REPRODUCTION IN DOMESTIC ANIMALS

SECOND EDITION

REPRODUCTION IN DOMESTIC ANIMALS

SECOND EDITION

Edited by

H. H. COLE AND P. T. CUPPS

Department of Animal Science
University of California
Davis, California

ACADEMIC PRESS   New York and London   1969

ACADEMIC PRESS, INC.
111 Fifth Avenue, New York, New York 10003

United Kingdom Edition published by
ACADEMIC PRESS, INC. (LONDON) LTD.
Berkeley Square House, London W.1

LIBRARY OF CONGRESS CATALOG CARD NUMBER: 68-26645

PRINTED IN THE UNITED STATES OF AMERICA

LIST OF CONTRIBUTORS

Numbers in parentheses refer to the pages on which the authors' contributions begin.

L. L. ANDERSON, Department of Animal Science, Iowa State University, Ames, Iowa (217, 541)

S. A. ASDELL, New York State College of Agriculture, Cornell University, Ithaca, New York (1)

C. R. AUSTIN, Physiological Laboratory, Cambridge University, Cambridge, England (355)

R. L. BALDWIN, Department of Animal Science, University of California, Davis, California (441)

HUBERT R. CATCHPOLE,* Department of Pathology, University of Illinois, Chicago, Illinois (415)

M. T. CLEGG, Tulane University, Delta Regional Primate Research Center, Covington, Louisiana (473)

H. H. COLE, Department of Animal Science, University of California, Davis, California (17, 217)

M. COUROT, Laboratoire de Physiologie de la Reproduction, I.N.R.A., 37 Nouzilly, France (251)

P. T. CUPPS, Department of Animal Science, University of California, Davis, California (217)

RALPH I. DORFMAN, Institute of Hormone Biology, Syntex Research, Division of Syntex Corporation, and Department of Pharmacology, School of Medicine, Stanford University, Palo Alto, California (113)

P. ECKSTEIN, Department of Anatomy, The University of Birmingham, Birmingham, England (385)

C. W. EMMENS, Veterinary Physiology Department, University of Sydney, Sydney, Australia (85)

R. H. FOOTE, Department of Animal Science, Cornell University, Ithaca, New York (313)

WILLIAM F. GANONG, Department of Physiology, University of California Medical Center, San Francisco, California (155, 473)

M. T. HOCHEREAU, Laboratoire de Physiologie de la Reproduction, I.N.R.A., Nouzilly, France (251)

* Present address: The Queen's University of Belfast, Department of Pathology, Grosvenor Road, Belfast, N. Ireland.

v

W. A. KELLY, Department of Anatomy, The Medical School, Bristol, England (385)

CLIFFORD L. KRAGT, Department of Physiology, University of California Medical Center, San Francisco, California (155)

F. W. LORENZ, Department of Animal Physiology, University of California, Davis, California (569)

T. MANN, A.R.C. Unit of Reproductive Physiology and Biochemistry, Cambridge, England (277)

P. MAULEON, Laboratoire de Physiologie de la Reproduction, Tours L'Orfrasiere, Nouzilly, France (187)

A. REES MIDGLEY, JR., Department of Pathology, University of Michigan, Ann Arbor, Michigan (47)

JOHANNES MOUSTGAARD, Department of Physiology, Endocrinology and Bloodgrouping, The Royal Veterinary and Agricultural College, Copenhagen, Denmark (489)

R. ORTAVANT, Laboratoire de Physiologie de la Reproduction, I.N.R.A., 37 Nouzilly, France (251)

JOHN W. OSEBOLD, Department of Veterinary Microbiology, University of California, Davis, California (517)

HAROLD PAPKOFF, Hormone Research Laboratory, University of California Medical Center, San Francisco, California (67)

FOREWORD TO THE FIRST EDITION

This treatise utilizes a unique opportunity. During the last few decades an immense body of accurate information on reproductive phenomena in all higher animals has been gleaned. F. H. A. Marshall had the distinction of producing a pioneer account of these phenomena in an era preceding the development of endocrinology.

The immense usefulness of domestic animals to man very quickly focused attention on the physiology of their reproduction. Their study constituted, of course, a very significant part of Marshall's classic treatise, but the detailed study of each of these forms has been the product of only the last twenty or thirty years. In this present volume the results of these studies have been brought together and synthesized.

The primary object of this effort consists in the attempt to bring about a fuller understanding of the complex mechanisms involved in reproduction in order to utilize such an understanding in breeding farm animals. Such an aim can be accomplished solely by sound knowledge of the intricate internal mechanisms (nervous and endocrine) of reproduction and of the external factors (food and environment) which play vital roles here. *The effort to understand these controlling mechanisms is set forth here.* Physiological phenomena are the main concern. Genetics is not treated in detail, although consideration has been given to the influence of heredity on many reproductive phenomena.

Perhaps one of the most striking series of events in the early history of study in this realm was created by three investigations concerning small laboratory animals. The three papers were those of Stockard and Papanicolaou on the guinea pig, of Long and Evans on the rat, and of Edgar Allen on the mouse. They demonstrated that the sequence of steps in the development of the so-called "estrous rhythm" could be clearly shown by the types of cells found free in the vaginal fluid. It appeared, indeed, for a time that the application of the vaginal smear method would be all that was required to segment the stages of the estrous cycle in all animals. Early studies by Hammond in the cow, by McKenzie in the sow, by Andrews and McKenzie in the mare, and by Cole in the cow and ewe did not substantiate this optimism; the beautifully distinct changes seen in the vaginal lochia of small rodents were peculiar for the smaller forms. Only in the dog, as determined by Evans and Cole, was the estrogen level high enough for pronounced vaginal cornification which divulges ovarian changes. We were quickly forced back to old-fashioned but eminently reliable observations of such matters, for instance, as changes in behavior.

In behavior changes the internal mechanisms, both endocrine and nervous, are, of course, at work. External controlling factors are also becoming known with increasing accuracy. Two domestic species, the ewe and the mare, are seasonal breeders. The reader will find here a discussion of the fact that the sexual season is induced in the ewe by withdrawal of light, and in the mare by increased light, as had been previously found in birds. The role of temperature is also definite, for it may delay the onset of the ewe's sexual season, cooling hastening this event.

The endocrine changes in pregnancy have led, as is well known, to dramatic discoveries, for example, that of the very high hemal titers in female sex hormone in the pregnant mare (subsequently amazingly found in the stallion) and in reliable pregnancy tests. Perhaps nothing is stranger than the similarity between the mare and women in high pregnancy estrogen and gonadotropin titers. In the mare, unlike the situation in women, the gonadotropin appears to be secreted by maternal structures called *endometrial cups* and not by the chorionic tissue of her offspring, although estrogens are secreted by the chorion in both forms. Explanations for the sudden great overproduction of these gonadotropins are not at hand.

The tremendous importance of artificial insemination in animal breeding has served as a stimulus for intensive research on spermatogenesis, on the biochemistry of semen, and on the factors influencing sexual *libido* and sperm production. It is perhaps in this area that some of our knowledge in domestic animals compares favorably with, and in some instances surpasses, that available in laboratory animals.

If this beautiful treatise can thus serve as an impetus for the acquisition of new, necessary, and especially quantitative data, measuring all of these phenomena, its essential purpose will have been abundantly fulfilled.

HERBERT M. EVANS

Institute of Experimental Biology
University of California, Berkeley, California
March, 1959

PREFACE

The first two-volume edition of this treatise is now in its second printing; apparently it served a useful purpose. After much consultation, we decided that the second edition should not only serve as a reference work but as a text for advanced students studying reproductive physiology as well. To accomplish this objective it became necessary to condense the material in the first edition and bring it up-to-date. It is our hope that this second edition will provide a fairly complete review of reproduction in domestic animals and, especially, that it will give a critical summary of recent work.

In order to accomplish our aim, it became necessary to delete some of the chapters appearing in the first edition. For example, the reviews on the anatomy of the reproductive organs were reluctantly omitted, but a considerable number of illustrations on anatomy appear throughout this work. The five chapters on the estrous cycle have been condensed into one. Several other contributions were deleted and the subject matter redistributed. However, we have been able to add four new chapters: The Chemistry of Gonadotropins, The Biochemistry of the Gonadal Hormones, Immunological Characterization of the Gonadotropins, and Oogenesis and Folliculogenesis.

We are greatly indebted to the authors for their diligence in preparing authoritative manuscripts promptly and for their forbearance with our suggestions for changes in order to obtain better integration of the contributions. During the period of planning the work, authors made many valuable suggestions. We are grateful for the assistance of Mrs. Mary Bigelow Horton in many phases of editing. We would like to thank the staff of Academic Press for their cooperation in the preparation of this work. This treatise would not have been completed without the assistance of many others, but to attempt to name each of them would only do injustice to those inadvertently overlooked.

As stated in the Preface to the first edition,
"For many years reproductive physiology has been greatly enriched by the signal contributions made by Dr. Herbert M. Evans and his colleagues. Many, including the senior editor, have benefited from a sojourn in the inspirational atmosphere of his laboratory." We are pleased to have the opportunity to reprint Dr. Evan's Foreword to the First Edition in his eighty-fourth year.

H. H. Cole
P. T. Cupps

Davis, California
January, 1969

CONTENTS

10. Spermatogenesis and Morphology of the Spermatozoon

R. ORTAVANT, M. COUROT, AND M. T. HOCHEREAU

11. Physiology of Semen and of the Male Reproductive Tract

T. MANN

12. Physiological Aspects of Artificial Insemination

R. H. FOOTE

13. Fertilization and Development of the Egg

C. R. AUSTIN

14. Implantation, Development of the Fetus, and Fetal Membranes

W. A. KELLY AND P. ECKSTEIN

15. Hormonal Mechanisms during Pregnancy and Parturition

HUBERT R. CATCHPOLE

1 HISTORICAL INTRODUCTION

S. A. ASDELL

I. Early History, Mostly Anatomical

The development of our knowledge of the working of the reproductive processes has been much slower than that of any other of the body functions. The reasons are not far to seek. For mammals the nonexistence of eggs that could be seen without the aid of the microscope and the time gap between mating and the ability to recognize the products of conception in the uterus were obstacles that could only be surmounted by the invention of suitable visual aids and the formulation of the cell theory. Also, the method of control by hormones, prominent in the functioning of the sexual organs, has been so recent a discovery that the delay is not surprising on this account alone.

Mankind has made up for the lack of physiological knowledge by an abundance of speculation. Probably more has been written and thought about reproduction in one form or another than about anything else. At one time or another every possible suggestion that might account for reproduction of the species or, at any rate, that might explain some facet of the process has been made and pressed with various degrees of plausibility. Most of this speculation and folklore had to be cleared away before explanations acceptable to science could be advanced.

Naturally enough, the Greeks had plenty of ideas on the subject, and it is now known that many of these ideas had been passed on to them by the wise men of the East, especially India, a country with which they had much contact, particularly at the time of Alexander the Great. Our first compre-

1

hensive treatise on reproduction, Aristotle's "Generation of Animals" (4), dates from this period. For a comparable treatise we had to wait over two thousand years until Marshall's "Physiology of Reproduction" (45), appeared (Fig. 1). True, Galen (130–200 AD), William Harvey in 1651 (35), discoverer of the circulation of the blood, and others had written books on reproduction, but these were hardly of the quality of the treatises of either Aristotle or Marshall.

The Greek view of reproductive physiology was quite logical if the limited range of the facts at their disposal is taken into account. The fetus

THE PHYSIOLOGY OF
REPRODUCTION

BY

FRANCIS H. A. MARSHALL
M.A. (Cantab.), D.Sc. (Edin.)
FELLOW OF CHRIST'S COLLEGE, CAMBRIDGE, AND UNIVERSITY LECTURER
IN AGRICULTURAL PHYSIOLOGY

WITH A PREFACE BY
Professor E. A. SCHÄFER, Sc.D., LL.D., F.R.S.

AND CONTRIBUTIONS BY
WILLIAM CRAMER, Ph.D., D.Sc.
AND
JAMES LOCHHEAD, M.A., M.D., B.Sc., F.R.C.S.E.

WITH ILLUSTRATIONS

LONGMANS, GREEN AND CO.
39 PATERNOSTER ROW, LONDON
NEW YORK, BOMBAY, AND CALCUTTA
1910

All rights reserved

FIG. 1. A portrait of F. H. A. Marshall and the title page of the original edition of Marshall's "Physiology of Reproduction" (45).

arose from the menstrual blood because this does not appear during pregnancy. This material was activated by the seminal fluid. Sex was determined in this way: the male is darker in color than is the female so, as fetal development depends upon the coagulation of the activated menses, this must, for a male, be conducted at a higher temperature (coagulation of an egg, for instance, requires heat) and this will darken the product. The right side of the body is more active and nobler than the left, so it must be the hotter side. Hence, male fetuses are developed on the right side. Even in present times, one occasionally hears that the right ovary gives rise to males and the left to females. As the two ovaries are said to alternate in their action it is possible, according to this view, to obtain a male or female at will by noting the sex of the previous offspring and counting subsequent cycles. Incidentally, the Greeks of this period had no knowledge of the ovaries. Credit for this discovery is given to the Alexandrine Greek, Herophilus, about a hundred years later (ca. 300 BC). He named them "the female testes," a name which they bore for many centuries. During this interval they were not recognized as equivalent to the ovaries of the bird. Aristotle knew of a bull that remained fertile for a time after it had been castrated and was led to deny a direct influence of the testes upon fertility. He suggested that the semen was derived from all parts of the body and that the testes were merely plummets that kept the necessary tubes from becoming kinked and, thus, stopped up. It is no wonder that these early authorities were confused about the ovaries. This doctrine of semen derivation, known as "pangenesis," was revived in more recent times by Darwin, who called the active particles "gemmules."

After the activities of the Greek Alexandrine School there is little to record until Fallopius (27), an anatomist at Padua (died 1562, at age 39 years), described the tubules that bear his name. In the intervening centuries there was nothing but practical treatises on obstetrics and recapitulations of the knowledge brought together by Aristotle, who with, the physician Galen (130–200 AD), was regarded as the final authority in biological matters. Galen was something of an experimentalist, and he added something to embryology by his dissection of hens' eggs. Then the study of anatomy eventually began to shake off this authoritarianism, and anatomists began to look at specimens for themselves, to dissect them, and to interpret what they saw. A student of Fallopius, Volcherus Coiter (14), in 1573 described the corpus luteum, and in 1672 Regnier de Graaf (23) described the Graafian follicle (Fig. 2). He suggested that it represented the egg, corresponding to the egg of the bird or frog. A few years previously, in 1667, the Danish anatomist Steno (61) had suggested that the female testes were in reality the mammalian equivalent of the ovaries of egg-laying animals, but he had no idea of the nature of the mammalian egg. However, his was a fruitful suggestion and it put the anatomists at last on the right path. De Graaf also killed rabbits at half-hourly intervals after copulation. He discovered that the number of cicatrices in the ovaries usually corresponded with the number of eggs or embryos in the uterus. But he recognized that the "ovum" in the uterus was much smaller than the follicle, which he regarded as the egg.

For many years William Harvey had been studying the subject of reproduction and in 1651, when he was 73 years' old, his views were published in book form (35). He had followed the development of the chick at regular intervals through incubation, as had others before him, and he added materially to our knowledge of embryology. In his mammalian studies he was not so fortunate. He studied the deer and the rabbit, but was baffled by the interval between the time of coitus and the time when something resembling an avian embryo could be found in the uterus. But he did recognize that the maternal and fetal circulations were distinct, a major contribution in itself.

A few years later an amateur biologist of Delft, Holland, made an observation that was to mark the beginning of the modern era in this field. He had improved the simple lens and had the curiosity to examine with his

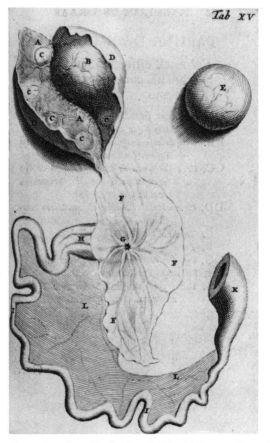

FIG. 2. An illustration from R. de Graaf, "De Mulierum Organis Generatione Inservientibus," 1672 edition (23). This gives the author's idea of the follicle that bears his name. He evidently regarded it as the egg.

instruments everything that came his way. A medical student named Hamm drew his attention to the presence of live animalcules in the semen of a man afflicted with a venereal disease. The biologist van Leeuwenhoek (68) soon found that similar animalcules were present in the semen of males from many species of animals, a fact that was published in print in 1677, though he seems to have informed others by letter several years previously. In those days there was an active correspondence between workers in several countries and this was an important factor in spreading the latest information. Publication was secondary. In most countries there were small societies or clubs of philosophical amateurs, who were avid students of the latest scientific discoveries.

This discovery by van Leeuwenhoek led to an immense amount of speculation, and biologists as well as numerous other philosophers keenly

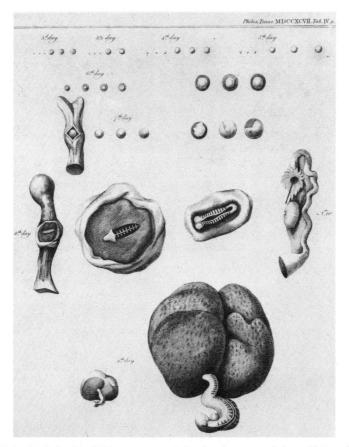

FIG. 3. Cruikshank's (*21*) sequence of the development of the rabbit embryo. His third day ova were taken from the oviduct.

debated its implications. They divided into two camps, one maintaining that the ovum, still undiscovered, gave rise to the embryo, while others were equally certain that this was the function of the "new" animalcules. Another controversy arose between the "preformationists" and the "epigenists." The former maintained that the embryo was present fully formed in either the egg or the sperm. Thus, one or other of these bodies must contain the eggs or sperm of the next generation and so on ad infinitum both up and down the line. Adam, or Eve, therefore, must have contained the germs of all their descendants. This absurd doctrine gave rise to much speculation, theological and otherwise, but one gets the impression that several of the writings on the subject may properly be classed in the category of "leg pulls." More sensible were the speculations of Swammerdam (1637–1680) (65), a superb dissector. He was puzzled concerning how the egg got into the oviduct of the frog. He described the external fertilization of the egg and observed its first cleavage. Yet, he was an ardent preformationist. The epigenists took the opposite view, namely, that the egg and the sperm had to be organized into the form of the embryo and that this took place anew

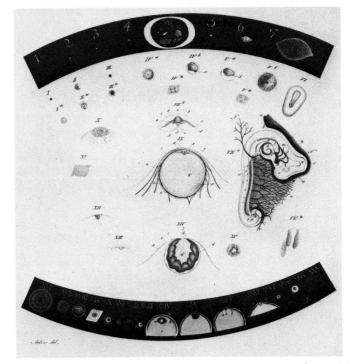

FIG. 4. An illustration from C. E. von Baer, "De Ovi Mammalian et Hominis Genesi," 1827 (69). This contains a timed sequence of ovum development and, in the lower band, the relations of ovum and follicle are clearly shown.

with each union of the two. However, there was still only speculation, but no proof, for mammals, that the newly discovered animalcules, or spermatozoa, entered the ovum, and it must be remembered that the actual mammalian ovum had not yet been discovered. Only the early embryo was yet known.

In 1780 the Italian priest Spallanzani (60), also working with the frog, attempted to answer the question of whether or not the spermatozoa were actually the fertilizing agents for the egg. His method was to filter semen through blotting paper. Fertility was lost in some instances, but not in all. He attempted other experiments of a similar nature, but none gave him the correct answer, as they did not absolutely exclude the spermatozoa. It remained for Dumas (24) in 1825 to provide definite proof by experiments with rabbits that spermatozoa are the fertilizing agents. Spallanzani did show that semen diluted to the extent of one drop in 25 pounds of water retained the ability to fertilize, and he was also the first in modern times to demonstrate the possibility of artificial insemination. He used the dog for this purpose.

Recognition of the mammalian ovum was hardly possible until the cell theory had been developed. Several workers seem to have seen ova enveloped by the discus proligerus and to have described these as ova. Cruikshank (21) in 1797 may have seen them in this form. He certainly described rabbit ova in the oviducts on the third day following impregnation (Fig. 3). Later, Prévost and Dumas (56) opened rabbit follicles and obtained from them bodies about 1 mm in diameter. These were less transparent than the smaller eggs which they found developing within the uterus. Definite recognition came in 1827 when von Baer (69) described the ovum and noted its relation to the discus proligerus and to the follicle (Fig. 4). He called the newly found object an "ovulum." In the same year Dumas (25) said that the spermatozoon and the ovum unite in the oviduct or uterus. He and Prévost saw a single spermatozoon in the egg of a frog and expressed the view that one is sufficient to fertilize the egg. In 1840 Barry (8) found for the first time spermatozoa in a mammalian egg. This was a rabbit egg. Three years later he described an embryo in the two-blastomere stage. Ten years after this (1853) Newport (52) described the penetration of a frog's egg by spermatozoa, and the modern age of reproductive biology had begun.

II. Sex Determination

Sex determination is one aspect of the subject that excited lively controversy, and the theories advanced to account for the sex of an individual, male or female, have been legion. Obviously, no correct answer could be forthcoming until the cell nucleus was recognized and the role of the chromosomes described.

In 1901 McClung (47) pointed out that a sex difference existed in the chromosomes, but his interpretation of it was at fault. It remained for Stevens (62) and Wilson (72), each working with insects, to work out the true relationship of the heterochromosomes to sex. The haploid nature of the germ cells had been recognized previously in 1883, by van Beneden (67), and the restoration of the diploid condition by the union of the gametes was already understood. It remained for the recognition of sex linkage by Bateson and Punnet (9) in 1908, a condition that, to clinch the matter, allowed recognition of the line of descent of individual chromosomes. More recent events in this field have been Barr's (7) discovery of the sex chromatin, use of more efficient technique in chromosome recognition, the finding that the Y chromosome of mammals is definitely concerned in male development, and, most recently, the discovery by Blackler (13) that, in the South African clawed toad, at any rate, the genetic composition of the gonads determines the sex, not the composition of the germ cells themselves. If this latter finding is confirmed in other species, and circumstantial evidence points in this direction, it is an important addition to our knowledge.

III. Sexual Cycles

One of the first to draw attention to the cyclic nature of the sexual process was Lataste (41), who worked at Bordeaux with a variety of rodents. This was pioneering work, and at the time it attracted but little attention. In fact, the physiology of reproduction was investigated very slowly. After the initial discoveries the attention of biologists seems to have been diverted in the direction of working out the changes that take place in the cell nucleus during division, and in the study of embryological development. Eventually, both of these led back to reproduction, in the case of embryology because of the demand for more accurately aged material.

Next came the work of Heape (36), who defined and named the various phases of the female cycle in mammals. He also pointed out the essential similarity between the reproductive processes in man and other mammals, a conclusion he reached as a result of his studies of the changes in the sexual organs of monkeys. Heape (37) also drew attention to the fact that ovulation in the rabbit is induced by coitus. This led to eventual recognition of the endocrine nature of much that goes on in the sexual cycle. He was the first to transfer successfully ova from one female to another.

As a result of Heape's work, Marshall (44) was able to differentiate between the physiological activities of the Graafian follicle and the corpus luteum in their relations to the accessory organs. This work was considerably extended by Ancel and Bouin (3). Later, Marshall (46) demonstrated the effects of changing light gradients in certain seasonal reproducers, thus helping to explain the nature of this phenomenon.

Further pioneer work was that of Deanesly and Parkes (22), who showed how, by a carefully contrived sampling system, together with a study of the histology of the tracts, much information may be obtained about reproduction in wild species that do not readily reproduce in captivity.

IV. Steroid Hormones

In 1849 Berthold (12) published the results of work in which he castrated roosters and, in a few, implanted the testes upon the intestines. In consequence, these birds did not display the usual results of castration, and he drew the correct inference that the testes produced blood-borne substances that maintained the accessory sexual structures and male behavior. But it was not until the turn of the century, after Bayliss and Starling (10) had enunciated their hormone theory, that attention was again given to this possibility. In the first decade or so of this century several workers injected various types of crude extracts of gonads or of uteri, and they occasionally obtained growth of the uterus, but, on the whole, the results were not encouraging. In searching for an active substance of totally unknown structure, usually present in very small amounts, a good biological test is essential during the earlier work. In 1917 Stockard and Papanicolaou (63) published their work on the estrous cycle of the guinea pig, and similar studies followed in 1922, on the mouse, by Allen (1) and on the rat, by Long and Evans (43a). These studies showed that the vaginal smear gave a valuable clue to the ovarian changes. In 1923, Allen and Doisy (1a) used this hint as a means of tracking down the follicular hormone, which was soon isolated. Its structure was worked out, and synthesis soon followed. It turned out to be a steroid substance, a member of a class of organic compounds just beginning to be recognized. At first it was obtained from natural sources only and in small amounts, but when Girard (30) introduced his series of reagents, the isolation in quantity of estradiol and related substances from human pregnancy urine soon followed. A dramatic moment in the history of this development occurred at a meeting called to discuss the possibility of setting up an international reference standard for the estrogens, which had not yet been obtained in an absolutely pure state. The American and British representatives were talking about donating milligrams to the pooled standard when Girard, who had been invited at the last moment, produced from his pocket several grams and promised a good many more.

Isolation of estrogens was quickly followed by that of progesterone from the corpora lutea of pigs by Corner and Allen (19). The role of this organ in maintaining pregnancy was known from the work in 1903 by Fraenkel (28), who is said to have received the hint from his professor, Born, while the latter was on his deathbed. The method of detection used by Corner and Allen was to use the extracts to build the endometrium of the ovariectomized rabbit to the level found during pseudopregnancy. The history of these exciting days is recounted in most interesting manner by Corner (18).

The male hormone, testosterone, was tracked down by Gallagher and Koch (29) in 1928–1929. They used the sensitivity of the rooster comb as their test. Interest in all these substances was lively, and a number of laboratories were involved in their purification, characterization, and synthesis. Among these may be mentioned the laboratories of Ruzicka, Butenandt, and Laqueur.

Another hormone, relaxin, has been obtained in impure form from the corpus luteum. It is not a steroid but a polypeptide, and its exact functions are still controversial. It was first described in 1928 by Hisaw (38).

V. Anterior Pituitary Hormones

In 1905 Heape (37) suggested that the activity of the gonads was controlled by a substance circulating in the blood. He gave it the provisional name "generative ferment." In 1925 this hypothesis was extended by Hammond and Marshall (33), who considered that the substance, whatever it might be, was also concerned in body growth and in lactation, since all these were linked in some way. Growth had to be considerable before the gonads began to function and estrous cycles tended to be suppressed during lactation. If one adds together the functions of several of the anterior pituitary hormones, they act much in the manner suggested by the generative ferment concept.

The first of the anterior hormones to be isolated and purified was prolactin. Evidence for the existence of a pituitary factor that influences milk secretion was first given by Stricker and Grueter (64) in 1928. Riddle and Braucher (57a) reported that this hormone stimulated the crop gland of pigeons, a finding which led to a favorite method of assay. It was partially purified and named by Riddle and Bates (57) in 1933. In 1929 Bellerby (11) had shown that an extract of the anterior pituitary gland would induce ovulation in the estrous rabbit, a species that ordinarily requires activation by coitus before ovulation occurs. This was followed by the work of P. E. Smith (59), who perfected the parapharangeal surgical technique for removing the rat pituitary, thus providing at the same time evidence regarding pituitary function and a convenient animal for testing the potency of extracts of the gland. The profound effects of the operation upon the gonads, which immediately atrophied, and the restorative effects of implants of the gland or of extracts were soon demonstrated. This work was followed up by Fevold et al. (27a) and Evans et al. (26a) and soon led to highly purified preparations of follicle stimulating hormone (FSH) and luteinizing hormone (LH, or ICSH). Like prolactin both of these were found to be proteins, and their separation proved to be difficult.

As a consequence of relying too much upon evidence from a single species, the rat, which is easier than most to work with, some of the earlier generalizations have not stood up under further test. For instance, prolactin was found to be the hormone that stimulates the corpus luteum to secrete progesterone. This is so in the rat and probably in many other rodents, but in those species of other orders of mammals about which we have information LH is the activating hormone.

These hormones are evidently used in the glands they stimulate because they have to be supplied continuously if they are to maintain the gonads. Furthermore, there is a relationship between the amount supplied and the amount of their effect. Before they were isolated Lipschütz (43) had deduced a "law" of follicular constancy. This was based on the fact that females tend to ripen a constant number of follicles at each heat period, and that if one ovary is removed, the other does the work of both. Evidently, the amount of FSH secreted determines the number of follicles that may mature at any one time. Additional injected FSH increases the number of ripening follicles, a fact that has proved useful in experimental work.

Information on the role of the placenta as an endocrine organ came from Aschheim and Zondek's (5) discovery in 1927 of a gonadotropic substance in the urine of pregnant women. It proved to be similar to LH in its physiological properties. This was followed in 1930 by Cole and Hart's discovery (16) of a substance resembling FSH in its physiology in the blood serum of the pregnant mare. Both discoveries were useful, as they provided abundant sources for these hormones. It was no longer necessary to rely upon the limited supply of pituitaries for hormones with gonadotropic activity. They were also useful in providing a test for pregnancy in these two species.

In 1937 Harris (34) showed that electrical stimulation of the hypothalamic region of the brain would cause the female rabbit to ovulate, while Markee and his students began to explore the effects of sympathetic and parasympathetic stimulating and blocking drugs upon reproduction. This soon became a very active field, and it is impossible to single out individuals whose contributions have led to the greatest development. It is sufficient to say that the hypothalamus is now recognized as the source of hormones, probably polypeptides, that travel to the anterior pituitary and there control the hormone output. It is by this pathway that exogenous stimuli such as light or the sense of smell or sight (Whitten and Bruce effects) are able to exert their effects.

VI. Physiology of Spermatozoa

By far the most important development in reproductive physiology has been that which has led to the widespread use of artificial insemination in animal breeding. This has obvious advantages in reducing the number of males that must be maintained, in increasing the possibilities of improvement by using only males that transmit to their offspring the most desirable characters, and, especially since the introduction of antibiotics, in controlling the spread of venereal diseases in livestock.

The work of Spallanzani (60), who successfully inseminated a dog, has been mentioned. After that initial work only sporadic attempts were made to put the discovery into practice until the beginning of this century, when the Russian Iwanow (39) began to investigate the possibility of collecting, preserving, and diluting the semen. His work was, at first, entirely with horses, but he gradually extended it to other domestic species, and after

World War I the results began to be used for large-scale purposes. Milovanov (50) was one of those who developed the techniques, and his name is especially associated with the use of semen diluters. In 1936 the first artificial-insemination cooperative was organized in Denmark, on the island of Samsø, by Sørensen and Gylling Holm, and from this time progress was rapid.

In the United States an experiment made in Minnesota from 1937 to 1938 proved successful with beef cattle. In 1938 E. J. Perry (54) organized the first American cooperative in New Jersey. Among those who were engaged in developing techniques and in improving the efficiency of operation were Walton (70), Phillips (55), and Willett and Salisbury (71). The latter, in cooperation with Knodt (40), introduced the addition of sulfa drugs to the semen as a means of reducing bacterial contamination and cutting down the incidence of venereal diseases. About the same time Almquist (2) further improved upon this by adding antibiotics to the semen diluters.

In 1950 Smith and Polge (58) found that by adding glycerol to bull semen it may be frozen and preserved at $-79°C$ or lower without undue loss of its fertilizing ability. This discovery, due to a fortunate accident in the laboratory together with the capacity of the investigators to interpret what had happened, has led to a considerable advance because semen of some species may now be kept for years if necessary; thus, semen banks may be used and specimens sent under refrigeration for very long distances.

Effective use of these new techniques demanded that the estrous cycles, as well as the optimum time in the cycle for insemination and the length of survival both for the sperm and the ovum, should be known in more detail than had previously been the case. Many workers have taken part in these explorations, and it is impossible to mention more than a few of them. In 1903 Marshall (44) published work on the estrous cycle of the sheep, and this was followed by papers by Cole and Miller (17) in 1935 and McKenzie and Terrill (49) in 1937. Murphey (51) was working with cattle in 1924, and Hammond (31) published on the subject in 1927. In 1926 McKenzie (48) dealt with the pig. This was followed in 1959 by a monograph by Nishikawa (53) on the horse.

In 1911 Lewis (42) pointed out that the life of the spermatozoon and of the ovum in the female tract of domestic animals was shorter than was usually realized and he gave approximate figures. This was followed in 1926 by a study of the subject in rabbits by Hammond and Asdell (32) which confirmed Lewis's pioneer work. This species was ideal for this type of problem because in it ovulation depends upon coitus, which it follows at a very definite interval. In 1943 Trimberger and Davis (66) obtained definite figures upon the relationship between estrus and ovulation in the cow and on the effect of the interval between insemination and ovulation upon fertility. Gradually, a satisfactory picture of this very practical phase of the subject has been built up.

In 1922 Crew (20) suggested that spermatogenesis required a lower temperature than that of the body and that, therefore, the testes were suspended in the scrotum, which serves as a thermoregulator. These facts were used by Asdell and Salisbury (6) in 1941 to work out the rate of spermatogenesis in the testis. Their results have been essentially confirmed by recent work in which radioactive tracers have given more precise figures.

VII. Miscellaneous Factors

So far nothing has been said about the effects of varying nutrition upon fertility. This is largely because under modern conditions of feeding domestic animals, quantitative and qualitative deficiencies are rarely seen. There is evidence that vitamin A and E deficiencies interfere with spermatogenesis in the rat [Evans and Burr, 1927 (26)] but other species do not seem to be as sensitive, and the same seems to be true for vitamin and other deficiencies that may occur during pregnancy. Adverse conditions have to be rather extreme for them to affect reproduction.

A practical problem in which progress has been made is that of synchronization of heats so that a number of females ovulate at a date chosen by the farmer or inseminator. This, when perfected, will make it much easier to arrange a breeding program and will lessen the amount of work and time involved in visiting farms for performing the inseminations. This line of enquiry is still very recent, and it is being pursued in several laboratories. Much of this work consists in screening various steroid derivatives and picking out the most effective ones. These substances are being produced in the research laboratories of many drug houses in connection with the search for the ideal contraceptive. A problem that needs further work is that the conception rate is lower than usual in the heat period immediately after these substances have been used. It is clear that we do not yet have the best stimulus for reactivating the ovary after it has been held inactive by the synchronizing drug.

It is easy to make a list of outstanding problems in reproduction, and a complete one would be very long. Ability to control the sex of the offspring is one that has attracted much attention, and frequent claims of success have been made, only to be followed by a silence that indicates that the method proposed has not been as successful as had at first been believed.

We may hope that the hypothalamic hormones and inhibitors will soon be known in more detail. If the present belief that they are relatively simple polypeptides is correct, we may expect fairly early synthesis. When they become available in this manner, we may expect to have far greater control over the anterior pituitary than is now possible. This would mean that the rest of the sexual organs will be brought under more certain control. The problem of pineal involvement, which has not been treated in this chapter, is another one that calls for elucidation. Hormone levels and feedback mechanisms also require much more work. The use of radioactive tracers to find the rate of loss of steroid hormones at each step of their assay has already helped in this respect, as it has made assay much more accurate than was possible in the past.

There are also many problems of a fundamental nature awaiting answer, such as: what do fertilization and activation of the egg actually involve, and why are they distinct? For that matter, why does a fertilized egg divide? What is the mechanism of reduction division and extrusion of polar bodies? How is ovulation brought about? What causes certain hormones to be so specific in their actions? What are the relationships between the structure of the hormone and that of the cells with which they react? What causes the uteri of some species to be so specific in the positions in which implantation of embryos may occur? And what determines the length of gestation? It is surprising how many of these important questions still await answers.

REFERENCES

1. Allen, E., Am. J. Anat. 30, 297 (1922).
1a. Allen, E., and Doisy, E. A., J. Am. Med. Assoc. 81, 819 (1923).
2. Almquist, J. O., J. Dairy Sci. 26, 483 (1943).
3. Ancel, P., and Bouin, P., Compt. Rend. Soc. Biol. 66, 454, 605 (1909).
4. Aristotle, "Generation of Animals," Transl. A. L. Peck, Loeb Classical Library. Heinemann, London, 1943.
5. Aschheim, S., and Zondek, B., Klin. Wochschr., 6, 1321 (1927).
6. Asdell, S. A., and Salisbury, G. W., Anat. Record 80, 145 (1941).
7. Barr, M. L., in "Modern Trends in Obstetrics and Gynecology" (K. Bowes, ed.). Butterworth, London and Washington, D. C., 1955.
8. Barry, M., Phil. Trans. Roy. Soc., London 133, 33 (1843).
9. Bateson, W., and Punnett, R. C., Science [N. S.] 27, 785 (1908).
10. Bayliss, W. M., and Starling, E. H., J. Physiol. (London) 28, 325 (1902).
11. Bellerby, C. W., J. Physiol. (London) 67, xxxiii (1929).
12. Berthold, A. A., Arch. Anat. Physiol., Leipzig 16, 42 (1849).
13. Blackler, A. W., Advan. Reproductive Physiol. 1, 9–28 (1966).
14. Coiter, V., "Externarum et Internarum Principalium Humani Corporis Partium Tabulae." T. Gerlatzeni, Noribergae, 1572. A facsimile (A. Schierback and B. W. T. Nuyens, eds.) was published: Opuscula Selecta Neerlandicorum Arte Med. 18 (1955); but see Harrison, R. J., Biol. Rev. 23, 296 (1948).
*15. Cole, F. J., "Early Theories of Sexual Generation." Oxford Univ. Press (Clarendon), London and New York, 1930.
16. Cole, H. H., and Hart, G. H., Am. J. Physiol. 93, 57 (1930).
17. Cole, H. H., and Miller, R. F., Am. J. Anat. 57, 39 (1935).

* The three books preceded by asterisks give good general accounts of their subjects. They cover in detail many aspects of this chapter and may be used as supplementary readings.

18. Corner, G. W., "The Hormones of Human Reproduction." Princeton Univ. Press, Princeton, New Jersey, 1947.
19. Corner, G. W., and Allen, W. M., *Am. J. Physiol.* **88**, 326 (1929).
20. Crew, F. A. E., *J. Anat.* **56**, 98 (1922)
21. Cruikshank, W. C., *Phil. Trans. Roy. Soc., London* **87**, 197 (1797).
22. Deanesly, R., and Parkes, A. S., *Phil. Trans. Roy. Soc., London, Ser. B* **222**, 47 (1933).
23. de Graaf, R., "De Mulierum Organis Generatione Inservientibus." Ex officina Hackiana, Lugd. Bat., 1672. A facsimile was published: *Dutch Classics Hist. Sci.* **13** (1965).
24. Dumas, J. B. A., *Dictionnaire Classique Hist. Nat., Paris* **7**, 194 (1825).
25. Dumas, J. B. A., *Ann. Sci. Nat.* **12**, 443 (1827).
26. Evans, H. M., and Burr, G. O., *Mem. Univ. Calif.* **8** (1927).
26a. Evans, H. M., Korpi, K., Pencharz, R. I., Simpson, M. E., and Wonder, D. H., *Univ. Calif. Publ. Anat.* **1**, 255 (1936).
27. Fallopius, G., "Opera Omnia," apud haered. A. Weckeli, Francofurti, 1600.
27a. Fevold, H. L., Hisaw, F. L., and Leonard, S. H., *Am. J. Physiol.* **97**, 291 (1931).
28. Fraenkel, L., *Arch. Gynaek.* **68**, 438 (1903).
29. Gallagher, T. F., and Koch, F. C., *J. Biol. Chem.* **84**, 495 (1929).
30. Girard, A., and Sandulesco, G., *Helv. Chim. Acta* **19**, 1095 (1936).
31. Hammond, J., "The Physiology of Reproduction in the Cow." Cambridge Univ. Press, London and New York, 1927.
32. Hammond, J., and Asdell, S. A., *Brit. J. Exptl. Biol.* **4**, 155 (1926).
33. Hammond, J., and Marshall, F. H. A., "Reproduction in the Rabbit." Oliver & Boyd, Edinburgh and London, 1925.
34. Harris, G. W., *Proc. Roy. Soc.* **B122**, 374 (1937).
35. Harvey, W., "Exertationes de Generatione Animalium, Quibus Accedunt quedam de Partu: de Membranis ac Humoribus Uteri et de Conceptione." O. Pulleyn, London, 1651; Willis, R., "The Works of William Harvey," Translated from the Latin with a Life of the Author. Sydenham Society, London, 1847. Reprinted by Edwards, Ann Arbor, Michigan, 1943.
36. Heape, W., *Quart. J. Microscop. Sci.* **44**, 1 (1900).
37. Heape, W., *Proc. Roy. Soc.* **B76**, 260 (1905).
38. Hisaw, F. L., *Physiol. Zool.* **2**, 59 (1929).
39. Iwanow, E. J., *Arch. Sci. Biol., St. Petersburg* **12**, 377 (1907).
40. Knodt, C. B., and Salisbury, G. W., *J. Dairy Sci.* **29**, 285 (1946).
41. Lataste, F., *Act. Soc. Linn. Bordeaux* **40**, 202 (1887).
42. Lewis, L. L., *Oklahoma Agr. Expt. Sta. Bull.* **96** (1911).
43. Lipschütz, A., *Biol. Rev.* **2**, 263 (1927).
43a. Long, J. A., and Evans, H. M., *Mem. Univ. Calif.* **6**, 1–148 (1922).
44. Marshall, F. H. A., *Phil. Trans. Roy. Soc, London*, **B196**, 47 (1903).
45. Marshall, F. H. A., "The Physiology of Reproduction," 1st ed. 1910; 2nd ed. 1922; 3rd ed. as "Marshall's Physiology of Reproduction" (A. S. Parkes, ed.). Longmans, Green, New York, 1956–1966.
46. Marshall, F. H. A., *Proc. Roy. Soc.* **B122**, 413 (1937).
47. McClung, C. E., *Anat. Anz.* **20**, 220 (1901).
48. McKenzie, F. F., *Missouri Univ. Agr. Expt. Sta., Res. Bull.* **86**, 1926.
49. McKenzie, F. F., and Terrill, C. E., *Missouri Univ. Agr. Expt. Sta., Res. Bull.* **264**, 1937.

50. Milovanov, V. K., "Isskusstvenoye Ossemenenie Selsko-Khoziasvennykh Jivotnykh" (Artificial Insemination of Farm Animals). Seljhozgiz, Moscow, 1938.
51. Murphey, H. S., *J. Am. Vet. Med. Assoc.* **65**, 598 (1924).
*51a. Needham, J., "A History of Embryology," 2nd ed. Abelard, New York, 1959.
52. Newport, G., *Phil. Trans. Roy. Soc., London* **143**, 233 (1853).
53. Nishikawa, Y., "Studies on Reproduction in Horses. Singularity and Artificial Control in Reproductive Phenomena." Japan Racing Assoc., Tokyo, 1959.
*53a. Parkes, A. S., "Sex, Science and Society." Oriel Press, Newcastle upon Tyne, 1966.
54. Perry, E. J., ed., "The Artificial Insemination of Farm Animals," 2nd ed. Rutgers Univ. Press, New Brunswick, New Jersey, 1952.
55. Phillips, P. H., and Lardy, H. A., *J. Dairy Sci.* **23**, 390 (1940).
56. Prèvost, J. L., and Dumas, J. B. A., *Ann. Sci. Nat.* **3**, 113 (1824).
57. Riddle, O., and Bates, R. W., *Endocrinology* **17**, 689 (1933).
57a. Riddle, O., and Braucher, P. F., *Am. J. Physiol.* **97**, 617 (1931).
58. Smith, A. U., and Polge, C., *Vet. Record* **62**, 115 (1950).
59. Smith, P. E., *Am. J. Anat.* **45**, 205 (1930).
60. Spallanzani, L., "Dissertations Relative to the Natural History of Animals and Vegetables, Translated from the Italian of the Abbè Spallanzani." J. Murray, London, 1784.
61. Steno, N., *Acta Med. Hafniensia* **2**, 81, 210 (1675).
62. Stevens, N. M., *Carnegie Inst. Wash. Publ.* **36**, 1905.
63. Stockard, C. R., and Papanicolaou, G. N., *Am. J. Anat.* **22**, 225 (1917).
64. Stricker, P., and Grueter, F., *Compt. Rend. Soc. Biol.* **99**, 1978 (1928).
65. Swammerdam, J., "Miraculum Naturae sive Uteri Muliebris Fabrica." S. Matthaei, Lugd. Bat., 1672.
66. Trimberger, G. W., and Davis, H. P., *Nebraska Univ. Agr. Expt. Sta., Res. Bull.* **129** (1943).
67. van Beneden, E., *Arch. Biol.* **4**, 265 (1883).
68. van Leeuwenhoek, A., *Phil. Trans. Roy. Soc., London* **12**, 1040 (1679).
69. von Baer, C. E., "De Ovi Mammalium et Hominis Genesi." Sumptibus L. Vossii, Lipsiae, 1827.
70. Walton, A., "Notes on Artificial Insemination of Sheep, Cattle and Horses, 2nd ed. Holborn Surgical Instrument Co., London, 1938.
71. Willett, E. L., and Salisbury, G. W., *Cornell Univ. Agr. Expt. Sta., Mem.* **249** (1942).
72. Wilson, E. B., *J. Exptl. Zool.* **2**, 507 (1905).

* The three books preceded by asterisks give good general accounts of their subjects. They cover in detail many aspects of this chapter and may be used as supplementary readings.

2 PHYSIOLOGICAL CHARACTERIZATION OF GONADOTROPINS

H. H. COLE

I. Introduction

Remarkable advances have been made in our knowledge of the chemistry and physiology of the gonadotropins since the initial discovery of the gonad-stimulating properties of human pregnancy urine by Aschheim and Zondek (14) and of the pituitary by Smith (141) and Smith and Engle (142) and Zondek and Aschheim (163). Shortly thereafter, Fevold et al. (58) obtained evidence which led them to propose that the pituitary secreted two gonadotropins, follicle stimulating hormone (FSH) and lutein-

17

izing hormone (LH). In spite of the progress which has been made, a thin veil of uncertainty persists concerning this dualistic hormone concept, which prompted Harris (73) to comment in 1966, "Although it cannnot be said with certainty that there are two separate gonadotrophic hormones, FSH and LH, it is simple for descriptive purposes to make this assumption. . . ." In the same vein, Meyer (96), in his comments following a paper on the physiology of the gonadotropins, expressed doubt concerning the existence of two pituitary gonadotropins. In commenting on pituitary extracts prepared by McShan he said, "All 'pure' preparations stimulated growth of follicles and ventral prostates in hypophysectomized and intact immature rats"; and again, "Such results have most often been explained on the basis of contamination with LH. They can be, however, ascribed to a single protein possessing a 'complete' gonadotropic function." The possibility exists that chemical manipulation may result in breaking a "complete" hormone into FSH and LH fragments, but findings during the past 2 years of varying proportions of FSH and LH in urine and blood, and separation of these two activities, come close to completely dispelling this interpretation. In fact, this discussion will be based upon the premise that two hormones, FSH and LH, are found in the pituitary and in the fluids and tissues of nonpregnant mammals. This assumption is made with some apprehension. Taymor et al. (149) have found, for example, that antiserum against pituitary FSH extracts reacted with FSH from both urinary and pituitary sources, but antiserum against urinary FSH reacted only partially against pituitary FSH. Further, some early studies with gonadotropin extracted from the blood of nonpregnant mares indicated that it behaved, as concerns the response to single versus multiple injections, more like PMSG than pituitary FSH and LH (34).

Nothing seemed more certain than that the human placenta secreted a single hormone, human chorionic gonadotropin (HCG), but Hamashige et al. (69), in a recent paper, concluded on the basis of immunological and physiological studies of urinary fractions that HCG ". . . consists of at least three distinct hormones possessing similar immunologic and biologic activities but of variable specific activities." Future studies will be necessary to determine if this merely represents denaturing of the native molecule or if, indeed, there are several molcules with similar properties. Kikutani and Tokuyasu (80) have presented evidence that HCG fragments retain some biological activity.

Other factors have contributed uncertainty regarding our concepts of the physiological nature of gonadotropins. For example, it was shown during the decade after discovery of the gonadotropins that many inert substances, including blood proteins, would enhance the ovarian response of the immature rat to pituitary extracts. More recently, Albert et al. (6) have shown that tannation of pituitary LH will enhance its effect on the ventral prostate, but depress the response by the ovarian ascorbic acid depletion (OAAD) assay.

Species specificity is another factor which has led to some false conclusions concerning the physiological properties of gonadotropins. On the basis of what is known about the chemical structure of luteinizing hormones, one might postulate that slight chemical differences will be found in all protein hormones (see Chapter 4), and these chemical differences may be reflected by slight variations in biological activity. Parlow (107) has reported differences in the half-life of LH preparations from several species and Parlow and Reichert (110) and Reichert (116) found differences in the slope in the Steelman-Pohley assay. Hutchinson et al. (76) found differences in the relative activity by the ventral prostate and OAAD assays of rat, mouse, equine, and human LH preparations. Geschwind (64) suggests that in all instances physiological differences may not reflect chemical differences, but rather binding of a hormone to an unique nonhormonal pituitary protein in one species, whereas in another species the chemically identical hormone may be unbound.

It is recognized that mammalian gonadotropins may have quantitative differences in responses, depending upon mammalian species receiving the mammalian hormone. Notable is the finding of Van Wagenen and Simpson (154) that ovulation can be regularly induced in monkeys with extracts of monkey pituitaries, whereas the use of other gonadotropins has resulted in highly erratic, and, for the most part, negative results. Dörner (44) has recently provided evidence, however, that this may not apply to all non-primate gonadotropins. He reported that porcine FSH followed by HCG was as effective in inducing ovulation in humans as was human pituitary FSH.

Synergism between luteinizing and follicle stimulating hormones and problems in the complete separation of these two activities continues to plague investigators attempting to make a physiological characterization of FSH. There is evidence that the use of immunological procedures to neutralize contaminating LH in FSH extracts may be helpful in determining the responses of the gonads which are specific to FSH (87). LH, however, is apparently available in pure form, and, thus, tests in hypophysectomized animals should accurately reflect the physiology of this hormone.

In determining the direct gonadal responses to a gonadotropin, one must take into account the fact that gonadal hormones act not only upon the accessory reproductive organs, the brain, and the pituitary (see Chapter 7) but also have a direct influence upon the gonads. Evidence that estrogenic hormone secreted by small follicles played an important role in the normal development of definitive follicles led Edgar Allen (9) to paraphrase, "The 'favored follicle' truly 'stands on the shoulders of its contemporaries.'" More recent evidence that estrogen influences follicular growth in intact and hypophysectomized immature rats has been reviewed by Young (161). Although ovulation has been induced in the excised ovary of the toad by progesterone (164), there is little evidence for direct intervention of progesterone on gonadal function.

In the male, androgens will maintain spermatogenesis in the hypophysectomized animal (40, 156). Nelson (101) found that male rats treated with androgen remained fertile and would copulate for 6 months after hypophysectomy.

In the discussion to follow, no attempt will be made to distinguish direct effect of gonadotropins upon the gonads from indirect ones in which gonadal hormones may participate in effecting certain responses. The known effects of gonadotropins, excepting prolactin, are, for the most part, directly upon the gonads or mediated through the gonads by virtue of the secretion of gonadal hormones. A conspicuous exception to this general rule is the direct effect of LH (and HCG or PMSG) upon the nuptial feathering in the male African orange weaver finch (*Pyromelana franciscana*), as shown by Witschi (*158*).

For more extensive coverage of many aspects of the physiology of gonadotropins, the reader is referred to a number of excellent recent reviews: (Anderson (*10*); Catchpole (*25*); Everett (*55*); Geschwind (*63*); Gemzell and Roos (*64*); Greep (*66*); Harris and Campbell (*73*); Lyons and Dixon (*90*); Rothchild (*125*); Rowlands (*127*); Segaloff (*133*); Savard *et al.* (*131*); Short (*135*); and Wolstenholme and Knight (*159*).

II. Follicle Stimulating Hormone (FSH)

A. PHYSIOLOGY OF FSH IN THE FEMALE

Because FSH and LH synergize, and because there is uncertainty as to whether the purest FSH preparations available are entirely free of LH, the specific effects of FSH upon the gonads are incompletely known. The one most significant fact is that as the purity increases the weight response of the ovaries of intact immature rats decreases. For example, the FSH fraction prepared by Fevold *et al.* (*57*) in 1933, in intact immature female rats, produced ovaries weighing more than 200 mg when large doses were given, whereas the purest preparations today scarcely affect ovarian weight (*87*). The writer considers the question open, therefore, as to whether the follicular integrity and growth attributed to FSH (see Figs. 1–3, 5, and 7) depend solely upon FSH or whether slight LH contamination of the FSH preparations may be important in eliciting these responses.

A common concept for some years was that FSH produced slight follicular growth which, in turn, resulted in estrogen secretion by the ovary. Estrogen secretion, in turn, produced a uterine weight increase. Greep *et al.* (*68*) were the first to challenge this viewpoint. They obtained a highly purified FSH extract from porcine pituitaries which produced a two fold increase in ovarian weight of hypophysectomized rats and definite follicular development, but the uteri remained infantile. It is this lack of estrogen secretion which distinguishes these results from those previously obtained. Proteolytic enzymes were used during the course of purification. This, of course, immediately raises the question as to whether the integrity of the hormone has been maintained. Segaloff (133) stated recently that he has not ". . . seen a preparation of follicle stimulating hormone even if subjected to proteolytic digestion which failed to stimulate an increase in uterine weight when sufficient was given to produce a regularly significant increase in ovarian weight." Lostroh and Johnson (88), however, using FSH pre-

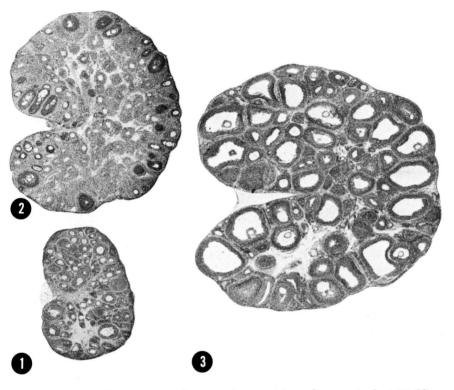

FIGS. 1–3. Cross sections of ovaries from rats hypophysectomized at 26–28 days of age with autopsy 10–12 days after the operation. Hematoxylin and eosin stain. × 19. From Simpson (137).
FIG. 1. Untreated control.
FIG. 2. LH treatment for 3 days. Interstitial cell repair, but follicles comparable to hypophysectomized control.
FIG. 3. FSH treatment for 3 days. Many follicles stimulated to partial development.

pared by the method of Papkoff et al. (105), reported that a certain amount of hormone doubled the ovarian weight, but the uteri were unaffected. Eshkol and Lunenfeld (48) obtained comparable results with FSH prepared from human menopausal urine. Similar findings concerning lack of estrogen secretion had been reported following immunological inactivation of LH in preparations having FSH activity (37, 87). In fact, studies of sera of mares immunized against HCG in immature female rats (37) suggest that FSH and LH are needed both for follicular growth and for estrogen secretion (Table I). Note that with 5 ml of serum the ovaries are enlarged, but the uteri are in the control range; whereas 30 ml of serum depresses both ovarian and uterine weights below those of untreated animals. This depression is interpreted as being due to the neutralization of endogenous LH of the rat by the anti-HCG. According to these findings, more LH is needed to produce estrogen secretion than is needed for ovarian growth, and the immature rat is producing sufficient amounts of endogenous LH to synergize with the exogenous FSH in the serum. If our interpretation is correct, the

TABLE I

GONADOTROPIC AND ANTIGONADOTROPIC ACTIVITY IN THE SERUM OF A
MARE IMMUNIZED AGAINST HCG AS SHOWN BY THE RESPONSE
IN INTACT IMMATURE FEMALE RATS[a,b]

Dose of serum (ml)	Ovary weight (mg)	Uterine weight (mg)
None (control)	17.3	38
1.25	19.3	90[c]
2.5	33.9[c]	59[c]
5.0	26.3[c]	37
30.0	13.8[d]	20[d]

[a] Six rats per dose level.

[b] From Cole and Snook (37).

[c] Significantly greater than control. This response depends upon FSH in the immune serum, which synergizes with LH from pituitary of recipients.

[d] Significantly less than control. This depression of ovarian and uterine weights depends upon inhibition of endogenous LH of the recipient rat by anti-HCG in the serum. The cross reactivity of anti-HCG against murine LH is low and thus is only observed when large amounts of serum are administered.

results of Greep et al. (68) and of Lostroh and Johnson (88) would indicate that their preparations contained sufficient LH for slight ovarian development, but not enough to synergize with FSH and stimuulate estrogen secretion.

In discussing the physiological action of FSH, it is pertinent to consider the effect of this hormone on metabolism and steroidogenesis. Meyer et al. (98) did not find an increase in succinic dehydrogenase in ovaries of rats treated either with FSH or unfractionated pituitary extracts.

Marsh and Savard (93) and Mason and Savard (95) found that NIH-FSH-S1 stimulated progesterone synthesis in vitro, but they provided convincing evidence that this activity depended upon contamination with LH. These studies on the effect of FSH on enzyme activity in the ovary provide no clue as to whether or not FSH by itself has an effect upon the ovary.

This discussion can be summarized by indicating that we are still not in a position to state unequivocally that FSH by itself has the ability to stimulate either follicular growth or estrogen secretion. The writer is disposed toward the position that in the female FSH only acts jointly with LH.

Though the commonly accepted view is that luteinization produced with FSH preparations is due to contaminating LH, the possibility exists that some degree of luteinization may be produced by FSH alone.

There has been a tendency to refer to LH as the ovulating hormone, but the evidence indicates that FSH and LH are equally competent in inducing ovulation of mature follicles. Lostroh and Johnson (88) found that 20 μg of either FSH or LH induced ovulation in 100% of hypophysectomized female rats treated 3 days previously with a combination of 3 μg of FSH and 1 μg of LH. As early as 1931, Leonard (84) reported that FSH and LH were equally effective in inducing ovulation in the estrous rabbit, a conclusion which has been confirmed using more highly purified preparations (23, 68).

Apparently, FSH plays no role in maintaining the functional activity of the corpus luteum; that is, it is not luteotropic. An FSH preparation from human menopausal urine did not stimulate progesterone synthesis in slices of bovine corpora lutea (48).

B. PHYSIOLOGY OF FSH IN THE MALE

The seminiferous tubules of the male are stimulated to increased growth by FSH (68). Simpson et al. (139) found that large amounts of their FSH preparation produced mature spermatozoa in Long-Evans males hypophysectomized at 40 days of age with amounts which failed to affect the sex accessories. It should be mentioned, however, that the Long-Evans strain is relatively refractory to LH by the ventral prostate assay. Synergism between FSH and HCG was demonstrated with small doses.

Though FSH has a marked stimulating effect upon the seminiferous tubules, it does not hasten the appearance of mature spermatozoa. Nelson (102) proposed that androgens may be necessary for the final stages of spermatogenesis, but this process is not hastened in the intact immature rat treated with PMSG, a situation in which the androgenic titer is very high, as judged by the response of the sex accessories (35).

C. ASSAY OF FSH

The minimal amount of FSH to reestablish follicular growth in hypophysectomized female rats has been used as the end point for assay of FSH by Evans and Simpson (52). This method involves sectioning of the ovaries and therefore is more cumbersome than the augmentation assay proposed by Steelman and Pohley (146). This latter procedure is based upon the synergistic response of FSH and LH. By giving an excess of LH (HCG), any interference with LH contaminating the extracts to be tested is obviated. Because of its reliability and simplicity it is widely used. Using the

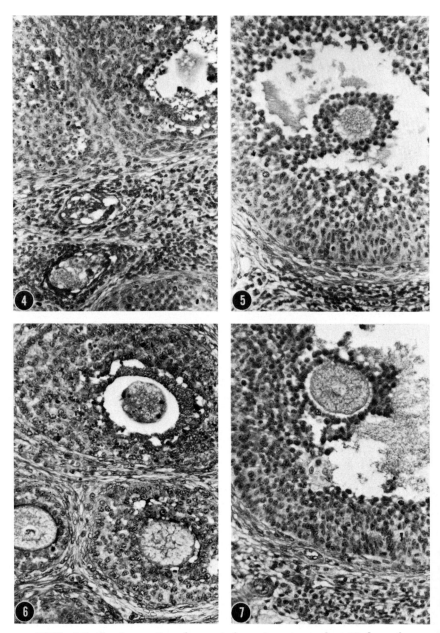

FIGS. 4–7. Ovarian sections from rats hypophysectomized at 28 days of age
and sacrificed 10 days later. Treated rats were injected once daily for 3 days, with
autopsy 72 hours after the initial injection. × 270. From Lostroh and Johnson
(88).

Steelman-Pohley assay, Parlow and Reichert (110) found that a reduction in the number of injections from 2 to 1 per day over a 3-day period decreased the mean value of the slope of porcine, ovine, equine, murine, and human FSH and that porcine FSH showed a greater decrease than did FSH from other species.

An assay based upon germ cell loss and Sertoli cell hypertrophy within 24 hours following the intratesticular injection of as little as 2 μg of NIH-FSH-S2 has been proposed by Murphy (99). The specificity of this procedure was not considered.

A sensitive method of assay of FSH based upon the synergism between FSH and LH using mice uterine weights as the end point has been suggested (78, 83). The studies of Uberoi and Meyer (152) and of DeReviers and Mauléon (42), however, indicate that the method lacks specificity.

A testicular augmentation assay for FSH proposed by Gans and van Rees (60) is based upon findings in earlier studies made by Paesi et al. (104). One rat testis is removed after hypophysectomy to serve as control. As in the Steelman-Pohley assay, an excess of LH (HCG) is given to obviate any influence of contaminating LH in the sample to be tested. It compares favorably in precision with the Steelman-Pohley assay.

Payne et al. (112) proposed an assay of FSH using hypophysectomized estrogen-treated immature rats. However, Meyer and Bradbury (95a) have reported that stilbestrol priming mainly augments the response to LH in the hypophysectomized rat. Since only partially purified preparations were used by both investigators, judgment on the specificity of the assay must be withheld.

III. Luteinizing Hormone (LH)

The discussion of LH, unless indicated otherwise, will refer to the hormone obtained from the pituitary gland. It is probable that LH, as it appears in the urine and blood of nonpregnant animals, is similar in nature. Many writers have referred to HCG as an "LH." Both HCG and PMSG have strong LH properties, as indicated by the response in the interstitial tissue of the testes of intact and hypophysectomized rats. Nonetheless, these hormones also have follicle stimulating properties and thus should be clearly distinguished from pituitary LH.

FIG. 4. Untreated control. The pycnotic nuclei of the interstitial cells and autolysis of the granulosa cells of the follicles bear witness to gonadotropin deficiency.

FIG. 5. FSH, 3 μg daily. Follicles now have antra and granulosa cells appear normal, but the interstitial cells are atrophic.

FIG. 6. ICSH, 1 μg daily. Interstitial cells repaired.

FIG. 7. ICSH, 1 μg daily and FSH, 3 μg daily. Healthy follicles and interstitial tissue.

Luteinizing hormone is frequently, and perhaps more correctly, referred to as interstitial cell stimulating hormone (ICSH). LH has the capacity to stimulate the interstitial tissue of the gonads of both the male and the female (see Figs. 2, 4–7, and 8). However, it acts in conjunction with FSH to influence follicular development in the female and by virtue of its ability to stimulate androgen secretion has an influence upon the seminiferous tubules of the male.

Parenthetically, the nomenclature of the gonoadotropins as a whole is extremely cumbersome and should be revised; attempts have been made periodically to revise it (15, 25, 29, 49), but unless an appropriate system can be adopted simultaneously by a number of leading journals in the field, there is little hope of overcoming the present confusing and extremely awkward terminology.

A. Physiology of LH in the Female

The development of the interstitial tissue of the gonads depends wholly, it seems clear, upon the presence of adequate amounts of LH in the blood (see Figs. 2 and 6).

The synergism between FSH and LH has been discussed previously. There is evidence that FSH and LH are being secreted at all phases of the estrous cycle. The output of both LH and FSH increases shortly before ovulation. According to one study (122), the increased release of FSH into the blood occurs slightly before LH. Faiman and Ryan (56) report two bursts of FSH release during the menstrual cycle, in some instances, with only one outpouring of LH. The release of FSH with LH at midcycle in normal women is a consistent finding (124). These data serve as additional evidence in favor of the view that FSH and LH participate in all phases of the development of the follicle up to the time of ovulation. As concerns ovulation there must be a sudden discharge of either or both FSH and LH in order for ovulation to occur. Normally, there is a discharge of both (56, 121, 130). Superovulation can readily be induced in either immature or mature females by repeated injections of FSH followed by LH or HCG (24, 157).

Though FSH extracts were found to stimulate progesterone synthesis in slices of bovine corpora lutea, the activity has been attributed by Mason and Savard (95) to contaminating LH. Extremely small amounts of LH are effective in stimulating progesterone synthesis in bovine luteal slices (72, 131). Interestingly, prolactin has no influence on progesterone synthesis in bovine corpora lutea slices *in vitro* (131). Short (135) was unable to raise the concentration of progesterone in peripheral blood of cows with corpora lutea in the ovaries by the administration of LH. Savard *et al.* (131) suggest that this may be due to refractory corpora lutea or to the possibility that the steroid synthesis is already maximal. Armstrong *et al.* (12) found that corpora early in the cycle were much more responsive to LH *in vitro* than were older corpora. LH is also effective in inducing progesterone synthesis in the human corpus luteum (131). Apparently, there is no synergism between FSH and LH in progesterone synthesis (120). Kilpatrick et al. (81) have shown that ovine pituitary LH will maintain the corpora lutea of hypophysectomized rabbits, whereas prolactin was ineffective in producing this response. Hansel and Siefart (72) showed that bovine LH prolonged the life of the corpus luteum in both intact and hysterectomized cows. These authors (136) also have studied incubation conditions for optimal progesterone synthesis of progesterone by slices of bovine corpora lutea. Armstrong et al. (13) found that bovine pituitary LH increased progesterone formation in the corpora lutea of superovulated rat ovaries.

B. Physiology of LH in the Male

LH stimulates the interstitial tissue of the male to secrete androgen. It may be that it is through androgen secretion that LH has an effect upon the seminiferous tubules of the hypophysectomized male. The weight increases induced by LH in the testes of hypophysectomized rats are not as great as those obtained with follicle stimulating hormone. The fact that the response of the testis to increasing doses of LH levels off relatively early explains how testis weight can be used as an assay for follicle stimulating hormone. Human LH is reported to be more potent than ovine LH (117, 145). Because the ventral prostate dose-response curve of human LH in saline is very flat, it is necessary to suspend the hormone in gelatin to quantitate its activity in terms of international units of HCG (89).

By the use of a sensitive LH assay (20), Gay and Bogdanove (62) studied the biological half-life of endogenous murine LH and exogenous ovine LH in the castrated, acutely hypophysectomized rat and reported half-lives ranging from 19.4 to 38.1 minutes. The differences between endogenous and exogenous values were not great. Earlier, Parlow and Ward (111) found half-lives of 15 and 17 minutes for exogenous ovine and murine LH, respectively.

C. Assay of LH

If great sensitivity is desired, radioimmunoassay will become the method of choice (see Chapter 3). The minimal effective dose (MED) biological assay is based upon the smallest amount of LH which will repair the interstitial tissue of the hypophysectomized female rat (52). In the hands of an experienced investigator it is a sensitive and reliable assay.

The ventral prostate weight assay proposed by Greep et al. (67) is not extremely sensitive, but the results can be expressed quantitatively and a dose-response curve can be constructed to limit the number of levels of injection necessary in order to express the results in terms of micrograms of a standard preparation. The ventral prostate response to LH has been shown by Segaloff et al. (132) to be augmented by concurrent injection of prolactin, and Parlow (109) has shown that it is also somewhat influenced by contamination with large amounts of FSH. Albert et al. (7) have shown that tannating pituitary LH extracts will enhance the ventral prostate weight response in hypophysectomized males. Rat or human serum used as a vehicle for injection of pituitary LH enhanced the ventral prostate weight response above that obtained with the hormone dissolved in saline (108). Finally, the response is greatly variable depending upon the strain of rats employed. The Long-Evans strain, for example, is relatively refractory.

The ovarian ascorbic acid depletion assay was developed by Parlow (106). This is a sensitive assay and has good precision when used on pituitary extracts. The response is depressed by tannating of pituitary extract, probably because the hormone is taken up less rapidly by the ovary from the bloodstream (7, 123). McCann and Ramirez (91) have suggested a modification of the Parlow assay which increases its sensitivity. Sakiz and Guillemin (128) have also suggested a modification of the procedure to increase its precision. Pelletier (113) has reported that plasma of hypophysectomized sheep produces a significant decrease in ascorbic acid. Gay and Bogdanove (61) have compared the use of PMSG alone as compared to PMSG plus HCG in preparing female rats for the OAAD. The differences obtained were not as striking as had been reported by Novella et al. (103).

Bell et al. (19) suggested an assay based on depletion of cholesterol following LH administration in the pseudopregnant rat, but others have reported it to be unsatisfactory (74, 140). Ellis (46) suggested an assay which apparently measured the blood flow through the gonad. It involves the intravenous injection of LH, followed by 2 μc of radioiodinated serum albumin 2 hours later. After 15 minutes both ovaries are excised and measured for contents of the tracer.

IV. Prolactin

Prolactin can be added to the list of gonadotropins only on the basis of its luteotropic action in the hypophysectomized rat. Lyons and Dixon (90) give an excellent discussion of the luteotropic action of this hormone. The evidence is irrefutable that it has luteotropic activity in the hypophysectomized rat. They conclude that HCG may exert its luteotropic action by virtue of its ability to stimulate estrogen secretion, which, in turn, causes the release of prolactin. The clear-cut evidence obtained in the rat by Evans et al. (54) in 1941 led to the generally accepted view that prolactin was the luteotropic hormone. Huang and Pearlman (75) were unable to increase the rate of synthesis of radioactive progesterone in vitro in slices of luteinized rat ovaries with ovine prolactin, while Armstrong et al. (13) have shown that highly purified bovine LH increases progesterone formation in vitro in these ovaries. Thus, it appears that the in vivo and in vitro studies with prolactin in the rat are in conflict. Savard *et al.* (*131*) state that prolactin is without activity as a luteotropin in the woman, the monkey, the sow, the ewe, the guinea pig, and the rabbit. They indicate that luteinizing hormone alone induces steroidogenesis in slices of the corpus luteum of the cow and the woman. However, Bartosik *et al.* (*18*) found that prolactin augmented the secretion of progesterone in bovine luteal ovaries perfused *in vitro*. The classification of prolactin as a gonadotropin nonetheless seems to hang from a tenuous thread.

V. Human Chorionic Gonadotropin (HCG)

A. EFFECT OF HCG IN THE FEMALE

The early literature describing many of the physiological effects of HCG is reviewed by Engle (*47*). HCG produces a true precocious sexual maturity in rats and mice. Ovulation and pregnancy subsequent to mating occur. In the immature rat, amounts of hormone which cause development of a few follicles will produce a typical estrous uterus, indicating that a rich estrogen secretion is initiated. The ovarian dose-response curve shows a moderately steep rise between 1 and 40 IU, between 40 and about 800 IU it is relatively flat, and with further increase in dosage another steep rise is manifested (*8, 71*).

In the hypophysectomized female rat the response is limited mainly to interstitial cell development when small amounts of hormone are given (Fig. 8); larger amounts produce marked follicular enlargement and partial luteinization (Figs. 9 and 11).

Within 2 to 4 hours after injection of HCG into intact immature female rats, ovarian hyperemia is manifested. HCG, like pituitary LH, augments the ovarian response to FSH. In the Steelman-Pohley assay for FSH, this synergism is used to obviate any effect of LH contaminating the FSH preparation being tested. Ovulation is induced by HCG in the isolated estrous rabbit. This is the basis for the widely used Friedman pregnancy test.

As early as 1934, Leonard and Smith (*86*) postulated that follicular development following treatment with HCG depended upon a contribution from the pituitary gland. FSH has been presumed to be the pituitary factor involved. Shiino and Rennels (*134*) showed that follicular growth induced by HCG in 19-day-old rats could be inhibited by giving anti-FSH. There seems to be little doubt but that endogenous FSH plays a role in follicular development of the intact immature rat. It is known that amounts of HCG in excess of 800 IU will produce follicular development in the hypophysectomized rat. Simpson (*138*) indicated that this may be due to pituitary FSH contaminating HCG extracts. This view receives further support by the finding of Crooke and Butt (*39*) that the equivalent of 4 mg of human

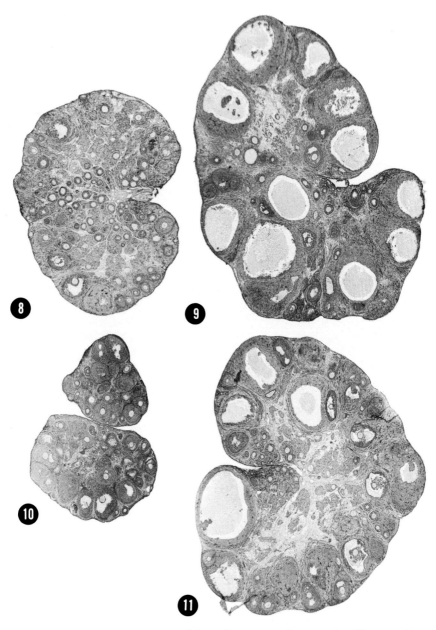

FIGS. 8–11. Cross sections of hypophysectomized rat ovaries. The operation was performed at 21 days of age. HCG was injected once daily on the 23rd, 24th, and 25th days of age. Anti-HCG was given as a single injection on the 23rd day. Autopsy was performed 96 hours after initial injection. × 29. From Cole and Bigelow (31).

menopausal gonadotropin (HMG20A) was excreted daily in the urine of women during pregnancy.

By giving anti-HCG with HCG to hypophysectomized Long-Evans female rats, evidence has recently been presented, however, to support the view, suggested earlier by Albert (2), that HCG has intrinsic follicle stimulating activities. The anti-HCG inhibited both the second rise in ovarian weights of immature rats and the follicular development of hypophysectomized rats in a manner expected if these responses depended upon HCG (see Figs. 8–11). The anti-HCG preparation used augmented the response to ovine FSH in the intact immature female rat, thus indicating that any contaminating pituitary FSH in the HCG preparation was not being inhibited. Furthermore, calculation of the amount of contamination of the HCG preparation with pituitary FSH which might be expected made it seem unlikely that FSH played any significant role in either the second rise of ovarian weight in the intact immature rat or the follicular development in the hypophysectomized female rat.

B. EFFECT OF HCG IN THE MALE

In the intact immature male, the main effect of HCG is upon the interstitial tissue, with consequent secretion of androgen and the development of the sex accessories. The seminiferous tubules are enlarged, but precocious spermatogenesis does not result. If mature male rats are hypophysectomized and treatment with HCG started immediately, complete testicular function is maintained. HCG is used successfully to induce descent of the testes in certain types of human cryptorchidism (151). HCG has an adrenotropic effect upon the male rat adrenal. This response is reported to be mediated by the testes (43). In toads and frogs, HCG induces spermiation.

C. ASSAY OF HCG

Any of the physiological responses to HCG may be used in pregnancy diagnosis or in biological assay. In pregnancy diagnosis, the rapidity of the test is important, whereas in assay, precision is desired. Zarrow (162) has discussed the pregnancy tests and points out that tests based on ovarian

FIG. 8. Ovary of hypophysectomized rat receiving 800 IU HCG plus 0.1 ml anti-HCG serum. The ovarian weight (19.2 mg) is greatly reduced in comparison to rat receiving 800 IU HCG without antiserum (see Fig. 9). The largest follicles are approximately the same size as that of hypophysectomized controls, but there is marked interstitial cell development.

FIG. 9. Ovary of hypophysectomized rat receiving 800 IU HCG. Note that the follicles are greatly enlarged and partly luteinized. Ovarian weight = 47.2 mg.

FIG. 10. Ovary of hypophysectomized control. Ovary weight = 10.2 mg.

FIG. 11. Ovary of rat receiving 1600 IU of HCG plus 0.2 ml of anti-HCG serum. This is a calculated dose of 1100 IU of HCG. Ovarian weight = 44.2 mg.

hyperemia of the rat, the extrusion of ova in *Xenopus laevis,* and spermia-tion in *Bufo arenarum* may be completed within a 4-hour period with an accuracy comparable to that of the corpora hemorrhagica test in the immature rat or the isolated rabbit.

It is important to remember that treatment and the vehicle for injection may greatly influence the assay. For example, Albert *et al.* (5) showed that tannates of HCG were 3.3 times as potent by the ventral prostate assay as untannated HCG and 1.8 times more potent by the ovarian ascorbic acid depletion assay. Simpson (137) lists the following physiological responses which have been used in assaying HCG: corpora lutea in ovaries of imma-ture rats or mice, uterine weight of immature rat, vaginal cornification in immature rat, ovulation in isolated rabbit, rat ovarian hyperemia, and the ventral prostate response in hypophysectomized male rats. To this list should be added spermiation in toads and frogs. For many purposes, no doubt, immunological procedures will supplant these biological tests. Be-cause denaturation may result in a loss of biological potency without a corresponding loss in immunological properties, it is unlikely that biological tests will be entirely replaced. Parenthetically, Hamburger (70) gives an interesting thumbnail sketch of the chronology of the development of our knowledge concerning gonadotropins including bioassay and immunoassay.

VI. *Pregnant Mare Serum Gonadotropin (PMSG)*

A. Effect of PMSG in the Female

The reader is again referred to Engle (47) for review of the early litera-ture dealing with the biological properties of PMSG. This hormone at a proper dosage level (6–15 IU) will produce superovulation in rats 25–28 days of age at the time of the injection. About 50% of these rats will mate and some will carry an abnormally large number of fetuses to term. A single injection of a large dose of PMSG into immature females will produce ovaries weighing in excess of 200 mg.

Two to four IU will bring about perceptible stimulation of the ovaries of hypophysectomized female rats. A single injection of 120 IU into these animals will produce ovaries weighing approximately 100 mg—about two-thirds of the weight one would expect to obtain in intact immature rats.

PMSG will produce ovulation in the estrous rabbit, but this animal is not nearly as sensitive to the hormone as is the rat. It will also produce ovulation in the anestrous ewe, and two injections spaced 17 days apart will induce both estrus and ovulation in variable numbers of treated ani-mals. In three prepuberal monkeys receiving 35, 75, and 400 RU of PMSG daily for 6–8½ months, cystic ovaries were induced and menstrua-tion was observed 19, 22, and 29 days after initiation of treatment (153).

A quiescent period followed, ranging from 57 to 170 days, after which regular cycles were established, in spite of continued injections. Two of the three monkeys became pregnant shortly after cessation of injection, indicating that the anti-PMSG present did not cross-react with the endogenous gonadotropin.

It has been recognized for some time (36, 51) that PMSG rarely produces ovulation in the hypophysectomized female rat, even though the follicles are luteinized. This is true even though this hormone has a balance of LH and FSH properties. One might, therefore, attribute the fact that it does readily produce ovulation in the intact animal to the participation of endogenous gonadotropin from the recipient's pituitary. Gay and Bogdanove (61) have provided evidence that PMSG administration resulted in a reduced content of pituitary LH in rats. The injection of PMSG into 25-day-old immature rats reduced pituitary FSH between 1:30 and 7:00 PM of the 27th day, whereas the pituitary LH content dropped later (118). Szontagh and associates (147, 148) found that the injection of PMSG caused a lowering of pituitary LH in ovariectomized as well as in the intact immature rat. Quinn and Zarrow (114, 115) reported that ovulation induced by PMSG in immature rats could be blocked by hypophysectomy, by administration of drugs, or by hypothalamic lesions. According to Wagner and Brown-Grant (155), the time of administering Nembutal to block ovulation in immature rats treated with PMSG at the beginning of the light period was longer than when the hormone was injected at the beginning of the dark period. Evidence has been provided that blocking of ovulation in the PMSG-treated immature rat by progesterone is brought about by blocking the release of endogenous FSH (22).

A PMSG half-life of 6 days in the gelding and about 26 hours in the rabbit and rat have been reported (26, 111). The half-life of endogenous PMSG in the mare hysterectomized during pregnancy was found to be essentially the same as reported previously for the gelding (32). Thus, it appears that the gonads have no appreciable influence upon the rate of disappearance of the hormone. Fitko (59), likewise, could find no evidence that rat or cow ovarian tissue metabolized gonadotropin. Studies on losses of PMSG in the urine and milk (32) indicate that the major portion of the hormone is metabolized rather than excreted. The ovary is not the site of this metabolism. According to Parlow and Ward (111), the half-life of PMSG in the rat (24–26 hours) is much longer than that of HCG (4.9 hours) or of 17 minutes for murine LH (Fig. 12). The long half-life of PMSG is consonant with the fact that a single injection is as effective as multiple injections (35). Connell (38) has attributed the slow disappearance from the bloodstream to the high molecular weight of PMSG (68,000). As discussed in Chapter 4, the question of the molecular weight is still unsettled. A value as low as 28,000 has been reported, but a larger molecule would make its long half-life, its prolonged action, and its failure to be influenced by tannation (4) more understandable.

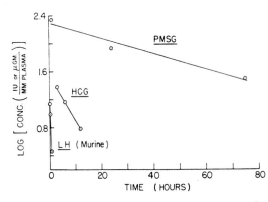

FIG. 12. Half-lives of murine LH (half-life = 26 hours; $b = -0.012$), HCG (half-life = 4.9 hours; $b = -0.064$), and PMSG (half-life = 26 hours; $b = -0.012$). From Parlow and Ward (*111*).

B. Effect of PMSG in the Male

In the immature male rat there is a remarkable development of the interstitial tissue of the testes if daily treatment with PMSG is instituted (Figs. 13–16). As with HCG, a true precocious maturity is not induced in the intact male. The hormone has a pronounced effect on both the interstitial tissue and the seminiferous tubules of the hypophysectomized male rat. The biological properties of purified PMSG (3000–4000 IU/mg) could not be differentiated from the effects of crude pregnant mare serum (*36*). Atrophy of the gonads and sex accessories of mature rats on a low protein diet (Fig. 17) can be corrected and fertility restored with PMSG (*35*).

C. Assay of PMSG

Cole and Erway (*33*) proposed a 48-hour method of assay based upon the ovarian weight response of 25-day-old immature female rats. A slight modification involves a two-point assay using younger (22-day-old) rats (*31*). This procedure is more rapid and simpler than the older 96-hour minimal response assays. It is more specific and probably more accurate than assays based on uterine weight.

VII. Effect of Gonoadotropins upon Metabolic Activity of Gonads

It is well known that gonadotropins influence directly or indirectly the synthesis of steroid hormones by the gonads and are also responsible for the growth of gonadal tissues. The dramatic effect of PMSG on the blood supply of the ovary was illustrated by Catchpole and Lyons (*27*).

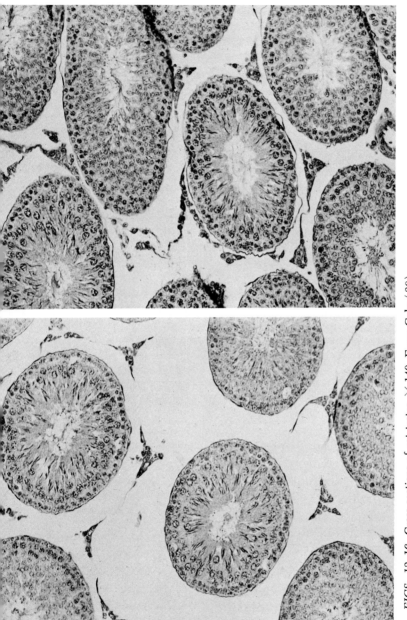

FIGS. 13–16. Cross sections of rat testes. × 140. From Cole (*30*).
FIG. 13. Untreated control rat sacrificed at 48th day of age.
FIG. 14. Rat receiving 2 RU of PMSG (1 RU essentially same as 1 IU) daily from 25th to 44th days with necropsy on 45th day.

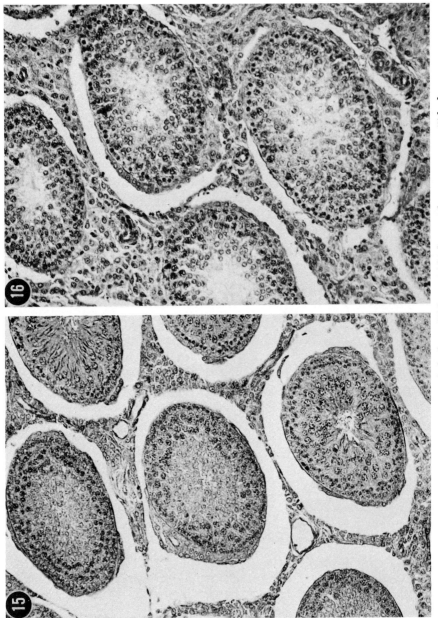

FIG. 15. Rat receiving 32 RU daily from 25th to 44th days with necropsy on 45th day.

FIG. 16. Rat receiving 32 RU daily from 25th to 47th days with necropsy on 48th day. Note the extreme development

The fact that progesterone is secreted in normal amounts following hypophysectomy in ewes indicates that a constant supply of LH is not necessary for continuing function of a formed corpus luteum (41, 135). Armstrong and Black (11) reported, however, that LH added to the incubation medium did increase the synthesis of progesterone by slices of bovine corpus luteum. LH or HCG has been found to increase testosterone production by testicular tissue both *in vivo* and *in vitro* (45, 77, 129). These data support the view that gonadotropins regulate the activities of the enzyme systems.

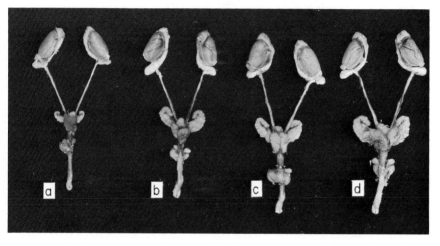

FIG. 17. Reproductive organs of male rats sacrificed at 130 days of age; (a) untreated rat on low protein diet; (b) rat on low protein diet receiving single injection of 500 RU (essentially, 1 RU = 1 IU) of PMSG; (c) untreated rat on normal diet; (d) rat on normal diet receiving a single injection of 500 IU of PMSG. From Cole *et al.* (35).

FSH administered 1 hour or more before sacrifice increased the incorporation of isotopic uridine and valine into the ovarian follicles of rabbits; LH and HCG pretreatment also stimulated incorporation into both follicles and interstitial tissue, but incorporation into the interstitial tissue was more marked (65). Ahren and Rubinstein (1) found that injection of FSH 4 hours before the ovaries were removed increased the incorporation of glycine-³H into ovarian protein, but the addition of FSH to the medium *in vitro* was without effect. They suggested that FSH influenced amino acid transport. Amounts of FSH plus HCG, which significantly influenced rat ovarian weights, increased total RNA and DNA and the RNA:DNA ratio (21).

Nagai *et al.* (*100*) reported an enhanced incorporation of ^{32}P into lipid phosphate in the ovarian microsomal fraction following treatment with HCG. McKerns (*92*) showed that the subcutaneous injection of PMSG resulted in a marked increase in specific and total activities of NADP+— specific dehydrogenases, and if the PMSG was followed by HCG, the increase was still greater. LH given 30 minutes or 3 hours prior to sacrifice stimulated the uptake of glucose and production of lactic acid in minced luteinized rat ovaries, but LH added *in vitro* was without effect (*28*).

VIII. The Progonadotropic Response

Sera of animals treated chronically with gonadotropins as antigens frequently display progonadotropic activity before antigonadotropic responses are obtained; later low doses of sera may augment the response to a gonadotropin given concurrently, whereas larger amounts of serum may completely inhibit it (*79, 94, 126, 150*). Meyer and Kupperman (*97*) and Kupperman *et al.* (*82*) showed ovarian hypertrophy of female rats in parabiotic union with rats pretreated with antiserum or precocious development of ovaries of infantile rats subsequent to treatment with antiserum. They attributed these effects as being due to the stimulation of the rat's pituitary by the antiserum. More recently, it has been shown, however, that sera with high antigonadotropic titers also have gonadotropic activity (*143, 144*). The basis for referring to "progonadotropic" activity was that the antiserum presumably had no gonadotropic activity when given alone. Immature female rats were used in testing the sera by these early investigators, however, and it has been shown more recently that certain antisera having no effect upon the immature female will produce a ventral prostate weight response in the hypophysectomized male rat (Cole, H. H., Snook, R. B., McDonald, P. G., and Dierschke, D., unpublished). Ahern, Geschwind, and Cole (unpublished) have shown that HCG antiserum markedly prolongs the half-life of ovine LH in the rat; this effect plus increased gonadotropic levels may account for the so-called progonadotropic response to antisera.

IX. The Pituitary Antagonist

Certain pituitary extracts given intraperitoneally to intact or hypophysectomized rats will inhibit the response to gonadotropins given subcutaneously (*50, 53, 85*). Woods and Simpson (*160*) have made the most exhaustive study of this phenomenon to date. Only gonadotropic extracts, among anterior and posterior hormone preparations, appear to have antagonistic properties. With increasing purification the property was lost in FSH preparations and diminished in LH extracts. The authors suggest that antagonism depends upon an unknown factor which is difficult to separate from LH.

X. Standards and International Units

In 1939, international standards for prolactin, PMSG, and HCG were established by the World Health Organization (WHO) of the League of Nations. The decisions concerning the standard and international units were made by the Third International Conference on the Standardization of Hormones (119).

The gonadotropic preparations used in setting up these standards were supplied by pharmaceutical houses. To facilitate quantitation the preparations were mixed with inert material and a certain weight of this material was designated as 1 IU. For example, 0.1 mg of the international standard for HCG was designated as the international unit. The unit was designed to produce some specific biological effect—1 IU of PMSG, for example, was the smallest amount which would induce follicular growth and luteinization in the ovaries of 22- to 25-day-old female rats. The supplies of the first standards of prolactin, HCG, and PMSG are exhausted and new standards have been established. The description of how the standards were prepared and tested is given in bulletins of WHO (e.g., 16, 17).

An international standard for human pituitary gonadotropin obtained from menopausal urine has recently been established. This standard has both FSH and LH activity. One IU of FSH or of LH has been defined as 0.229 mg of this international standard. Albert (3) gives amounts of international standard (2nd International Reference Preparation, IRP) needed to produce specific biological responses in male and female rats.

The National Institute for Medical Research (Division of Biological Standards, Medical Research Council, National Institute for Medical Research, Mill Hill, London, England) has accepted the responsibility for collecting, testing, packaging, and storing the standards. Samples are distributed upon request to scientists throughout the world.

In addition to the international standards, the National Institute of Health of the U.S. Public Health Service has relatively pure preparations of pituitary FSH and LH which, in a sense, serve as standards.

REFERENCES

1. Ahren, K., and Rubinstein, L., *Acta Physiol. Scand.* **64**, 463 (1965).
2. Albert, A. (ed.), *in* "Human Pituitary Gonadotropins," p. 132. Thomas, Springfield, Illinois, 1961.
3. Albert, A., *Acta Endocrinol. Suppl.* **106** (1966).
4. Albert, A., Bennett, G., Carl, G., Rosemberg, E., Keller, P., and Lewis, W. B., *Endocrinology* **76**, 499 (1965).

5. Albert, A., Bennett, D., Carl, G., Rosemberg, E., Keller, P., and Lewis, W. B., *Endocrinology* **76**, 506 (1965).
6. Albert, A., Derner, I., Rosemberg, E., and Lewis, W. B., *Endocrinology* **76**, 19 (1965).
7. Albert, A., Derner, I., Rosemberg, E., and Lewis, W. B., *Endocrinology* **76**, 139 (1965).
8. Albert, A., and Kelly, S., *J. Clin. Endocrinol. Metab.* **18**, 1067 (1958).
9. Allen, E., *in* "Glandular Physiology and Therapy," pp. 142–167. Am. Med. Assoc., Chicago, Illinois, 1942.
10. Anderson, L. L., Schultz, J. R., and Melampy, R. M., *in* "Gonadotropins, Their Chemical and Biological Properties and Secretory Control" (H. H. Cole, ed.), pp. 171–219. Freeman, San Francisco, California, 1964.
11. Armstrong, D. T., and Black, D. L., *Endocrinology* **78**, 937 (1966).
12. Armstrong, D. T., Black, D. L., and Core, C. E., *Federation Proc.* **23**, 462 (1964).
13. Armstrong, D. T., O'Brien, J., and Greep, R. O., *Endocrinology* **75**, 488 (1964).
14. Aschheim, S., and Zondek, B., *Klin. Wochschr.* **7**, 1404 (1928).
15. Astwood, E. B., and Greep, R. O., *Science* **89**, 81 (1939).
16. Bangham, D. R., Mussett, M. V., and Stack-Dunne, M. P., *Bull. World Health Organ.* **29**, 721–728 (1963).
17. Bangham, D. R., and Woodward, P. M., *Bull. World Health Organ.* (in press) (1968).
18. Bartosik, D., Romanoff, E. B., Watson, D. J., and Scricco, E., *Endocrinology* **81**, 186 (1967).
19. Bell, E. T., Mukerji, S., and Loraine, J. A., *J. Endocrinol.* **28**, 321 (1964).
20. Bogdanove, E. M., and Gay, V. L., *Endocrinology* **81**, 1104 (1967).
21. Callantine, M. R., Humphrey, R. R., and Lee, S., *Endocrinology* **76**, 332 (1965).
22. Callantine, M. R., and Humphrey, R. R., *Endocrinology* **77**, 921 (1965).
23. Carter, F., Woods, M. C., and Simpson, M. E., *in* "Control of Ovulation" (C. A. Villee, ed.), pp. 1–21. Pergamon, Oxford, 1961.
24. Casida, L. E., Meyer, R. K., McShan, W. H., and Wisnicky, W., *Am. J. Vet. Res.* **4**, 76 (1943).
25. Catchpole, H. R., *in* "Gonadotropins, Their Chemical and Biological Properties and Secretory Control" (H. H. Cole, ed.), pp. 40–70. Freeman, San Francisco, California, 1964.
26. Catchpole, H. R., Cole, H. H., and Pearson, P. B., *Am. J. Physiol.* **112**, 21 (1935).
27. Catchpole, H. R., and Lyons, W. R., *Am. J. Anat.* **55**, 167 (1934).
28. Channing, C. P., and Villee, C. A., *Biochim. Biophys. Acta* **115**, 205 (1966).
29. Coffin, H. C., and Van Dyke, H. B., *Science* **93**, 61 (1941).
30. Cole, H. H., *Am. J. Anat.* **59**, 299 (1936).
31. Cole, H. H., and Bigelow, M., *Anat. Record* **157**, 19 (1967).
32. Cole, H. H., Bigelow, M., Finkel, J., and Rupp, G. R., *Endocrinology* **81**, 927 (1967).
33. Cole, H. H., and Erway, J., *Endocrinology* **29**, 514 (1941).
34. Cole, H. H., and Goss, H., *Am. J. Physiol.* **127**, 702 (1939).

35. Cole, H. H., Guilbert, H. R., and Goss, H., *Am. J. Physiol.* **102**, 227 (1932).
36. Cole, H. H., Pencharz, R. I., and Goss, H., *Endocrinology* **27**, 548 (1940).
37. Cole, H. H., and Snook, R. B., *Proc. 5th Intern. Congr. Animal Reprod. Artificial Insemination, Trento* **2**, 143–147 (1964).
38. Connell, G. M., *Nature* **207**, 412 (1965).
39. Crooke, A. C., and Butt, W. R., *J. Obstet. Gynaecol. Brit. Commonwealth* **66**, 297 (1959).
40. Cutuly, E., and Cutuly, E. C., *Endocrinology* **26**, 503 (1940).
41. Denamur, R., Martinet, J., and Short, R. V., *Acta Endocrinol.* **52**, 72 (1966).
42. DeReviers, M. M., and Mauléon, P., *Compt. Rend. Acad. Sci.* **261**, 540 (1965).
43. Dinerstein, J., and Lanmon, J. T., *Endocrinology* **68**, 164 (1961).
44. Dörner, G., *Acta Endocrinol. Suppl.* **119**, 112 (1967).
45. Eik-Nes, K. B., and Hall, P. F., *J. Reprod. Fertility* **9**, 233 (1965).
46. Ellis, S., *Endocrinology* **68**, 334 (1961).
47. Engle, E. T., *in* "Sex and Internal Secretions" (E. Allen, ed.), 2nd ed., pp. 1003–1044. Williams & Wilkins, Baltimore, Maryland, 1939.
48. Eshkol, A., and Lunenfeld, B., *Acta Endocrinol.* **54**, 91 (1967).
49. Evans, H. M., *Western J. Surg. Obstet. Gynecol.* March–April (1936).
50. Evans, H. M., Korpi, K., Pencharz, R. I., and Simpson, M. E., *Univ. Calif. Publ. Anat., Berkeley* **1**, 237 (1936).
51. Evans, H. M., Meyer, R. K., and Simpson, M. E., *Mem. Univ. Calif.* **11**, 151 (1933).
52. Evans, H. M., and Simpson, M. E., *in* "The Hormones" (G. Pincus and K. V. Thimann, eds.), Vol. 2, pp. 351–404. Academic Press, New York, 1950.
53. Evans, H. M., Simpson, M. E., and Austin, P. K., *J. Exptl. Med.* **58**, 545 (1933).
54. Evans, H. M., Simpson, M. E., Lyons, W. R., and Turpeinen, K., *Endocrinology* **28**, 933 (1941).
55. Everett, J. W., *in* "Sex and Internal Secretion" (W. C. Young, ed.), Vol. 1, pp. 497–555. Williams & Wilkins, Baltimore, Maryland, 1961.
56. Faiman, C., and Ryan, R. J., *J. Clin. Endocrinol. Metab.* **27**, 1711 (1967).
57. Fevold, H. L., Hisaw, F. L., Hellbaum, A., and Hertz, R., *Am. J. Physiol.* **104**, 710 (1933).
58. Fevold, H. L., Hisaw, F. L., and Leonard, S. L., *Am. J. Physiol.* **97**, 291 (1931).
59. Fitko, R., *Endokrynol. Polska* **16**,, 289 (1965).
60. Gans, E., and van Rees, G. P., *Acta Endocrinol.* **52**, 573 (1966).
61. Gay, V. L., and Bogdanove, E. M., *Endocrinology* **78**, 1268 (1966).
62. Gay, V. L., and Bogdanove, E. M., *Endocrinology* **82**, 359 (1968).
63. Gemzell, C., and Roos, P., *in* "The Pituitary Gland" (G. W. Harris and B. T. Donovan, eds.), Vol. 1, pp. 492–517, Butterworth, London and Washington, D.C., 1966.
64. Geschwind, I. I., *in* "The Pituitary Gland" (G. W. Harris and B. T. Donovan, eds.), Vol. 2, pp. 589–612, Butterworth, London and Washington, D.C., 1966.

65. Given, M., Brown, C. B., and Hilliard, J., *Biochim. Biophys. Acta* **114**, 127 (1966).
66. Greep, R. O., *in* "Sex and Internal Secretions" (W. C. Young, ed.), Vol. 1, pp. 240–301. Williams & Wilkins, Baltimore, Maryland, 1961.
67. Greep, R. O., Van Dyke, H. B., and Chow, B. F., *Proc. Soc. Exptl. Biol. Med.* **46**, 644 (1941).
68. Greep, R. O., Van Dyke, H. B., and Chow, B. F., *Endocrinology* **30**, 635 (1942).
69. Hamashige, S., Astor, M. A., Arguilla, E. R., and Van Thiel, D. H., *J. Clin. Endocrinol. Metab.* **27**, 1690 (1967).
70. Hamburger, C., *in* "Gonadotropins: Physicochemical and Immunological Properties" (G. E. W. Wolstenholme and J. Knight, eds.), pp. 1–10. Little, Brown, Boston, Massachusetts, 1965.
71. Hamburger, C., and Johnsen, S., *in* "Human Pituitary Gonadotropins" (A. Albert, ed.), p. 161. Thomas, Springfield, Illinois, 1961.
72. Hansel, W., and Siefart, K. H., *J. Dairy Sci.* **50**, 1948 (1967).
73. Harris, G. W., and Campbell, H. J., *in* "The Pituitary Gland" (G. W. Harris and B. T. Donovan, eds.), Vol. 2, pp. 99–165. Butterworth, London and Washington, D.C., 1966.
74. Heald, P. J., and Furnival, B. E., *J. Endocrinol.* **34**, 525 (1966).
75. Huang, W. Y., and Pearlman, W. H., *J. Biol. Chem.* **237**, 1060 (1962).
76. Hutchinson, J. S. M., Armstrong, D. T., and Greep, R. O., *Acta Endocrinol. Suppl.* **119**, 111 (1967).
77. Ibayashi, H., Nakamura, M., Uchikawa, T., Murakawa, S., Yoshida, S., Nakao, K., and Okinaka, S., *Endocrinology* **76**, 347 (1965).
78. Igarashi, M., and McCann, S. M., *Endocrinology* **74**, 440 (1964).
79. Katman, P. A., Wade, N. J., and Doisy, E. A., *Endocrinology* **41**, 27 (1947).
80. Kikutani, M., and Tokuyasu, K., *J. Biochem.* (*Tokyo*) **57**, 598 (1965).
81. Kilpatrick, R., Armstrong, D. T., and Greep, R. O., *Endocrinology* **74**, 453 (1964).
82. Kupperman, H. S., Meyer, R. K., and Finerty, J. C., *Am. J. Physiol.* **136**, 293 (1942).
83. Lamond, D. R., and Bindon, B. M., *J. Endocrinol.* **34**, 365 (1966).
84. Leonard, S. L., *Am. J. Physiol.* **198**, 406 (1931).
85. Leonard, S. L., *Proc. Soc. Exptl. Biol. Med.* **31**, 1157 (1934).
86. Leonard, S. L., and Smith, P. E., *Anat. Record* **58**, 175 (1934).
87. Li, C. H., Moudgal, N. R., Trenkle, A., Bourdel, G., and Sadri, K., *Ciba Found. Colloq. Endocrinol.* **14**, 20 (1962).
88. Lostroh, A. J., and Johnson, R. E., *Endocrinology* **79**, 991 (1966).
89. Lostroh, A. J., Squire, P. G., and Li, C. H., *J. Endocrinol.* **26**, 215 (1963).
90. Lyons, W. R., and Dixon, J. S., *in* "The Pituitary Gland" (G. W. Harris and B. T. Donovan, eds.), Vol. 1, pp. 527–581, Butterworths, London, 1966.
91. McCann, S. M., and Ramirez, V. D., *Recent Progr. Hormone Res.* **20**, 131 (1964).
92. McKerns, K. W., *Biochim. Biophys. Acta* **97**, 542 (1965).
93. Marsh, J. M., and Savard, K., *J. Biol. Chem.* **239**, 1 (1964).
94. Marvin, H. N., and Meyer, R. K., *Endocrinology* **32**, 271 (1943).
95. Mason, N. R., and Savard, K., *Endocrinology* **74**, 664 (1964).

95a. Meyer, J. E., and Bradbury, J. T., *Endocrinology* **66,** 121 (1960).
 96. Meyer, R. K., *in* "Gonadotropins: Their Chemical and Biological Properties and Secretory Control" (H. H. Cole, ed.), p. 71. Freeman, San Francisco, California, 1964.
 97. Meyer, R. K., and Kupperman, H. S., *Proc. Soc. Exptl. Biol. Med.* **42,** 285 (1939).
 98. Meyer, R. K., McShan, W. H., and Erway, W. F., *Endocrinology* **37,** 431 (1945).
 99. Murphy, H. D., *Proc. Soc. Exptl. Biol. Med.* **120,** 671 (1966).
100. Nagai, K., Matsumoto, K., Kotoh, K., Hanai, J., and Okala, K., *Med. J. Osaka Univ.* **16,** 321 (1966).
101. Nelson, W. O., *Cold Spring Harbor Symp. Quant. Biol.* **5,** 123 (1937).
102. Nelson, W. O., *Ciba Found. Colloq. Endocrinol.* **4,** 271 (1952).
103. Novella, M., Alloiteau, J., and Ascheim, P., *Compt. Rend. Acad. Sci.* **259,** 1553 (1964).
104. Paesi, F. J. A., Wijnas, and de Jongh, S. E., *Acta Endocrinol.* **8,** 251 (1951).
105. Papkoff, H., Gospodarowicz, D., and Candiotti, A., *Arch. Biochem.* **111,** 431 (1965).
106. Parlow, A. F., *in* "Human Pituitary Gonadotropins" (A. Albert, ed.), pp. 300–310. Thomas, Springfield, Illinois, 1961.
107. Parlow, A. F., *Program 43rd. Meeting Endocrine Soc., New York* p. 8 (1961).
108. Parlow, A. F., *Endocrinology* **73,** 377 (1963).
109. Parlow, A. F., *Endocrinology* **73,** 456 (1963).
110. Parlow, A. F., and Reichert, L. E., Jr., *Endocrinology* **73,** 740 (1963).
111. Parlow, A. F., and Ward, D. N., *in* "Human Pituitary Gonadotropins" (A. Albert, ed.), pp. 204–209. Thomas, Springfield, Illinois, 1961.
112. Payne, R. W., Runser, R. H., Hagans, J. A., and Morrison, R. D., *Endocrinology* **65,** 389 (1959).
113. Pelletier, J., *Compt. Rend. Acad. Sci.* **260,** 5624 (1965).
114. Quinn, D. L., and Zarrow, M. X., *Endocrinology* **74,** 309 (1964).
115. Quinn, D. L., and Zarrow, M. X., *Endocrinology* **77,** 255 (1964).
116. Reichert, L. E., Jr., *Endocrinology* **80,** 1180 (1967).
117. Reichert, L. E., Jr., and Parlow, A. F., *Endocrinology* **75,** 815 (1964).
118. Rennels, E. G., and O'Steen, W. K., *Endocrinology* **80,** 82 (1967).
119. Rept. 3rd Intern. Conf. Standardization Hormones, *League Nations Bull. Health Organ.* **7,** *Extract* No. 32, p. 887.
120. Rice, B. F., Hammerstein, J., and Savard, K., *J. Clin. Endocrinol. Metab.* **24,** 606 (1964).
121. Robertson, H. A., and Hutchinson, J. S. M., *J. Endocrinol.* **24,** 143 (1962).
122. Robertson, H. A., and Rakha, A. M., *J. Endocrinol.* **35,** 177 (1966).
123. Rosemberg, E., and Albert, A., *Endocrinology* **82,** 187 (1968).
124. Rosemberg, E., and Keller, P. J., *J. Clin. Endocrinol. Metab.* **25,** 1262 (1965).
125. Rothchild, I., *Vitamins Hormones* **23,** 209–327 (1965).
126. Rowlands, I. W., *J. Physiol. (Proc. Physiol. Soc.)* **91,** 6 (1937).
127. Rowlands, I. W., *in* "Gonadotropins, Their Chemical and Biological Properties and Secretory Control" (H. H. Cole, ed.), pp. 74–107. Freeman, San Francisco, California, 1964.

128. Sakiz, E., and Guillemin, R., *Endocrinology* **72**, 804 (1963).
129. Sandler, R., and Hall, P. F., *Comp. Biochem. Physiol.* **19**, 833 (1966).
130. Santolucito, J. A., Clegg, M. T., and Cole, H. H., *Endocrinology* **66**, 273 (1960).
131. Savard, K., Marsh, J. M., and Rice, B. F., *Recent Prog. Hormone Res.* **21**, 285 (1965).
132. Segaloff, A., Steelman, S. L., and Flores, A., *Endocrinology* **59**, 233 (1956).
133. Segaloff, A., *in* "The Pituitary Gland" (G. W. Harris and B. T. Donovan eds.), Vol. 1, pp. 518–526, Butterworth, London and Washington, D.C., 1966.
134. Shiino, M., and Rennels, E. G., *Endocrinology* **81**, 1379 (1967).
135. Short, R. V., *Recent Progr. Hormone Res.* **20**, 303 (1964).
136. Siefart, K. H., and Hansel, W., *Endocrinology* **82**, 232 (1968).
137. Simpson, M. E., *in* "Reproduction in Domestic Animals," (H. H. Cole and P. T. Cupps, eds.), 1st ed., pp. 59–110. Academic Press, New York, 1959.
138. Simpson, M. E., *in* "Human Pituitary Gonadotropins" (A. Albert, ed.), pp. 127–128. Thomas, Springfield, Illinois, 1961.
139. Simpson, M. E., Li, C. H., and Evans, H. M., *Endocrinology* **48**, 370 (1951).
140. Skosey, J. L., and Goldstein, D. P., *Endocrinology* **78**, 218 (1966).
141. Smith, P. E., *Proc. Soc. Exptl. Biol. Med.* **24**, 131 (1926).
142. Smith, P. E., and Engle, E. T., *Am. J. Anat.* **40**, 159 (1927).
143. Snook, R. B., and Cole, H. H., *Endocrinology* **74**, 52 (1964).
144. Snook, R. B., and Cole, H. H., and Geschwind, I. I., *J. Reprod. Fertility* **15**, 239 (1968).
145. Squire, P. G., Li, C. H., and Anderson, R., *Biochemistry* **1**, 412 (1962).
146. Steelman, S. L., and Pohley, F. M., *Endocrinology* **53**, 604 (1953).
147. Szontagh, F. E., Uhlarik, S., and Jakobovits, A., *Kiserl. Orvastud.* **15**, 526 (1963).
148. Szontagh, F. E., and Uhlarik, S., *J. Endocrinol.* **29**, 203 (1964).
149. Taymor, M. L., Tamada, T., Soper, M., and Blatt, W. F., *J. Clin. Endocrinol. Metab.* **27**, 708 (1967).
150. Thompson, K. W., *Proc. Soc. Exptl. Biol. Med.* **35**, 640 (1937).
151. Thompson, W. O., Bevan, A. D., Kechek, N. J., McCarthy, E. R., and Thompson, P. K., *Endocrinology* **21**, 220 (1937).
152. Uberoi, N. K., and Meyer, R. K., *Fertility Sterility* **18**, 420 (1967).
153. Van Wagenen, G., and Cole, H. H., *Am. J. Physiol.* **123**, 208 (1938).
154. Van Wagenen, G., and Simpson, M. E., *Fertility Sterility* **9**, 386 (1958).
155. Wagner, J. W., and Brown-Grant, K., *Endocrinology* **76**, 958 (1965).
156. Walsh, E. L., Cuyler, W. K., and McCullagh, D. R., *Am. J. Physiol.* **107**, 508 (1934).
157. Willett, E. L., McShan, W. H., and Meyer, R. K., *Proc. Soc. Exptl. Biol. Med.* **79**, 396 (1952).
158. Witschi, E., *Proc. Soc. Exptl. Biol. Med.* **35**, 484 (1936).
159. Wolstenholme, G. E. W., and Knight, J. (eds.), "Gonadotropins: Physicochemical and Immunological Properties." Little, Brown, Boston, Massachusetts, 1965.
160. Woods, M. C., and Simpson, M. E., *Endocrinology* **68**, 647 (1961).
161. Young, W. C., ed., *in* "Sex and Internal Secretions," pp. 449–496. Williams & Wilkins, Baltimore, Maryland, 1961.

162. Zarrow, M. X., *in* "Sex and Internal Secretions" (W. C. Young, ed.), 3rd
     ed., Vol. 2, p. 986. Williams & Wilkins, Baltimore, Maryland, 1961.
163. Zondek, B., and Aschheim, S., *Klin. Wochschr.* **6,** 248 (1927).
164. Zwarenstein, H., *Nature* **139,** 112 (1937).

3 IMMUNOLOGICAL CHARACTERIZATION OF THE GONADOTROPINS[*]

A. REES MIDGLEY, JR.[†]

I. Introduction

Historically, immunoendocrinology began in 1934 when Collip (*10*) showed that foreign protein hormones lose their effectiveness after repeated injection through the formation of circulating "anti-hormones." Several investigators felt that "anti-hormones" were equivalent to antibodies, but lack of correlation between results from classical immunological methods and results from neutralization studies made this interpretation so difficult to accept that uncertainty as to their identity persisted through 1950 (*21, 41, 87*). The modern era of immunoendocrinology began in the late 1950's with preparation of highly purified hormones suitable for immunochemical studies (*43*), development of immunodiffusion procedures for immunologi-

[*] The preparation of this chapter was supported in part by grants from the National Institutes of Health (HD 02193 and HD 02929) and the Population Council.

[†] Career Development Awardee of the National Institute of Child Health and Human Development.

47

cal analysis (12, 75), and use of adjuvant techniques for immunization and quantitative immunochemical techniques for measurement (38).

This chapter will focus on immunological studies with gonadotropins which have been reported during the last 10 years. Since a reasonable understanding of immunological principles is required for proper interpretation of such studies, Section II will be a brief consideration of underlying immunological theory. Further information concerning the immunological properties of hormones is available in a number of reviews (3, 28, 31, 43, 106, 107).

II. General Immunological Considerations

While the interaction of an antigen with its antibody is inherently specific, the overall specificity of such a reaction depends on the number and kind of these interactions involved under given experimental conditions. Endocrinologists utilizing immunological procedures have often taken false comfort in the knowledge that antigen-antibody reactions are specific and have failed to determine the number and nature of such reactions. No immunological study is now complete without a careful immunochemical characterization of appropriate reagents.

Antigenicity of a protein, i.e., its ability to elicit formation of antibodies in a suitable test animal, is dependent on many poorly defined factors. Most antigenic proteins have a relatively large size, with molecular weights in excess of 20,000, although the minimum size for antigenic polypeptide hormones has been found to be considerably less. Thus, insulin with a molecular weight approximating 6000, glucagon, with a molecular weight of 3485, and preparations of vasopressin with molecular weights less than 1100 are all antigenic (86). Smaller substances may be antigenic when covalently linked to larger molecules (38).

An animal does not normally form antibodies to endogenous proteins in its circulation. However, when foreign proteins are injected into an animal under conditions optimal for immunization, antibodies are formed which react not only with the injected protein but often with related proteins in the immunized animal as well. Thus, rabbits immunized with bovine LH developed testicular and epididymal atrophy (78) and rats immunized with ovine LH developed antibodies which neutralized their endogenous LH (98, 99).

For a small amount of protein to be maximally effective as an antigen, it must be presented to immunologically competent cells in an efficient fashion. This is usually done by emulsifying the protein solution in complete Freund's adjuvant (see description, Section III). The effects of this procedure are to delay absorption of the antigen and thus prevent rapid loss by excretion or catabolism, and to provoke a vigorous, granulomatous inflammatory response in which the immunologically competent cells are found (36, 38).

A single antigenic protein can react with more than one antibody. Protein molecules contain numerous, overlapping, antigenic determinant sites, each of which is capable of eliciting the formation of a spectrum of antibodies. Some of these antibodies react avidly with their complementary antigenic sites, others weakly. Thus, the number of antibodies bound to a protein will depend on the ratio of antibody molecules to antigenic determinant sites, the size of these sites, the energy of the reactions, and steric effects.

For unknown reasons, and regardless of the method employed for immunization, the concentration and avidity of antibodies directed against antigenic determinant sites vary greatly between different animals of the same species and to a lesser extent between bleedings from a single animal. Although protein molecules may possess markedly different physical, chemical, and biological properties, they may possess limited regions of structural and antigenic similarity, sometimes called a "common core." The existence of a core common to two or more proteins can give rise to immunological cross-reactivity.

The regions on the surface of a hormone molecule responsible for biological activity do not always coincide with the sites responsible for immunological reactivity with all antibodies. Thus, degraded or modified protein hormones may possess different ratios of biological to immunological activity.

Finally, for all practical purposes it is impossible to obtain an absolutely pure protein hormone free of antigenic contaminants. Often, these impurities are better antigens than the protein being studied, and this gives rise to the production of higher antibody titers against the impurities than against the major protein. This is particularly true when immunogenicity of a protein mixture is enhanced by use of appropriate adjuvants or by frequent injections (i.e., hyperimmunization). These undesirable antibodies can often be removed by absorption with known amounts of preparations containing the impurities. It is also possible to inject the impurities into newborn animals and thus render the animals tolerant to later injection of the same materials. Antisera obtained from tolerant animals should be free of antibodies to the impurities.

III. Development of Antisera

The success of any immunological study depends in large measure on the quality and specificity of antiserum employed. Although, as just outlined, a number of factors influence the properties of resulting antiserum, immunization procedures are highly empirical. Most investigators have employed an adjuvant. While this could consist of adsorbing the antigen on an insoluble substance, most investigators have used complete Freund's adjuvant, which is a water-in-oil emulsion of the hormone with heat killed mycobacteria added. While a variety of animals have been employed for immunization, guinea pigs and rabbits have been used most often. These animals have been chosen since they are known to be capable of producing suitable antisera against a wide number of antigens, they are easy to maintain in a laboratory, and a reasonable volume of serum may be obtained at frequent intervals. One might expect, however, that animals phylogenetically further removed from the animals supplying the purified hormone would prove to be more suitable in developing high-titered antiserum. Several different routes and injection schedules have been employed. Probably the most unique procedure has been the intraperitoneal injection of mice with extracts of sheep anterior pituitary gland or HCG. This resulted in the production of abundant antibody-containing ascitic fluid (35). One satisfactory method of immunization which has been employed in the author's laboratory is to emulsify 0.25 mg or less of highly purified hormone in 0.5 ml saline with 0.5 ml of complete Freund's adjuvant. One-tenth milliliter of this emulsion is then injected into each of the four foot pads of a rabbit and the remaining 0.6 ml is injected into 6 to 10 subcutaneous sites. This procedure is repeated at intervals of 3 weeks. Suitable antisera are often obtained after the second set of injections. Forty-five milliliters of blood may then be removed at weekly intervals until the antibody titer drops. At this point the rabbit can be given a booster injection to increase the antibody titer rapidly.

IV. Immunological Methods of Analysis

A. Precipitation of Hormone-Antibody Complexes

Immunoprecipitation techniques are utilized for quantitative and qualitative analysis of antigens and antibodies and involve an examination of the precipitate which forms when these two components are allowed to interact under suitable conditions. This precipitate does not form as the result of a simple chemical reaction, but occurs in at least two steps. The initial interaction of antigenic determinant sites with antibody-combining groups results in the formation of soluble complexes. If the antibody combining groups are saturated by an excess of antigenic molecules ("antigen excess"), the complexes remain soluble. When these complexes form with optimal proportions of the two reactants, a second stage of aggregation occurs, resulting in the formation of a visible precipitate. With appropriate standards, either antigen or antibody can be quantified by measuring the precipitate ("quantitative precipitin test"). Li et al. (43) have probably made the widest use of this technique. With specific antisera they have been able to measure a minimum of 1 μg of ovine LH and 1 μg of human LH. This technique is capable of considerable precision, reproducibility, and specificity, but it is not as sensitive as several other quantitative immunochemical procedures. Furthermore, incubation conditions have to be carefully adjusted to insure maximal precipitation, and some antibodies often react with the antigen without precipitate formation. The presence of non-precipitating antibodies must always be considered when one interprets a negative precipitin reaction.

If antigens and antibodies are allowed to diffuse toward each other through semisolid medium, a zone of equivalence develops in which the precipitating antibody and its antigen are present in optimal proportions. With suitable conditions, a precipitate forms in this region. Other antigens and antibodies will also seek out their regions of optimal proportions, form-ing several zones of maximal precipitation. The number of such regions provides a minimum estimate of the number of antigen-antibody interacting systems. Although this procedure is not as suitable for quantification as the liquid precipitin test, it is capable of distinguishing between two or more antigenically dissimilar substances and indicating the presence of contami-nating antigens. The resolving power of immunodiffusion techniques is enhanced by prior separation of the antigenic mixture into its various com-ponents by electrophoresis, chromatography, etc., prior to the immuno-diffusion step with antibody. Excellent descriptions of the theoretical and practical applications of these procedures have been published (12, 75).

Immunoprecipitation procedures have been used extensively to charac-terize antisera to different gonadotropins. In this way antibodies against contaminating substances have been demonstrated, the unwanted antibodies removed by absorption, and the absorbed antiserum shown to contain anti-bodies capable of precipitating only a single hormone (16, 53). Although immunodiffusion techniques are not usually utilized for quantification, Richards was able to combine a "polygon plate method" with an absorbed antiserum prepared in turkeys against pregnant mare serum gonadotropin to develop a simple procedure for the diagnosis of pregnancy in mares. This procedure was capable of detecting a minimum of 2.5 IU of pregnant mare serum gonadotropin per ml (83).

B. COMPLEMENT FIXATION

The word complement refers to a group of components, found in sera of animals, which combine with antigen-antibody complexes. Complement fixation tests are based upon the binding of these components to antigen-antibody complexes with the decrease in free complement being measured by a separate indicator system, usually hemolysis. Complement present in the sample under study is destroyed by heating at 57–58°C, and then a known amount of complement is added. This method can be used as a quantitative technique since the ability of complexes to fix complement is essentially a linear function of antigen concentration. This test possesses moderately high sensitivity and is particularly useful for the detection of antibodies to soluble antigens. It has been used to measure human FSH and ovine LH in amounts from 0.01 to 0.06 μg per assay tube (60, 95) and HCG in concentrations from 0.1 to 0.5 IU/ml (7). This method requires rigorous control of many factors in order to obtain consistent results, and it cannot be used for assaying materials with anticomplementary substances.

C. AGGLUTINATION INHIBITION

Agglutination-inhibition tests depend upon the ability of an antigen to prevent or reverse antibody-mediated agglutination of antigen-coated particles (usually fresh or formalin-fixed red blood cells or particles of latex). Various modifications of this principle have formed the basis for a large number of commercially available kits for the diagnosis of human pregnancy (34, 50). These methods have also been used to estimate concentrations of a number of different gonadotropins (9, 56, 100, 104). The procedures are relatively easy to perform, are relatively sensitive, but have several disadvantages. First, the assays at best result in semiquantitative measurements, since the end points are difficult to judge and are based on subjective impressions. Second, numerous factors affect the pattern of the agglutinated particles at the end points. Third, the methods cannot be used with many substances unless nonspecific inhibitors are removed by extraction (13, 55).

D. IMMUNOHISTOCHEMICAL ANALYSIS

Immunohistochemical procedures involve the use of labeled antibodies to localize antigens in sections of tissues prepared for histologic examination (63). To make certain that apparent sites of localization represent the antigen in question, studies must be performed with adjacent serial sections and appropriate control procedures, and must be accompanied by independent demonstration of immunochemical specificity of the labeled antiserum. With these methods HCG has been localized in syncytiotrophoblast (42, 52, 77), LH has been localized in the S1 mucoid cells of the human pituitary gland (47), and antibodies to ovine LH, ovine FSH, and porcine FSH have been shown to localize in beta cells of the pituitary gland of the pig and sheep (11, 82).

Most immunohistochemical studies have employed fluorescent compounds for the antibody label. Although valuable information has been derived from use of antibodies labeled in this manner, the method has several limitations. Tissues reacted with this antibody conjugate have to be examined by ultraviolet fluorescence microscopy, considerable care must be taken to distinguish specific fluorescence from autofluorescence in tissues, sections must be examined and photographed promptly before the fluorescence fades, and, finally, sections must be stored at low temperature. Recently, a better method, free of these limitations (65), was described. The method utilized antibodies labeled with enzymes for localization of tissue antigens at both the light and electron microscopic level. Tissue sections containing the antigen in question were allowed to react with the enzyme-labeled antibody, and then the antibody was located by histochemical staining for the enzyme. The latter step results in deposition of reaction products at the sites of the antigens. Since the reaction products are electron opaque, the antigens can be localized at the ultrastructural level as well. A modification of the method has been developed for the simultaneous localization of multiple antigens in the same tissue sections (64). After localizing one antigen in the usual way, the enzyme-labeled antibody was eluted from the section without removing the colored reaction products. A second antigen was then localized by reacting it with its enzyme-labeled antibody followed by histochemical staining and deposition of reaction products with a different color. By extending this procedure it has been possible to localize up to three different antigens in the same tissue section (64). With this method it is easy to determine whether a single cell contains more than one hormone. Preliminary studies with sections from rat pituitary glands have shown that growth hormone, prolactin, ACTH, TSH, and LH are all located in different cells. The only exception to the one cell-one hormone relationship appears to be with LH and FSH. Although some cells contain only LH and some cells only FSH, many cells appear to contain both hormones. Differences in the distribution of these two hormones and results from reciprocal absorption studies with highly purified ovine FSH and ovine LH strongly support the contention that these two hormones can be produced in the same cell (Nakane, unpublished observations). By comparison with immunohistochemically standardized antisera it should now be possible to assess the specificity of unknown antisera to pituitary hormones. At the ultrastructural level, rat LH has been located in granules of castration cells (66).

E. Radioimmunologic Analysis

Radioimmunoassay is now the most widely used technique for measuring levels of protein hormones in blood. This method, based on the report of Berson et al. (4), depends upon competition between unlabeled hormone and highly purified radioactively labeled hormone for limited, specific binding sites on antibody molecules. This principle is illustrated in Fig. 1. In the absence of unlabeled hormone (top reaction), the labeled hormone has maximal opportunity to react with the limited antibody-binding sites. However, if some of the limited antibody-combining sites are allowed to react with unlabeled hormone (bottom reaction), fewer sites will be left to react with the labeled hormone which results in a decrease in antibody-bound radioactivity. The labeled and unlabeled hormones are bound to the antibody in a ratio which is proportional to their concentration. Since antigen-antibody complexes are soluble at the high dilutions used in radioimmunoassays, a separate step must be used to separate antibody-bound hormone from free hormone. Details of the various procedures employed have been described elsewhere (106). A standard curve may be constructed with known amounts of hormone, as illustrated in Fig. 2. The amount of hormone in unknown samples can be determined by comparison with this standard curve.

Radioimmunoassay possesses the advantage of great sensitivity; as little as 10 picograms (0.01 mμg) of HCG can be detected in a single assay tube. Furthermore, the specificity of this method, which depends on the purity of the labeled hormone much more than upon the specificity of the antisera, is better than most other immunoassays. The method is affected very little by "toxic" factors, "anticomplementary" substances, etc., or by wide changes in pH, temperature, or ionic composition of buffer. This is not true for other commonly employed methods for immunological analysis (3). Radioimmunoassays can, therefore, be used to measure concentrations of hormones in a wide variety of extracts and tissue fluids including serum.

A number of radioimmunoassays have now been described for human gonadotropins (1, 22, 23, 26, 48, 49, 67, 73, 85, 101–103). With these

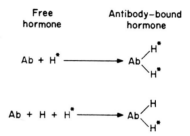

FIG. 1. Principle of radioimmunoassay.

methods a sharp peak in serum levels of LH and FSH has been found during the middle of the menstrual cycle 1–2 days before the rise in basal body temperature (24, 51, 51a, 84). The levels of both gonadotropins are higher during the follicular phase than during the luteal phase of the cycle. The individual components of oral contraceptives, when given alone in the usual dosage or in combination, result in a suppression of the peaks of serum LH and FSH which are usually seen at the middle of the menstrual cycle (37a). In postmenopausal women or in women following ovariectomy, the levels of both gonadotropins increase, with FSH rising proportionately higher. Serum from hypophysectomized patients have low or undetectable levels of both gonadotropins. Children show low levels until ages 10–12, when they begin to show adult levels (Midgley and Jaffe, unpublished observations). No evidence of rhythmicity or cyclic peaking in LH or FSH has been seen in male subjects. Male subjects treated with large doses of ethinyl estradiol show a decrease in both gonadotropins, while subjects treated with testosterone for 3 days show a decrease only in LH. Male subjects treated with clomiphene citrate show a rise in LH and FSH (75a).

Radioimmunoassays for LH in rats (58, 69), sheep (70), and cows

(71) have been developed. All three of these radioimmunoassays have given relative potency estimates remarkably close to those obtained by bioassay of preparations varying widely in their content of LH and in ratios of LH to other glycoprotein hormones. Thus, for rat preparations with widely varying LH/TSH and LH/FSH ratios, the estimate of LH obtained by bioassay divided by the estimate of LH obtained by radioimmunoassay (Index of Discrimination) ranged from 0.79 to 1.29. Similarly, beef preparations varying by as much as 64-fold in LH/TSH ratios and 164,200-fold in LH/FSH ratios have shown indices of discrimination ranging from 0.67

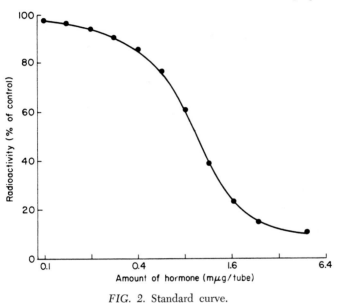

FIG. 2. Standard curve.

to 1.6. With the ovine LH radioimmunoassay, preparations with LH/TSH ratios varying as much as 102-fold and LH/FSH ratios varying by as much as 340,000-fold have shown indices of discrimination ranging from 0.75 to 1.26. Samples of serum obtained serially from rats during the estrous cycle have been found to contain a peak of LH on the afternoon of proestrus (59). Similarly, samples obtained from postpartum rats have revealed peaks in serum levels of LH occurring between 4–11 hours after delivery (80). Peaks in LH have also been found in sera from cattle and sheep during the first day of estrus. Castration in all three animals is followed by a rise in radioimmunoassayable LH, and hypophysectomy is followed by a decrease to undetectable levels. With all three assays the levels of LH as estimated by radioimmunoassay appear to be considerably less than those obtained with the ovarian ascorbic acid-depletion bioassay. The reasons for this discrepancy remain to be determined.

With the use of these highly sensitive and specific radioimmunoassays it should be possible to explore many aspects of reproductive endocrinology which, in the past, have had to be examined by indirect means. One interesting application of the rat LH radioimmunoassay has been the development of a sensitive and specific *in vitro* assay for LH-releasing factor (88; Caligaris *et al.*, unpublished observations). Using the technique of *in vitro* incubation developed by Piacsek and Meites (76), LH released into the media can be measured repeatedly in flasks containing only one-half of an anterior pituitary gland. In this manner, each donor rat can provide two pituitary halves, one of which can be used as a control for the other. The present results suggest a considerable increase in precision, specificity, and sensitivity with this combination of techniques. It should soon be possible to measure the content of LH-releasing factor in hypothalami and sera from individual rats.

F. Neutralization of Biological Activity

1. Exogenous Hormones

The ability of an antiserum to neutralize the biological activity of a hormone was not only the first (*10*) but also the best indication that antibodies to the hormone exist in the antiserum. However, this procedure is not a critical test for the presence of antibodies. A negative result is of little significance in ruling out the existence of specific antibodies because they may be present in too low a concentration for this relatively insensitive technique. However, evidence of neutralization is of little help unless correlated with other quantitative immunochemical procedures since the neutralization may be due to antibodies which bear no relationship to those responsible for results obtained by other methods of immunochemical analysis. The observed neutralization also must be shown to be specific for the hormone in question since some bioassays require the presence of other hormones for activity to be demonstrated. Thus, the ability of FSH to induce steroidogenesis depends upon the presence of at least some LH (*43*), and in an assay like the mouse uterine-weight method antibodies against LH will effectively neutralize the activity of FSH (*20*). Likewise, antibodies against human LH will cross-react with and neutralize HCG (*47*) which is a necessary part of the ovarian augmentation bioassay for FSH.

Neutralization of biological activity is not proof that antibody has reacted with the site on the molecule responsible for biological activity. Antibody-hormone complexes might be rapidly removed from circulation; complexes might render the hormone physically unable to fit into some receptor site on the surface of cells; and complexes might prevent hormone from entering target cells.

Numerous methods have been employed to demonstrate neutralization. There seems to be little difference whether the hormone and antiserum are mixed together and incubated first with subsequent removal of any formed precipitate, or whether the reactants are simply mixed and injected directly, or whether the hormone and antiserum are injected in separate sites in the animals.

2. Endogenous Hormones

Neutralization of endogenous hormonal activity is not as amenable to quantitative analysis as is neutralization of exogenous hormonal activity. It is usually seen either as the development of resistance to injections of exogenous hormones or in experiments in which exogenous antibodies are injected in an attempt to induce a transient, selective, functional hypophysectomy. Wakabayashi and Tamaoki have shown that active immunization of rats and rabbits with ovine LH resulted in a marked atrophy of the testis, seminal vesicles, and prostate which they interpreted as suggesting the production of LH antibody which inhibited the action of endogenous LH (98, 99). Similar results were obtained in rabbits immunized with bovine LH (78).

Hypophysectomy is a procedure designed to remove the role of pituitary function from experimental consideration. There are two major disadvantages to this procedure: It is difficult to be certain that all functional tissue has been removed, and it is difficult to interpret the resulting phenomena since all pituitary hormones have been removed and the animals are no longer in an optimal state of health. Providing one can obtain sufficient quantities of high titer, well-characterized specific antiserum, these objections can be overcome. Thus, it is possible to guarantee that all effective circulating hormone has been neutralized and that this has been done without removing other hormones from consideration. The procedure has obvious limitations, one of which is the development of antibodies to the heterologous antiserum being injected. This limits the use of this technique to short-term procedures of a few days duration or necessitates the use of antiserum prepared in homologous animals. Lostroh et al. (44) provided one of the most interesting examples of this technique. Rabbit antiovine LH was injected into male rats 2 months after hypophysectomy. By usual criteria hypophysectomy had been complete in these rats, yet the injections of antiserum resulted in further atrophy of the testes. The authors drew the conclusion that practically all of their untreated hypophysectomized experimental animals showed "some evidence of residual gonadotropic activity." It was postulated that this residual activity originated in cells present in the region of the infundibular stalk above the diaphragma sella. LH has been demonstrated by immunohistochemistry in comparable cells in the human pars tuberalis (47).

Injections of rabbit antiovine LH into male rabbits (79) and male and female rats (5, 30) have resulted in atrophy of gonads and secondary reproductive organs. Injections of rabbit antiovine LH into female rats during the estrous cycle have been used as an indirect means of determining the role of LH in ovulation. Injection of rabbit antiovine LH into rats 36 hours prior to expected ovulation blocked both the subsequent estrus and its associated ovulation (6). When rabbit antiovine LH was injected into rats at either 12:30 PM or 1:00 PM the afternoon of proestrus, the expected fall in pituitary LH concentration and the subsequent estrus were not abolished, but ovulation was blocked. These data strongly suggest that a peak in serum LH occurred in the afternoon of proestrus, that this circulating LH was neutralized by the antibody, and that this peak in LH was not responsible for the estrous smear seen on the subsequent day (39, 90). Female rats injected daily for several days showed persistent diestrous smears with subsequent resumption of cycling approximately 10 days after the injections were discontinued (6, 108). Injection of rabbit antiovine LH into pregnant rabbits between days 3–18 of pregnancy resulted in regression of corpora lutea and resorption of embryos (94). This was interpreted as being the result of a fall in estrogen levels secondary to neutralization of circulating rabbit LH.

V. Application of Immunological Procedures

A. PURIFICATION AND ISOLATION OF GONADOTROPINS

Antibodies have been used to remove contaminants from partially purified hormones and to selectively remove small amounts of a single hormone from a crude mixture. Thus, antiserum against serum from hypophysectomized rats has been used to remove serum protein contaminants from rat hormones prior to using them for immunization of rabbits (27). Antiovine LH has been quantitatively added to highly purified ovine FSH to remove a known, small amount of contaminating LH. This antibody-purified FSH was injected into hypophysectomized test rats and shown to be capable of inducing follicular development, but incapable of promoting steroidogenesis unless remixed with a small amount of LH (43). Similarly, human urinary FSH free of LH by treatment with antibodies against HCG promoted follicular development in intact infantile mice, but did not stimulate uterine growth (15, 20). These observations support the earlier conclusions of Greep that FSH is not capable of promoting steroidogenesis in the absence of LH (29). Cole suggests (Chapter 2) that LH is probably necessary for follicular growth as well as for steroidogenesis. Although these studies have all employed antibodies in solution with subsequent removal of the antigen-antibody complexes by centrifugation or column chromatography, the possibility of using insolubilized antibodies (i.e., antibodies adsorbed, trapped, or conjugated to an insoluble substance) should be kept in mind. This type of procedure would decrease the contamination of the resulting hormone by serum proteins contained in the antiserum and should make it possible to recover the antibody-bound antigens by elution with appropriate procedures.

Possibilities of making use of the exquisite specificity of antibodies to obtain small amounts of highly purified hormones has just begun to be realized. Thus, Wakabayashi and Tamaoki have utilized rabbit antiovine LH to isolate rat LH containing leucine-^{14}C from pituitary homogenates (97). With this procedure, an increased incorporation of amino acids into LH was shown in pituitary glands from rats immunized with ovine LH (98, 99). This increased biosynthesis of LH was presumed to be due to the castration-like changes secondary to the neutralization of circulating LH. A comparable method has been used by Samli and Geschwind, who showed that dinitrophenol and oligomycin could inhibit 75% of the incorporation of leucine-^{14}C into LH and yet not affect the release of LH (88). These results suggested to the authors that synthesis of LH is independent of release.

B. IMMUNOCHEMICAL ANALYSIS OF GONADOTROPINS

Relatively few studies have employed immunochemical techniques to explore physical and chemical properties of gonadotropic hormones. It is to be anticipated that as more specific antisera are developed and characterized, studies of this sort will play an important role in our understanding of the molecular composition of these hormones. From studies with a number of hormones it is known that sites responsible for biological activity do not necessarily correspond to sites responsible for immunological activity. Thus, with the use of antibodies prepared against porcine and ovine ACTH, a study was made of modified and intact, natural and synthetic molecules of ACTH and a complete dissociation of immunologic and biologic activity was found (37). Rabbit antisera against HCG have been shown capable of forming a precipitate with human LH and HCG after these hormones were heated for 30 minutes at 100°C, but not after they were treated with hydrogen peroxide (93). With the use of complement fixation and immunoprecipitation techniques, rabbit antiovine LH antibodies were shown capable of combining with ovine LH which had been oxidized with periodate, but not with ovine LH which had been oxidized with performic acid (96). Since the biological activity of ovine LH was destroyed by treatment with periodate, Trenkle et al. concluded that the carbohydrate moiety on ovine LH was not required for immunochemical activity (96). In a like manner, Barr and Colee showed that with the use of a commercially available hemagglutination-inhibition test that removal of sialic acid from HCG results in a loss of biological activity with no effect on immunochemical reactivity (2).

A number of immunochemical studies have suggested that several glycoprotein hormones possess a similar immunochemically reactive region, a "common core." With the use of a number of immunochemical procedures, bovine LH and TSH were specifically examined for this possibility. The studies suggested that TSH and LH are capable of eliciting distinct antibodies, but they also suggested the possibility that they might, in addition, share a peptide core (92). Antibodies to human TSH were shown to cross-react with antibodies to human LH and HCG (74). With a hemagglutina-tion-inhibition test for human FSH, the conclusion was reached that a non-specific antigenic component originated in the pituitary and was common to preparations of LH and FSH (104). Probably the best support for the concept of a common core has come from recent attempts to develop a radioimmunoassay for human FSH (49, 54, 72). Most rabbits immunized with preparations of human FSH developed antibodies which react equally well with highly purified preparations of human FSH, human LH, human TSH, and HCG. At an antibody concentration capable of binding most of the labeled FSH, highly purified preparations of these other hormones were equally capable of completely displacing the labeled FSH from its antibody. It is difficult to conceive of any possibility other than a common core to explain these observations.

C. Immunological Species Specificity of Gonadotropins

That gonadotropins from one species exhibit biological activity in an-other species has been known for years. This suggests that the region on the surface of the molecule which is responsible for biological activity has a similar configuration on molecules from different species. One can assume, furthermore, that at least some antibodies ought to preferentially react with this region and thus exhibit species cross-reactivity. A large number of immunological studies have been done which do show that antibodies pre-pared against LH or FSH from one species cross-react with comparable hormones in other species. This does not answer the question, however, as to whether this cross-reaction is by way of the biologically active site or with some other nonbiologically active region on the gonadotropin mole-cule. Few generalities can be made except that the extent of species cross-reactivity depends somewhat upon the taxonomic relatedness of species, the procedure used to demonstrate the cross-reactivity, the titer of the antiserum utilized, properties in the antiserum relating to unique features of the animal immunized, and the method of immunization. Thus, antiserum from rabbits hyperimmunized for prolonged periods tends to show wider species cross-reactivity than antiserum from rabbits given only a few suboptimal injec-tions of the same hormone. As would be expected, hormones from widely different species such as frog, turtle, human, and chicken have not shown significant cross-reactivity.

Table I lists a number of studies which bear upon this problem of spe-cies cross-reactivity. No attempt has been made in assembling this table to evaluate critically the specificity of the reported cross-reactions. Therefore, some of the examples of cross-reactivity may in reality be cross-reactions with contaminating substances. Furthermore, several of the studies did not employ extracted hormones, but rather were studies in which a biological activity was measured. For these studies the hormone presumed to be re-

TABLE I

SPECIES SPECIFICITY OF GONADOTROPINS BY IMMUNOLOGICAL PROCEDURES

Active material injected[a]	Animal immunized	Active material analyzed	Positive reaction (methods used)[b]	Negative reaction (methods used)[b]
BLH	Rabbit	BLH, OLH, PLH, RLH	C, N, P, R (70, 78, 81)	
		ELH, HLH	N (81)	C, P (81)
		HCG, PMSG	N (81)	
		RbLH	P (78)	
CLH	Guinea pig	BLH, OLH		P (8)
		CLH	P (8)	
ELH	Rabbit	BLH, ELH, OLH, RLH	C, N, P (14)	
		CLH, HCG		P (14)
		PMSG	C, P (14)	
HCG	Rabbit and mouse	BLH, PLH, PMSG		P (93)
		HLH	P (93)	
		HCG	N, P (35, 40, 93)	
		MLH		N (18, 40)
		OLH		N, P (35, 93)
		RLH	I (57)	N (35)
HLH	Guinea pig and rabbit	BLH, ELH, OLH, PLH		C, N, P, R (25, 81)
		HLH	C, N, P, R (25, 68, 81)	
		HCG	C, N, P (81)	
		PMSG		C, N, P (81)
		FLH, HsLH, MLH, RLH, RbLH, TLH		R (25)
		SLH		R (25, 68)
OLH	Rabbit, mouse, and rat	OLH	A, I, N, P, R (8, 9, 17, 33, 61, 70, 79, 105)	
		BLH	A, N, P, R (8, 9, 62, 70)	
		HLH	A, N, P (9, 61, 62)	P (61)
		RLH	I, N, P, R (5, 6, 19, 30, 35, 39, 61, 70, 98, 99, 108)	
		ELH	A, P (9)	

TABLE I (Continued)

Active material injected[a]	Animal immunized	Active material analyzed	Positive reaction (methods used)[b]	Negative reaction (methods used)[b]
		HCG	N, P (16, 17, 62)	N, P (8, 33)
		OxLH	N, P (33)	
		PLH	I, P, R (8, 61, 62, 70, 105)	N, P (33)
		MLH	N (18)	
		RbLH	N (79, 94)	
		CLH		N (8, 61)
		PMSG	N, P (9, 16, 17, 61, 62)	P (61)
PLH		PLH, OLH, BLH, RLH	R (70)	
PMSG	Rabbit and turkey	MLH	N (18)	
		PMSG	N (83)	
RLH	Rabbit	MLH, RLH	N, R (45, 58)	
		BLH, OLH, RbLH	R (58)	
		HLH		P (45)
		HCG		P, R (45, 58)
HFSH	Guinea pig and rabbit	HFSH	A, C, P, R (25, 46, 60, 68, 89)	
		SFSH	A (46)	R (25, 68)
		OFSH		A, C, P, R (25, 46, 60, 89)
		PFSH, PMSG		A, C, R (25, 46, 60)
		BFSH		A, R (25, 46)
		EFSH	P (89)	A (25, 89)
		DFSH, FFSH, HsFSH, MFSH, RFSH, RbFSH, TFSH		R (25)
OFSH	Rabbit	RFSH	N (32)	P (91)
		OFSH	N, P (32, 91)	
		PMSG		P (91)

[a] Abbreviations for species of origin of the various hormones: B, bovine; C, chicken; D, dog; E, equine; F, frog; H, human; Hs, hamster; M, mouse; O, ovine; P, porcine; R, rat; Rb, rabbit; S, simian; T, turtle.

[b] Numbers in parentheses are references. Abbreviations for methods used: A, agglutination inhibition; C, complement fixation; I, immunohistochemistry; N, neutralization; P, precipitation; and R, radioimmunoassay.

sponsible for the biological activity measured has been listed in the table. Finally, no attempt has been made to interpret examples of apparent disagreement since, as should be obvious to the reader, numerous plausible explanations exist for each discrepancy.

REFERENCES

1. Aono, T., Goldstein, D. P., Taymor, M. L., and Dolch, K., *Am. J. Obstet. Gynecol.* **98**, 996 (1967).
2. Barr, W. A., and Collee, J. G., *J. Endocrinol.* **38**, 395 (1967).
3. Berson, S. A., and Yalow, R. S., in "The Hormones" (G. Pincus, K. V. Thimann, and E. B. Astwood, eds.), Vol. 4, p. 557. Academic Press, New York, 1964.
4. Berson, S. A., Yalow, R. S., Bauman, A., Rothschild, M. A., and Newerly, K., *Northwest Med.* **55**, 541 (1956).
5. Bourdel, G., *Gen. Comp. Endocrinol.* **1**, 375 (1961).
6. Bourdel, G., and Li, C. H., *Acta Endocrinol.* **42**, 473 (1963).
7. Brody, S., and Carlstrom, G., *J. Clin. Endocrinol. Metab.* **22**, 564 (1962).
8. Bullock, D. W., Mittal, K. K., and Nalbandov, A. V., *Endocrinology* **80**, 1182 (1967).
9. Chen, B.-L., and Ely, C. A., *Gen. Comp. Endocrinol.* **9**, 193 (1967).
10. Collip, J. B., *J. Mt. Sinai Hospital* **1**, 28 (1934).
11. Corte, F. D., and Biondi, A., *Riv. Biol.* **57**, 359 (1964).
12. Crowle, A. J., "Immunodiffusion." Academic Press, New York, 1961.
13. Davajan, V., and Mishell, D. R., *Obstet. Gynecol.* **29**, 515 (1967).
14. Desjardins, C., and Hafs, H. D., *J. Animal Sci.* **24**, 347 (1965).
15. Donini, P., Puzzuoli, D., D'Alessio, I., Lunenfeld, B., Eshkol, A., and Parlow, A. F., *Acta Endocrinol.* **52**, 186 (1966).
16. Ely, C. A., and Chen, B.-L., *Endocrinology* **79**, 362 (1966).
17. Ely, C. A., and Chen, B.-L., *Endocrinology* **81**, 1033 (1967).
18. Ely, C. A., and Tallberg, T., *Anat. Record* **148**, 369 (1964).
19. Ely, C. A., Tuercke, R., and Chen, B.-L., *Cancer Res.* **26**, 1441 (1966).
20. Eshkol, A., and Lunenfeld, B., *Acta Endocrinol.* **54**, 91 (1967).
21. Evans, H. M., and Simpson, M. E., in "The Hormones" (G. Pincus and K. V. Thimann, eds.), p. 351. Academic Press, New York, 1950.
22. Faiman, C., and Ryan, R. J., *Proc. Soc. Exptl. Biol. Med.* **125**, 1130 (1967).
23. Faiman, C., and Ryan, R. J., *J. Clin. Endocrinol. Metab.* **27**, 444 (1967).
24. Faiman, C., and Ryan, R. J., *J. Clin. Endocrinol. Metab.* **27**, 1711 (1967).
25. Faiman, C., Ryan, R. J., Greslin, J. G., and Reichert, L. E., Jr., *Proc. Soc. Exptl. Biol. Med.* **125**, 1232 (1967).
26. Franchimont, P., *Thèse de Medécine*, Editions Arscia, Bruxelles, 1966.
27. Furth, J., and Moy, P., *Endocrinology* **80**, 435 (1967).
28. Geschwind, I. I., in "Gonadotropins, Their Chemical and Biological Properties and Secretory Control" (H. H. Cole, ed.), p. 1. Freeman, San Francisco, California, 1964.
29. Greep, R. O., *Recent Progr. Hormone Res.* **15**, 139 (1959).
30. Hayashida, T., *J. Endocrinol.* **26**, 75 (1963).
31. Hayashida, T., in "The Pituitary Gland" (G. W. Harris and B. T. Donovan, eds.), Vol. 2, p. 613. Univ. of California Press, Berkeley, California, 1966.
32. Hayashida, T., and Chino, S., *Anat. Record* **139**, 236 (1961).

33. Henry, S. S., and Van Dyke, H. B., *J. Endocrinol.* **16**, 310 (1958).

34. Hobson, B. M., *J. Reprod. Fertility* **12**, 33 (1966).

35. Hooverman, L. L., Sager, D. B., Meyer, R. K., Wolf, R. C., and Miller, M., *Proc. Soc. Exptl. Biol. Med.* **123**, 848 (1966).

36. Humphrey, J. H., *Ciba Found. Colloq. Endocrinol.* **14**, 6 (1962).

37. Imura, H., Sparks, L. L., Grodsky, G. M., and Forsham, P. H., *J. Clin. Endocrinol. Metab.* **25**, 1361 (1965).

37a. Jaffe, R. B., and Midgley, A. R., Jr., *in* "Progress in Conception Control" (D. Moyer, ed.), p. 13. Lippincott, Philadelphia, Pennsylvania, 1968.

38. Kabat, E. A., and Mayer, M. M., "Experimental Immunochemistry," 2nd ed. Thomas, Springfield, Illinois, 1961.

39. Kelly, W. A., Robertson, H. A., and Stansfield, D. A., *J. Endocrinol.* **27**, 127 (1963).

40. Land, R. B., and McLaren, A., *J. Reprod. Fertility* **13**, 321 (1967).

41. Leathem, J. H., *Recent Progr. Hormone Res.* **4**, 115 (1949).

42. Leznoff, A., and Davis, B. A., *Can. J. Biochem.* **41**, 2517 (1963).

43. Li, C. H., Moudgal, N. R., Trenkle, A., Bourdel, G., and Sadri, K., *Ciba Found. Colloq. Endocrinol.* **14**, 20 (1962).

44. Lostroh, A. J., Johnson, R., and Jordan, C. W., Jr., *Acta Endocrinol.* **44**, 536 (1963).

45. Lunenfeld, B., Eshkol, A., Baldratti, G., and Suchowsky, G. K., *Acta Endocrinol.* **54**, 311 (1967).

46. McGarry, E. E., and Beck, J. C., *Fertility Sterility* **14**, 558 (1963).

47. Midgley, A. R., Jr., *J. Histochem. Cytochem.* **14**, 159 (1966).

48. Midgley, A. R., Jr., *Endocrinology* **79**, 10 (1966).

49. Midgley, A. R., Jr., *J. Clin. Endocrinol. Metab.* **27**, 295 (1967).

50. Midgley, A. R., Jr., *Clin. Obstet. Gynecol.* **10**, 119 (1967).

51. Midgley, A. R., Jr., and Jaffe, R. B., *J. Clin. Endocrinol. Metab.* **26**, 1375 (1966).

51a. Midgley, A. R., Jr., and Jaffe, R. B., *J. Clin. Endocrinol. Metab.* (in press) (1968).

52. Midgley, A. R., Jr., and Pierce, G. B., Jr., *J. Exptl. Med.* **115**, 289 (1962).

53. Midgley, A. R., Jr., Pierce, G. B., Jr., and Weigle, W. O., *Proc. Soc. Exptl. Biol. Med.* **108**, 85 (1961).

54. Midgley, A. R., Jr., and Reichert, L. E., Jr., *Excerpta Med. Intern. Congr. Ser.* **161**, Part I, p. 117 (1968).

55. Mishell, D. R., Wide, L., and Gemzell, C. A., *J. Clin. Endocrinol. Metab.* **23**, 125 (1963).

56. Mishell, D. R., Jr., *Am. J. Obstet. Gynecol.* **95**, 747 (1966).

57. Monroe, S. E., and Midgley, A. R., Jr., *Federation Proc.* **25**, 315 (1966).

58. Monroe, S. E., Parlow, A. F., and Midgley, A. R., Jr., *Endocrinology* **83**, 1004 (1968).

59. Monroe, S. E., Rebar, R. W., and Midgley, A. R., Jr., *Federation Proc.* **27**, 371 (1968).

60. Mori, K. F., *Endocrinology* **81**, 1241 (1967).

61. Moudgal, N. R., and Li, C. H., *Arch. Biochem. Biophys.* **95**, 93 (1961).

62. Munshi, S. R., and Rao, S. S., *Indian J. Exptl. Biol.* **3**, 136 (1965).

63. Nairn, R. C., "Fluorescent Protein Tracing." Livingstone, Edinburgh and London, 1962.

64. Nakane, P. K., *J. Histochem. Cytochem.* (in press) (1968).
65. Nakane, P. K., and Pierce, G. B., Jr., *J. Cell Biol.* 33, 307 (1967).
66. Nakane, P. K., and Pierce, G. B., *J. Histochem. Cytochem.* 15, 758 (1967).
67. Neill, J. D., Johansson, E. D. B., Data, J. K., and Knobil, E., *J. Clin. Endocrinol. Metab.* 27, 1167 (1967).
68. Neill, J. D., Peckham, W. D., and Knobil, E., *Nature* 213, 1014 (1967).
69. Niswender, G. D., Midgley, A. R., Jr., Monroe, S. E., and Reichert, L. E., Jr., *Proc. Soc. Exptl. Biol. Med.* 128, 807 (1968).
70. Niswender, G. D., Midgley, A. R., Jr., and Reichert, L. E., Jr., (*in* "Gonadotropins 1968" (E. Rosenberg, ed.), Geron-X, Los Altos, California (in press) (1968).
71. Niswender, G. D., Reichert, L. E., Jr., and Midgley, A. R., Jr., submitted for publication.
72. Odell, W. D., Reichert, L. E., and Bates, R. W., *Excerpta Med. Intern. Congr. Ser.* 161, Part I, p. 124 (1968).
73. Odell, W. D., Ross, G. T., and Rayford, P. L., *Metabolism* 15, 287 (1966).
74. Odell, W. D., Wilber, J. F., and Paul, W. E., *J. Clin. Endocrinol.* 25, 1179 (1965).
75. Ouchterlony, O., "Handbook of Immunodiffusion and Immunoelectrophoresis." Ann Arbor Sci. Press, Ann Arbor, Michigan, 1968.
75a. Peterson, N. T., Midgley, A. R., Jr., and Jaffe, R. B., *J. Clin. Endocrinol. Metab.* 28, 1473 (1968).
76. Piacsek, B. E., and Meites, J., *Endocrinology* 81, 535 (1967).
77. Pierce, G. B., Jr., and Midgley, A. R., Jr., *Am. J. Pathol.* 43, 153 (1963).
78. Pineda, M. H., Luecker, D. C., Faulkner, L. C., and Hopwood, M. L., *Proc. Soc. Exptl. Biol. Med.* 125, 665 (1967).
79. Quadri, S. K., Harbers, L. H., and Spies, H. G., *Proc. Soc. Exptl. Biol. Med.* 123, 809 (1966).
80. Rebar, R. W., and Nakane, P. K., *Federation Proc.* 27, 371 (1968).
81. Reichert, L. E., Jr., and Treadwell, P. E., *Endocrinology* 81, 591 (1967).
82. Rennels, E. G., *in* "Cytologie de l'Adenohypophyse" (J. Benoit and C. Da Lage, eds.), p. 201. C.N.R.S., Paris, 1963.
83. Richards, C. B., *Nature* 215, 1280 (1967).
84. Ross, G. T., Odell, W. D., and Rayford, P. L., *Science* 155, 1679 (1967).
85. Rosselin, G., and Dolais, J., *Presse Med.* 75, 2027 (1967).
86. Roth, J., Glick, S. M., Klein, L. A., and Petersen, M. J., *J. Clin. Endocrinol. Metab.* 26, 671 (1966).
87. Rowlands, I. W., and Parkes, A. S., *in* Marshall's "Physiology of Reproduction" (A. S. Parkes, ed.), 3rd ed., Vol. III, p. 26. Little, Brown, Boston, Massachusetts, 1966.
88. Samli, M. H., and Geschwind, I. I., *Endocrinology* 82, 225 (1968).
89. Saxena, B. B., and Henneman, P. H., *J. Clin. Endocrinol. Metab.* 24, 1271 (1964).
90. Schwartz, N. B., and Gold, J. J., *Anat. Record* 157, 137 (1967).
91. Segal, S. J., Niu, L., and Hakin, S., *Acta Endocrinol. Suppl.* 51, 1093 (1960).
92. Selenkow, H. A., Saravis, C. A., and Garcia, A. M., *Acta Endocrinol.* 51, 32 (1966).
93. Shahani, S. K., and Rao, S. S., *Acta Endocrinol.* 46, 317 (1964).
94. Spies, H. G., and Quadri, S. K., *Endocrinology* 80, 1127 (1967).

95. Trenkle, A., Moudgal, N. R., Sadri, K. K., and Li, C. H., *Nature* **192,** 260 (1961).

96. Trenkle, A., Li, C. H., Sadri, K. K., and Robertson, H., *Arch. Biochem. Biophys.* **99,** 288 (1962).

97. Wakabayashi, K., and Tamaoki, B. I., *Endocrinology* **77,** 264 (1965).

98. Wakabayashi, K., and Tamaoki, B., *Endocrinology* **79,** 477 (1966).

99. Wakabayashi, K., and Tamaoki, B., *Endocrinology* **79,** 643 (1966).

100. Wide, L., and Hobson, B., *Acta Endocrinol.* **54,** 105 (1967).

101. Wide, L., and Porath, J., *Biochim. Biophys. Acta* **130,** 257 (1966).

102. Wilde, C. E., Orr, A. H., and Bagshawe, K. D., *Nature* **205,** 191 (1965).

103. Wilde, C. E., Orr, A. H., and Bagshawe, K. D., *J. Endocrinol.* **37,** 23 (1967).

104. Wolf, A., *Nature* **211,** 942 (1966).

105. Wolf, J. E., and Rennels, E. G., *Anat. Record* **148,** 351 (1964).

106. Wright, A. D., and Taylor, K. W., *in* "Hormones in Blood" (C. H. Gray and A. L. Bacharach, eds.), Vol. 1, p. 24. Academic Press, New York, 1967.

107. Wright, P. H., *Vitamins Hormones* **23,** 61 (1965).

108. Young, W. P., Nasser, R., and Hayashida, T., *Nature* **197,** 1117 (1963).

4 CHEMISTRY OF THE GONADOTROPINS

HAROLD PAPKOFF[*]

I. Introduction

Following the convincing physiological demonstrations that there were substances present in pituitary extracts, blood and urine which profoundly affected reproductive processes, it became the role of the biochemist with his techniques of purification and characterization to firmly associate unique chemical substances with specific biological activities. By the early 1940's,

*Career Development Awardee, Institute of General Medical Sciences, National Institute of Health.

it was known that the gonadotropins were protein in nature, and with the exception of prolactin, contained carbohydrate as well. Progress in developing the chemistry of the gonadotropins has been slow, however, in contrast to other protein hormones such as insulin, growth hormone, and adrenocorticotropin. In part, this has been due to the small quantities of gonadotropin present in pituitary tissue, to difficulties in purification, and problems of lability. In the past decade, however, with the development of new techniques of purification such as ion-exchange chromatography and gel filtration, there has been a revitalization of research into the chemistry of the gonadotropins.

This chapter will deal primarily with those gonadotropins which have been obtained in a state of purity such that meaningful chemical data have been obtained. These will include the hormones from the pituitary gland, luteinizing hormone (LH, ICSH), follicle stimulating hormone (FSH), and prolactin. In addition, human chorionic gonadotropin (HCG) will be discussed, as well as pregnant mare serum gonadotropin (PMSG). Although much work has been done on urinary gonadotropins, especially human, their state of purity at present does not warrant extensive treatment. For a discussion of earlier work, the reader is referred to articles by Li (28), White (68), Geschwind (10a), and Wolstenholme and Knight (70).

II. Luteinizing Hormone (LH, ICSH)

A. Purification

Methods have been described in recent years for the purification of luteinizing hormone from ovine, bovine, human, porcine, and equine pituitaries. By far the greatest progress has been made with ovine LH. Procedures for the preparation of ovine LH have been described by Papkoff et al. (40), Reichert and Parlow (49), Squire and Li (56), and Ward et al. (66). These procedures also appear to be applicable to the purification of bovine LH. With the method of Ward et al. (66), porcine LH may be purified. Reichert (45) has also described methodology for porcine LH. The purification of equine LH has been studied by Reichert and Wilhelmi (50). Human LH in recent years has been the subject of much research, and fractionation techniques have been reported by Hartree (18), Papkoff (38), Parlow et al. (43), and Squire et al. (57).

In general, these methods all consist of initial purification of pituitary extracts by alcohol, salt, or pH fractionation, followed by ion exchange chromatography on Amberlite IRC-50, CM-cellulose, DEAE-cellulose, sulfo-ethyl-Sephadex, and, more recently, by gel filtration on columns of Sephadex, usually G-100.

As examples of the methods employed in the purification of LH, the procedures of Papkoff *et al.* (*40*) and Ward *et al.* (*66*) for the preparation of ovine LH will be described in greater detail. In the method of Papkoff *et al.*, the pituitary glands are ground and extracted at pH 4.0. Precipitation of inert proteins is accomplished by titration of the extract to pH 3.0 with metaphosphoric acid, and the crude LH fraction is salted out with ammonium sulfate at half-saturation, pH 6.5–7.0. Further purification is achieved by adsorption and elution from sulfoethyl-Sephadex C-50 (SE-C50). The hormone is adsorbed by the gel from a 0.01 M Na_2HPO_4 solution and eluted with 0.1 M Na_2HPO_4, resulting in an eight- to ten-fold purification. Final purification is performed by gel filtration on a column of Sephadex G-100. The typical pattern obtained shows one main peak containing the LH, with smaller peaks before and after. The yield of the isolated material amounts to 300 mg/kg of sheep pituitaries, has an activity of about two times the NIH-LH-S1 standard, and is essentially free of other hormonal contaminants.

In contrast, Ward *et al.* initially perform an alcoholic extraction of the glands according to the procedure of Koenig and King (*24*). The crude gonadotropin fraction obtained is submitted to chromatography on CM-cellulose. The LH is absorbed to the cellulose at pH 6.0, and following buffers of higher ionic strength and pH, the hormone is eluted with a pH 8.2 buffer of 0.04 M borate containing 0.2 M NaCl. The final step is gel filtration on Sephadex G-100 in which the major peak constitutes the purified ovine LH. The yield of hormone and the purity are comparable to that described by Papkoff *et al.* (*40*).

As LH is a protein, and as such is subject to denaturation, the usual precautions are taken, when indicated, such as avoidance of extremes of pH and temperature in its handling. Although only two procedures are compared here, others are similar in nature and the interested reader is referred to the specific references given previously for further information.

B. CHARACTERIZATION STUDIES

1. Ultracentrifugation and Molecular Weight Considerations

Ovine LH, when prepared by the methods of Papkoff *et al.* (*40*), Ward *et al.* (*66*), or Squire and Li (*56*), is shown to behave as a monodisperse material when examined in the ultracentrifuge. Determination of the sedimentation coefficient ($s_{20,w}$) in neutral or slightly alkaline solutions of the preparations described previously have been remarkably similar, varying from 2.67 to 2.74 $s_{20,w}$.

Calculations indicate the molecular weights of both ovine (*56, 66*) and bovine LH (*66*) (Table I) are close to 30,000. When either LH is examined in strongly acidic solutions, however, a different result is obtained. Li and Starman (*30*) found that in a solution of pH 1.3 (HCl-KCl), the sedimentation coefficient of ovine LH drops to 1.64 $s_{20,w}$, suggesting a dissocia-

TABLE I

MOLECULAR WEIGHTS AND ISOELECTRIC POINTS OF SEVERAL GONADOTROPINS

Hormone	Molecular weight	Isoelectric point
LH (ovine)	28,000–30,000	7.1–7.3
LH (bovine)	30,000	—
LH (human)	26,000	5.4
FSH (ovine)	25,000–30,000	4.5
FSH (porcine)	29,000	5.1
FSH (human)	—	5.6
HCG	30,000	2.95
PMSG	28,000	1.8
Prolactin	24,200	5.7

tion into smaller units. Sedimentation-equilibrium experiments reveal the molecular weight in acidic solution to be close to 15,000, half the value obtained in neutral or slightly alkaline media. Similar results were obtained for bovine LH (38) and have been confirmed by Ward et al. (66). The implication that ovine and bovine LH have a monomer molecular weight of 15,000 must be held in abeyance, however, as other studies, to be detailed later, suggest the presence of two *nonidentical* subunits, each of about 15,000 molecular weight.

Human LH was found by Squire et al. (57) to have a sedimentation coefficient of 2.71 $s_{20,w}$ in slightly alkaline solution, and a molecular weight of 26,000 was calculated from sedimentation-equilibrium studies (see Table I). Porcine LH also appears to have a molecular weight of about 30,000, but does not behave like ovine or bovine LH in strongly acidic solutions (65). Reichert and Jiang (47), on the basis of gel-filtration studies and sucrose density-gradient centrifugation experiments, concluded that ovine, bovine, and porcine LH had molecular weights in the range of 25,000–33,000. Equine LH behaved as a much higher molecular weight material on gel-filtration columns of Sephadex G-100.

2. Electrophoretic Analyses

Ovine LH has been examined by the classic free-boundary electrophoresis technique (56, 63), zone electrophoresis in troughs of starch (22, 23), columns of cellulose (22, 23) and on cellulose acetate (40), and by the disc electrophoretic technique on columns of polyacrylamide (49, 66). Although most of the studies just discussed indicate ovine LH to behave as a homogeneous protein, certain discrepancies have been noted, depending upon the system employed and the preparation. Thus, Jutisz and Squire (22, 23) observed several biologically active components when ovine LH was submitted to column electrophoresis at pH 5.2. Reichert and Parlow (49) have obtained two components by the disc electrophoresis method. However, Ward et al. (66), by this latter technique, obtained a single band. The significance of the observed electrophoretic heterogeneity is still obscure and may possibly be explained by either the subunit nature of ovine LH or the presence of several closely related molecules, all possessing biological activity. The isoelectric point of ovine LH was determined to be in the vicinity of pH 7.1–7.3 (*56, 66*) (see Table I).

Human LH has been examined by free-boundary electrophoresis and found to be homogeneous. Its isoelectric point is at pH 5.4 (*57*) (see Table I). Few data are presently available for the other species of LH cited previously.

3. Terminal Groups, Amino Acid, and Carbohydrate Content

It would appear from recently reported dinitrophenylation studies (*46, 66*) that LH, regardless of species, does not possess a free N-terminal amino acid. Ward and Coffey (*62*) have speculated that it may be acetylated. Studies on the C-terminus of LH, by means of the carboxypeptidase and hydrazinolysis reactions (*46, 67*), have shown the presence of small amounts of aspartic acid and serine, as well as several other amino acids, but the data are, presently, not conclusive. The only amino acid analyses reported thus far have been for ovine LH (*64, 40*). Shown in Table II is the analysis reported by Papkoff *et al.* (*40*). Of interest is the fact that tryptophan is absent, and the content of cystine and proline is very high.

Both Papkoff *et al.* (*40*) and Walborg and Ward (*61*) have reported on the carbohydrate content of ovine LH. In addition, Papkoff (*38*) has re-

TABLE II
AMINO ACID CONTENT OF VARIOUS GONADOTROPINS[a]

Amino acid	LH (ovine)	FSH (human)	PMSG	Prolactin (ovine)
Lysine	13	15	4	10
Histidine	6	5	1	8
Arginine	10	7	7	11
Aspartic acid	12	20	4	23
Threonine	16	8	5–6	9
Serine	14	11	8–9	15
Glutamic acid	15	15	6	24
Proline	25	10	8–9	12
Glycine	13	13	4	11
Alanine	16	15	4–5	10
Half-cystine	18	11	6	6
Valine	13	11	4	10
Methionine	5	2	2	7
Isoleucine	7	4	4	10
Leucine	12	15	6	24
Tyrosine	6	7	3–4	7
Phenylalanine	7	8		6
Tryptophan	0	2	—	2

[a] Expressed as residue per molecule; analysis taken from reference cited in text.

ported data for human and bovine LH. All three species of LH contain hexoses, fucose, and hexosamines. In the case of ovine LH (61), it is known that the hexoses are of two kinds, mannose and galactose, and the two common hexosamines, glucosamine and galactosamine, are present. Sialic acid is low or absent (40, 38) in ovine and bovine LH, as indicated by chemical analysis and by treatment with neuraminidase, which does not release any of the sugar and does not affect either the biological activity or the electrophoretic mobility of the hormone. The total carbohydrate content of the several species studied varies from 12–16% (Table III).

TABLE III

CARBOHYDRATE CONTENT OF VARIOUS GONADOTROPINS[a]

Hormone	Hexose	Hexosamine	Fucose	Sialic acid
LH (ovine)	6.5	7.8	1.4	0.37
LH (bovine)	5.5	6.5	0.9	—
LH (human)	5.9	5 1	0.6	0.68
FSH (ovine)	5.7	4.5	1.1	2.8
FSH (porcine)	2.6	3.7	1.1	—
FSH (human)	3.9	2.4	0.4	1.4
HCG	11.0	8.7	1.2	8.5
PMSG	18.6	14.1	1.4	10.4

[a] Grams per 100 gm glycoprotein.

4. Structural Considerations

The molecular-kinetic data cited previously suggested that ovine LH is a glycoprotein with a molecular weight of 15,000 which dimerizes in neutral or slightly alkaline solutions. Studies on the nature of the carbohydrate moiety of ovine LH by Papkoff (35, 36) and Ward et al. (65) show that there are two distinct carbohydrate units of different composition present in ovine LH. In addition, the enzyme degradation studies which led to the isolation of these glycopeptides showed that there were different amino acid sequences associated with each carbohydrate moiety. Further, Ward et al. (67) suggested the presence of two different C-terminal amino acid residues, aspartic acid and serine. The conclusion to be drawn is that ovine LH does, indeed, dissociate into units of about 15,000 molecular weight in acidic solution, but that these are nonidentical structures. Most recently, Papkoff and Samy (39) have strengthened this concept by the isolation and partial characterization of the individual subunits. Ovine LH was submitted to countercurrent distribution in a solvent system consisting of 40% $(NH_4)_2SO_4$-0.2% dichloroacetic acid-n-propanol-ethanol (60:60:27:33). The ovine LH resolves into two fractions, one of high partition coefficient, and one of low partition coefficient. These were each shown to be homogeneous by disc electrophoresis. Chemical analysis shows that the two fractions differ considerably in both the carbohydrate and amino acid contents. The individual subunit fractions retain a low level of biological activity (7–8%), but whether this represents intrinsic biological activity or a lowering of potency due to inactivation remains to be resolved.

Virtually nothing is known regarding the structures of other species of LH, aside from the chemical and physical data mentioned in the characterization studies.

C. STABILITY STUDIES

The knowledge gained of the stability of a protein hormone when subjected to various experimental procedures is often very useful and can be used to advantage in the development of purification procedures. In addition, it is often possible to gain some insight into the relationship between structure and biological activity from such experiments. The studies to be reported here all concern ovine LH, and their applicability to other species of LH is not presently known.

When ovine LH is treated with performic acid, a reagent which oxidizes disulfide bonds, the hormonal activity is completely abolished (2). Agents which reduce disulfide bridges, such as thioglycolate and dimercaptopropanol, were also found to result in reduced biological activity (2); thus, it appears that the integrity of the —S—S— bond is important for the maintenance of the biological activity of ovine LH.

The hormone is also susceptible to extremes of pH. Exposure to 0.01 M HCl or 0.07 M HCl, either at room temperature or −20°C, will very rapidly result in diminished activity (2, 40). Short treatment, 15 minutes at a pH of 12, leads to a 14% loss of activity (2), and longer periods would undoubtedly increase the loss. Heating a solution of ovine LH at 100°, pH 7.4, for 6 minutes leads to a 96% inactivation (2), but a lyophilized preparation may be heated in a vacuum oven at 100° for 24 hours and is only partially inactivated (2, 40).

A number of studies (2, 9, 37, 60) have been published which show that ovine LH loses its biological activity when incubated in high concentrations (6 M or greater) of urea. This is in contrast to the behavior of ovine FSH, which will be discused in the next section and can be used to preferentially inactivate LH contamination found in FSH preparations. Llosa et al. (31) have evidence that strong urea solutions dissociate ovine LH into its subunits.

Many reports can be found in the older literature (28, 68) which suggest that various carbohydrases such as ptyalin and Taka-diastase destroy the activity of the various gonadotropins, including ovine LH. Proteolytic enzymes such as trypsin and chymotrypsin also inactivate ovine LH (2).

Finally, it should be noted that the carbohydrate of ovine LH is susceptible to periodate oxidation. Geschwind and Li (11) showed that incubation of LH for 5–10 minutes at room temperature in 0.02 M sodium metaperiodate would destroy about 90% of the biological activity.

III. Follicle Stimulating Hormone (FSH)

A. PURIFICATION

The purification of FSH to a state of high chemical purity has proved to be a much more difficult task than in the case of LH. In part, this has been due to the smaller quantities of the hormones present in pituitary tissue and to problems of inactivation encountered during purification. The preparation of ovine FSH in highly purified form and some of its properties have been reported by Hashimoto et al. (19), Jutisz (21), and Papkoff et al. (41). Studies on porcine FSH have been reported by Steelman and Segaloff (59). In recent years, the isolation of human FSH has been pursued by a number of investigators. Human FSH of high potency has been prepared by Amir et al. (3), Papkoff et al. (42), Parlow et al. (43), and Roos and Gemzell (53, 54). Methods for the partial purification of equine FSH (55) and bovine FSH (48) are in the literature. The method employed has been similar to that for the purification of LH. In general, advantage is taken of the solubility of FSH in half-saturated $(NH_4)_2SO_4$ solutions and in ethanol-water mixtures. Ion exchangers such as DEAE-cellulose and CM-cellulose, as well as preparative polyacrylamide electrophoresis, have been used. Virtually all reports employ gel filtration on Sephadex G-100 as a purification step. Yields have been low, from 4–5 mg/kg for ovine FSH (42) to 10 mg/kg for human FSH (53, 54), although Papkoff et al. (42) have reported a yield of 110 mg human FSH/kg pituitaries.

B. CHARACTERIZATION STUDIES

1. Physical Studies

The ovine FSH preparations cited previously have all been examined by one or more techniques of ultracentrifugation. Sedimentation-velocity studies by Papkoff et al. (41) of 1% protein solutions in 0.1 M $NaHCO_3$ showed the $s_{20,w}$ to be 3.02 S. Sedimentation-equilibrium studies under the conditions just described resulted in the calculation of a molecular weight of 21,800. The experiments also suggested an aggregating system. Hashimoto et al. (19), employing lower concentrations (0.24 and 0.14%) and a buffer of pH 5.0, calculated the $s_{20,w}$ to be 2.63 S and the molecular weight, from sedimentation-equilibrium, to be 32,500. Jutisz (21) has estimated the molecular weight by ultracentrifugation in a sucrose density gradient and obtained a value of 30,000. Papkoff et al. (41) also report the $s_{20,w}$ in acid solutions of pH 1.3 to be 1.54 S. It would appear, then, that an uncertainty exists with respect to the true molecular weight of ovine FSH. For purposes of expressing data, however, a value of 25,000 has been selected (see Table I).

Porcine FSH was found to behave as a single component in the ultracentrifuge with an $s_{20,w}$ of 2.49 S (59). Together with diffusion data, the molecular weight was calculated to be 29,000 (see Table I).

Data for human FSH are still sparse, although Roos and Gemzell (53) have reported an $s_{20,w}$ of 2.95, and Papkoff et al. (42), a value of 4.63 S, different conditions being used for these experiments.

The electrophoretic properties of ovine, human, and porcine FSH have been examined by a variety of techniques and have been shown to behave as highly purified materials. The isoelectric point (pI) of ovine FSH has been estimated to be pH 4.5–4.6 (44). The pI of porcine FSH, pH 5.1–5.2 (59) is similar, but human FSH appears to be somewhat more basic. Its pI was determined by the free boundary technique to be at pH 5.6 (42) (Table I).

2. Terminal Groups, Amino Acid, and Carbohydrate Content

Analysis by the fluorodinitrobenzene technique has failed to reveal any N-terminal amino acids in either sheep (41) or human (42) FSH. No data is available for porcine FSH. In addition, treatment with carboxypeptidase failed to release significant quantities of C-terminal amino acids from either sheep (41) or human FSH (42). It would appear then, that FSH is similar to LH by virtue of the absence of terminal groups.

Amino acid data are available for ovine (41), human (42), and porcine FSH (59). The data which are summarized in Table III are unremarkable in that all the commonly expected amino acids are encountered. Of interest from a structural point of view is the high content of cystine found in FSH, and when the data for the three species are compared, numerous differences are found in the content of individual amino acids. For human (42) and porcine FSH (59), the amino acid content, together with the carbohydrate analysis (to be discussed), accounted for 87% and 88% of the material, uncorrected for moisture and ash.

Carbohydrate analyses have shown that FSH contains the same type of sugars as LH (hexoses, fucose, and hexosamines), but, in addition, the presence of sialic acid is found (41, 42). The data summarized in Table III show that ovine FSH has a greater carbohydrate content than either human or porcine FSH. The sialic acid content is of particular interest, and the values suggest two residues of this sugar per molecule of ovine FSH, but only one residue per molecule of human FSH. Insofar as LH does not contain sialic acid, this is an important means of chemical distinction between FSH and LH. Of further interest is the relationship of the sialic acid to biological activity to be discussed later.

C. Stability Studies

It was stated earlier that workers attempting to purify FSH have persistently been plagued by problems of capricious inactivation. In part, this appears to be due to the action of proteolytic enzymes on the hormone. It is known from the work of Adams and Smith (1) and Ellis (8) that there are two general classes of proteolytic enzymes present in pituitary tissue, with pH optima at about 4.0 and 8.5, respectively. The studies of Papkoff et al. (41) suggest that these enzymes, particularly those with an optimum of pH 4.0, must be inactivated or removed if the biological stability of FSH is to be achieved. FSH appears, however, to be resistant to the commonly encountered proteolytic enzymes from the pancreas, such as trypsin and chymotrypsin (3, 28, 59).

As with LH, however, carbohydrases appear to markedly affect FSH (28). In particular, neuraminidase is very effective in destroying the activity of FSH preparations, presumably by its action in releasing sialic acid (17, 37). In the case of ovine FSH (41), it was shown that neuraminidase completely liberates the sialic acid present.

Treatment of FSH with periodate, which preferentially oxidizes carbohydrate, results in a diminished biological activity. Geschwind and Li (11) showed that the same conditions of oxidation employed for LH ($0.02\ M$ sodium metaperiodate, 5–10 minutes, room temperature) resulted in a loss of 85% of the biological activity of ovine FSH. More recently, Butt et al. (5) reported similar findings for human FSH.

There is considerable evidence to show that FSH is markedly more stable in strong urea solutions ($6–8\ M$) than LH (9, 37, 60), a property which can be used to differentially inactivate the LH contamination in preparations of FSH (37).

IV. Pregnant Mare Serum Gonadotropin (PMSG)

A. PURIFICATION PROCEDURES

There have been few studies reported on the preparation of highly purified PMSG. The most recent of these are the studies by Bourrillon and Got (4), Gospodarowicz and Papkoff (12), and Legault-Demare et al. (26, 27). Further information on fractionation studies and the characterization of PMSG can be found in the review by Legault-Demare and Clauser (25). Legault-Demare et al. (26, 27) obtained PMSG by means of alcohol fractionation, chromatography on columns of Permutit, adsorption on barium carbonate, and countercurrent distribution. Their preparation had an activity of 15,000–16,000 IU/mg. Gospodarowicz and Papkoff (12) obtained a product of similar activity by a much simpler procedure which utilized metaphosphoric acid precipitation of inert proteins, alcohol fractionation, gel filtration, and chromatography on sulfoethyl-Sephadex C-50. The preparation of Bourrillon and Got (4) assayed 8000 IU/mg, but was reported homogeneous by various physicochemical criteria. The characterization of PMSG cited later is summarized from the just cited authors.

B. Characterization Studies

The highly purified preparations of PMSG mentioned previously have all been shown to be electrophoretically homogeneous by one or more methods. The isoelectric point has been determined to be at pH 1.8 (see Table I). The extremely low pI is undoubtedly a reflection of the very high content of sialic acid found in PMSG. The molecular weight of PMSG has been calculated to be 28,000 (see Table I). The sedimentation and diffusion values for this calculation were obtained in water as a solvent. In a phosphate buffer of pH 7.3, the sedimentation coefficient remained the same, 3.75 S, but the diffusion coefficient shifted from $D_{20} = 10.2 \times 10^{-7}$ cm^2 sec^{-1} to 4.2×10^{-7} cm^2 sec^{-1}. The resultant molecular weight is now 68,000. The possibility must be considered, then, that PMSG undergoes an aggregation or association process. In this connection, it should be noted that PMSG behaves as a much larger molecule than 28,000 in gel-filtration experiments (12, 34).

Amino acid analyses have shown a polypeptide content of about 30–40%. The low amino acid content—in particular, tyrosine—is reflected by the low ultraviolet absorption of the hormone (1 mg/ml at 280 mμ = 0.259). The values (see Table III) indicate a high content of serine, threonine, proline, and cystine. No terminal-group data are presently available. The remainder of the hormone consists of carbohydrate, which totals 45% of the weight of PMSG (see Table II). Most noteworthy is the extremely high content of sialic acid, 10.4%. The hexoses of PMSG amount to 18.6% and consist mainly of galactose, with smaller quantities of mannose and glucose. Both commonly encountered hexosamines, galactosamine and glucosamine, are present to the extent of 2.4% and 11.8%, respectively. Finally, two methyl pentoses, fucose and rhamnose, are found in PMSG (1.4% and 0.7%, respectively).

PMSG is inactivated by strong urea solutions, nitrous acid, disulfide reducing agents, peroxide, and periodate. In addition, proteolytic enzymes such as trypsin, chymotrypsin, pepsin, and papain, as well as certain carbohydrases such as ptyalin, Taka-diastase, and neuraminidase, promote loss of biological activity.

V. Human Chorionic Gonadotropin (HCG)

A. Purification Studies

As was the case with PMSG, there are relatively few studies which report the purification of HCG in a state of purity such that meaningful chemical and physical data can be obtained. Got and Bourrillon (14, 16) have developed procedures yielding HCG from pregnancy urine and characterized their preparation to a considerable extent. Their method employed adsorption of HCG on benzoic acid, extraction and fractionation with alcohol, adsorption on kaolin, and chromatography on Decalso and Dowex-2 ion-exchangers. The purified HCG had an activity of 10,000–12,000 IU/mg. Midgley (33) has reported that commercial HCG preparations can be further purified by DEAE-cellulose chromatography and gel filtration on Sephadex G-100. Although it remains to be seen whether the product is identical to the normal urinary HCG, Reisfeld and Hertz (51) and Wilde and Bagshawe (69) have prepared HCG of high potency from trophoblastic tumors.

B. CHARACTERIZATION STUDIES

The studies reported here are derived from the work of Got and Bourrillon (13–16). Their preparation of HCG was shown to be homogeneous by a number of techniques such as boundary and zone electrophoresis, sedimentation-velocity analysis in the ultracentrifuge, solubility and diffusion studies, and immunoelectrophoresis. The free-boundary electrophoresis studies yielded a pI of pH 2.95 (see Table I). From the sedimentation coefficient (2.7 S) and the diffusion coefficient ($D_{20} = 8.2 \times 10^{-7}$ cm²/sec) a molecular weight of 30,000 was calculated (see Table I).

Chemical analysis indicates that HCG, like PMSG, contains a very high carbohydrate content, and, as a result, it is found that the polypeptide portion of the molecule accounts for but 57% of the hormone. All of the commonly encountered amino acids are present, although there is some doubt about the presence of tryptophan. If tryptophan, is, indeed, absent, HCG would resemble ovine and bovine LH in this respect. There is a very high content of cystine present (9.0%), which, on the basis of a molecular weight of 30,000, would represent 13 cystine residues. No N-terminal groups were detected by the fluorodinitrobenzene technique. This result, too, is in accord with the negative results obtained with other gonadotropins. Reaction with carboxypeptidase, however, showed glycine to be at the C-terminus of the molecule.

The remainder of the HCG molecule consists of carbohydrate (see Table II). Analysis shows the presence of 11% hexoses (5.5% each of mannose and galactose), 1.2% fucose, 8.7% hexosamines (7.0% glucosamine and 1.7% galactosamine), and 10.4% sialic acids, which have been identified as both N-acetylneuraminic acid and N-glycolylneuraminic acid.

As is true of the other glycoprotein gonadotropins, the carbohydrate of HCG appears to be essential if full biological activity is to be manifested. Thus, as expected, periodate treatment of HCG results in profound losses of activity (11, 16). The same is found to be true of the action of certain carbohydrases. When HCG was treated with neuraminidase, an 80% loss of activity was observed with a concomitant loss of 60% of the sialic acid (15). Treatment with ptyalin and Taka-diastase also results in marked inactivation of HCG (16).

VI. Prolactin (Lactogenic Hormone; Mammotropin; Luteotropin; LTH)

A. PURIFICATION OF OVINE PROLACTIN

Prolactin was one of the first of the pituitary hormones to be isolated in a state of reasonable chemical purity. Although there is some question as to whether or not prolactin should be classified as a gonadotropin, it will be briefly discussed here because of its importance in various phases of reproduction and mammary gland function.

The preparation of ovine prolactin has been described by Cole and Li (6), Jiang and Wilhelmi (20), and Reisfeld et al. (52). It would appear that the methods discussed here can also be employed for the purification of bovine prolactin. Recent studies on porcine prolactin have been reported by Eppstein (10) and Jiang and Wilhelmi (20). Earlier studies on the purification and properties of prolactin have been reviewed by White (68) and more recently, by Dixon and Li (7), Li (29), and Lyons and Dixon (32). In the case of the human pituitary, considerable prolactin activity, as measured by the crop-sac test, is found to be associated with human growth hormone, and, thus, it appears to be an intrinsic biological activity of that molecule. Whether a discrete prolactin exists in human pituitaries is as yet an unsettled question. This entire problem is reviewed by Lyons and Dixon (32).

The purification techniques employed in the references cited previously all rely on initial extraction and concentration by conventional methods. Advantage is taken, however, of the fact that prolactin is quite insoluble near its isoelectric point and in the presence of relatively low concentrations of salt. In addition, prolactin withstands inactivation by extremes of pH and organic solvents. Thus, Cole and Li (6) prepared an acid-acetone powder of the pituitaries and performed salt and isoelectric precipitations to obtain an enriched prolactin fraction. Final purification was achieved by countercurrent distribution in the solvent system 2-butanol-0.4% dichloro-acetic acid (1:1). After 15 transfers in this system, the purified hormone was found in tubes 8–11 and a yield of 2 gm/kg of glands was obtained. The potency was found to be 35 IU/mg.

In the procedure of Jiang and Wilhelmi (20), glands which have been serially extracted to remove other hormones are treated with alkaline ethanol to obtain a crude prolactin fraction. This material is further purified by a simple salt fractionation prior to a chromatographic step employing DEAE-cellulose. Yields of about 0.5 gm/kg of pituitaries are obtained which have an activity comparable to that reported by Cole and Li (6). The characterization studies to be discussed relate largely to ovine prolactin as isolated by the Cole and Li (6) procedure. These studies are extensively reviewed in the references cited previously.

B. CHARACTERIZATION OF OVINE PROLACTIN

1. Physical Properties

When ovine prolactin was examined by ultracentrifugation in slightly alkaline buffers, it was found to behave as a homogeneous, monodisperse substance. In 0.1 M NaHCO$_3$ the sedimentation coefficient was found to be 2.19 S. Together with the determined diffusion coefficient (D_{20}) of 8.44 × 10^{-7} and a partial specific volume of 0.739, the molecular weight was calculated to be 24,200 (see Table I). Values very close to this figure have also been obtained by sedimentation-equilibrium studies, osmotic pressure experiments, and from amino acid data. Bovine prolactin is of a similar molecular weight.

Electrophoresis experiments showed the isoelectric point to be at pH 5.73 for both the ovine and bovine preparations of prolactin (see Table I). Certain types of electrophoretic techniques (starch gel and polyacrylamide), however, have indicated that ovine prolactin preparations consist of several different electrophoretic components. In part, this suggested heterogeneity has been resolved by gel-filtration experiments (58) in which it was shown that prolactin could be resolved into "monomer," "dimer," and "polymer" fractions. Each fraction, however, possessed biological activity and was identical with respect to amino acid content. Other experiments have suggested that varying degrees of aggregation of prolactin occurs when the hormone is subjected to lyophilization and extremes of pH. Thus, the very mechanics of isolation may, in part, be responsible.

2. Chemical Properties

The amino acid content of ovine prolactin is shown in Table III. All the commonly expected amino acids are found to be present. Aspartic acid, glutamic acid, and leucine are in highest concentration, and tryptophan is present to the extent of only two residues. In total, 205 amino acid residues are present.

Terminal-group analysis showed that the NH$_2$-terminal residue is threonine. In addition, the sequences of a few of the adjacent residues have been determined, leading to the following structure:

$$NH_2\text{-Thr}\cdot\text{Pro}\cdot\text{Val}\cdot\text{Thr}\cdot\text{Pro}\cdots$$

When the conventional methods were applied to the C-terminus, however, no terminal amino acid residue was indicated. It was postulated that one of the cystine residues present in prolactin was present at the terminus of the polypeptide chain, forming a loop through its —S—S— bond. This was proved by studies in which prolactin was treated with mercaptoethanol in order to reduce the —S—S—bonds of cystine to —SH groups. Reoxidation was prevented by alkylation of the —SH group with iodoacetamide. When the reduced, alkylated prolactin was digested with carboxypeptidase, it was demonstrated that the alkylated cysteine derivative occupied the C-terminus and was followed by residues of asparagine, leucine, and tyrosine. These structural studies can be summarized in the following representation:

$$\underset{1\quad\ 2\quad\ 3\quad\ 4\quad\ 5}{NH_2\text{-}Thr\cdot Pro\cdot Val\cdot Thr\cdot Pro}\cdots \underset{202\ \ 203\ \ 204}{Tyr\cdot Leu\cdot Asp\,(NH_2)}\cdot \underset{205}{CyS\text{-}COOH}$$

C. PROPERTIES OF PORCINE PROLACTIN

The only data available on porcine prolactin are those of Eppstein (10). This preparation was reported to be homogeneous and had a molecular weight of 25,000, similar to the ovine and bovine preparations. The isoelectric point, however, was somewhat more acidic and was found to be at pH 4.9. Differences were found in the amino acid composition, the greatest being that porcine prolactin contains 7 cystine residues, compared to 3 for ovine prolactin. In addition, it was found that the N-terminal residue is alanine rather than threonine.

VII. Concluding Remarks

This has necessarily been a brief survey. Many details and aspects of the chemistry of the gonadotropins have been omitted in order to emphasize several main points. It is evident from the data available that far too few species of gonadotropins have been purified and studied for generalizations to be made. It is clear, however, that with the exception of prolactin, gonadotropins having either FSH or LH activity may be expected to contain carbohydrate as part of the molecule in addition to the peptide components. Further, it is evident that the carbohydrate plays an important role in manifesting the biological activity of the hormone. Indeed, in the case of ovine FSH, the selective removal of the sialic acid by neuraminidase completely abolishes the biological activity.

We have seen, too, that the same hormone isolated from different species is not chemically identical. Thus, LH from human and ovine pituitaries show differences in isoelectric point, carbohydrate, and amino acid content. The same is true for human and ovine FSH. Findings of this nature are not unexpected in view of the comparative chemical studies which have been made on other protein and polypeptide hormones (i.e., growth hormone, insulin, corticotropin, etc.). One may expect, however, that, despite chemical differences, a common polypeptide sequence is present which may be regarded as the active center of the hormone.

In conclusion, it may be reiterated that there is a great continuing need for new and more efficient methods to prepare gonadotropins. Only when it can be unequivocally established that a hormone is pure and free of other pituitary factors and contaminants can the biological effects of the hormone be established without question.

REFERENCES

1. Adams, E., and Smith, E. L., *J. Biol. Chem.* **191,** 651 (1951).
2. Adams-Mayne, M., and Ward, D. N., *Endocrinology* **75,** 333 (1964).
3. Amir, S. M., Barker, S. A., Butt, W. R., and Crooke, A. C., *Nature* **209,** 1092 (1966).
4. Bourrillon, R., and Got, R., *Acta Endocrinol.* **24,** 82 (1957).
5. Butt, W. R., Crooke, A. C., Cunningham, F. J., and Evans, A. J., *Biochem. J.* **79,** 64 (1961).
6. Cole, R. D., and Li, C. H., *J. Biol. Chem.* **213,** 197 (1955).
7. Dixon, J. S., and Li, C. H., *Metab. Clin. Exptl.* **13,** 1093 (1964).
8. Ellis, S., *J. Biol. Chem.* **233,** 63 (1958).
9. Ellis, S., *in* "Human Pituitary Gonadotropins" (A. Albert, ed.), pp. 378–380. Thomas, Springfield, Illinois, 1961.
10. Eppstein, S., *Nature* **202,** 899 (1964).
10a. Geschwind, I. I., *in* "Gonadotropins: Their Chemical and Biological Properties and Secretory Control" (H. H. Cole, ed.), p. 1. Freeman, San Francisco, California, 1966.
11. Geschwind, I. I., and Li, C. H., *Endocrinology* **63,** 449 (1958).
12. Gospodarowicz, D., and Papkoff, H., *Endocrinology* **80,** 669 (1967).
13. Got, R., and Bourrillon, R., *Biochim. Biophys. Acta* **39,** 241 (1960).
14. Got, R., and Bourrillon, R., *Biochim. Biophys. Acta* **42,** 505 (1960).
15. Got, R., and Bourrillon, R., *Nature* **189,** 234 (1961).
16. Got, R., and Bourrillon, R., *in* "Etudes d'Endocrinologie" (R. Courrier and M. Jutisz, eds.), p. 39. Hermann, Paris, 1961.
17. Gottschalk, A., Whitten, W. K., and Graham, E. R. B., *Biochim. Biophys. Acta* **38,** 183 (1960).
18. Hartree, A. S., *Biochem. J.* **100,** 754 (1966).
19. Hashimoto, C., McShan, W. H., and Meyer, R. K., *Biochemistry* **5,** 3419 (1966).
20. Jiang, N-S., and Wilhelmi, A. E., *Endocrinology* **77,** 150 (1965).
21. Jutisz, M., *Ciba Found. Study Group* **22,** 113 (1965).
22. Jutisz, M., and Squire, P. G., *Bull. Soc. Chim. Biol.* **40,** 122 (1958).
23. Jutisz, M., and Squire, P. G., *Acta Endocrinol.* **37,** 96 (1961).
24. Koenig, V. L., and King, E., *Arch. Biochem. Biophys.* **26,** 219 (1950).
25. Legault-Demare, J., and Clauser, H., *in* "Etudes d'Endocrinologie" (R. Courrier and M. Jutisz, eds.), pp. 69–91. Hermann, Paris, 1961.
26. Legault-Demare, J., Clauser, J., and Jutisz, M., *Biochim. Biophys. Acta* **30,** 169 (1958).
27. Legault-Demare, J., Clauser, J., and Jutisz, M., *Bull. Soc. Chim. Biol.* **43,** 897 (1961).
28. Li, C. H., *Vitamins Hormones* **7,** 223 (1949).
29. Li, C. H., *Advan. in Protein Chem.* **12,** 269 (1957).
30. Li, C. H., and Starman, B., *Nature* **202,** 291 (1964).
31. de la Llosa, P., Courte, C., and Jutisz, M., *Biochem. Biophys. Res. Comm.* **26,** 411 (1967).
32. Lyons, W. R., and Dixon, J. S., *in* "The Pituitary Gland" (G. W. Harris and B. T. Donovan, eds.), Vol. 1, pp. 527–581. Butterworths, London and Washington, D.C., 1966.

33. Midgley, A. R., Jr., *Endocrinology* **79**, 10 (1966).
34. Morris, C. J. R. O., *Acta Endocrinol. Suppl.* **90**, 163 (1964).
35. Papkoff, H., *Biochim. Biophys. Acta* **78**, 384 (1963).
36. Papkoff, H., *Abstr. 46th Meeting Endocrinol. Soc., San Francisco,* p. 129, (1964).
37. Papkoff, H., *Acta Endocrinol.* **48**, 439 (1965).
38. Papkoff, H., *Proc. 6th Pan-Am. Congr. Endocrinol., Mexico City, 1965. Excerpta Med. Found. Intern. Congr. Ser.* **112**, 334 (1966).
39. Papkoff, H., and Samy, T. S. A., *Biochim. Biophys. Acta* **147**, 175 (1967).
40. Papkoff, H., Gospodarowicz, D., Candiotti, A., and Li, C. H., *Arch. Biochem. Biophys.* **111**, 431 (1965).
41. Papkoff, H., Gospodarowicz, D., and Li, C. H., *Arch. Biochem. Biophys.* **120**, 434 (1967).
42. Papkoff, H., Mahlmann, L-J., and Li, C. H., *Biochemistry,* **6**, 3976 (1967).
43. Parlow, A. F., Condliffe, P. G., Reichert, L. E., Jr., and Wilhelmi, A. E., *Endocrinology* **76**, 27 (1965).
44. Raacke, I. D., Lostroh, A. J., and Li, C. H., *Arch. Biochem. Biophys.* **77**, 138 (1958).
45. Reichert, L. E., Jr., *Endocrinology* **75**, 970 (1964).
46. Reichert, L. E., Jr., *Endocrinology* **78**, 186 (1966).
47. Reichert, L. E., and Jiang, N. S., *Endocrinology* **77**, 78 (1965).
48. Reichert, L. E., and Jiang, N. S., *Endocrinology* **77**, 124 (1965).
49. Reichert, L. E., and Parlow, A. F., *Endocrinology* **73**, 285 (1963).
50. Reichert, L. E., and Wilhelmi, A. E., *Endocrinology* **76**, 762 (1965).
51. Reisfeld, R. A., and Hertz, R., *Biochim. Biophys. Acta* **43**, 540 (1960).
52. Reisfeld, R. A., Tong, G. L., Rickes, E. L., Brink, N. G., and Steelman, S. L., *J. Am. Chem. Soc.* **83**, 3717 (1961).
53. Roos, P., and Gemzell, C. A., *Biochim. Biophys. Acta* **93**, 217 (1964).
54. Roos, P., and Gemzell, C. A., *Ciba Found. Study Group* **22**, 11 (1965).
55. Saxena, B. B., McShan, W. H., and Meyer, R. K., *Biochim. Biophys. Acta* **65**, 394 (1962).
56. Squire, P. G., and Li, C. H., *J. Biol. Chem.* **234**, 520 (1959).
57. Squire, P. G., Li, C. H., and Andersen, R. N., *Biochemistry* **1**, 412 (1962).
58. Squire, P. G., Starman, B., and Li, C. H., *J. Biol. Chem.* **238**, 1389 (1963).
59. Steelman, S. L., and Segaloff, A., *Rec. Progr. Horm. Res.* **15**, 115 (1959).
60. Visutakul, P., Bell, E. T., Loraine, J. A., and Fisher, R. B., *J. Endocrinol.* **36**, 15 (1966).
61. Walborg, E. F., Jr., and Ward, D. N., *Biochim. Biophys. Acta* **78**, 304 (1963).
62. Ward, D. N., and Coffey, J., *Biochemistry* **3**, 1575 (1964).
63. Ward, D. N., McGregor, R. F., and Griffin, A. C., *Biochim. Biophys. Acta* **32**, 305 (1959).
64. Ward, D. N., Walborg, E. F., and Adams-Mayne, M., *Biochim. Biophys. Acta* **50**, 224 (1961).
65. Ward, D. N., Fujino, M., and Lamkin, W. M., *Federation Proc.* **25** (2), 348 (1966).
66. Ward, D. N., Adams-Mayne, M., Ray, N., Balke, D. E., Coffey, J., and Showalter, M., *Gen. Comp. Endocrinol.* **8**, 44 (1967).

67. Ward, D. N., Fujino, M., Showalter, M., and Ray, N., *Gen. Comp. Endo-crinol.* **8**, 289 (1967).
68. White, A., *Vitamins Hormones* **7**, 253 (1949).
69. Wilde, C. E., and Bagshawe, K. D., *Ciba Found. Study Group* **22**, 46 (1965).
70. Wolstenholme, G. E. W., and J. Knight, eds., "Gonadotropins: Physico-chemical and Immunological Properties." Little, Brown, Boston, Massachusetts, 1965.

5 PHYSIOLOGY OF GONADAL HORMONES AND RELATED SYNTHETIC COMPOUNDS

C. W. EMMENS

I. Androgens

A. INTRODUCTION

As the chemistry of the gonadal hormones and related compounds is dealt with in a separate chapter, reference should be made to it for an explanation of the types of structure concerned, their interrelations and biogenesis. It is sufficient here to point out that the androgens are not characterized by potent series of nonsteroidal compounds as are the estrogens, although some nonsteroids of very low androgenic activity are now known—mostly, those which act as antiandrogens at another dosage level. The potent androgens are all steroids; the natural androgens are typified by testosterone. Testosterone is found in the testes of many species, and in the spermatic vein, but it is apparently not formed in the adrenal cortex. Other androgens occur in the adrenals, the gonads of both sexes, and probably, the placenta. The blood of both males and females, therefore, contains androgens, which perform various functions in both sexes, but only male blood typically contains testosterone. However, it has only been chemically detected in spermatic vein blood (*17*) in the dog and in man.

Beside the actions to be discussed later in more detail, androgens cause nitrogen retention, promptly lost on cessation of administration (*100, 147*). A main effect is on skeletal muscle and occurs in the absence of the testis and various other endocrine glands. Increased sebaceous gland development (*45, 78*) and characteristic male behavior (*10, 15, 138*) are also androgen dependent. Modified androgens such as some of the nortestosterones have lost much of their androgenic activity, although more so in rodents than in man, and are used for their anabolic effects in convalescence or to stimulate growth. Some such compounds have much greater ratios of anabolic to androgenic activity; many of them, in addition, are potent progestogens.

B. Normal Role at Puberty and the Breeding Season

There is little evidence for significant secretory activity of the testis as an endocrine gland prior to the approach of puberty. While embryonic development may be disturbed by the administration of sex hormones, it still seems very dubious that such a mechanism is physiological, even in the production of freemartins (*97*). From excretion studies, it would appear that the human urinary content of 17-ketosteroids (which supposedly reflects the male hormone content of the blood), or of actual androgens, is so low as to be negligible in the normal subject until puberty commences, as shown in Figs. 1 and 2. Thereafter, it rises rapidly and remains high until senescence. No corresponding data are available from any animal species, so it has to be conjectured that a similar course of events occurs.

Prior to puberty, the accessory organs can respond to sex hormones. It is, thus, reasonable to assume that the quiescent prepubertal sex tract is receiving very little stimulus, since it could respond more if it were. Puberty may be stimulated by normal testicular activity at a varying time in relation to body growth in different species. In most rodents studied, puberty occurs at about half the adult body weight, whereas in primates general body growth is much more advanced (*7*). Also, puberty and sexual maturity tend to be almost synonymous in rodents and other small animals, whereas in many of the larger domestic animals and man himself, sexual maturity follows only after an interval of months or years. We must, therefore, differentiate the two phenomena: puberty, the time when reproduction is possible, and sexual maturity, when full reproductive capacity is reached.

In animals which show little or no breeding season—and these are surprisingly few—the production of androgens continues at a presumably steady pace. In most species, a breeding season, bred out to a varying extent in domestic animals, is normal, although it is less obvious in the male than in the female. Marshall's account of the breeding season (118) should be consulted for the almost infinite variety of cyclic activity offered by lower forms; we shall confine ourselves to vertebrates and, largely, to mammals. Various stimuli in vertebrates act on the hypothalamus and cause gonado-tropin release; changes in the diurnal period of illumination are common in

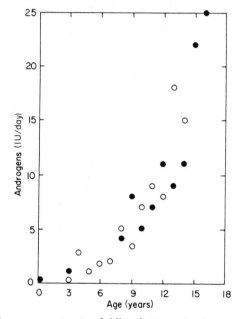

FIG. 1. Androgen excretion in childhood. From Dorfman and Shipley (43), p. 396.

higher vertebrates as a triggering mechanism. These changes are reflected by variation in gonadal hormone output and in development of the repro-ductive tract, spermatogenesis, and sexual activity. Puberty occurs once, but sexual activity in many species recurs periodically.

C. Effects of Castration

The effects of castration have been known in part from antiquity, par-ticularly as regards man and some of the domestic animals. The testes of all vertebrates would appear to secrete androgens; they contain the relevant cells, Leydig cells of the interstitial tissue, in fishes (*34, 37*), amphibia, reptiles (*98*), birds, and mammals. The androgens from fish testes stimulate comb growth in capons or chicks (*84, 150*), and it seems reasonable to suppose that they are of a similar chemical nature in all vertebrates. Similarly, synthetic androgens cause characteristic changes in fishes (*89*).

The main actions of male sex hormones are shown by changes following castration or by the failure to develop particular characteristics after prepubertal castration. Thus, from the lizard (*121, 122*) and bird (*140*) to man, castration is followed by failure to develop secondary sexual characteristics or their subsequent loss, by fat deposition in many instances, by the appearance, in general, of a neutral sexual condition, and the loss or absence of libido.

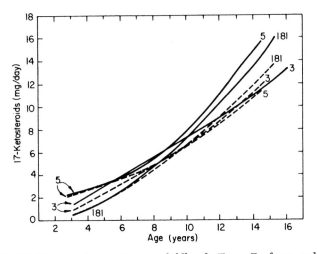

FIG. 2. 17-Ketosteroid excretion in childhood. From Dorfman and Shipley (*43*), p. 397. (Numbers accompanying the smoothed curves indicate references in the original article.)

Extensive work on castration and the effects of male hormone has been done in the domestic fowl. Castration is followed in the cockerel by regression of the comb and wattles, by loss of the capacity to crow, involution of the vas deferens, loss of aggressive behavior, and, in some breeds, by assumption of a neutral plumage not previously seen. In normal breeds, the plumage of the cock and the capon is identical, but in the so-called henny-feathered breeds (*142*) the cock responds to male hormone as does the hen to estrogens, and the two sexes, thus, have identical plumage. On caponization, the neutral plumage appears. Castration of the chick prevents the development of male characteristics in the first instance. The cooperation of androgens and estrogens, rather than progesterone and estrogens, seems to be of importance in the development of the sex tract of pullets (19).

In mammals, involution of various organs is seen if castration is performed postpubertally, or failure to develop is seen if it is performed prepubertally. The development and maintenance of the penis, scrotum, prostate gland, seminal vesicles, Cowper's gland, vas deferens, epididymis, of the characteristic laryngeal changes and hair distribution in some species, such as man and the lion, and normal sexual behavior depend on the testes. The glandular secretions fail on castration. The seminal plasma in an early castrate stage fails to contain the characteristic fructose, citric acid, and other constituents (116), and in a later stage plasma itself is not produced. Male castrates typically accumulate body fat, a well-recognized fact in farm animals, and true also for such laboratory animals as the rat (101). However, clinical experience of men and animals shows that the castrate is not always fat and that the distribution of body fat is, in addition, only partly controlled by the gonads (79).

In both birds and mammals, castration affects the pituitary gland. The anterior pituitary gland increases in size (56) and changes profoundly in histology. The basophil cells increase in number and size, and the acidophils decrease in number and appear to regress to chromophobes (82). Accompanying this, in some species, is a vacuolization of the basophils, resulting in the so-called signet-ring cell, or castration cell, with a large vacuole in the center and the nucleus looking like the signet in a ring of protoplasm (2, 168). In the rat, the normal pituitaries studied by Ellison and Wolfe (46) had 5.5% basophils, those of castrates showed 17% basophils, of which 1.4% were typical signet-ring cells. Another pituitary change is an increase in content of gonadotropin, mostly of follicle stimulating hormone (FSH) activity (110). This increased production has been shown parabiotically (119) by biological assay of pituitary extracts, or by assays of serum or urine (27, 75). Urinary gonadotropin in castrated men may rise tenfold compared with normals.

D. Effects on the Male Reproductive Organs

1. External Genitalia

In the rat, the penis hypertrophies with an excess of androgen, and androgen treatment prevents castration atrophy (105). Hypertrophy of the penis is expected when treating boys with chorionic gonadotropin for undescended testicle. An extensive survey of the effects of various androgens on the glans penis and the prepuce is given by Burrows (23). The musculature of the rat penis is particularly sensitive to androgens, for example; Wainman and Shipounoff (183) found that the weight of the perineal muscles after the injection of 500 μg of testosterone propionate daily for 35 days increased from an average of 1.21 to 1.94 gm.

The scrotum is similarly dependent on male hormone, and adequate treatment prevents the shrinkage and depigmentation that otherwise occurs on castration (76, 77). Twenty immature male rats given 19 daily injections of testosterone, commencing at 14 days of age, had scrota 1.5 to 3 times the weight of those of uninjected controls. Scrotal enlargement is also seen in boys treated for undescended testes by gonadotropin injections, due, as with hypertrophy of the penis, to excessive androgen secretion.

2. Internal Genitalia

The prostate gland is stimulated to both growth and secretory activity by androgens, and castration involution is prevented by androgen therapy (134). In some rodents, the immature animal's adrenal, with a persistent X zone, may produce enough androgen to maintain prostatic activity to a marked extent (90, 91, 152). In the adult, however, with an involuted X zone, castration is followed by full prostatic degeneration. This is mentioned because the need for, and effectiveness of, androgens in maintaining the prostate may seem uncertain with some experiments on rodents. Parabiotic experiments by Martins and Rocha (119), in which two male rats were joined, showed that excess of androgen may cause prostatic hypertrophy. When one partner of two males is castrated, its own pituitary gonadotropin rises and the testes of the other partner are stimulated to secrete excess of androgen. This results in hypertrophy of the noncastrate's prostate gland.

The principal effect of androgens is on the secretory part of the prostate gland. Estrogens stimulate the stroma and, thus, a cooperative effect may occur (106). In addition, an anomalous result may be seen on giving weak androgens in older males, when an inhibitory effect on the pituitary output of gonadotropin may result in such a fall in endogenous secretion of androgen that an overall lower androgen level is the result. When this occurs, the prostrate and other glands may actually decrease in weight (103).

Prostatic secretion has been recognized as dependent on androgen for some time [(94); see also the many later papers by Huggins et al.]. Since the work of Mann and his colleagues, a good deal of attention has been focused on the biochemical side of this phenomenon, much of which has recently been reviewed by Mann (115, 116). Fructose is produced as a result of androgenic stimulation from the dorsal prostate and coagulating gland in the rat, from the ventral prostate in the rabbit, but by the seminal vesicles in man. In dog, apparently no fructose is produced at all. Other components of the semen, such as citric acid and acid phosphatase, have been shown to be hormone dependent (93, 114).

The coagulating gland was shown by Camus and Gley (25, 26) to release a specific enzyme causing coagulation of vesicular fluid; it is distinct from the rest of the prostate in the guinea pig and some other rodents. This gland is often not separately mentioned when discussing the prostate. It is equally dependent on androgen for maintenance.

The seminal vesicles produce a fluid which clots on mixture with the products of the coagulating gland (72); this is responsible for the vaginal plug in many rodents. The degree of clotting varies with species, depending not only on whether a seminal vesicle is present but also on the activity of the mixture. The enzyme just mentioned, vesiculase, acts on a protein from the seminal vesicles, strongly in the rat or mouse, weakly in man, just barely or not at all in the horse or bull. In most species the seminal vesicle is the main source of fructose (115, 116). Androgens repair castration changes in these glands or stimulate precocious growth (132, 133); as with the other glands, secretion is dependent on androgens (117).

The preputial glands and Cowper's gland have been quite extensively studied, although the significance of their secretions remains in part obscure. They are androgen dependent (125, 181) and subject to greater growth under simultaneous treatment with estrogen, as with many of the male secondary sexual organs. The epididymis and the vas deferens are, likewise under the control of androgens, and castration changes may be prevented by experimental therapy (95, 127, 180).

The testis itself falls into a somewhat different category from the foregoing in that it is the site of production of the androgen concerned. Earlier workers tended to assume that its own secretion did not affect the testis, except, perhaps, via the pituitary gland; now, however, a direct action on the seminiferous tubules is recognized. Moore and Price (131) showed that bull testis extract caused damage to immature rat testes, including the germinal epithelium, and suggested a pituitary influence. Later workers have shown that the exact effects produced depend on age, dosage level, the androgen used, duration of treatment, and species or strain of animals. The subject is well reviewed by Dorfman and Shipley (43). Most of the work has been on intact rats, and has shown that even 2 μg of testosterone propionate per day causes degeneration in the very young rat, but that much higher doses are ineffective at 70 days of age or more. Very high doses (30 mg/week or more) produced testicular enlargement due to a direct effect (discussed later) in which the tubules are stimulated but the Leydig cells degenerate. The most intense damage is with testosterone or methyltestosterone, at about 1 mg/day, and is progressive with time up to 195 days (171). Similar effects have been demonstrated in the guinea pig (18) and ground squirrel (163), but in the mouse a high and probably protective dose of 5 mg/day did not cause damage (100), while no effect of high or low dosage (0.5 or 5.0 mg/day) followed Moore and Morgan's experiments with the opossum (130). This testicular damage is not always readily reversible, particularly if caused by early, high dosage.

The involvement of the pituitary gland is shown by decreased amounts of gonadotropin in glands from treated animals (132) and by the fact that testicular atrophy can be prevented by the simultaneous injection of gonadotropic hormone (18).

The direct effect of testosterone (or other androgens) on the testis was first demonstrated after hypophysectomy in the rat (184, 185). Degeneration of interstitial cells still occurred, but the seminiferous tubules were maintained. These experiments were amply confirmed by later workers, and the effect has been shown in the ground squirrel, pigeon, and primates. In the rat, spermatogenesis was best maintained by androstenediol rather than testosterone, which in Masson's (120) experiments failed to maintain it, while maintaining testis weight quite well. The consensus of recent views would seem to be that some yet undefined early stages of spermatogenesis are pituitary dependent, but that later stages can be maintained by androgens.

These results illustrate a typical relationship between the pituitary gland and one of its dependent glands. Excessive production of the target gland's own hormone is followed by a decrease in the pituitary output of the tropic hormone concerned, and, thus, by a lowered output of the target gland and a new balance. In the case of the testis, a complication arises in that one of the tissues affected by testosterone—the seminiferous tubules—is part of the testis itself.

E. Effects on the Female

Since the adrenal glands and perhaps even the ovaries secrete male hormone, the presence of a certain amount of circulating androgen is normal —in the human female, the total blood level of 17-ketosteroids and their excretion in the urine is about the same as in the male, but it is not clear how much represents original androgen.

In lower vertebrates, androgens may produce seemingly odd effects. Thus, the female South African clawed toad (*Xenopus laevis*) ovulates under androgenic stimulation (169), even the excised toad ovary doing so (170). The comb and wattles of the domestic hen grow when androgens are injected or inuncted, and various other characteristic androgen responses are elicited in other birds (189, 190). Androgens stimulate the oviduct as do estrogens, and they also cause follicular stimulation (30, 170). In some ways, therefore, androgens act as gonadotropins in birds and amphibia.

In mammals, androgens affect the female reproductive tract in an important variety of ways. The uterus of spayed females is maintained in weight by the so-called metrotropic activity of androgens, affecting both the myometrium and the mucosa (102, 104, 135, 137). The estrogen-primed uterus may be used to show the progestational effect of androgens, which is never so pronounced as with progesterone itself (52, 99, 124). The progestational effect is fully developed with ethynyltestosterone (53, 78), which is metrotropic and androgenic and estrogenic, although it seems probable that each activity may be due to a different metabolite—the estrogenic activity certainly is (48). The nortestosterones, which can hardly be called typical androgens, however, supply examples of molecules with much greater progestational activity than progesterone itself, and they are also active by mouth. Another progesterone-like action of androgens is a dampening of uterine motility (160).

A single dose of androgen (or estrogen) at birth affects the development of the reproductive system in rodents and hamsters (*134a, 178*). The results are similar in the different species examined. A single dose of testosterone propionate reduces testis size, increases adrenal weight in females, but does not affect ovarian or uterine weight, or external genitalia. Cyclic ovulation fails to occur, and the appearance of the uterus suggests a constant secretion of estrogen.

Premature opening and cornification of the vagina in rodents follow administration of some androgens, such as androstenediol (*24, 47*), subsequently shown by Rubinstein et al. (*163*) to be due to direct action of the compounds concerned. This is not confirmed by the tests of Emmens (*48*) in which the proestrogenic character of such androgens was established, so that although the pituitary or ovary may not be concerned, the androgens are not themselves the cause of the vaginal response; instead, a metabolite is presumably responsible. Androgens will normally prevent the vaginal cornification caused by estrogens (*50, 161*).

The female preputial glands and prostate (Skene's ducts) are affected by androgens shadowing the corresponding effects on the male. Thus, glands of supranormal size may be produced and may, in the case of the prostate, secrete increased citric acid (*153*). Growth of the clitoris to a penislike organ under androgenic stimulation is a well-known phenomenon, seen also in virilizing conditions in women. The female urethra may also exhibit hypospadias.

The ovary may be affected directly or via the pituitary gland. Most effects described fall into the latter class. Follicular maturation occurs in the rat, followed often by luteinization without ovulation (*164*)—a response abolished by hypophysectomy. This would appear to be consequent upon depression of LH output and stimulation of FSH output. In general, it would seem that short treatment with testosterone causes increased pituitary output of FSH in the rat or mouse, whereas longer treatment (several months) causes ovarian atrophy due to pituitary suppression. Again, this resembles the effects of progesterone. Noble (*137*) suggests a direct effect on the ovary in maintaining corpora lutea.

Androgens have been found to stimulate sexual desire in the human female—perhaps copying the effects of progesterone in this regard. Thus, patients treated with androgen for such conditions as breast cancer show in most cases a heightened sex drive and easier attainment of orgasm (*67, 165*). The ovariectomized woman does not lose libido, but the adrenalectomized woman does.

F. EFFECTS ON THE EMBRYO

Gallien (*61–63, 65*) showed that, in *Rana temporaria*, genetic females may be completely transformed to males by administration of testosterone propionate to the tadpole or frog. The modified sex is stable and fertile, and is not reversed by subsequent treatment with estradiol. Not all amphibia respond as fully, and intersexuals may result, depending on species, dosage, time of treatment, etc.

In the chick, injection of developing eggs causes partial sex reversal, affecting testes and secondary sexual characters. Testosterone does not much affect males, but causes ovaries to become testislike, and stimulates the wolffian ducts of genetic females. Other androgens, such as androsterone, have a feminizing effect as well, and stimulate both the wolffian and müllerian ducts (128); androsterone also causes both testes and ovaries to become ovotestes.

In mammals, mainly the rat and the opossum, even less effect is seen, with no sex reversal or even hermaphroditism. Secondary masculine sexual structures are stimulated by androgens in both sexes, and again, derivatives of both the wolffian and müllerian ducts may be stimulated by androgen in the opossum (69). Gonadectomy of the early opossum embryo (128) does not affect development of the reproductive tract, but in the rabbit, Jost (97) found failure of müllerian duct development if castration of the male fetus occurred before the 19th day. Various anomalous findings, and the absence of any very complete response the higher one ascends the vertebrate phylum, make it seem unlikely that the normal sex hormones are responsible for the embryonic development of the gonads or sex tracts. There is, in fact, no evidence that, whatever "hormone" the early embryonic gonad may secrete, it is testosterone or estradiol or a steroid at all.

II. Estrogens

A. INTRODUCTION

As well as the steroidal estrogens, there are very extensive series of synthetic substances such as stilbestrol, most of which copy in practically every way the actions of the steroids. Some more recently investigated synthetics have antiestrogenic actions, usually accompanied by weak estrogenicity.

Estrogens produce general body metabolic effects different from those with androgens. A possible exception is the protein anabolic effect, especially prominent in ruminants; this may be an indirect effect, however, involving the stimulation of the secretion of androgenic substances by the adrenal cortex (31) or of the secretion of growth hormone from the anterior pituitary gland. Growth of bones is inhibited and ossification is intensified. This may cause sufficient narrowing of the marrow cavity to result in anemia, an effect particularly marked in birds, but seen also in mammals (166). In the dog, less prominently in other mammals, fatal anemia may follow which is not entirely due to bone marrow effects.

Another effect of estrogens is vasodilation and consequent edema, not confined to any one area and apparently unaffected by innervation. The "sex skin" of some primates shows this phenomenon especially, but following prolonged treatment for several weeks, the edema may spread over most of the body surface, even in males (9, 54).

Estrogens affect the pituitary gland more profoundly than do androgens; a virtual chemical hypophysectomy is possible with continued high dosage, resulting in inhibition of growth and in gonadal regression. In rodents of both sexes, pituitary tumors may eventually develop and may cause blindness and death [for review of the earlier work see Burrows (23)]. The same reciprocal relationship exists between the ovary and the hypophysis as between the testes and hypophysis, but with much greater complexity in the normal cyclic female.

B. NORMAL ROLE AT PUBERTY AND THE BREEDING SEASON

Blood estrogen in normal cycles in women reaches a peak of about 6 μg/liter, with high variability (29, 179), it rises spectacularly in pregnancy to as much as 2 mg/liter at term (139, 151), most of which is estriol. No extensive figures are available for farm or laboratory animals.

As with the testis, there is no good evidence that the ovary secretes steroid hormones prior to the onset of puberty. The human urinary content of estrogens is lower prior to puberty, and that which occurs can reasonably be attributed to products of the adrenal cortex. Again, as in the male, the sex tract can respond to estrogens, and the lack of any marked response further argues that the amounts present are small.

When significant ovarian secretion commences, it does so in a cyclic manner, continuing apart from pregnancy or anestrus until the breeding age is past. There is a sudden increase in ovarian size at puberty due to secretion of liquor folliculi, but the full development of estrous cycles is a gradual phenomenon, preceded by anovulatory and otherwise incomplete cycles. This characterizes the period of adolescent sterility, during which cyclic activity and the overt onset of puberty is accompanied by few or no fertile cycles. In the human, this phase may last for several years. The menarche, therefore, is not synonymous with fertility. Thereafter, full sexual maturity is gradually attained, although most animals are less fecund at first. In rodents and pigs, the first litter is smaller than subsequent ones, and in sheep, the proportion of singles at the first lambing is very high (7).

In some species, the breeding season seems to be more sharply defined for the female than for the male. Thus, spermatogenesis in Merino rams is present all the year round, but the ewes show a definite breeding season, although with good nutrition, breeding does not cease completely in the free state at any time of year.

C. EFFECTS OF OVARIECTOMY

As with orchidectomy, ovariectomy is characterized by regression of, or failure to develop, secondary sexual characters. The younger the age of ovariectomy, the more profound the results are likely to be. All vertebrates appear to secrete estrogens, and the effects of ovariectomy are similar in the different classes. Attempts have been made to extract ovarian hormones from fish (42, 55), and small amounts of estrogen have been found. Fish urine contains substances suggestive of estrogenic steroids, but their identity has not yet been established (20). Thus, even so far down the vertebrate scale, estrogens exist, but may not be steroids. In the female as in the male, however, steroid estrogens of mammalian or synthetic origin act in fishes as do the natural hormones (41).

In birds, ovariectomy, besides affecting breeding behavior and the reproductive tract, may affect the plumage, causing the hen to revert in many breeds of domestic fowl to the neutral plumage of the capon or poularde Another rather anomalous result in this class may be the activation of the right gonadal element, which may grow to become ovotestis or even, in extremely rare cases, a functional testis. The same result may follow naturally after extensive ovarian disease.

In the mammal, spaying of the immature female results in failure of development of the Fallopian tubes, uterus, vagina, and accessory glands, of the mammary glands and teats, and of the typical female bone formation and fat distribution in many species. Regression toward the neutral type occurs in postpubertal gonadectomy. A natural "spaying" occurs over the somewhat extended period of the menopause in the human subject, and is accompanied by various regressive changes, as indicated previously, sometimes also by psychotic disorders.

Gonadectomy affects the pituitary gland, which increases in size and gonadotropin output, but the size change would appear, in some species at least, to be less than is seen with the male (82, 83). There is in particular an increase in FSH activity, again as in the male (193), and the urinary gonadotropin of postmenopausal women is mainly FSH in nature.

Mention has been made of the adrenal cortex as a source of estrogen, and it is interesting that in old female mouse castrates, sufficient estrogen may come from this source to cause activation of the reproductive tract (191).

D. Effects on the Female Reproductive Organs

The effect of estrogens on the ovariectomized female rodent in causing cornification of the vagina has in the past, overshadowed their other activities to an almost alarming extent. Thus, many a compound pronounced to be estrogenic has never been tested, except by this one criterion. The test, fortunately, appears to be very specific. More recently, uterine weight increase in immature or spayed rodents has tended to replace the vaginal smear test; this test is much less specific and cannot be used as a criterion of estrogenic activity with any real justification.

In discussing the effects of estrogens, therefore, it has to be recalled that vaginal cornification or effects on the uterus are not synonymous with the production of true estrus or readiness to mate, which often depends on the interaction of hormones rather than the effects of any single compound. In the mouse, for instance, only very few animals respond to cornifying or even very much higher doses of estrogen by a simultaneous readiness to accept the male.

Estrogen administered to castrates prevents atrophy of the vagina and, if in high enough dosage, causes rodent vaginal cornification or changes similar to it in other species, thus providing the test referred to previously, an elaboration by Allen and Doisy (4, 6) of the original observations of Stockard and Papanicolaou (177). A full discussion of the earlier work and of the detailed changes seen under estrogenic treatment is found in Burrows (23). Glycogen deposition follows estrogen treatment (14, 44) and may be responsible, via lactic acid production, for the lowered pH which also occurs (146). The initial responses of the vagina include RNA increases and uptake of amino acids, perhaps following direct interaction of estrogens with genes (49), followed by the mitosis and the development of stratification and mucification and, finally, cornification in some species of the vaginal layers farthest from the basement membrane (13). These latter phenomena have been duplicated in vitro, using slices of mouse vagina, and are apparently independent of blood supply or of other hormones (81).

The early responses of the uterus are similar to those in the vagina, followed by water uptake (8, 35), and then by a hypertrophy of both myometrium and endometrium (188). The water uptake reaches a stage of frank edema, particularly in rodents, but the same sequence of events is seen in all species—in normals, castrates, and hypophysectomized animals alike (175). A phase of glycogenesis occurs with glycogen deposition (16) —an effect which has not yet been produced in vitro—and it is interesting that glycogen deposition in the primate uterus appears to depend on progesterone instead.

Activity of the uterus is much affected by estrogen, which causes both spontaneous activity and sensitivity to oxytocin increase (156). The effects vary to some extent in different species, being much more striking in the rabbit and mouse than in many others. In these species, both in vivo and in vitro, spontaneous contractions and sensitivity to oxytocin increase under estrogenic treatment. Estrogens also prepare the uterus for the action of progesterone, which alone produces little effect.

Prolonged treatment with estrogens causes various uterine disturbances, starting with metaplasia and proceeding to pyometria, adenoma, and cancer (23). Infertility is naturally a concomitant result, and one which attained economic importance in Australia after World War II, where the wide-spread use of early subterranean clover was associated with dystocia and infertility in sheep (11). Later, the clover was found to contain large amounts of various estrogenic isoflavones.

In rodents, a combination of estrogen and progestogen is needed for implantation (123), and it is supposed that a surge of estrogen from the ovary is needed at the time of arrival of the blastocyst in the uterus (172, 173). This surge of estrogen is supposed to release histamine from mast cells, which sensitizes the endometrium and induces decidualization at the site of implantation, but this extension of the hypothesis has been widely criticized.

Remarkably little work has been done on the effects of estrogens on the fallopian tubes, although a cyclic influence on tubal structure and activity occurs, and tube locking or acceleration of ova in the tube are readily brought about by estrogen dosage (149, 186).

The ovary itself is affected, as is the testis, via the pituitary gland. Estrogens are much more potent than androgens in suppressing gonadotropin output, and, also, the output of other anterior pituitary hormones. They may be used to produce a state closely resembling hypophysectomy if given in sufficient dosage for a period of time. However, the first effect of physiological doses is an apparent release of LH (109), but on continued administration, general suppression of both LH and FSH output occurs. Again, as with androgens, a direct gonadotropic action of estrogen itself may be demonstrated in suitable circumstances. Thus, Williams (187) found that diethylstilbestrol prevents the atrophy of the ovary, which normally follows hypophysectomy in the immature female rat, and increased the response to gonadotropin (PMS). The same treatment did not affect the ovary weight of normal controls. Payne and Hellbaum (143) have obtained similar results with a series of estrogens. A fourfold increase in ovarian weight above controls was obtained with diethylstilbestrol in hypophysectomized rats by Pencharz (144). Reviewing the influence which estrogen secretion by smaller follicles has upon the definitive follicle led Allen (5) to paraphase, "The 'favored follicle' truly 'stands upon the shoulders of its contemporaries.'"

While it is possible that pituitary or other gonadotropins maintain the ovarian follicles by stimulating the local production of estrogen, this seems unlikely, since the greater part of the estrogen produced by the ovary comes from the follicles themselves, and the situation is not quite the same as with the testis, where the interstitial tissue may support tubular growth. Follicular growth in the presence of excess systemic estrogen is, however, definitely inhibited by suppression of the release of pituitary gonadotropin.

The effects of estrogens on the mammary gland are dealt with at greater length in Chapter 16. It is sufficient to note here that in some species estrogens alone cause mammary growth and even lactation, while in others, progesterone and possibly other, adrenal steroids are needed for full mammary development. Folley's book on the subject (57) should be consulted for details.

As with androgens, a single dose of estrogen to the newborn female has lasting effects, causing failure of cyclic ovarian activity and the appearance of constant estrogen secretion (134a, 178).

E. EFFECTS ON THE MALE

The estrogen output from the adrenal cortex means that, as in the female, a balance of androgenic and estrogenic activity normally exists in the male, so that he is accustomed to a certain level of estrogenic stimulation. In some cases, such as the stallion, whose testes produce large amounts of estrogen, the normal male is adapted to a very high level indeed.

The general effects of estrogens on males of both lower and higher vertebrates are feminization, with suppression of male secondary sexual characters and behavior. In the male, as in the female, a state of chemical hypophysectomy may be achieved with prolonged dosage. In birds, the plumage assumes the female character, and other secondary organs, such as the comb and wattles of the cock, regress. Chemical caponization, a milder form of the condition mentioned previously, may be achieved in cockerels or male birds of other species by regulated dosage with estrogens. Usually, a pellet is implanted into the neck.

Under prolonged estrogen treatment (22, 66) the male mammal suffers decalcification of the pubic symphysis and resultant hernia, testicular atrophy, and then atrophy of the secondary reproductive tract and sterility (182). These effects are reviewed in detail by Emmens and Parkes (54). The dosage of estrogen required in any one species to cause a particular effect varies widely; thus, mice are much more resistant than are rats and rabbits. Varying strains of mice have also been studied with reference to hyperplasia of the Leydig cells in the testis. This occurs with Strong albino mice quite readily on prolonged dosage with estrogens (23), but not in other strains, and is another aspect of effects on the pituitary gonadotropin output, which varies in different strains and, thus, causes resultant varying degrees of androgen production and protection from the results of estrogen dosage.

The ejaculate is reduced in volume by treatment with estrogens. Huggins and Clark (92) reported that, in dogs, 0.6 mg or more per day of diethylstilbestrol caused a rapid fall in sperm count and in ejaculate volume to nil or almost nil within a month. Similar effects have been reported for boars and men, although with 4–5 mg/day absorbed from tablets, two Suffolk rams treated by Chang (28) remained fertile and rose in sperm production at first. Later, sperm production fell below controls and would, presumably, have fallen further if the experiment had been continued. In the bull, supplementary estrogen causes the formation of spermatozoa with looped tails (37a), and the effect occurs in the tail of the epididymis (37b).

As indicated previously, males and females chronically dosed with estrogen, particularly if from early life, may be rendered not only sterile and eunuchoid but also present a state resembling hypophysectomy. That this is due to a general pituitary suppression may be demonstrated by injecting growth hormone, when growth is resumed. The plateaued rat, with a body weight of about 120 gm and exhibiting no further growth, is, in fact, used as a test for growth hormone. Even regression of the thyroid gland has been reported (12), so that the degree of "chemical hypophysectomy" may be quite advanced. However, there is no exact parallel, for hypophysectomized rats themselves plateau at about 70 gm, and there is good evidence that estrogen inhibits bone growth directly as well as doing so via the pituitary gland.

Direct changes in the accessory male reproductive organs also follow estrogen treatment. Estrogen causes stratification and metaplasia of the urethral epithelium (129), muscular growth in the seminal vesicles (58), and enlargement of the prostate gland (108). Much work has been done in various species, particularly since estrogen treatment has proved beneficial in prostatic enlargement or carcinoma. It would seem that müllerian elements enter into the structure of tissues showing an epithelial response, and that the inhibitory effect of estrogen on structures arising from the wolffian ducts is not in disaccord with this view (194, 195).

The mammary gland of the male shows a remarkable capacity to respond to estrogens, and has been used extensively for studies of the effects of these hormones on mammary development (54, 57).

The normal male is much more resistant to the effects of estrogens than is the castrate. This is because his androgens protect him from some of the effects, and are locally antagonistic to the action of estrogens. Castrates may be protected by injection of androgens simultaneously with estrogens. Such inhibition requires very much more androgen than estrogen. Thus, de Jongh (96) found that about 300 μg of androsterone would inhibit the effects of 1 μg of estrone on the prostate gland of rats. Emmens and Bradshaw (50) found that 500 μg of testosterone and some other androgens were needed to inhibit the response of spayed mice to 0.12 μg of estrone. The reverse phenomenon, the inhibition of androgen by estrogen, occurs with a much smaller ratio. Thus, the comb growth produced in brown leghorn capons by 600 μg of injected androsterone could be 50% inhibited by about 2 mg of estradiol and totally inhibited by about 10 mg. This is in line with the much greater amounts of androgenic steroids needed physiologically, as compared with estrogenic steroids.

F. Effects on the Embryo

The embryos of lower vertebrates are more affected by estrogen treatment than are those of mammals. In amphibia, estrogens induce ovary development in both sexes (154); in the fowl, the same result is seen (even though androgens do not, in the fowl, cause full testis development). Thus, Gallien (64) obtained 100% of female newts (Pleurodeles waltlii) by keeping the tadpoles in estradiol benzoate solution (600 μg/liter), and the resulting adults laid eggs. The left testis more readily becomes an ovary in the fowl (60), but even the right gonads may be feminized (38, 39). However, fertility does not seem to have been reported in such birds. The derivatives of the müllerian ducts (oviduct, etc.) are stimulated and those of the wolffian ducts are repressed, but as the birds grow up, there is a tendency for reversion to a more normal type in the genetic males.

In the mammal, attempts to produce feminization depend on failure to cause abortion or fetal resorption. Green et al. (68, 70, 71) injected pregnant rats with estrogens on the 13th, 14th, and 15th day of gestation and caused varying degrees of male hypospadias, visible nipples at birth, and abdominal testis and vaginal development, with inhibition of development of seminal vesicles and prostate, right vas deferens, scrotum, and penis. However, in these and many other similar studies, the male gonad has never been modified, and, as with treatment of the female with androgens, we must conclude that the sex hormones of the adult may not be the determining factors in embryonal gonadal development in the mammal.

III. Progestogens

A. NORMAL ROLE IN THE NONPREGNANT FEMALE

Except when given in high doses to the nonpregnant female, progesterone has less effect on general bodily functions than have androgens or estrogens. It acts somewhat like adrenal steroids in causing decreases in circulating eosinophils in adrenalectomized rats (33), but does not copy these steroids in many other ways. Various actions of this and other steroids on the extragenital system are summarized by Pincus (147).

The main source of progesterone, the only natural progestogen, in the nonpregnant female is the corpus luteum, which develops cyclically in the ovary and releases progesterone for a period that varies in different species. Progesterone is normally released in quantity after a period of estrogenic stimulation, and many of its effects are not developed unless the animal has been primed with estrogen in this manner. This hormone has been little investigated as regards its action on the male or on the embryo, but, in general, it acts rather like an androgen.

In the adult female, progesterone causes vaginal mucification, the characteristic progestational phase of the estrous cycle shows a stratified, mucus-saturated epithelium. Ovulation and estrus are suppressed (141). Responses to estrogen are themselves suppressed, even 2 mg of estrone per day may fail to cause cornification in the rat in the presence of corpora lutea of pregnancy. This has been shown to be due to the progesterone produced by the corpus luteum; thus, Selye et al. (167) found that 400 µg of progesterone abolishes the rat's response to 30 µg of estrone, the animals showing only mucification of the vagina.

The outstanding effects of progesterone are seen on the uterus. After a certain amount of response to estrogen, the uterus is in a state to undergo proliferation under the influence of progesterone, which particularly affects the endometrium. It greatly enlarges, and the tubular glands increase in depth and tortuosity. Uterine motility is decreased and the response of the uterus to estrogen and to oxytocin from the posterior pituitary gland is decreased or abolished (*107, 159*).

A considerable amount of rather contradictory work has been done on blood levels of progesterone, which in earlier years resulted in a very

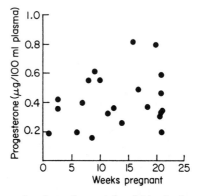

FIG. 3. Progesterone levels in the peripheral blood of pregnant ewes (normal duration of pregnancy 21 weeks). From Short (*174*), p. 416.

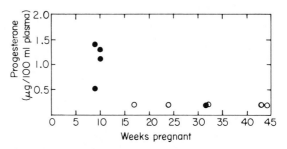

FIG. 4. Progesterone levels in the peripheral blood of pregnant mares (normal duration of pregnancy 48 weeks. Open circles show negative results.) From Short (*174*), p. 415.

large overall discrepancy between biological and chemical methods of assay. Chemical methods now available seem reliable as measures of true progesterone levels (*174*) and indicate that detectable plasma levels of progesterone occur in the normal cycle in the mare, cow, ewe, and sow. An increasing level is seen during the course of pregnancy in women and, probably, ewes (Fig. 3). In the mare, cow, and sow, however, the highest level would seem to occur early in pregnancy (Figs. 4–6).

As do the other steroids so far considered, progesterone depresses the gonadotropic output of the pituitary gland. The amounts required and the activity seen resemble those of androgens rather than estrogens. Herlant

(85) administered progesterone to adult female rats, removed the pituitaries at varying periods, and implanted them into immature females. Implants from rats receiving 1 mg daily for only 4 days caused ovarian and uterine enlargement greater than in controls, but implants from rats receiving only 0.5 mg/day or less for 10–14 days caused no such growth.

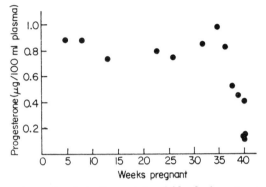

FIG. 5. Progesterone levels in the peripheral blood of pregnant cows (normal duration of pregnancy 40 weeks). From Short (174), p. 415.

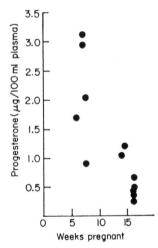

FIG. 6. Progesterone levels in the peripheral blood of pregnant sows (normal duration of pregnancy 16 weeks). From Short (174), p. 418.

This is interpreted as an increased LH production at first, followed by suppression. Other investigators have produced similar results in long-term tests.

The effect of progesterone on the ovary may, thus, be both direct and indirect. Despite Herlant's finding in short-term progesterone tests, it is generally agreed that progesterone suppresses ovulation, presumably by suppressing LH output. The earlier work commenced with Loeb (*111*), who found that extirpation of guinea pig corpora lutea led to early ovulation, and later investigators have found that daily doses of progesterone inhibit ovulation and estrus in rats, guinea pigs, and rabbits (*40, 112, 113, 145*). The development of oral contraceptives (*148*) has depended on these findings, although in the human ovulation is not readily suppressed by progestogen alone.

The interrelationships between progesterone and the ovary, pituitary gland, and central nervous system are reviewed by Rothchild (*162*), where the relationships between its ovulation-suppressing and ovulation-inducing properties are discussed. Medroxyprogesterone and chlormadinone have been found to suppress ovulation in cattle, and the former also in sheep, but the general situation seems to be that whether a progestogen suppresses ovulation or causes it depends on timing—chronic treatment suppresses, acute treatment just prior to the expected time of ovulation induces it.

Cooperation between progesterone and estrogens in producing psychic estrus is probably normal, but the exact relationship between the two hormones varies from species to species. At one extreme, the rat, mouse, or guinea pig requires an estrogenic stimulus followed by progesterone to produce sexual receptivity; at the other, a relatively long course of progesterone in the ewe is needed before a full response can be obtained to estrogen itself (*157*). This explains the phenomenon of "silent heat" in that species, since the first estrous cycle of the season may not elicit receptivity in the absence of progesterone pretreatment, but subsequent cycles do so because of the preceding corpora lutea.

In the ewe, progestogens alone will suppress ovulation, which tends to occur on the cessation of progestational stimulation. After administering injections of progesterone followed by gonadotropin or estrogen (*158*), Robinson and his colleagues have evolved techniques employing intravaginal sponges, impregnated with synthetic progestogens, which are withdrawn after a suitable period so as to give a relatively abrupt ending to the progestational phase (*158*) and synchronous heat and ovulation in the majority of animals. The technique is particularly successful in anestrus, although the cycle which follows that induced by treatment seems to be the more fertile one. A similar technique seems possible in cows. The subject is reviewed by Hansel and Zimbelman (*80, 192*).

B. Normal Role in the Pregnant Female

In pregnancy, there is, essentially, a continuation of the progestational phase of the estrous cycle. Progesterone is essential for the maintenance of pregnancy in all its stages, and its withdrawal is followed by absorption, abortion, or premature birth. The source of progesterone during pregnancy varies in different species, being mainly ovarian in the early stages and mainly placental in the later stages of pregnancy in most domestic animals. At one extreme, animals like the mouse or goat provide so little placental progesterone that ovariectomy is followed by abortion at all stages of pregnancy, whereas in the mare or female primate, at the other extreme, only early removal of the ovary causes abortion, and a fully functional corpus luteum is not present in late pregnancy (7). Progesterone injections or corpus luteum extract will prolong a normal pregnancy if given when birth is to be expected (136). This depends on the maintenance of a functional placenta by progesterone and also on the prevention of responses to estrogen and oxytocin, which normally occur at birth. Thus, in preparing the uterus for implantation, in maintaining the integrity of the placenta and its relationship with the uterus, and in maintaining uterine growth (together with estrogen), progesterone plays its role throughout pregnancy.

While the events in the uterus are proceeding, mammary growth also occurs. It has been mentioned that different species show varying degrees of completeness of mammary development in response to experimental treatment with estrogens. In general, it is concluded by Folley (57) that normal midpregnant morphology (by which time the greater part of mammary growth is complete) is shown only on treatment with both estrogen and progesterone, but that three main categories of animal exist. The first category includes the domestic ruminants and the guinea pig, in which functional mammary glands can be developed by estrogen alone. The second includes the rat, rabbit, and cat, in which although both duct and alveolar growth can be developed by sufficiently prolonged estrogen treatment, full alveolar growth typically depends on progesterone. The last category, represented so far only by the bitch, shows little or no mammary development from estrogen alone, not even duct development. Even in the first category, it seems certain that normal mammary development depends in part on the action of progesterone; experimentally, in cows, combinations of estrogen and progesterone give more normal-looking glands than estrogen alone (36) and glands which secrete more milk (155).

C. Effects on the Embryo

Progesterone has no known undesirable effects on the embryo, even when given in excess early in pregnancy, but some of the newer progestogens have additional properties which may be reflected in embryonic abnormalities. Thus, some of the nortestosterones cause failure of implantation or the formation of abnormal implants (51), presumably because of either their estrogenic or antiestrogenic activities. It is possible that such mechanisms as sex behavior patterns could be affected in the human by steroids administered for progestational effects in early pregnancy, but which also possess androgenic or estrogenic activity. If so, the demonstration of such effects could be difficult.

IV. Relaxin

A. NATURE AND DISTRIBUTION

The biochemistry and physiology of relaxin have been the subject of two fairly recent reviews (59, 88). Relaxin is a substance of protein or polypeptide nature, capable of relaxing the pelvic tissues of certain species after prior sensitization with estrogen. Relaxation in the primed guinea pig when given progesterone is due to the formation of relaxin in the reproductive tract itself. There also seems to be a number of related substances, probably very close to relaxin in constitution, which may copy one action or another of relaxin.

Hisaw and his colleagues have concentrated particularly on relaxin in the guinea pig, and in the most recent review, cited previously, they carefully define the relaxin they are discussing as the hormone producing effects in that species. It is possible to separate that activity, to some extent, from a similar activity in the mouse.

Relaxin has been found in the blood, placenta, and reproductive organs of mammals, and the ovary, uterus, and placenta have been suggested as sites of formation (86, 88). Castrated pregnant guinea pigs relax normally and show a normal blood concentration of relaxin (88, 126). The placenta also contains more relaxin than the uterus in the rabbit, suggesting the former as the source of hormone. Hall and Newton (74), however, believe that in the mouse the placenta acts by stimulating the ovary to produce relaxin. The ovary of the pregnant sow contains vast quantities of the hormone (3, 87), and there would seem to be little doubt as to its formation in the corpora lutea. There would, thus, seem to be species differences resembling others met with in endocrine research; in some mammals the ovary, while in others the placenta, appears to be the main site of relaxin production. Relaxin has been reported in tissues from the sow, guinea pig, rabbit, human, dog, cat, mare, and even the chicken.

Clinical interest in relaxin has stimulated some recent attempts to isolate and purify it. Material of high biological activity has been obtained from the sow ovary (32), assaying at 1800 units/mg, but still showing heterogeneity. Relaxin has still not been isolated in pure form.

B. PHYSIOLOGICAL ACTION

Relaxation of the human pelvic articulations in pregnancy and parturition was described by Snelling (176), and has been recorded by other authors in the guinea pig, mouse, dog, mole, cow, ewe, seal, and pocket gopher. Only the guinea pig and mouse have been studied in any detail.

Early studies with the guinea pig by Hisaw and his colleagues were considerably clouded by the fact that estrogen and combinations of estrogen and progesterone can cause pelvic relaxation. They showed, however, that the castrated guinea pig, sensitized by prior estrogen treatment, responds to relaxin preparations; the studies were confirmed by others (1, 21). Hisaw and his colleagues then showed that relaxin causes relaxation within 6 hours, while progesterone takes 72–96 hours and is only effective in animals with a uterus. Finally, it was shown that progesterone can act by causing the formation of relaxin in the uterus, and that very potent relaxin extracts may have no steroid action.

Relaxation with estrogen in the guinea pig causes a resorption of bone and proliferation of loose fibrous tissue; relaxation with relaxin causes a splitting of the collagenous fibers into thin threads and a breakdown of glycoproteins. Progesterone causes the same phenomena as does relaxin (88). In the mouse, treatment with estrogen causes pubic separation, with the formation of a gap 2–3 mm long, occupied by an interpubic ligament. Relaxin causes a separation more rapidly, which reaches something like twice the dimensions of that caused by estrogen. In the estrogenized mouse, progesterone does not cause pubic separation (73, 74).

Relaxin has other actions than relaxation, surveyed in the reviews cited previously. It appears to synergize with estrogen and progesterone in the rat in causing mammary growth; it has an antidiuretic action in the rabbit; it inhibits the deciduoma reaction of the rat uterus and the rhythmic contractions of the uterus in guinea pigs and rats. It also seems to cause a pregnancy anemia in rabbits, an erythrocyte and hematocrit drop of about 33%, and a rise in reticulocytes.

REFERENCES

1. Abramson, D., Hurwitt, E., and Lesnick, G., *Surg. Gynecol. Obstet.* **65,** 335 (1937).
2. Addison, W. H. F., *J. Comp. Neurol.* **28,** 441 (1917).
3. Albert, A., Morey, W. L., and Zarrow, M. X., *Endocrinology* **40,** 370 (1947).
4. Allen, E., *Am. J. Anat.* **30,** 297 (1922).
5. Allen, E., *in* "Glandular Physiology and Therapy," p. 145. Am. Med. Assoc., Chicago, Illinois, 1942.
6. Allen, E., and Doisy, E. A., *J. Am. Med. Assoc.* **81,** 819 (1923).
7. Asdell, S. A., "Patterns of Mammalian Reproduction." Cornell Univ. Press (Comstock), Ithaca, New York, 1946.
8. Astwood, E. B., *Endocrinology* **23,** 25 (1938).
9. Bachman, C., Collip, J. B., and Selye, H., *Proc. Roy. Soc.* **B117,** 16 (1935).
10. Beach, F. A., "Hormones and Behaviour," p. 220. Harper (Hoeber), New York, 1948.
11. Bennetts, H. W., Underwood, E. J., and Shier, F. L., *Australian Vet. J.* **17,** 85 (1946).
12. Bialet-Laprida, Z., *Comp. Rend. Soc. Biol.* **114,** 727, 733 (1933).
13. Biggers, J. D., *Nature* **170,** 895 (1952).
14. Biggers, J. D., *J. Anat.* **87,** 327 (1953).

15. Blair, A., J. *Exptl. Zool.* **103**, 365 (1946).
16. Boeltinger, E. G., *J. Cellular Comp. Physiol.* **27**, 9 (1947).
17. Bongiovanni, A. H., and Darrel Smith, J., *in* "Hormones in Blood" (C. H. Gray and A. L. Bacharach, ed.), p. 355. Academic Press, New York, 1961.
18. Bottomley, A. C., and Folley, S. J., *J. Physiol. (London)* **94**, 26 (1938).
19. Breneman, W. R., *Endocrinology* **58**, 262 (1956).
20. Brill, L., and Cuypers, Y., *Arch. Intern. Physiol.* **62**, 70 (1954).
21. Brouha, L., and Simonnet, H., *Compt. Rend. Soc. Biol.* **99**, 1769 (1928).
22. Burrows, H., *Brit. J. Surg.* **21**, 507 (1934).
23. Burrows, H., "Biological Actions of Sex Hormones." Cambridge, Univ. Press, London and New York, 1945.
24. Butenandt, A., and Kudszus, H., *Z. Physiol. Chem.* **237**, 75 (1935).
25. Camus, L., and Gley, E., *Compt. Rend. Soc. Biol.* **48**, 787 (1896).
26. Camus, L., and Gley, E., *Compt. Rend. Soc. Biol.* **49**, 787 (1897).
27. Catchpole, H. R., Hamilton, J. B., and Hubert, G. R., *J. Clin. Endocrinol.* **2**, 181 (1942).
28. Chang, M. C., *J. Endocrinol.* **3**, 192 (1942).
29. Christiansen, E. G., *Danish Med. Bull.* **3**, 229 (1956).
30. Chu, J. P., and You, S. S., *Proc. Chinese Physiol. Soc. (Chengtu)* **2**, 89 (1944).
31. Clegg, M. T., and Cole, H. H., *J. Animal Sci.* **13**, 108 (1954).
32. Cohen, H. *Trans. N.Y. Acad. Sci.* [2], **25**, 313 (1963).
33. Coste, F., Laurent, F., and Delabarre, F., *Compt. Rend. Soc. Biol.* **145**, 838 (1951).
34. Courrier, R., *Compt. Rend. Soc. Biol.* **85**, 939 (1921).
35. Courrier, R., and Potvin, R., *Compt. Rend. Soc. Biol.* **94**, 878 (1926).
36. Cowie, A. T., Folley, S. J., Malpress, F. H., and Richardson, K. C., *J. Endocrinol.* **8**, 64 (1952).
37. Craig-Bennett, A., *Phil. Trans. Roy. Soc. London* **B219**, 197 (1931).
37a. Cupps, P. T., and Briggs, J. R., *J. Dairy Sci.* **48**, 1241 (1965).
37b. Cupps, P. T., Lahen, R. C., and Mead, S. W., *J. Dairy Sci.* **43**, 1135 (1960).
38. Dantchakoff, V., *Compt. Rend. Soc. Biol.* **122**, 168, 1307 (1936).
39. Dantchakoff, V., *Compt. Rend. Soc. Biol.* **124**, 195 (1937).
40. Dempsey, E. W., *Am. J. Physiol.* **120**, 126 (1937).
41. Dodd, J. M., *Mem. Soc. Endocrinol.* **4**, 166 (1955).
42. Donahue, J. K., *Endocrinology* **28**, 419 (1941).
43. Dorfman, R. I., and Shipley, R. A., "Androgens." Wiley, New York, 1956.
44. Dyke, H. B. Van, and Chen, G., *Am. J. Anat.* **58**, 473 (1936).
45. Ebling, F. J., *J. Endocrinol.* **5**, 297 (1948).
46. Ellison, E. T., and Wolfe, J. M., *Endocrinology* **19**, 160 (1935).
47. Emmens, C. W., *J. Physiol. (London)* **93**, 416 (1938).
48. Emmens, C. W., *J. Endocrinol.* **2**, 444 (1941).
49. Emmens, C. W., *Advan. Reproductive Physiol.* **2** (1967).
50. Emmens, C. W., and Bradshaw, T. E. T., *J. Endocrinol.* **1**, 378 (1939).
51. Emmens, C. W., and Finn, C. A. *J. Reprod. Fertility* **3**, 239 (1962).
52. Emmens, C. W., and Parkes, A. S., *J. Endocrinol.* **1**, 323 (1939).
53. Emmens, C. W., and Parkes, A. S., *J. Endocrinol.* **1**, 332 (1939).
54. Emmens, C. W. and Parkes, A. S., *Vitamins Hormones* **5**, 233 (1947).
55. Fellner, O. O., *Klin. Wochschr.* **4**, 1651 (1925).

56. Fichera, G., *Arch. Ital. Biol.* **43**, 504 (1905).
57. Folley, S. J., "The Physiology and Biochemistry of Lactation." Oliver & Boyd, Edinburgh and London, 1956.
58. Freud, J., *Biochem. J.* **27**, 1438 (1933).
59. Frieden, E. H., and Hisaw, F. L., *Recent Progr. Hormone Res.* **8**, 333 (1953).
60. Gallagher, T. F., and Koch, F. C., *J. Pharmacol. Exptl. Therap.* **55**, 97 (1935).
61. Gallien, L., *Compt. Rend. Acad. Sci.* **205**, 375 (1937).
62. Gallien, L., *Bull. Biol. France Belg.* **72**, 269 (1938).
63. Gallien, L., *Bull. Biol. France Belg.* **78**, 257 (1944).
64. Gallien, L., *Compt. Rend. Acad. Sci.* **231**, 919 (1950).
65. Gallien, L., *Mem. Soc. Endocrinol.* **4**, 188 (1955).
66. Gardner, W. U., *Proc. Soc. Exptl. Biol. Med.* **33**, 104 (1935).
67. Greenblatt, R. B., Mortara, F., and Torpin, R., *Am. J. Obstet. Gynecol.* **44**, 658 (1942).
68. Greene, R. R., Burrill, M. W., and Ivy, A. C., *Science* **88**, 130 (1938).
69. Greene, R. R., Burrill, M. W., and Ivy, A. C., *Am. J. Anat.* **65**, 415 (1939).
70. Greene, R. R., Burrill, M. W., and Ivy, A C., *Am. J. Anat.* **67**, 305 (1940).
71. Greene, R. R., Burrill, M. W., and Ivy, A. C. *Physiol. Zool.* **15**, 1 (1942).
72. Grobstein, C., *Proc. Soc. Exptl. Biol. Med.* **49**, 477 (1942).
73. Hall, K., and Newton, W. H. *Lancet* **i**, 54 (1946).
74. Hall, K., and Newton, W. H., *J. Physiol. (London)* **106**, 18 (1947).
75. Hamburger, C., *Acta Pathol. Microbiol. Scand. Suppl.* **17** (1933).
76. Hamilton, J. B., *Proc. Soc. Exptl. Biol. Med.* **35**, 386 (1936).
77. Hamilton, J. B., *Endocrinology* **21**, 649 (1937).
78. Hamilton, J. B., *J. Clin. Endocrinol.* **1**, 570 (1941).
79. Hamilton, J. B., *Recent Progr. Hormone Res.* **3**, 257 (1948).
80. Hansel, W., *U.S. Dept. Agr. Misc. Publ.* **1005** (1965).
81. Harrison, R. J., *Biol. Revs. Cambridge Phil. Soc.* **23**, 296 (1948).
82. Hatai, S., *Am. J. Anat.* **15**, 87 (1913).
83. Hatai, S., *J. Exptl. Zool.* **15**, 297 (1913).
84. Hazelton, L. W., and Goodrich, F. J., *J. Am. Pharm. Assoc. Sci. Ed.* **26**, 420 (1937).
85. Herlant, M., *Compt. Rend. Soc. Biol.* **131**, 1315, 1318 (1939).
86. Hisaw, F. L., *Proc. Soc. Exptl. Biol. Med.* **23**, 661 (1926).
87. Hisaw, F. L., and Zarrow, M. X., *Proc. Soc. Exptl. Biol. Med.* **69**, 395 (1948).
88. Hisaw, F. L., and Zarrow, M. X., *Vitamins Hormones* **8**, 151 (1950).
89. Hoar, W. S., *Mem. Soc. Endocrinol.* **4**, 5 (1955).
90. Howard, E., *Am. J. Anat.* **62**, 381 (1938).
91. Howard, E., *Am. J. Anat.* **65**, 105 (1939).
92. Huggins, C., and Clark, P. J., *J. Exptl. Med.* **72**, 747 (1940).
93. Huggins, C., and Hodges, C. V., *Cancer Res.* **1**, 293 (1941).
94. Huggins, C., Masina, M. H., Eichelberger, L., and Wharton, J. D., *J. Exptl. Med.* **70**, 543 (1939).
95. Itho, M., and Kon, T., *Compt. Rend. Soc. Biol.* **120**, 678 (1935).
96. Jongh, S. E. de, *Arch. Neerl. Physiol.* **5**, 28 (1935).
97. Jost, A., *Recent Progr. Hormone Res.* **8**, 379 (1953).

98. Kehl, R., and Combescot, C., *Mem. Soc. Endocrinol.* **4**, 57 (1955).

99. Klein, M., and Parkes, A. S., *Proc. Roy. Soc.* **B121**, 574 (1937).

100. Kline, I. T., and Dorfman, R. I., *Endocrinology* **48**, 345 (1951).

101. Korenchevsky, V., *J. Pathol. Bacteriol.* **33**, 607 (1930).

102. Korenchevsky, V., and Hall, K., *J. Pathol. Bacteriol.* **45**, 687 (1937).

103. Korenchevsky, V., and Hall, K., *Brit. Med. J.* **I**, 4 (1939).

104. Korenchevsky, V., and Hall, K., *J. Pathol. Bacteriol.* **50**, 295 (1940).

105. Korenchevsky, V., Dennison, M., and Kohn-Speyer, A., *Biochem. J.* **26**, 2097 (1932).

106. Korenchevsky, V., Hall, K., Burburk, R. C., and Ross, M. A. *Biochem. J.* **33**, 36 (1939).

107. Kraus, H., *J. Physiol. (London)* **61**, 383 (1926).

108. Lacassagne, A., *Compt. Rend. Soc. Biol.* **131**, 580 (1933).

109. Lane, C. E., and Hisaw, F. L., *Anat. Record* **60**, 52 (1934).

110. Leonard, S. L., *Endocrinology* **21**, 330 (1937).

111. Loeb, L., *Biol. Bull.* **27**, 1 (1914).

112. Makepeace, A. W., Weinstein, G. L., and Friedman, M. H., *Proc. Soc. Exptl. Biol. Med.* **35**, 269 (1936).

113. Makepeace, A. W., Weinstein, G. L., and Friedman, M. H., *Am. J. Physiol.* **119**, 512 (1937).

114. Mann, T., *Advan. Enzymol.* **9**, 329 (1949).

115. Mann, T., *Recent Progr. Hormone Res.* **12**, 353 (1956).

116. Mann, T., "The Biochemistry of Semen." Methuen, London, 1964.

117. Mann, T., Rudolph, G. G., and Samuels, L. T., *Endocrinology* **44**, 190 (1949).

118. Marshall, F. H. A., *in* "Marshall's Physiology of Reproduction" (A. S. Parkes, ed.), Vol. 1, Part 1. Longmans, Green, London, 1956.

119. Martins, T., and Rocha, A., *Compt. Rend. Soc. Biol.* **106**, 510 (1931).

120. Masson, G., *Am. J. Med. Sci.* **209**, 324 (1945).

121. Matthay, R., *Z. Zellforsch. Mikroskop. Anat.* **8**, 671 (1929).

122. Matthay, R., *Bull. Soc. Vaudoise Sci. Nat.* **57**, 71 (1929).

123. Mayer, G. *Mem. Soc. Endocrinol.* **6**, 76 (1959).

124. Mazer, M., and Mazer, C., *Endocrinology* **26**, 662 (1940).

125. Meller, R. E., *J. Pathol. Bacteriol.* **27**, 751 (1930).

126. Merrick, E. H., *Anat. Record* **39**, 193 (1928).

127. Moore, C. R., *in* "Sex and Internal Secretions" (E. Allen, ed.), 2nd ed., p. 353. Williams & Wilkins, Baltimore, Maryland, 1939.

128. Moore, C. R., "Embryonic Sex Hormones and Sexual Differentiation." Thomas, Springfield, Illinois, 1947.

129. Moore, C. R., and McLellan, A. M., *J. Urol.* **40**, 641 (1938).

130. Moore, C. R., and Morgan, C. F., *Endocrinology* **30**, 990 (1942).

131. Moore, C. R., and Price, D., *Am. J. Anat.* **50**, 13, (1932).

132. Moore, C. R., and Price, D., *Endocrinology* **21**, 313 (1937).

133. Moore, C. R., and Price, D., *Anat. Record* **71**, 59 (1938).

134. Moore, C. R., Gallagher, T. F., and Koch, F. C., *Endocrinology* **13**, 367 (1929).

134a. Morris, G. W., *Endocrinology* **75**, 627 (1964).

135. Nelson, W. O., and Merkel, C. G., *Proc. Soc. Exptl. Biol. Med.* **36**, 823 (1937).

136. Nelson, W. O., Pfiffner, J. J., and Haterius, H. O., *Am. J. Physiol.* **91**, 690 (1930).
137. Noble, R. L., *J. Endocrinol.* **1**, 184 (1939).
138. Nussbaum, N., *Ergeb. Anat. Entwicklungsgeschichte* **15**, 39 (1905).
139. O'Donnell, V. J., and Preedy, J. R. K., *in* "Hormones in Blood" (C. H. Gray and A. L. Bacharach, eds.), p. 303. Academic Press, New York, 1961.
140. Oort, G. J. van, and Junge, G. C. A., *Acta Brevia Neerl. Physiol. Pharmacol. Microbiol.* **3**, 15 (1933).
141. Papanicolaou, G. N., *Anat. Record* **18**, 251 (1920).
142. Parkes, A. S., and Emmens, C. W., *Vitamins Hormones* **2**, 361 (1944).
143. Payne, R. W., and Hellbaum, A. A., *Endocrinology* **57**, 193 (1955).
144. Pencharz, R. I., *Science* **91**, 554 (1940).
145. Phillips, W. A., *Am. J. Physiol.* **119**, 623 (1937).
146. Pincus, G., *in* "The Hormones" (G. Pincus and K. V. Thimann, eds.), Vol. 2, Chapter 1. Academic Press, New York, 1950.
147. Pincus, G., *in* "The Hormones" (G. Pincus and K. V. Thimann, eds.), Vol. 3, Chapter 13. Academic Press, New York, 1955.
148. Pincus, G., "The Control of Fertility." Academic Press, New York, 1965.
149. Pincus, G., and Kirsch, R. E., *Am. J. Physiol.* **115**, 219 (1936).
150. Potter, G. D., and Hoar, W. S., *J. Fisheries Res. Board Can.* **11**, 63 (1954).
151. Preedy, J. R. K., and Aitken, Elsie H., *Lancet* **i, 191** (1957).
152. Price, D., *Am. J. Anat.* **60**, 79 (1936).
153. Price, D., *Intern. Congr. Biochem., 1st Congr., Cambridge, Engl., Abstr. Communs.* p. 388 (1949).
154. Raynaud, A., *Compt. Rend. Soc. Biol.* **127**, 215 (1937).
155. Reineke, E. P., Meites, J., Cairey, C. F., and Huffman, C. F., *Proc. Book. Ann. Meeting Am. Vet. Med. Assoc.* p. 325 (1952), quoted by Folley (57).
156. Reynolds, S. R. M., "Physiology of the Uterus." Harper (Hoeber), New York, 1942.
157. Robinson, T. J., *J. Endocrinol.* **12**, 163 (1955).
158. Robinson, T. J., *Nature* **206**, 39 (1965).
159. Robson, J. M., *J. Physiol. (London)* **85**, 145 (1935).
160. Robson, J. M., *Quart. J. Exptl. Physiol.* **26**, 355 (1937).
161. Robson, J. M., *J. Physiol. (London)* **92**, 371 (1938).
162. Rothchild, I. *Vitamins Hormones* **23**, 209 (1965).
163. Rubinstein, H. S., Abarbanel, A. R., and Nader, D. N., *Proc. Soc. Exptl. Biol. Med.* **39**, 20 (1938).
164. Salmon, U. J., *Proc. Soc. Exptl. Biol. Med.* **38**, 352 (1938).
165. Salmon, U. J., and Geist, S. H., *J. Clin. Endocrinol.* **3**, 235 (1943).
166. Selye, H., "Textbook of Endocrinology." Acta Endocrinol., Montreal, Canada, 1947.
167. Selye, H., Browne, J. S. L., and Collip, J. B., *Proc. Soc. Exptl. Biol. Med.* **34**, 198, 472 (1936).
168. Severinghaus, A. E., *Anat. Record* **57**, 149 (1933).
169. Shapiro, H. A., *Chem. Ind. (London)* **55**, 1031 (1936).
170. Shapiro, H. A., and Zwarenstein, H., *J. Physiol. (London)* **89**, 38P (1937).
171. Shay, H., Gershon-Cohen, J., Paschkis, K. E., and Fels, S. S., *Endocrinology* **28**, 485 (1941).
172. Shelesnyak, M. C., *Endeavour* **19**, 87 (1960).

173. Shelesnyak, M. C., *in* "Techniques in Endocrine Research" (P. Eckstein and F. Knowles, eds.). Academic Press, New York, 1963.
174. Short, R. B., *in* "Hormones in Blood" (C. H. Gray and A. L. Bacharach, eds.), p. 379. Academic Press, New York, 1961.
175. Smith, P. E., *Am. J. Physiol.* **99**, 345, 349 (1932).
176. Snelling, F. G., *Am. J. Obstet. Gynecol.* **2**, 561 (1870).
177. Stockard, C. R., and Papanicolaou, G., *Am. J. Anat.* **22**, 225 (1917).
178. Swanson, H. H., *J. Endocrinol.* **36**, 376 (1966).
179. Varangot, J., Seeman, A., and Cedard, L., *Compt. Rend. Soc. Biol.* **150**, 923 (1956).
180. Vatna, S., *Biol. Bull.* **58**, 322 (1930).
181. Voss, H. E., *Z. Zellforsch. Mikroskop. Anat.* **14**, 200 (1931).
182. Wade, N. J., and Doisy, E. A., *Endocrinology* **19**, 77 (1935).
183. Wainman, P., and Shipounoff, G. C., *Endocrinology* **29**, 975 (1941).
184. Walsh, E. L., Cuyler, W. K., and McCullagh, D. R., *Proc. Soc. Exptl. Med.* **30**, 848 (1933).
185. Walsh, E. L., Cuyler, W. K., and McCullagh, D. R., *Am. J. Physiol.* **107**, 508 (1934).
186. Whitney, R., and Burdick, H. O. *Endocrinology* **22**, 639 (1937).
187. Williams, P. C., *Nature* **145**, 388 (1940).
188. Williams, M. F., *Am. J. Anat.* **83**, 247 (1948).
189. Witschi, E., *Proc. Soc. Exptl. Biol. Med.* **33**, 484 (1936).
190. Witschi, E., and Fugo, N. W., *Proc. Soc. Exptl. Biol. Med.* **45**, 10 (1940).
191. Woolley, G. W., and Little, C. C., *Cancer Res.* **5**, 203 (1945).
192. Zimbelman, R. G., *U.S. Dept. Agr. Misc. Publ.* **1005** (1965).
193. Zondek, B., *Am. J. Obstet. Gynecol.* **24**, 836 (1932).
194. Zuckerman, S., *Proc. Roy. Soc.* **B118**, 22 (1936).
195. Zuckerman, S., *Biol. Revs. Cambridge Phil. Soc.* **15**, 231 (1940).

6 THE BIOCHEMISTRY OF GONADAL HORMONES AND RELATED COMPOUNDS

RALPH I. DORFMAN

The earliest biochemical studies on gonadal hormones were done on tissues and body fluids in domestic animals. Bull testis served as an important source for androgen studies and, in fact, the first isolation of testosterone was from this source (29). Pregnant mare's urine (40) and stallion's urine (33) were important early sources of estrogens. In more recent years, however, a good portion of the development of steroid metabolism has shifted to studies on human and rodent tissues and fluids, while studies in the domestic animals have somewhat lagged behind.

This chapter summarizes the present status of the biochemistry of gonadal hormones of domestic animals, excluding pets. The gonadal hormones include androgens, estrogens, and progesterone and are biosynthesized in the testes, ovaries, adrenal gland, and placenta. On a sequential basis it is proper, as will be discussed in some detail, to consider progesterone as the first of the gonadal hormones formed from cholesterol. In addition to the physiological function of progesterone in the sexual cycles of the female and in pregnancy, the compound may be considered to be an important direct biosynthetic intermediate in the formation of androgens and indirectly in the formation of estrogens. In a recent study, a new role for progesterone has been suggested (35). It is quite likely that progesterone, on the basis of its antiandrogenic and antiestrogenic activity, protects the fetus from excessive concentrations of both androgens and estrogens during pregnancy.

I. Pregnenolone and Progesterone

Tables I–IV summarize the isolation of progesterone, pregnenolone, and related steroids from various tissues, blood, bile, and urine, respectively, of

113

TABLE I

PREGNENOLONE, PROGESTERONE, AND RELATED STEROIDS
IN TISSUES OF DOMESTIC ANIMALS

Species	Steroids	Tissue	Reference
Porcine	3β-Hydroxy-5α-pregnan-20-one	Ovary	(*21b, 51, 59, 189, 210*)
	Progesterone 20α-Hydroxypregn-4-en-3-one	Ovary	(*131*)
	Progesterone	Ovary Corpus luteum, over 5 mm—5.1 μg/g Corpus luteum, under 5 mm—0.39 μg/g Follicles—0.09 μg/g	(*199*)
	Progesterone	Ovary	(*21, 51, 189, 210*)
	Progesterone	Ovary	(*36*)

Cycle day	μg/g
4	23
8	213
12	335
16	311
18	0

	Progesterone	Ovary corpus luteum	(*22*)
	17α-Hydroxyprogesterone	Ovary follicular fluid	(*184, 185*)
	Pregnenolone	Adrenal	(*4, 129*)
	20α-Hydroxypregn-4-en-3-one	Adrenal	(*129*)
	Pregnenolone 3β-Hydroxy-5α-pregnan-20-one 3α-Hydroxy-5α-pregnan-20-one	Testis	(*45, 159*)
	Progesterone	Testis	(*130*)
	Progesterone	Ovary	(*36*)

Day of pregnancy	μg/g
16	477
48	578
102	120

	Progesterone	Ovary, pregnancy, corpus luteum, maximum levels—65 μg/g	(*155*)

TABLE I (Continued)

Species	Steroids	Tissue	Reference
Equine	Progesterone 20α-Hydroxypregn-4-en-3-one 17α-Hydroxyprogesterone	Ovary luteal tissue	(185)
	Progesterone 20β-Hydroxypregn-4-en-3-one	Ovary follicular fluid Placenta	(184) (181)
Ovine	20α-Hydroxypregn-4-en-3-one	Placenta	(183)
Bovine	Progesterone	Placenta	(14)
	Progesterone	Adrenal	(8, 19, 54)
	Pregnenolone	Adrenal	(162, 179, 192)
	3β-Hydroxy-5α-pregnan-20-one	Adrenal	(129)

animals of the porcine, equine, and bovine species. Biosynthetic reactions demonstrated in these species are presented in Tables V and VI.

Pregnenolone is the primary steroid on the route to steroid hormone formation from cholesterol. In recent years the biosynthetic mechanism has been elucidated. Shimizu et al. (178) demonstrated that 20α-hydroxycholesterol could be cleaved at the side chain to give isocaproic acid. The C_{21} steroid nuclear moiety, pregnenolone, was subsequently demonstrated by use of adrenal homogenate preparations. The human placenta and the rat testes performed these transformations as well (179). The conversion was also demonstrated with a bovine corpus luteum homogenate (198). The incubation of 20α22R-dihydroxycholesterol with the bovine adrenal homogenate yielded pregnenolone. Constantopoulos and Tchen (26) have confirmed the studies indicating the pathway of cholesterol conversion to pregnenolone.

Two monohydroxy derivatives of cholesterol are possible as the first intermediate, one with the hydroxyl group in the 20α position and one with a hydroxyl group in the 22R position (24). Either monohydroxylated intermediate could be further hydroxylated to the dihydroxy compound 20α,22R-dihydroxycholesterol which, with the action of the 20,22R-desmolase, forms pregnenolone and isocaproic aldehyde. In many of the systems in which this reaction has been shown to take place in vitro, the isocaproic aldehyde is oxidized further to the corresponding isocaproic acid.

Progesterone is formed from pregnenolone in gonadal tissue and in the placenta by the action of 3β-ol dehydrogenase (see Table VI).

After Duncan et al. (36) demonstrated the in vitro formation of proges-

TABLE II

PREGNENOLONE, PROGESTERONE, AND RELATED STEROIDS
IN BLOOD OF DOMESTIC ANIMALS

Species	Steroid	Study	Reference
Bovine	Progesterone		(181)
	Progesterone	Pregnancy	(182)
	17α-Hydroxy-progesterone	Spermatic vein	(168)
Porcine	Progesterone		(181)
	Progesterone	Ovarian vein	(119)

Cycle day	μg/ml
1	0.36 ± 0.01
8	3.04 ± 0.3
14	1.45 ± 0.5
16	0.23 ± 0.1
18	0.17 ± 0.1

Pregnancy

Day of gestation	μg/ml
14	2.28 ± 0.2
18	2.6 ± 0.3
102	1.3 ± 0.3
112	0.9 ± 0.2

Species	Steroid	Study	Reference
	Progesterone	0.77 μg/ml	(172)
	Progesterone	Sow	(42)

Day of cycle	μg/100 ml
1	3 ± 1.0
10–12	107 ± 13
19–21	4 ± 1

Species	Steroid	Study	Reference
	Pregnenolone	Immature	(58)
	Progesterone		
Ovine	Pregnenolone Progesterone 20α-Hydroxypregn-4-en-3-one	Ovarian vein	(186)
	Progesterone		(181)
		Adrenal venous	(181)
	20α-Hydroxypregn-4-en-3-one		(181, 183)

TABLE II (Continued)

Species	Steroid	Study	Reference

Caprine	Progesterone	Normal cycle
		  11-day corpus luteum,
		    ovarian vein—1400[a]
		Pregnancy
		  120 days, jugular
		    vein—8.2
		  119 days, two corpora lutea
		    in left and one in right:
		    left ovarian vein—
		    1600
		    right ovarian
		      vein—620
		Anestrus
		  jugular vein—8.5
		  no corpora lutea—8
		Pregnancy
			(57)
			
			(181)

[a] In micrograms per milliliter.

terone by porcine luteal tissue, Mason et al. (117) demonstrated the in vitro stimulation of progesterone biosynthesis by gonadotropins.

Using this bovine corpus luteum slice system, Savard and Casey (170) incubated acetate-1-^{14}C and showed that LH (luteinizing hormone) produces a threefold to fivefold increase in progesterone-^{14}C and an equal increase in total progesterone. The addition of TPNH caused eightfold to fifteen-fold increase in mass of progesterone, but no increase in ^{14}C progesterone. In a further report, 3',5'-AMP increased both acetate-1-^{14}C incor-

TABLE III

THE PRESENCE OF PREGNENOLONE, PROGESTERONE, AND RELATED STEROIDS
IN THE BILE OF DOMESTIC ANIMALS

Species	Steroid	Remarks	Reference
Bovine	Pregnanolone	Pregnancy	(139)
	5β-Pregnane-3α,20β-diol	Pregnancy	(141)
	5α-Pregnane-3β,20β-diol		(137)

	Pregnanediol
	Presumptive:
	  5α-Pregnane-3α,20α-diol
	  5α-Pregnane-3β,20α-diol
	  5α-Pregnane-3β,20β-diol
		Pregnancy	(1)

	Estrone 17α-Estradiol	Newborn calves	(156)

TABLE IV
PREGNENOLONE, PROGESTERONE, AND RELATED COMPOUNDS
IN THE URINE OF DOMESTIC ANIMALS

Species	Steroid	Reference
Bovine	5β-Pregnane-3α,20α-diol (Pregnanediol)	(64, 108, 109)
	5α-Pregnane-3β,20α-diol	(107, 109)
	5α-Pregnane-3α,20α-diol	(108, 109)
	5β-Pregnane-3,20-dione Pregnanolone Pregnanediol	(65)
Porcine	3α-Hydroxy-5β-pregnan-20-one 3β-Hydroxy-5α-pregnan-20-one	(112)
	3α-Hydroxy-5β-pregnan-20-one 3β-Hydroxy-5α-pregnan-20-one 5β-Pregnane-3α,20α-diol	(173)

poration into steroid and total mass of progesterone as was found for LH, but different than that found for TPNH (113). Marsh and Savard (112a) suggest, on the basis of puromycin experiments, that protein synthesis is a requisite for stimulation of progesterone synthesis by LH and 3′,5′-AMP in the bovine corpus luteum.

Mason and Savard (118) investigated the specificity of gonadotropin stimulation of progesterone synthesis in bovine corpus luteum slices and concluded that LH stimulation is produced with as little as 0.01–0.02 μg/ gm of luteal tissue which is estimated to be 1×10^{-10} M.

A soluble enzyme preparation has been obtained from bovine corpus luteum which converts cholesterol to pregnenolone and progesterone in addition to the isocaproic aldehyde and the corresponding acid, and the activity for the overall reaction is present in the mitochondrial, microsomal, and supernatant fractions (73). Halkerston et al. (47) also found the overall cholesterol to pregnenolone and isocaproic acid activity in all adrenal homogenate fractions. The major activity for the adrenal tissue was in the mitochondrial fraction, while the supernatant of the bovine corpus luteum contained the bulk of the activity. In experiments involving acetone powders of whole homogenates of corpus luteum, all the activity may be accounted for in the soluble portion, that is, the fraction not sedimented at 105,000 g. Acetone powders were about ten times more active than fresh tissue on a wet-weight tissue basis.

Cleavage did not occur in the absence of added cofactor. TPN and DPN alone were more effective than small and moderate concentrations of TPNH. High concentrations of TPNH were inhibitory.

TABLE V
BIOSYNTHESIS OF PREGNENOLONE AND PROGESTERONE
IN DOMESTIC ANIMALS *in Vitro*

Substrate	Product	Test system	Species	Reference
Cholesterol	Pregnenolone	Adrenal homogenate	Bovine	(*161*)
	Progesterone	Corpora lutea	Bovine	(*190*)
	Pregnenolone	Adrenal	Bovine	(*54, 192*)
	Progesterone	homogenate		
Acetate	Progesterone	Adrenal slices and cell-free preparation	Porcine	(*5*)
		Ovary mince	Bovine	(*195*)
Pregnenolone	Progesterone	Adrenal homogenate	Bovine	(*144*)
β,β-Dimethylacrylate	Progesterone	Adrenal slices and cell-free preparation	Porcine	(*5*)
20α-Hydroxy-cholesterol	Pregnenolone Progesterone	Adrenal homogenate	Bovine	(*179*)
	Pregnenolone	Adrenal homogenate	Bovine	(*26*)
20α,22x-Dihydroxy-cholesterol	Pregnenolone	Adrenal homogenate	Bovine	(*180*)
20α-Hydroxy-cholesterol	Pregnenolone	Corpus luteum	Bovine	(*198*)
Acetate	Progesterone	Adrenal homogenate	Bovine	(*19*)
22-Hydroxy-cholesterol	Pregnenolone	Adrenal mitochondria	Bovine	(*24*)
Cholesterol 20α,22-Dihydroxy-cholesterol	Pregnenolone plus isocaproaldehyde	Adrenal cortex	Bovine	(*27*)

DPN at concentrations of 1–50 μg added to optimal concentrations of TPN elicited increased rates of side-chain cleavage over that observed for the same concentrations of DPN alone. A similar effect was obtained when TPN in concentrations from 1–100 μg were added to an optimal concentration of DPN and when DPN or TPN were added to optimal concentrations of TPNH. However, TPNH added to optimal concentrations of DPN did not influence the rate of side-chain cleavage. The effects obtained by the various pyridine nucleotide combinations suggested, on the one hand, a requirement for both the reduced and oxidized form of the nucleotide for the reaction sequence from C_{27} to C_{21} steroid to proceed optimally. On the other hand, since such extremely low levels of nucleotide added in the presence of high concentrations of other nucleotides produced such large increases in rate of cleavage, it is suggested that perhaps transhydrogenation

RALPH I. DORFMAN

TABLE VI
BIOSYNTHESIS OF PREGNENOLONE, PROGESTERONE, AND 20-DIHYDRO
DERIVATIVES IN DOMESTIC ANIMALS *in Vitro*

Species	Substrate	Product	Test system	References
Bovine	None	Pregnenolone	Adrenal and corpus luteum mitochondria	(67)
	Pregnenolone	Progesterone	Minced ovarian tissue	(125)
	Acetate	Progesterone 20β-Hydroxypregn-4-en-3-one	Corpus luteum slice	(134)
	Cholesterol	Pregnenolone	Adrenal cortex mitochondria	(48)
	Progesterone	5α-Pregnane-3,20-dione	Adrenal homogenate	(87)
	20α-Hydroxy-cholesterol	Pregnenolone Progesterone	Adrenal homogenate	(49)
	Mevalonate acetate	Progesterone	Corpus luteum slices	(66)
	Cholesterol	Pregnenolone	Adrenal mitochondria	(84)
	Endogenous	Progesterone	Corpus luteum	(6)
	Cholesterol sulfate	Pregnenolone sulfate	Adrenal mitochondria	(150)
	Cholesterol	Pregnenolone		
	Pregnenolone	Progesterone	Ovarian slices (studies during estrous cycle)	(96)
	Cholesterol 20α,22R-Dihy-droxycholesterol	Pregnenolone		(27)
	Cholesterol	Progesterone	Corpus luteum slice	(118)
	Pregnenolone acetate	Progesterone 20β-Hydroxy-pregn-4-en-3-one	Corpus luteum slices	(171)
	20α-Hydroxy-cholesterol	Pregnenolone	Adrenal homogenate	(26)

TABLE VI *(Continued)*

Species	Substrate	Product	Test system	Reference
	Cholesterol	Pregnenolone	Adrenal homogenate	*(161)*
		Progesterone	Corpora lutea	*(190)*
		Pregnenolone Progesterone	Adrenal homogenate	*(54, 192)*
	Pregnenolone	Progesterone	Adrenal homogenate	*(144)*
	Acetate	Progesterone	Corpus luteum slices and minces	*(46)*
	Acetate cholesterol	Progesterone	Corpus luteum slices	*(113)*
	Cholesterol 20α,20-Dihydroxycholesterol	Pregnenolone plus isocaproicaldehyde	Adrenal cortex	*(27)*
	22-Hydroxycholesterol	Pregnenolone	Adrenal mitochondria	*(24)*
	20α,22-Dihydroxycholesterol	Pregnenolone	Adrenal homogenate	*(180)*
	20α-Hydroxycholesterol	Pregnenolone	Corpus luteum	*(198)*
	20α-Hydroxycholesterol	Pregnenolone Progesterone	Adrenal homogenate	*(179)*
	Acetate	Progesterone	Adrenal homogenate	*(19)*
	Acetate	Progesterone	Ovary mince	*(195)*
	Acetate	Progesterone 20β-Hydroxypregn-4-en-3-one	Corpus luteum	*(171)*
	Pregnenolone	Progesterone 20β-Hydroxypregn-4-en-3-one		
	Progesterone	20β-Hydroxypregn-4-en-3-one		
	Cholesterol	Progesterone	Adrenal cortical slices	*(97)*
	Cholesterol	Progesterone	Corpus luteum slices	*(50)*

TABLE VI (Continued)

Species	Substrate	Product	Test system	Reference
Porcine	β,β-Dimethyl-acrylate Acetate	Progesterone	Adrenal slices and cell-free preparation	(5)
	None	Progesterone, 43 μg/gm of luteal tissue	Perfusion corpora lutea	(22)
	Acetate	Progesterone		
Equine	None	Progesterone (I) 20α-Hydroxy-pregn-4-en-3-one (II) 17α-Hydroxypro-gesterone (III)	Graafian follicles, 2–6 cm in diameter, 20,000–40,000 live cells, (7-days)	(23)

Product	μg formed
I	340
II	89
III	35

TABLE VII

The Catabolism of Progesterone in Domestic Animals *in Vitro*

Test system (species)	Product	Reference
Blood protein (bovine)	5β-Pregnane-3,20-dione	(157)
Liver slices (chicken)	20β-Hydroxypregn-4-en-3-one 20α-Hydroxypregn-4-en-3-one	(126)
Blood (bovine)	20α-Hydroxypregn-4-en-3-one	(28)
Sperm (boar) (stallion)	20β-Hydroxypregn-4-en-3-one	(176)
Corpus luteum (bovine)	20β-Hydroxypregn-4-en-3-one	(53a)
Ovary microsomes (porcine)	16α-Hydroxyprogesterone	(79)

between the pyridine nucleotides is satisfying a possible requirement for the reduced forms of both pyridine nucleotides. Some reduction of added pyridine nucleotide takes place in the absence of any added reduced-nucleotide generating system. The enzyme system contained a glucose 6-phosphate dehydrogenase system which rapidly reduced added TPN in the presence of glucose 6-phosphate and enzyme preparation alone.

The biosynthesis of progesterone may be summarized in the following

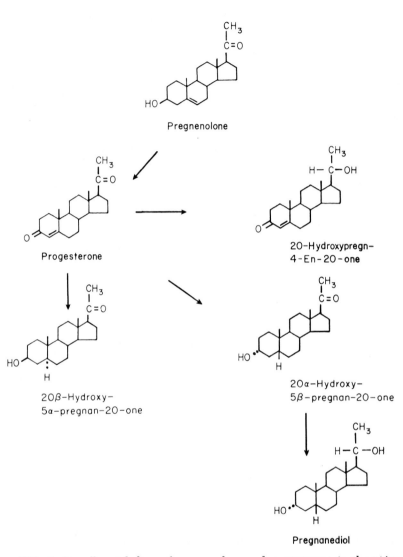

FIG. 1. Overall metabolism of pregnenolone and progesterone in the ovine species.

manner. Cholesterol→20α-hydroxycholesterol (or 22R-hydroxycholesterol) →20α,22R-dihydroxycholesterol→pregnenolone→progesterone.

The limited number of catabolic studies on progesterone in domestic animals yielded three dihydro compounds, namely, 5β-pregnane-3,20-dione and the 20α- and 20β-dihydro derivatives of progesterone (Table VII). To

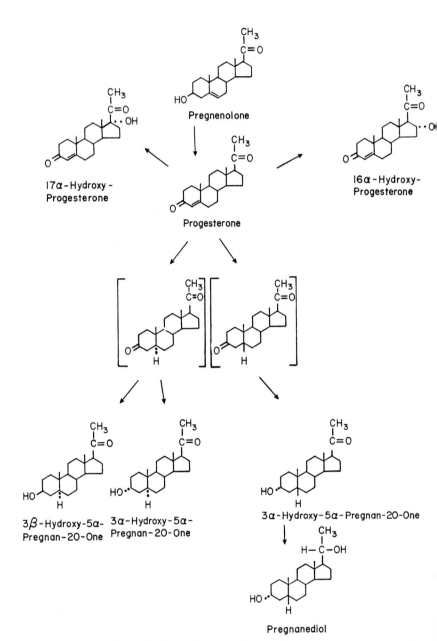

FIG. 2. Overall metabolism of pregnenolone and progesterone in the porcine species.

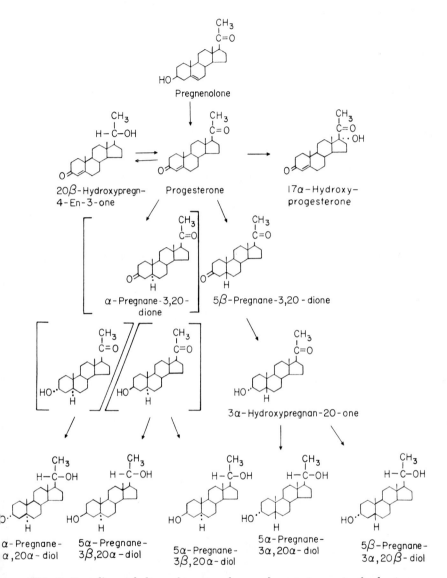

FIG. 3. Overall metabolism of pregnenolone and progesterone in the bovine species.

these derivatives is added the 16α-hydroxy of progesterone when the steroid is incubated with porcine ovary microsomes.

The metabolic interrelationship between pregnenolone, progesterone, and their metabolites is illustrated in Fig. 1 for the ovine species, Fig. 2 for the porcine species, and Fig. 3 for the bovine species. Compounds designated in brackets are those expected to be present but which have not been demonstrated. At this stage of development of the field of steroid metabolism, the fact that more metabolites are known in the bovine species is not necessarily significant, except as it relates to the greater amount of effort expended on steroid metabolism in this species.

II. Androgens

Androgens are substances which possess characteristic biological activity affecting the sex characters of various animals. The detailed physiological aspects are discussed in Chapter 5.

Small amounts of androgenic material occur in the testis, blood, and in the urine, and it was from the latter that the first active crystalline substance was isolated in 1931 by Butenandt and Tscherning (21a) and named "androsterone." In 1935, David et al. (29) isolated testosterone from bull testis, and this steroid is still the most active naturally occurring androgen known.

Testosterone has been isolated from the testis of many species, including the human, bull, stallion, rabbit, and pig. Concentrations in testes are usually of a low order, and there is a steady production of the hormone under the control of pituitary gonadotropic hormones and a steady extrusion into the bloodstream. Androst-4-ene-3, 17-dione, which differs from testosterone by virtue of a ketone in place of the 17β-hydroxyl group, is isolated as a companion substance in both the testis tissue and the spermatic venous effluent. A variety of C_{19} and C_{21} biosynthetic precursors and/or metabolites of testosterone have been found. These compounds include dehydroepiandrosterone, pregnenolone, progesterone, and various 17α-hydroxylated derivatives. Table VIII summarizes the androgens demonstrated in adrenal, testis, and ovary of domestic animals. 11-Oxygenated androgens have been realized only from adrenal tissue. Tables IX–XI list the androgens and related compounds from blood, bile, and urine.

References to experimental data dealing with the biosynthesis of androgens are listed in Tables XII–XIV. It is on the basis of this information that various pathways of androgen formation may be suggested. A mechanism, which has been described for all steroid-producing tissues and which was first reported by Slaunwhite and Samuels (188) and soon thereafter by Savard et al. (166), involves 17α-hydroxyprogesterone, the formation of androst-4-ene-3, 17-dione by a desmolase reaction, and the reduction of the 17-keto group to testosterone. This pathway is known for the testis (166, 188), the ovary (81, 190), and the adrenal (151).

Another pathway leads to the formation of dehydroepiandrosterone and involves the successive formation of pregnenolone, 17α-hydroxypregnenolone and dehydroepiandrosterone.

TABLE VIII

ANDROGEN AND RELATED STEROIDS IN THE TISSUES OF DOMESTIC ANIMALS

Species	Steroid	Tissue	Reference
Bovine	Androst-4-ene-3,17-dione	Adrenal	(13, 19, 37)
	Adrenosterone	Adrenal	(13, 152)
	11β-Hydroxyandrost-4-ene-3,17-dione	Adrenal	(13, 19)
	11β-Hydroxyepiandrosterone	Adrenal	(37, 153)
	6β-Hydroxyandrost-4-ene-3,17-dione 6α-Hydroxyandrost-4-ene-3,17-dione	Adrenal	(124)
Porcine	11β-Hydroxyandrost-4-ene-3,17-dione	Adrenal	(208)
	3-Keto-11β,18-dihydroxy-Δ^4-etienic acid	Adrenal	(127)
	11β-Hydroxyandrosterone 11β-Hydroxyepitesterosterone	Adrenal Adrenal	(129)
	Testosterone	Testis	(15)
	5α-Androst-16-en-3α-ol 5α-Androst-16-en-3β-ol	Testis	(159)
	Dehydroepiandrosterone	Testis	(128)
	Testosterone	Testis	(72)
	Androst-4-ene-3,17-dione		
	Dehydroepiandrosterone		
	Dehydroepiandrosterone sulfate		
Equine	Testosterone	Testis	(197)
Bovine	Adrenosterone	Testis	(130)
	Epiandrosterone		
	17α,20β-Dihydroxypregn-4-en-3-one	Testis	(98, 99) (130)
	17α,20α-Dihydroxypregn-4-en-3-one	Testis	(98, 99) (130)
	17α-Hydroprogesterone	Testis	(130)
	Testosterone	Testis	(29)
Equine	Epitestosterone	Ovary (follicular fluid)	(184)
	Androst-4-ene-3,17-dione		
	19-Norandrost-4-ene-3,17-dione		

TABLE IX
ANDROGENS AND RELATED STEROIDS IN BLOOD OF DOMESTIC ANIMALS

Species	Steroid	Tissue	Reference
Ovine	11β-Hydroxyandrost-4-ene-3,17-dione	Adrenal venous	(20)
Porcine	Dehydroepiandrosterone Dehydroepiandrosterone sulfate Androst-4-ene-3,17-dione Testosterone	Spermatic vein	(72)
	Presumptive: Androst-4-ene-3,17-dione 16α-Hydroxyprogesterone 17α-Hydroxyprogesterone 11β-Hydroxyandrost-4-ene-3,17-dione	Adrenal venous	(55)
	11β-Hydroxyandrosterone-3,17-dione	Adrenal venous	(58)
Bovine	Androst-4-ene-3,17-dione		(93)
	Androst-4-ene-3,17-dione	Spermatic vein	(168)
	Testosterone	Spermatic vein	(93, 168)

TABLE X
ANDROGENS IN BILE OF DOMESTIC ANIMALS

Species	Compound	Reference
Bovine	5β-Androstane-3α,17α-diol	(141)

Kadis (79) has demonstrated the presence of a 16α-hydroxylase in porcine ovaries, and this enzyme acts on the substrates testosterone, androst-4-ene-3, 17-dione, and dehydroepiandrosterone. The 16α-hydroxylation of these substrates appears to be related to the eventual formation of estriol (page 137) by the ovary.

The androgen 11β-hydroxyandrost-4-ene-3, 17-dione is formed by the action of 11β-hydroxylase (in bovine adrenal tissue) on androst-4-ene-3, 17-dione. Adrenosterone is formed, secondarily, by the action of 11β-dehydrogenase.

The presence of androsta-1, 4-diene-3, 17-dione in a bovine polycystic ovary has been reported by Gawienowski *et al.* (39) and may indicate a pathway of estrogen biosynthesis with this steroid as an intermediate. The same role is assigned with more confidence to 19-hydroxyandrost-4-ene-3, 17-dione. In the latter case the diene would be expected to go spontaneously to estrone after 19-hydroxylation.

It has been known for many years that porcine testes contain C_{19}-Δ^{16}

TABLE XI

ANDROGENS AND RELATED COMPOUNDS IN THE URINE OF DOMESTIC ANIMALS

Species	Steroid	Remarks	Reference
Bovine	Dehydroepiandrosterone		*(69, 107, 110)*
	Androsterone		*(110, 111)*
	Etiocholanolone		*(69)*
	5β-Androstene-3α,17α-diol	Pregnancy	*(83)*
	5α-Androstane-3α,17α-diol	Pregnancy	*(83)*
	11β-Hydroxyandrost-4-ene-3,17-dione		*(69)*
	Epiandrosterone	Ketonic fraction	*(64, 65)*
	Etiocholanolone		
	Androsterone		
	5α-Androstane-3,17-dione		
	5β-Androstane-3,17-dione		
	5β-Androstane-3α,17α-diol		
	5α-Androstane-3β,17α-diol		
	5β-Androstane-3α,17α-diol	Pregnancy	*(64)*
	5α-Androstane-3β,17α-diol		
Porcine	3β-Cl-Androst-5-en-17-one		*(72)*
	Dehydroepiandrosterone		*(72)*
	Epiandrosterone		
	Androsterone		
	Etiocholanolone		
	Dehydroepiandrosterone	Boar	*(71)*
	3β-Chloroandrost-5-en-17-one		
	Dehydroepiandrosterone	Hog (boar)	*(25)*
	Androsterone	Hog (boar)	*(25)*
	Etiocholanolone	Hog (boar)	*(25)*
	11β-Hydroxyetiocholanolone	Hog	*(25)*
	11-Ketoetiocholanolone	Hog	*(25)*
Equine	3β-Hydroxy-5α-androstan-16-one	Pregnancy	*(60, 70, 133)*
	5α-Androstane-3β,16β-diol	Pregnancy	*(17, 18)*
	5α-Androstane-3β,16α-diol	Pregnancy	

TABLE XII

THE BIOSYNTHESIS OF ANDROGENS IN BOVINE TISSUES BY PERFUSION

Substrate	Product	Gland	Reference
Androst-4-ene-3,17-dione	11β-Hydroxyandrost-4-ene-3,17-dione	Adrenal	(75, 76)
Progesterone	11β-Hydroxyandrost-4-ene-3,17-dione	Adrenal	(86)
Dehydroepiandrosterone	11β-Hydroxyandrost-4-ene-3,17-dione	Calf adrenal	(158)

steroids, but the synthetic route to these compounds has not been entirely elucidated. Gower and Ahmed (44) have made substantial contributions when they demonstrated that, using minced porcine testis or adrenals, pregnenolone may be converted to three C_{19}-Δ^{16} steroids. The mechanism by which this biosynthetic route operates is still to be elucidated.

The catabolic reactions of androgens both of the $C_{19}O_2$ and $C_{19}O_3$ are summarized in Table XIV. Similar studies have been done in the equine species, but mention should be made of the three $C_{19}O_2$ steroids which are known only from this source and which have oxygen substituents at C-3 and C-16, while lacking C-17 oxygen function (Fig. 4). In the case of the porcine species, more information is available and outlined in Fig. 5. This

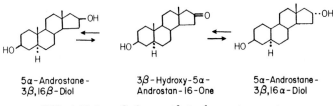

| 5α–Androstane-3β,16β-Diol | 3β-Hydroxy-5α-Androstan-16-One | 5α-Androstane-3β,16α-Diol |

FIG. 4. Unique $C_{19}O_2$ steroids in the equine species.

figure emphasizes the presence of $C_{19}O_2$ compounds, the presence of sulfate esters and, finally, the presence of androsterone and etiocholanolone as metabolites of androst-4-ene-3, 17-dione, an interrelation so well established in many species, including man (34). The 11β-hydroxy-$C_{19}O_2$ compounds are also represented in Fig. 5. In the bovine species the interrelationship between testosterone and ring A reduced metabolites is well documented (Fig. 6), and, in addition, the 11-oxygenated $C_{19}O_2$ are represented. In the catabolism of testosterone, three $C_{19}O_2$ diols have been noted (Fig. 6). In the ovine species the 11β-hydroxyandrost-4-ene-3, 17-dione and ring-A-reduced 17α-hydroxy derivatives have been reported. These and their possible metabolic interrelations are presented in Fig. 7.

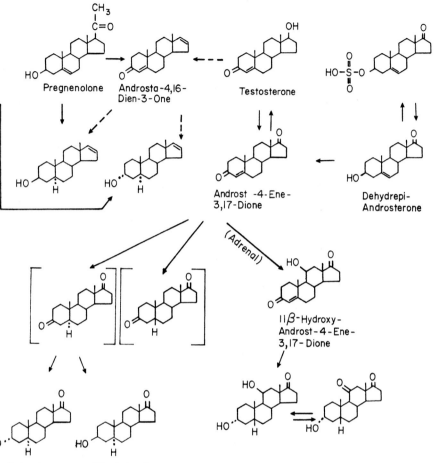

FIG. 5. Overall metabolism of $C_{19}O$, $C_{19}O_2$, and $C_{19}O_3$ steroids in the porcine species.

III. Estrogens

The biological activity of estrogens is described in Chapter 5. This section deals with the various biochemical aspects of this group of hormones.

Four estrogens, estrone, 17α- and 17β-estradiol, and estriol, have been detected in the steroid-forming tissues of domestic animals (Table XV). Tables XVI and XVII summarize the data on estrogens in blood and bile, respectively, while Table XVIII deals with urinary estrogens.

Estrogen biosynthesis in domestic animals has been studied rather ex-

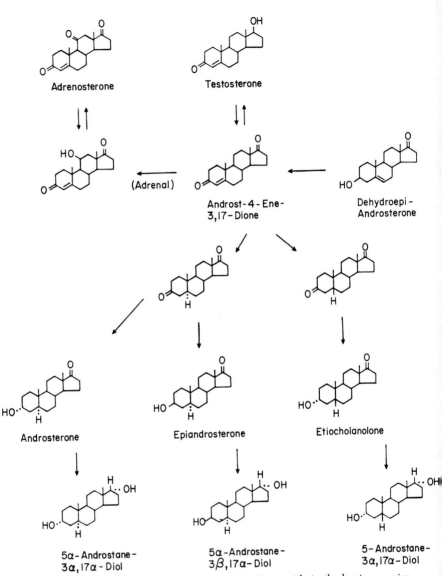

FIG. 6. Overall metabolism of $C_{19}O_2$ and $C_{19}O_3$ steroids in the bovine species.

tensively by *in vivo* (Table XIX) and *in vitro* (Table XX) methods. The pathways indicated in these species seem to be rather similar to those found in the human, such as the pathway acetate → cholesterol → pregnenolone → $C_{19}O_2$ (such as dehydroepiandrosterone, androst-4-ene-3, 17-dione, and/or testosterone) → 19-hydroxy-$C_{19}O_2$ → estrone and/or 17β-estradiol.

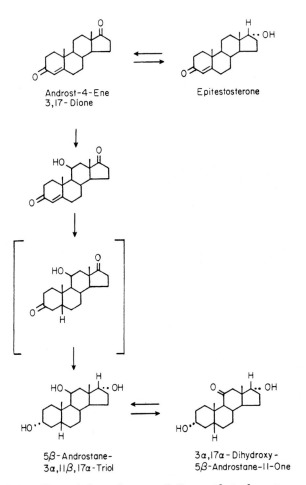

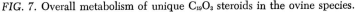

FIG. 7. Overall metabolism of unique $C_{19}O_3$ steroids in the ovine species.

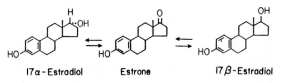

FIG. 8. Overall metabolism of estrogens in the bovine and porcine species.

An alternative pathway involving $C_{19}O_2$ steroids → 19-hydroxy-$C_{19}O_2$ → 19-oxo-$C_{19}O_2$ → estrone and/or 17β-estradiol is strongly indicated in the equine species (192a). The conversion of 19-norandrost-4-ene-3, 17-dione to estrone in the bovine species (122) seems to point to the decarboxylation

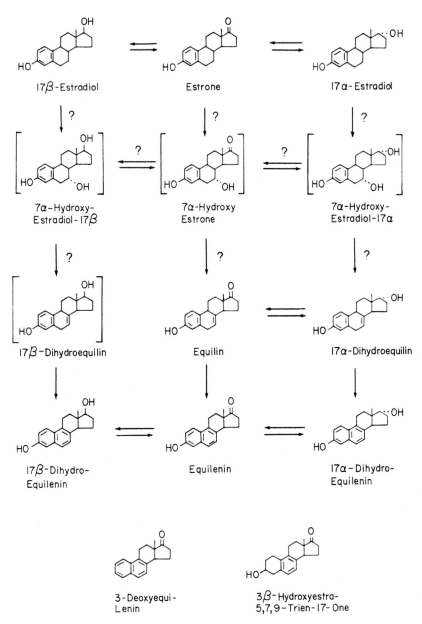

FIG. 9. Overall metabolism of estrogens in the equine species.

TABLE XIII

THE BIOSYNTHESIS OF ANDROGENS *in Vitro* BY DOMESTIC ANIMALS

Species	Substrate	Product	Test system	Reference
Porcine	Progesterone	Androst-4-ene-3,17-dione	Adrenal cell-free extract	(151)
	Acetate	Androst-4-ene-3,17-dione	Adrenal homogenate	(12, 63)
	Androst-4-ene-3,17-dione	3β-Hydroxyandrost-4-en-17-one Dehydroepiandrosterone	Acetone powder sheep adrenal microsomes	(204)
	Acetate	Testosterone	Testis slice	(15)
	Androst-4-ene-3,17-dione	3β-Hydroxyandrost-4-en-17-one Dehydroepiandrosterone	Acetone powder adrenal microsomes	(205)
	Androst-5-ene-3,17-dione	Dehydroepiandrosterone		
	Pregn-4-ene-17α,20α-diol-3-one	Testosterone Androst-4-ene-3,17-dione	Adrenal homogenate	(74)
	17α-Hydroxyprogesterone	Suggested pathway from pregn-4-ene-17α,20α-diol to androst-4-ene-3,17-dione		
	Testosterone	16α,17β-Dihydroxyandrost-4-en-3-one	Ovary mitochondria	(79)
	Androst-4-ene-3,17-dione	16α-Hydroxyandrost-4-ene-3,17-dione		
	Dehydroepiandrosterone	3β,16α-Dihydroxyandrost-5-en-17-one	Ovary mitochondria	(79)
	17α-Hydroxyprogesterone	Testosterone Androst-4-ene-3,17-dione	Adrenal homogenate	(74)
	17α,20α-Dihydroxypregn-en-3-one			
	Progesterone	Adrenosterone	Adrenal slices	(196)
	Pregnenolone	Androsta-4,16-dien-3-one 5α-Androst-16-en-3α-ol 5α-Androst-16-en-3β-ol	Minced testis or adrenal	(44)

TABLE XIII (Continued)

Species	Substrate	Product	Test system	Reference
Bovine	Androst-4-ene-3,17-dione	11β-Hydroxyandrost-4-ene-3,17-dione	Adrenal homogenate	(53)
	Androst-4-ene-3,17-dione	11β-Hydroxyandrost-4-ene-3,17-dione Adrenosterone 6α-Hydroxyandrost-4-ene-3,17-dione 6β,11β-Dihydroxy-androst-4-ene-3-17-dione	Adrenal homogenate	(124)
	Androst-4-ene-3,17-dione	19-Hydroxyandrost-4-ene-3,17-dione	Adrenal homogenate	(123)
	Dehydroepi-androsterone	11β-Hydroxyandrost-4-ene-3,17-dione	Adrenal homogenate	(122)
	17α-Hydroxy-pregnenolone	Dehydroepiandros-terone	Testis adrenal (homogenates)	(80)
	Progesterone	Androsta-1,4-diene-3,17-dione	Ovary (polycystic) (normal, no product)	(39)
	Acetate	Androst-4-ene-3,17-dione 11β-Hydroxyandrost-4-ene-3,17-dione	Adrenal homogenate	(19)
	Progesterone	Androst-4-ene-3,17-dione	Ovarian homogenate	(191)
	Testosterone	Testosterone sulfate	Homogenate supernatant of liver	(68)
	Dehydroepi-androsterone	Dehydroepiandroste-rone sulfate	Homogenate supernatant of placenta, Liver, adrenal pituitary, intestine, kidney, uterus	
	Progesterone	Androst-4-ene-3,17-dione	Testis, isotonic KCl homogenate	(74)
	17α-Hydroxy-progesterone	Testosterone (also, 17α,20α-Dihydroxy-pregn-4-en-3-one)		
	Progesterone	Androst-4-ene-3,17-dione Testosterone	Minced testis	(11)

TABLE XIII (*Continued*)

Species	Substrate	Product	Test system	Reference
Equine	Testosterone	10-Nortestosterone	Granulosa cell ovary	(160)
	Progesterone	Various androgens	Homogenates of ovarian follicular cells	(105)
	Progesterone	Testosterone Androst-4-ene-3,17-dione	Corpus luteum	
	17α-Hydroxy-progesterone	Testosterone Androst-4-ene-3,17-dione	Corpus luteum follicles Corpus hemor-rhagicum	
	Dehydroepi-androsterone	Androst-4-ene-3,17-dione	Ovarian follicular slices	(207)
	Endogenous precursors	Androst-4-ene-3,17-dione	Granulosa cells in tissue culture + HCG + PMS	(23)

of a 19-oxygenated $C_{19}O_2$ compound during estrogen biosynthesis. An example of this pathway would be: testosterone → 19-hydroxytestosterone → 19-oxotestosterone → 19-carboxytestosterone → 19-nortestosterone → 17β-estradiol.

The sow ovary is capable of estriol formation from 16α-hydroxyprogesterone (77, 78). This may occur by a route involving 16α, 17α-dihydroxyprogesterone → 16α-hydroxyandrost-4-ene-3, 17-dione → 16α-hydroxyestrone → estriol. Other alternatives can be visualized, and the route will require detailed studies.

A list of estrogen catabolism studies in domestic animals by *in vivo* and

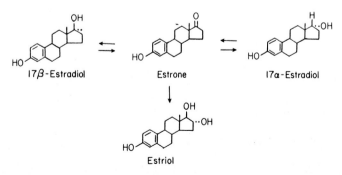

FIG. 10. Overall metabolism of estrogens in the ovine species.

TABLE XIV
The Catabolism of Androgens and Related Steroids in Domestic Animals

Substrate	Product	Test system (species)	Reference
Androst-4-ene-3,17-dione	Testosterone Epitestosterone	Blood (bovine)	(90)
Testosterone	Etiocholanolone 3β-Hydroxy-5β-androstan-17-one	Liver homogenate (fowl)	(163, 164)
Dehydroepiandrosterone	Dehydroepiandrosterone sulfate	Liver homogenate (bovine)	(31, 32)
Testosterone	Androsterone	Sperm (bovine)	(175)
11β-Hydroxyandrost-4-ene-3,17-dione	Adrenosterone	Adrenal homogenate (bovine)	(124)
Testosterone	Androsterone	In vivo wether (ovine)	(135)
Androst-4-ene-3,17-dione	Epitestosterone	Blood (ovine)	(95)
11β-Hydroxyandrost-4-ene-3,17-dione	11β,17α-Dihydroxy-androst-4-en-3-one 5β-Androstane-3α,11β,17a-triol 3α,17α-Dihydroxy-5β-androstan-11-one		
Testosterone	Epitestosterone 17α-Hydroxy-5β-androstan-3-one	In vivo (bovine, steer)	(116)

in vitro methods is detailed in Table XXI. These studies are further represented by a series of figures. In the bovine and porcine species, estrone occupies a central position since this compound is reduced both to the 17α- and 17β-stereoisomers (Fig. 8). The metabolism of estrogens in the equine studies has been studied extensively (Fig. 9). An overall scheme of estrogen metabolism in the ovine species indicates that estrone may be reduced to both the 17α- and 17β-stereoisomers of estradiol and that estriol may be formed (Fig. 10).

A rather extensive list of studies on stimulation of steroid hormone biosynthesis in bovine tissues has been published (Table XXII). The bovine

TABLE XV
ESTROGENS AND RELATED STEROIDS IN TISSUES OF DOMESTIC ANIMALS

Species	Steroid	Tissues	Reference
Bovine	Estrone	Adrenal	(9, 10)
	17β-Estradiol 17α-Estradiol Estrone	Placenta	(43)
Chicken	17β-Estradiol Estrone Estriol	Ovary	(88)
Porcine	17β-Estradiol	Ovary	(103)
	Estrone	Ovary	(209)
	Estrone 17β-Estradiol	Ovary	(100)
Equine	17β-Estradiol Estrone	Ovary follicular fluid	(184)
	17β-Estradiol Estrone	Testis	(10)

TABLE XVI
ESTROGENS AND RELATED STEROIDS IN BLOOD OF DOMESTIC ANIMALS

Species	Steroid	Tissues	Reference
Ovine	Estrone 17β-Estradiol	Ovarian vein	(186)

TABLE XVII
ESTROGENS AND RELATED COMPOUNDS IN THE BILE OF DOMESTIC ANIMALS

Species	Steroid	Remarks	Reference
Bovine	Estrone	Pregnancy	(138)
		Calves	(156)
	Estrone 17α-Estradiol	Bull	(142)
	17α-Estradiol	Calves	(156)
		Pregnancy	(2)
	17β-Estradiol	Pregnancy	(140)
Porcine	Estrone		(155)

TABLE XVIII

ESTROGENS AND RELATED COMPOUNDS IN THE URINE OF DOMESTIC ANIMALS

Species	Steroid	Remarks	Reference
Ovine	17α-Estradiol Estrone Estriol	Pregnant ewe	*(38)*
Bovine	Estrone		*(110, 111)*
	Estrone	Pregnancy	*(145, 155)*
	17α-Estradiol Estrone	Pregnancy	*(83)*
	17α-Estradiol	Pregnancy	*(200)*
	Estrone 17α-Estradiol 17β-Estradiol	Pregnancy	*(64)*
	17β-Estradiol (I) 17α-Estradiol (II) Estrone (III)	About 3 days before parturition	*(121)*

Steroid	μg/hour/100 kg
I	39 ± 6
II	386 ± 23
III	226 ± 10

Species	Steroid	Remarks	Reference
Equine	3-Deoxyequilenin	Pregnancy	*(147)*
	3β-Hydroxyestra-5,7,9- trien-17-one	Pregnancy	*(61, 41)*
	Equilin	Pregnancy	*(40)*
	Estrone	Pregnancy	*(30, 168)*
	17α-Estradiol 17α-Dihydroequilin 17α-Dihydroequilenin	Pregnancy	*(40a)*
	Estrone	Stallion	*(33, 52, 143)*
	17β-Estradiol	Pregnancy	*(211)*
		Stallion	*(89, 143)*
	Dihydroequilenin-17β	Pregnancy	*(211)*
	17α-Estradiol	Pregnancy	*(67a)*
	Equilenin	Pregnancy	*(40, 165)*
	Dihydroequilenin-17α	Pregnancy	*(174, 212)*

TABLE XVIII (Continued)

Species	Steroid	Remarks	Reference
Porcine	Estrone	Sow (n = 5)	(102)

Day of estrus	µg/24 hours
−2	32.5 ± 19.8
−1	51.1 ± 42.2
0	87.3 ± 37.6
+1	11.3 ± 4.8
+2	7.4 ± 2.4

Species	Steroid	Remarks	Reference
	Estrone	Pregnant sow	(149)
	Estradiol-17β Estrone	Nonpregnant sow	(148)
	Estrone 17β-Estradiol Estriol	Pregnant	(85)
	Estrone	Swine, pregnancy	(16, 154)
	Estrone		(201, 203)
	17β-Estradiol		(201)
	Estrone 17α-Estradiol	Boar	(201)
Caprine	Estrone 17α-Estradiol		(82)

TABLE XIX
BIOSYNTHESIS OF ESTROGENS in Vivo OR BY PERFUSION

Species	Substrate	Product	Test system	Reference
Equine	Acetate	Estrone Equilin Equilenin	Pregnancy in vivo	(63, 167)
	Testosterone	Estrone	Pregnancy in vivo	(62, 206)
	Acetate	Estrone 17β-Estradiol	Testis perfusion	(132)
Bovine	17β-Estradiol	Estriol 16β-Epiestriol 15α-Hydroxy-17β-estradiol	Adrenal perfusion	(92)

TABLE XX

THE BIOSYNTHESIS OF ESTROGENS *in Vitro* IN TISSUES OF DOMESTIC ANIMALS

Species	Substrate	Product	Test system	Reference
Equine	Testosterone	Estrone 17β-Estradiol 19-Nortestosterone	Granulosa and theca cells (preovulatory ovarian follicle)	(160)
	Testosterone Androst-4-ene- 3,17-dione	Estrogens	Corpus luteum	(105)
	Testosterone	Estrone 17β-Estradiol	Ovarian granulosa and theca cells	(160)
	Dehydroepi- androsterone	17β-Estradiol Estrone	Ovarian follicular slides	(207)
	Testosterone	Estrone 17β-Estradiol	Placental homogenate	(192)
	19-Hydrotestosterone			
	19-Oxoandrost-4-ene- 3,17-dione			
	Endogenous substances	17β-Estradiol	Granulosa cells tissue culture	(23)
	Dehydroepi- androsterone Androst-4-ene- 3,17-dione	Estrone 17β-Estradiol	Placental homogenate fraction	(3)
Bovine	17β-Estradiol	17β-Estradiol Sulfate Estrone Sulfate	Soluble prepara- tion ovary, corpus luteum, adrenal	(136)
	Androst-4-ene- 3,17-dione	Estrone	Ovarian follicular fluid	(123)
	19-Norandrost-4-ene- 3,17-dione			
	19-Hydroxy-androst- 4-ene-3,17-dione			
	Androst-1,4-diene- 3,17-dione 19-Norandrostan-4- ene-3,17-dione			

TABLE XX (Continued)

Species	Substrate	Product	Test system	Reference
	Estrone	Estrone Sulfate	Homogenate Supernatant of many cells	(68)
	Estrone	11β-Hydroxyestrone 16α-Hydroxyestrone	Adrenal mince	(83a)
	Dehydroepi- androsterone Androst-4-ene- 3,17-dione	17α-Estradiol 17β-Estradiol Estrone	Placental homogenate fractions	(3)
	Pregnenolone	17β-Estradiol Estrone (tentative)	Minced ovary	(125)
Porcine	16α-Hydroxy- progesterone	Estriol	Minced ovary	(78)
	Pregnenolone Testosterone Estrone	17β-Estradiol	Ovary	(194)
	16α-Hydroxy- progesterone	Estriol	Homogenate of ovary	(77)
	Dehydroepi- androsterone Androst-4-ene- 3,17-dione	Estrone 17β-Estradiol	Placental homogenate fractions	(3)
Ovine	Dehydroepi- androsterone Androst-4-ene- 3,17-dione	Estrone 17α-Estradiol 17β-Estradiol	Placental homogenate fractions	(3)

corpus luteum slice has been extensively studied. This preparation responds to luteinizing hormone (114) and cyclic 3′,5′-adenosine monophosphate (3′,5′-AMD) (50, 113). The stimulation of the bovine corpus luteum slice by the latter compound is in keeping with the idea that the luteinizing hormone acts through the stimulation of 3′, 5′-AMP as has been previously described for the stimulation of adrenocortical tissue by ACTH.

Inhibition of steroid hormone biosynthesis by bovine corpus luteum cell-free preparations can be accomplished with a variety of naturally occurring steroids, including pregnenolone (46, 73) and progesterone, 17α-hydroxyprogesterone, testosterone, dehydroepiandrosterone, and cortisol (73). The significance of this inhibition in vivo is yet to be established.

Table XXIII reviews the production and/or secretion rate of gonadal hormones in domestic animals.

TABLE XXI

THE CATABOLISM OF ESTROGENS AND RELATED COMPOUNDS
IN DOMESTIC ANIMALS

Substrate	Product	Test system (species)	Reference
17β-Estradiol	Estrone	Porcine (sow)	(100)
		Hen	(104)
Estriol	16-Epiestriol	Hen	(104)
17β-Estradiol	Estrone 17α-Estradiol	Bovine (calf)	(202)
Estrone	17α-Estradiol		
16-Keto-17β-estradiol	16-Epiestriol	Erythrocyte preparation (bovine)	(146)
Estrone	17β-Estradiol	Blood (bovine)	(7)
17β-Estradiol Estrone	Estrone 17β-Estradiol	Sperm (porcine) (bovine)	(176)
17β-Estradiol	Estrone 17α-Estradiol (as glucuronide)	IV in bull	(142)
17β-Estradiol	Estrone 17α-Estradiol	*In vivo* bovine (estrus cow)	(120)

TABLE XXII

STIMULATION OF STEROID BIOSYNTHESIS IN BOVINE TISSUES

Stimulation	Test system	Result	Reference
NADPH	Corpus luteum	Increased production of progesterone	(118)
Oxytocin	In vivo (cow)	Stimulates progesterone and 20α-Hydroxy-pregn-4-en-3-one formation in corpus luteum	(106)
Pituitary LH	Corpus luteum slice	Stimulates progesterone formation	(66)
LH, 3′,5′-AMP	In vitro corpus luteum slice	Progesterone and 20β-hydropregn-4-ene-3-one maximum formation at 30 minutes	(115)
ICSH, 3′,5′-cyclic AMP	Cholesterol to progesterone corpus luteum slice	Stimulated progesterone formation	(50)
3′,5′-AMP LH	Bovine corpus luteum	Increase formation of progesterone; maximum stimulation by 3′ cannot be increased by LH	(113)
Pregnant mare serum (PMS)	Ovary slice	17β-Estradiol (about 100% increase)	(193)
Luteinizing hormone	Corpus luteum	Stimulates progesterone formation	(46)

TABLE XXIII

PRODUCTION AND/OR SECRETION RATE OF GONADAL HORMONES
IN DOMESTIC ANIMALS

Steroids	Species	Method	Production and/or secretion rate	Reference
Testosterone	Bovine (calves)	Direct	Body wt. (lb) mg/day	(94)
			89 0.6	
			123 1.5	
			128 1.8	
			137 9.4	
			175 4.0	
			178 11.1	
			200 2.6	
Androst-4-ene-3,17-dione	Bovine (calves)	Direct	89 3.0	
			123 10.4	
			128 0.6	
			137 4.1	
			175 1.2	
			178 0.7	
			200 0.2	
Testosterone	Bovine (calves)		0.03 mg/hr	(93)
Androst-4-ene-3,17-dione	Bovine (calves)		After GH—0.04 mg/hr After GH—1.08 mg/hr	
Testosterone	Ovine (ram)	Direct	mg/day ± S.E. Underfed 0.4 ± 0.2 Well fed 3.5 ± 0.7	(177)
Pregnenolone (I)	Porcine	Adrenal blood under anesthesia	Secretion Rate	(58)
Progesterone (II)			Steroid μg/adrenal	
11β-Hydroxy-androst-4-ene-3,17-dione (III)			I 10 II 13 III 14	
Progesterone	Bovine (cow)		3 mg/day	(185a)
Progesterone	Caprine	Ovarian vein sample	Secretion rate (ng/min)	(58)
			Normal cycle 11-day corpus luteum, right ovarian vein —7000 no corpus luteum, left ovarian vein—80	

TABLE XXIII (Continued)

Steroids	Species	Method	Production and/or secretion rate	Reference
Progesterone	Caprine	Ovarian vein sample	Secretion rate (ng/min) Anestrus no corpus luteum —10–20 Pregnancy, day 119 corpora lutea, right ovary— 2232 two corpora lutea, left ovary—5120	(57)
Progesterone	Ovine	Direct cannulation ovarian vein	Secretion rate, 9th and 15th day of cycle—150 µg/hr	(186)
Estradiol	Ovine	Direct cannulation ovarian vein	Secretion rate—3.3– 7.4 µg/hr	

REFERENCES

1. Adlercreutz, H., and Luukkainen, T., Ann. Med. Exptl. Biol. Fenniae (Helsinki) 42, 161 (1964).
2. Adlercreutz, H., and Luukkainen, T., Biochim. Biophys. Acta 97, 134 (1965).
3. Ainsworth, L., and Ryan, K. J., Endocrinology 79, 875 (1966).
4. Anliker, R., Rohr, O., and Marti, M., Helv. Chim. Acta 39, 1100 (1956).
5. Aprile, M. E., Bligh, E. G., Webb, J. L., and Heard, R. D. H., Rev. Can. Biol. 15, 232 (1956–1957).
6. Armstrong, D. T., and Black, D. L., Endocrinology 78, 937 (1966).
7. Axelrod, L. R., and Werthessen, N. T., Arch. Biochem. Biophys. 86, 53 (1960).
8. Beall, D., Biochem. J. 32, 1957 (1938).
9. Beall, D., Nature 144, 76 (1939).
10. Beall, D., J. Endocrinol. 2, 81 (1940).
11. Becker, W. G., Snipes, C. A., and Migeon, C. J., Endocrinology 78, 737 (1966).
12. Bligh, E. G., Heard, R. D. H., O'Donnell, V. J., Webb, J. L., Saffran, M., and Schonbaum, E., Arch. Biochem. Biophys. 58, 249 (1955).
13. Bloch, E., Dorfman, R. I., and Pincus, G., Proc. Soc. Exptl. Biol. Med. 85, 106 (1954).

14. Bowerman, A. M., and Melampy, R. M., *Proc. Soc. Exptl. Biol. Med.* **109**, 45 (1962).

15. Brady, R. O., *J. Biol. Chem.* **193**, 145 (1951).

16. Bredeck, H. E., and Mayer, D. T., *Reprod. Infertility, 3rd Symp. Fort Collins, Colorado, 1957*, p. 157 (1958).

17. Brooks, R. V., and Klyne, W., *Biochem. J.* **62**, 21P (1956).

18. Brooks, R. V., and Klyne, W., *Biochem. J.* **65**, 663 (1957).

19. Bryson, M., and Sweat, M. L., *Arch. Biochem. Biophys.* **96**, 1 (1962).

20. Bush, I. E., and Fergusen, K. A., *J. Endocrinol.* **10**, 1 (1953).

21. Butenandt, A., *Wien. Klin. Wochschr.* **47**, 936 (1934).

21a. Butenandt, A., and Tscherning, K., *Z. Angew. Chem.* **44**, 905 (1931).

21b. Butenandt, A., and Westphal, U. *Z. Physiol. Chem.* **67**, 1140 (1934).

22. Cardeilhac, P. T., Morrissette, M. C., and Calle, J. D., *Proc. Soc. Exptl. Biol. Med.* **123**, 343 (1966).

23. Channing, C. P., *Nature* **210**, 1266 (1966).

24. Chaudhuri, A. C., Harada, Y., Shimizu, K., Gut, M., and Dorfman, R. I., *J. Biol. Chem.* **237**, 703 (1962).

25. Clark, A. F., *Federation Proc.* **22**, 468 (1963).

26. Constantopoulos, G., and Tchen, T. T., *Am. Chem. Soc. Abstr., St. Louis, 1961*, p. 31C.

27. Constantopoulos, G., Satch, P. S., and Tchen, T. T., *Biochem. Biophys. Res. Commun.* **8**, 50 (1962).

28. Coyle, M. G., and Romanoff, E. B., *Federation Proc.* **23**, 462 (1964).

29. David, K., Dingemanse, E., Freud, J., and Lacqueur, E., *Z. Physiol. Chem.* **233**, 281 (1935).

30. De Jongh, S. E., Kober, S., and Lacqueur, E., *Biochem. Z.* **240**, 247 (1931).

31. De Meio, R. H., and Lewycka, C., *Endocrinology* **56**, 489 (1955).

32. De Meio, R. H., Lewycka, C. M., and Wizerkaniuk, M., *Federation Proc.* **5**, 241 (1956).

33. Deulofeu, V., and Ferrari, J., *Z. Physiol. Chem.* **226**, 192 (1934).

34. Dorfman, R. I., and Ungar, F., "Metabolism of Steroid Hormones." Academic Press, New York, 1965.

35. Dorfman, R. I., *Anat. Record* **157**, 547 (1967).

36. Duncan, G. W., Bowerman, A. M., Hearn, W. R., and Melampy, R. M., *Proc. Soc. Exptl. Biol. Med.* **104**, 17 (1960).

37. Euw, J. von, and Reichstein, T., *Helv. Chim. Acta* **24**, 879 (1941).

38. Fevre, J., Piton, C., and Rombauts, P., *Compt. Rend. Acad. Sci.* **261**, 2517 (1965).

39. Gawienowski, A. M., Lee, S. L., and Marion, G. B., *Endocrinology* **69**, 388 (1961).

40. Girard, A., Sandulesco, G., Friederson, A., and Rutgers, J. J., *Compt. Rend. Acad. Sci.* **195**, 981 (1932).

40a. Glen, W. L., Barber, R., McConkey, H. M., and Grant, G. A., *Nature* **177**, 753 (1956).

41. Glen, W. L., Barber, R., and Papineau-Couture, G., *Nature* **182**, 1308 (1958).

42. Gomes, W. R., Herschler, R. C., and Erb, R. E., *J. Animal Sci.* **24**, 722 (1965).

43. Gorski, J., and Erb, R. E., *Endocrinology* **64**, 707 (1959).

44. Gower, D. B., and Ahmed, N., *Biochem. J.* **100**, 67P (1966).
45. Haines, W. L., Johnson, J. H., Goodwin, M. P., and Kuizenga, M. H., *J. Biol. Chem.* **174**, 925 (1948).
46. Haksar, A., Romanoff, E. B., Hagino, N., and Pincus, G., *Steroids* **9**, 405 (1967).
47. Halkerston, I. D. K., Eichhorn, J., and Hechter, O., *J. Biol. Chem.* **236**, 374 (1961).
48. Hall, P. F., and Koritz, S. B., *Biochim. Biophys. Acta* **93**, 441 (1964).
49. Hall, P. F., and Koritz, S. B., *Biochemistry* **3**, 129 (1964).
50. Hall, P. F., and Koritz, S. B., *Biochemistry* **4**, 1037 (1965).
51. Hartmann, M., and Wettstein, A., *Helv. Chim. Acta* **17**, 878 (1934).
52. Haussler, E. P., *Helv. Chim. Acta* **17**, 531 (1934).
53. Hayano, M., and Dorfman, R. I., *J. Biol. Chem.* **201**, 175 (1953).
53a. Hayano, M., Lindberg, M. C., Wiener, M., Rosenkrantz, H., and Dorfman, R. I., *Endocrinology* **55**, 326 (1964).
54. Hayano, M., Saba, N., Dorfman, R. I., and Hechter, O., *Recent Progr. Hormone Res.* **12**, 79 (1956).
55. Heap, R. B., and Holzbauer, M., *J. Physiol. (London)* **183**, 11P (1965).
56. Heap, R. B., and Deanesley, R., *J. Endocrinol.* **34**, 417 (1966).
57. Heap, R. B., and Linzell, J. L., *J. Endocrinol.* **36**, 389 (1966).
58. Heap, R. B., Holzbauer, M., and Newport, H., *J. Endocrinol.* **36**, 159 (1966).
59. Heard, R. D. H., *J. Am. Chem. Soc.* **60**, 493 (1938).
60. Heard, R. D. H., and McKay, A. F., *J. Biol. Chem.* **131**, 371 (1939).
61. Heard, R. D. H., and Hoffman, M. M, *J. Biol. Chem.* **138**, 651 (1941).
62. Heard, R. D. H., Jellinck, P. H., and O'Donnell, V. J., *Endocrinology* **57**, 200 (1955).
63. Heard, R. D. H., Bligh, E. G., Cann, M. C., Jellinck, P. H., O'Donnell, V. J., Rao, B. G., and Webb, J. L., *Recent Progr. Hormone Res.* **12**, 45 (1956).
64. Heitzman, R. J., and Thomas, G. H., *Biochem. J.* **96**, 22P (1965).
65. Heitzman, R. J., and Thomas, G. H., *J. Endocrinol.* **33**, 455 (1965).
66. Hellig, H. R., and Savard, K., *J. Biol. Chem.* **240**, 1957 (1965).
67. Hirschfield, I. N., and Koritz, S. B., *Endocrinology* **78**, 165 (1966).
67a. Hirschmann, H., and Wintersteiner, O., *J. Biol. Chem.* **122**, 303 (1937).
68. Holcenberg, J. S., and Rosen, S. W., *Arch. Biochem.* **110**, 551 (1965).
69. Holtz, A. H., *Nature* **174**, 316 (1954).
70. Huffman, M. N., and Lott, M. H., *J. Am. Chem. Soc.* **73**, 878 (1951).
71. Huis in't Veld, L. G., Louwerens, B., and Reilingh, W., *Acta Endocrinol.* **46**, 185 (1964).
72. Huis in't Veld, L. G., *Acta Physiol. Pharmacol. Neerl.* **13**, 102 (1965).
73. Ichii, S., Forchielli, E., and Dorfman, R. I., *Steroids* **2**, 631 (1963).
74. Ichii, S., Kobayashi, S., and Matsuba, M., *Steroids* **5**, 123 (1965).
75. Jeanloz, R. W., Levy, H., Jacobsen, R. P., Hechter, O., Schenker, V., and Pincus, G., *Am. Chem. Soc. Abstr., 118th Meeting, Chicago, Illinois, 1950,* p. 12C.
76. Jeanloz, R. W., Levy, H., Jacobsen, R. P., Hechter, O., Schenker, V., and Pincus, G., *J. Biol. Chem.* **203**, 453 (1953).
77. Kadis, B., *Biochim. Biophys. Acta* **82**, 639 (1964).
78. Kadis, B., *Biochemistry* **3**, 2016 (1964).

79. Kadis, B., *Biochemistry* **5**, 3604 (1966).
80. Kahnt, F. W., Neher, R., Schmid, K., and Wettstein, A., *Experientia* **17**, 19 (1961).
81. Kase, N., Forchielli, E., and Dorfman, R. I., *Acta Endocrinol.* **37**, 19 (1961).
82. Klyne, W., and Wright, A. A., *Biochem. J.* **66**, 92 (1957).
83. Klyne, W., and Wright, A. A., *J. Endocrinol.* **18**, 32 (1959).
83a. Knuppen, R., and Breuer, H., *Biochim. Biophys. Acta* **58**, 147 (1962).
84. Koritz, S. B., and Hall, P. F., *Biochemistry* **3**, 1928 (1964).
85. Kubomichi, M., *Animal Health Quart.* **6**, 33 (1966).
86. Kushinsky, S., Ph.D. Thesis, Boston Univ., Boston, Massachusetts, 1955.
87. Lantos, C. P., Raman, P. B., Graves, J. M. H., Dorfman, R. I., and Forchielli, E., *Steroids* **6**, 69 (1965).
88. Layne, D. S., Common, R. H., Maw, W. A., and Fraps, R. H., *Nature* **181**, 351 (1958).
89. Levin, L., *J. Biol. Chem.* **158**, 725 (1945).
90. Levy, H., Saito, T., Schepis, J. P., Takeyama, S., and Merrill, A. P., *Biochim. Biophys. Acta* **71**, 749 (1963).
91. Levy, H., Saito, T., Takeyama, S., Merrill, A. P., and Schepis, J. P., *Biochim. Biophys. Acta* **69**, 198 (1963).
92. Levy, H., Hood, B., Cha, C. H., and Carlo, J. J., *Steroids* **5**, 677 (1965).
93. Lindner, H. R., *Nature* **183**, 1605 (1959).
94. Lindner, H. R., *J. Endocrinol.* **23**, 139 (1961).
95. Lindner, H. R., *Steroids Suppl.* **2**, 133 (1965).
96. Lisse, K., and Schürenkämper, P., *Acta Endocrinol.* **50**, 429 (1965).
97. Lommer, D., and Wolff, H. P., *Acta Endocrinol. Suppl.* **100**, 69 (1965).
98. Lynn, W. S., Jr., and Brown, R., *J. Biol. Chem.* **232**, 1005 (1958).
99. Lynn, W. S., Jr., and Brown, R., *J. Biol. Chem.* **232**, 1015 (1958).
100. Lunaas, T., *Acta Endocrinol.* **42**, 514 (1963).
101. Lunaas, T., *Acta Endocrinol.* **44**, 529 (1963).
102. Lunaas, T., *Am. Vet. Sci.* **6**, 3 (1965).
103. Mac Corquodale, D. W., Thayer, A. S., and Doisy, E. A., *J. Biol. Chem.* **115**, 435 (1936).
104. MacRae, H. F., Layne, D. S., and Common, R. H., *Poultry Sci.* **38**, 684 (1959).
105. Mahajan, D. K., and Samuels, L. T., *Federation Proc.* **22**, 531 (1963).
106. Mares, S. E., and Casida, L. E., *Endocrinology* **72**, 78 (1963).
107. Marker, R. E., *J. Am. Chem. Soc.* **60**, 210 (1938).
108. Marker, R. E., *J. Am. Chem. Soc.* **60**, 2442 (1938).
109. Marker, R. E., *J. Am. Chem. Soc.* **60**, 2931 (1938).
110. Marker, R. E., *J. Am. Chem. Soc.* **61**, 944 (1939).
111. Marker, R. E., *J. Am. Chem. Soc.* **61**, 1287 (1939).
112. Marker, R. E., and Rohrman, E., *J. Am. Chem. Soc.* **61**, 3476 (1939).
112a. Marsh, J. M., and Savard, K., *Abstr. 46th Meeting Endocrine Soc., San Francisco*, p. 51 (1964).
113. Marsh, J. M., and Savard, K., *Steroids* **8**, 133 (1966).
114. Marsh, J. M., Mason, N. R., and Savard, K., *Federation Proc.* **20**, 187 (1961).
115. Marsh, J. M., Savard, K., Butcher, R. W., and Sutherland, E. W., *Proc.*

6th Pan Am Congr. Endocrinol., 1965. Excerpta Med. Intern. Congr. Ser. 99, E42 (1966).

116. Martin, R. P., Endocrinology 78, 907 (1966).
117. Mason, N. R., Marsh, J. M., and Savard, K., J. Biol. Chem. 236, PC34 (1961).
118. Mason, N. R., and Savard, K., Endocrinology 75, 215 (1964).
119. Masuda, H., Anderson, L. L., Henricks, D. M., and Melampy, R. M., Federation Proc. 25, 444 (1966).
120. Mellin, T. N., and Erb, R. E., Steroids 7, 589 (1966).
121. Mellin, T. N., Erb, R. E., and Estergreen, V. L., J. Animal Sci. 25, 955 (1966).
122. Meyer, A. S., Biochim. Biophys. Acta 24, 1435 (1955).
123. Meyer, A. S., Experientia 11, 99 (1955).
124. Meyer, A. S., Hayano, M., Lindberg, M. C., Gut, M., and Rodgers, O. G., Acta Endocrinol. 18, 148 (1955).
125. Miller, W. R., and Turner, C. W., Steroids 2, 657 (1963).
126. Nakao, T., Omori, Y., and Morisugi, M., Jikeikai Med. J. 6, 61 (1959).
127. Neher, R., Folio Endocrinol. (Pisa) 8, 55 (1960).
128. Neher, R., and Wettstein, A., Acta Endocrinol. 35, 1 (1960).
129. Neher, R., and Wettstein, A., Helv. Chim. Acta 43, 1171 (1960).
130. Neher, R., and Wettstein, A., Helv. Chim. Acta 43, 1628 (1960).
131. Neill, J. D., Day, B. N., and Duncan, G. W., Steroids 4, 699 (1964).
132. Nyman, M. A., Geiger, J., and Goldziehr, J. W., J. Biol. Chem. 234, 16 (1959).
133. Oppenauer, R., Z. Physiol. Chem. 270, 97 (1941).
134. Oriol-Bosch, A., and Romanoff, E. B., Acta Endocrinol. Suppl. 100, 95 (1965).
135. Osborne, W. B., Wong, P. K., and Garnett, J. L., Australian J. Biol. Sci. 19, 1101 (1966).
136. Payne, A. H., and Mason, M., Steroids 5, 21 (1965).
137. Pearlman, W. H., J. Biol. Chem. 166, 473 (1946).
138. Pearlman, W. H., Rakoff, A. E., Cantarow, A., and Paschkis, K. E., J. Biol. Chem. 170, 173 (1947).
139. Pearlman, W. H., Federation Proc. 7, 178 (1948).
140. Pearlman, W. H., Rakoff, A. E., Cantarow, A., and Walkling, A. A., J. Biol. Chem. 173, 175 (1948).
141. Pearlman, W. H., Ciba Found. Colloq. Endocrinol. 2, 309 (1952).
142. Pearson, J. R., and Martin, R. P., Endocrinology 78, 914 (1966).
143. Pigon, H. Lunaas, T., and Velle, W., Acta Endocrinol. 36, 131 (1961).
144. Plager, J. E., and Samuels, L. T., Federation Proc. 11, 383 (1952).
145. Pope, G. S., McNaughter, M. L., and Jones, M. E. H., Biochem. J. 66, 206 (1957).
146. Portius, J., and Repke, K., Arch. Exptl. Pathol. Pharmakol. 239, 299 (1960).
147. Prelog, V., and Führer, J., Helv. Chim. Acta 28, 583 (1945).
148. Raeside, J. I., Can. J. Biochem. Physiol. 41, 2013 (1963).
149. Raeside, J. I., J. Reprod. Fertil. 6, 427 (1963).
150. Raggatt, P. R., and Whitehouse, M. W., Biochem. J. 101, 819 (1966).
151. Rao, B. G., and Heard, R. D. H., Arch. Biochem. Biophys. 66, 504 (1957).
152. Reichstein, T., Helv. Chim. Acta 19, 29 (1936).

153. Reichstein, T., and von Euw, J., *Helv. Chim. Acta* **21**, 1197 (1938).
154. Rombouts, P., *Ann. Biol. Animale Biochim. Biophys.* **2**, 151 (1962).
155. Rommel, P., *Acta Endocrinol.* **45**, 605 (1964).
156. Rommel, P., and Zschintzsch, A., *Acta Endocrinol.* **50**, 47 (1965).
157. Rongone, E. L., Strength, D. R., Bockage, B. C., and Doisy, E. A., *J. Biol. Chem.* **225**, 959 (1957).
158. Rosenfeld, G., Ungar, F., Dorfman, R. I., and Pincus, G., *Endocrinology* **58**, 708 (1955).
159. Ruzicka, L., and Prelog, V., *Helv. Chim. Acta* **26**, 975 (1943).
160. Ryan, K. J., and Short, R., *Endocrinology* **76**, 108 (1965).
161. Saba, N., Hechter, O., and Stone, D., *J. Am. Chem. Soc.* **76**, 3862 (1954).
162. Saba, N., and Hechter, O., *Federation Proc.* **14**, 775 (1955).
163. Samuels, L. T., *Recent Progr. Hormone Res.* **4**, 65 (1949).
164. Samuels, L. T., Sweat, M. L., Levedahl, B. H., Pottner, M. N., and Helmreich, M. L., *J. Biol. Chem.* **183**, 231 (1950).
165. Savard, K., *Endocrinology* **68**, 411 (1961).
166. Savard, K., Dorfman, R. I., Baggett, B., and Engel, L. L., *J. Clin. Endocrinol. Metab.* **16**, 1629 (1956).
167. Savard, K., Andrec, K., Brooksbank, B. W. L., Reyneri, C., Dorfman, R. I., Heard, R. D. H., Jacobs, R., and Solomon, S. S., *J. Biol. Chem.* **231**, 765 (1958).
168. Savard, K., Mason, N. R., Ingram, J. T., and Gassner, F. X., *Endocrinology* **69**, 324 (1961).
169. Savard, K., Gut, M., Dorfman, R. I., Gabrilove, J. L., and Soffer, L. J., *J. Clin. Endocrinol. Metab.* **21**, 165 (1961).
170. Savard, K., and Casey, P. J. L., *Federation Proc.* **22**, 530 (1963).
171. Savard, K., and Telegdy, G., *Steroids Suppl.* **2**, 205 (1965).
172. Schomberg, D. W., Jones, P. H., Erb, R. E., and Gomes, W. R., *J. Animal Sci.* **25**, 1181 (1966).
173. Schomberg, D. W., Jones, P. H., Featherston, W. R., and Erb, R. E., *Steroids* **8**, 277 (1966).
174. Schwenk, E., and Hildebrandt, F., *Naturwissenschaften* **20**, 658 (1932).
175. Scott, T. W., Baggett, B., and White, I., *Australian J. Exptl. Biol. Med. Sci.* **41**, 363 (1963).
176. Seamark, R. F., and White, I. G., *J. Endocrinol.* **30**, 307 (1964).
177. Setchall, B. P., Waiter, G. M. H., and Lindner, H. R., *J. Reprod. Fertility* **9**, 149 (1965).
178. Shimizu, K., Dorfman, R. I., and Gut, M., *J. Biol. Chem.* **235**, PC25 (1960).
179. Shimizu, K., Hayano, M., Gut, M., and Dorfman, R. I., *J. Biol. Chem.* **236**, 695 (1961).
180. Shimizu, K., Gut, M., and Dorfman, R. I., *J. Biol. Chem.* **237**, 699 (1962).
181. Short, R. V., *Ciba Found. Colloq. Endocrinol.* **11**, 362 (1957).
182. Short, R. V., *J. Endocrinol.* **16**, 426 (1958).
183. Short, R. V., and Moore, N. W., *J. Endocrinol.* **19**, 288 (1959).
184. Short, R. V., *J. Endocrinol.* **20**, 147 (1960).
185. Short, R. V., *J. Endocrinol.* **24**, 59 (1962).
185a. Short, R. V., *J. Endocrinol.* **23**, 401 (1962).
186. Short, R. V., McDonald, M. F., and Rowson, L. E. A., *J. Endocrinol.* **26**, 155 (1963).

187. Short, R. V., Shorter, D. R., and Linzell, J. L., *J. Endocrinol.* **27**, 327 (1963).
188. Slaunwhite, W. R., Jr., and Samuels, L. T., *J. Biol. Chem.* **220**, 341 (1956).
189. Slotta, K. H., Rushing, H., and Fels, E., *Ber. Deut. Chem. Ges.* **67**, 1270 (1934).
190. Solomon, S., Vande Wiele, R., and Lieberman, S., *Am. Chem. Soc. Abstr., 126th Meeting, New York, 1956,* p. 29C.
191. Solomon, S., Vande Wiele, R., and Lieberman, S., *J. Am. Chem. Soc.* **78**, 5453 (1956).
192. Staple, E., Lynn, W. S., Jr., and Gurin, S., *J. Biol. Chem.* **219**, 845 (1956).
192a. Starka, L., Breuer, J., and Breuer, H., *Naturwissenschaften* **19**, 540 (1965).
193. Suzuki, M., Takahashi, K., and Murakami, Y., *Tohoku J. Exptl. Med.* **74**, 28 (1961).
194. Suzuki, M., Takahashi, K., Hirano, M., and Shindo, K., *Tohoku J. Exptl. Med.* **76**, 89 (1962).
195. Sweat, M. L., Berliner, D. L., Bryson, M. J., Nabors, C., Jr., Haskell, J., and Holmstrome, E. G., *Bicohim. Biophys. Acta* **40**, 289 (1960).
196. Syao, L., *Probl. Endokrinol. i Gormonoterap.* **8**, 17 (1962).
197. Tagmann, E., Prelog, V., and Ruzicka, L. H., *Chem. Abstr.* **29**, 440 (1946).
198. Tamaoki, B. I., and Pincus, G., *Endocrinology* **69**, 527 (1961).
199. Telegdy, G., *Kiserl. Orvostud.* **14**, 527 (1962).
200. Velle, W., *Acta Endocrinol.* **27**, 64 (1958).
201. Velle, W., *Acta Endocrinol.* **28**, 255 (1958).
202. Velle, W., *Am. J. Vet. Res.* **19**, 405 (1958).
203. Velle, W., *Acta Vet. Scand.* **1**, 19 (1959).
204. Ward, M. G., and Engel, L. L., *J. Biol. Chem.* **239**, PC 3604 (1964).
205. Ward, M. G., and Engel, L. L., *J. Biol. Chem.* **241**, 3147 (1966).
206. West, C. D., Damast, B. L., Sarro, S. D., and Pearson, O. H., *J. Biol. Chem.* **218**, 409 (1956).
207. West, C. D., and Naville, A. H., *Biochemistry* **1**, 645 (1962).
208. Wettstein, A., and Anner, G., *Experientia* **10**, 397 (1954).
209. Westerfield, W. W., MacCorquodale, D. W., Thayer, S. A., and Doisy, E. A., *J. Biol. Chem.* **126**, 195 (1938).
210. Wintersteiner, O., and Allen, W. M., *J. Biol. Chem.* **107**, 321 (1934).
211. Wintersteiner, O., Schwenk, E., Hirschmann, H., and Whitman, B., *J. Am. Chem. Soc.* **58**, 2652 (1936).
212. Wintersteiner, O., and Hirschmann, H., *J. Biol. Chem.* **119**, CVIII (1937).

7 ROLE OF THE NERVOUS SYSTEM IN REPRODUCTIVE PROCESSES

WILLIAM F. GANONG AND CLIFFORD L. KRAGT

I. Introduction

The nervous system is involved, with varying degrees of directness, in almost every aspect of the physiology of reproduction. Reflexes integrated at various levels of the nervous system are involved in sperm transport, parturition, and lactation. Copulation itself is made up of a series of reflexes and reaction patterns integrated into a coordinated whole, and sexual behavior is manifestly a subject for psychological and neurophysiological investigation.

In recent years, increasing attention has been focused on another aspect of the role of the nervous system in reproductive physiology—the regulation by the brain of gonadal function through hypothalamic regulation of anterior pituitary gonadotropin secretion. The brain exercises a major influence on the amount and type of pituitary gonadotropic hormones liberated into the circulation. The hormones act on the gonads to bring about, in both sexes, the state of readiness in the reproductive organs and the maturation of the germ cells necessary for successful procreation.

Such preparation would, of course, be in vain if it were not associated, in both sexes, with appropriate sexual behavior. This behavior is known to

155

be dependent on an adequate level of circulating gonadal steroids. Thus, the gonads are involved in a kind of "feedback" mechanism. The brain controls the secretion of the gonadotropins; the gonadal hormones are secreted in response to stimulation by these tropic hormones; and the gonadal secretions act back on the brain to initiate the behavior necessary for successful reproductive performance.

Interesting new data make it apparent that the brain not only regulates gonadotropin secretion in adulthood but that it also is responsible for the timing and coordination of the increase in the secretion of the gonadotropins that brings about sexual maturation. There is evidence that puberty occurs when the brain becomes less sensitive to the feedback effects of gonadal steroids.

The actions of gonadal hormones on the brain have also been shown to play a key role in the development and differentiation of hypothalamic function. In rats, both the adult pattern of gonadotropin secretion and sexual behavior depend on the pattern of sex steroid secretion during infancy, and in other species hormones may exert similar inductive effects during fetal life. Thus, brain-endocrine interrelations determine the development and sexual differentiation of the individual as well as his reproductive capacity once sexual maturity has been reached.

The role of the nervous system in several reproductive processes and various aspects of brain-endocrine interactions are discussed elsewhere in this book. Neural mechanisms involved in parturition are discussed in Chapter 14 and the neuroendocrine reflex responsible for oxytocin-induced milk letdown is described in Chapter 16. The pronounced effects of light and the ancillary effects of other environmental stimuli on gonadotropin secretion are discussed in Chapter 17. Sexual behavior and its neural and endocrine control are considered in Chapter 20. In this chapter, the basic neural substrates of copulation are considered briefly, and attention is focused on the brain-gonad relationship in adulthood, the mechanisms regulating the onset of puberty, and the inductive effects of sex steroids on the brain early in life.

II. Neural Substrates of Mating Behavior

Mating behavior may be legitimately divided into two components. It includes, first, activity consequent to the urge to copulate—the interest in or drive to sexual congress. Secondly, it includes the act of copulation itself. Sexual interest and the instinctual mating drives basic to the preservation of the species depend on neural circuits in the limbic lobe of the brain and the hypothalamus (see 7, 38, 101, 123 and Chapter 20). Copulation itself is made up of a collection of reflexes and reaction patterns, including erection, the necessary postural adjustments, the pelvic thrusts in the male, the lordotic adjustment of the pelvis in the female, ejaculation, and orgasm.

The reflex arcs and the centers in the nervous system controlling the motor patterns of the sexual act have been studied in considerable detail. It is known, for instance, that most of the postural adjustments for coitus in both the male and female are integrated at the spinal level (1). In dogs with spinal cord transections, stimulation of the genitalia leads to erection and pelvic thrusts in males, and perineal stimulation produces elevation of the pelvis in females.

Erection may be initiated in humans by purely psychic stimuli, but the reaction is primarily a reflex one, initiated by genital stimulation and integrated in the sacral segments of the spinal cord. The efferent pathway is parasympathetic. The motor fibers pass to the genitalia in a relatively well-defined bundle, and since these fibers are also involved in ejaculation, the bundle has come to be called, rather appropriately, the "nervus erigens." The vascular engorgement responsible for erection is produced in part by closure of the so-called small sluice channels within the corpora cavernosa, but the main factor involved is arterial dilatation with consequent compression of venous drainage (97).

Ejaculation in the male is initiated by stimulation of the glans, the adequate stimulus being gentle friction and the efferent pathway, the internal pudendal nerve. Ejaculation is usually divided into two parts, emission and ejaculation proper (135). The first event, emission, is the delivery of the semen into the urethra. It is primarily a sympathetic response integrated in the upper lumbar segments of the spinal cord and produced by impulses that reach the smooth muscle of the vas deferens and associated organs via fibers in the hypogastric plexus. Ejaculation proper follows emission and is the expulsion of the seminal fluid from the urethra. This response is primarily parasympathetic, but it also involves a contraction of somatic musculature which aids the expulsion. It is integrated in the upper sacral and lower lumbar portion of the spinal cord, and the motor fibers pass through the internal pudendal nerves and the nervus erigens. Ejaculation can still occur after sympathectomy, but because there is no contraction of the internal vesicle sphincter, the ejaculate usually spills into the bladder (97).

Uterine contractions may occur in response to a spinal reflex during coitus in the female. A neuroendocrine reflex involving the posterior pituitary may also be involved. There is considerable evidence that genital stimulation during coitus initiates reflex release of oxytocin from the posterior pituitary (50). Some investigators have argued that the oxytocin acts on the uterus to initiate a series of contractions which facilitate the transport of sperm from the vagina to the fallopian tubes. However, there are great variations in the rate of sperm transport in different mammalian species, and Fitzpatrick concludes, after a thorough review of the subject (50), that there is no proof that oxytocin secretion is an essential physiological component of mating.

III. Regulation of the Secretion of Pituitary Gonadotropins by the Nervous System

A. THE MECHANISM BY WHICH THE NERVOUS SYSTEM REGULATES PITUITARY SECRETION

Many lines of evidence indicate that the brain regulates gonadotropin secretion. Sexual cycles in animals are correlated with changes in the seasons, an observation which is difficult to explain except in terms of the intermediation of the nervous system between the environment and the endocrine system. Temperature and rainfall changes may be responsible in part for seasonal variations, but in birds and mammals fluctuation in the incident light is the major environmental factor involved (see Chapter 17). In certain mammalian species (e.g., the cat, the rabbit, the ferret, and the mink) ovulation occurs only after copulation, and this reflex ovulation has been shown to occur in response to afferent stimuli that converge on the hypothalamus from the genitalia, the eyes, the nose, and other organs (24). Gonadal abnormalities are seen in humans with brain pathology. Several detailed studies of the endocrine symptoms of brain disease (5, 120) make it clear that hypogonadism and, alternatively, precocious puberty are relatively common complications of disease processes involving the hypothalamus.

The effects of hypothalamic diseases in humans have been duplicated by experimental lesions in laboratory animals. Gonadal atrophy and inhibition of gonadotropin secretion have been observed following hypothalamic lesions in rats, cats, dogs, monkeys, sheep, and a variety of other species (33, 43, 51). Histological changes in the pituitary have been observed following such lesions, but they are related to altered secretion and not to ischemia or direct destruction of the pituitary by the lesions (13). The other pituitary hormones are under neural control as well. Thus, at least as far as these hormones and the hormones of their target glands are concerned, the endocrine system can be regarded as one of the effector arms of the nervous system (57).

The possibility that the hypothalamic control of the anterior pituitary is exerted via nerve fibers to the gland has received considerable attention. There are nerve fibers which reach the anterior lobe from the cervical sympathetic ganglia along blood vessels. Parasympathetic fibers also reach the gland by way of the greater superficial petrosal nerve. Harris (74) has reviewed in detail the controversy about direct innervation of the anterior pituitary from the hypothalamus and concludes that "the available evidence indicates that the pars distalis receives very few if any nerve fibers." Fried-good, on the basis of studies in rats, has claimed a role for the cervical sympathetic fibers in transmitting to the anterior pituitary the "neural stimuli which initiate pseudopregnancy" (53). However, complete sympa-thectomy does not prevent ovulation in the rabbit or pregnancy in other species. There is, similarly, little evidence for and considerable evidence against the parasympathetic supply to the anterior lobe being of significance in the control of hormone secretion (55). Simple section of the pituitary stalk in female laboratory animals, provided it does not infarct the pituitary or interfere with its revascularization by the portal vessels, permits a return of normal estrous cycles in a relatively short period of time (55). This interval is too short a period for regeneration of nerve fibers, if such re-generation can, indeed, be expected to occur from the hypothalamus. Thus,

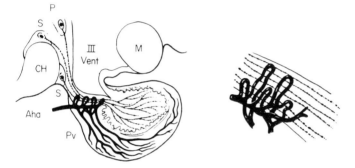

FIG. 1. Hypophyseal portal vessels. Left: saggital section of the hypothalamus showing a branch of the anterior hypophyseal artery (Aha) breaking up into capillary loops which penetrate the median eminence. The loops drain into the portal vessels (Pv) that end in capillaries in the anterior pituitary. Ch, optic chiasm; S, supraoptic nucleus; P, paraventricular nucleus; M, mammillary body; III Vent., third ventricle. Right: detail of capillary loops penetrating median eminence. From Ganong (58), reproduced with permission.

it is unlikely that nerve fibers to the adenohypophysis play any important role in the control of its secretory function.

There is, however, a unique vascular connection between the brain and the anterior pituitary. The blood supply to the hypothalamus and pituitary in mammals is derived from the carotid arteries and the circle of Willis, the anastomotic arterial ring at the base of the brain. Branches of these vessels form capillary loops which penetrate the median eminence (ventral por-tion of the hypothalamus overlying the pituitary) and the posterior pituitary. From these loops, the blood is channeled into sinusoidal portal vessels which pass down the pituitary stalk and end in capillaries in the anterior pituitary (Fig. 1). The portal vessels that originate from the median eminence are referred to as "long portal vessels" and those that originate from the neuro-hypophysis are referred to as "short portal vessels." The hypophyseal portal system is a true portal system that begins and ends in capillaries without going through the heart, and it provides a direct vascular pathway between the brain and the anterior pituitary.

The hypophyseal portal system is a constant anatomical feature in higher vertebrates (68). There was originally some confusion about the direction of blood flow in it, but direct observations in amphibians, rats, and ducks indicated that most of the flow was from the brain to the pituitary (8, 69, 83). Recently, it has been claimed that there are a few portal vessels in which the flow is in the other direction (140), but certainly the major part of the flow is to the pituitary (31). In many species of mammals and in all birds studied (31) the portal vessels provide essentially all the blood supply reaching the anterior lobe.

To determine the importance of the vascular connections to the hypothalamus in the control of anterior pituitary secretion, the effects of cutting the pituitary stalk and the effects of transplanting the pituitary away from the hypothalamus have been extensively studied. The portal vessels have a marked capacity for regrowth, and valid conclusions can be drawn from stalk section experiments only if such regeneration is prevented by insertion of a barrier between the hypothalamus and the pituitary (84). The usual effect of stalk section when performed with the insertion of such a plate is a marked decrease in FSH and LH secretion. Some of this may be due to infarction of the pituitary, but this is not the only explanation, since prolactin secretion is concurrently increased (108).

An animal's own anterior pituitary or adenohypophyseal tissue from closely related animals may be successfully transplanted. Such transplants have been observed to "take" particularly well in the anterior chamber of the eye and under the capsule of the kidney. In the initial, generally short-term experiments with such transplants in hypophysectomized donors, marked gonadal atrophy was usually reported (55). Retransplantation of the pituitary tissue from the kidney back to the median-eminence region has been shown to be associated with recrudesence of gonadal function once the portal vessels have regrown (118). However, more and more investigators have found reduced but still remarkably high levels of end-organ function in animals in which the pituitary has been transplanted (54, 66). Generally, these observations have been made in animals with transplants studied for prolonged periods of time. This does not mean, however, that the anterior pituitary tissue is secreting autonomously, because in animals with transplants it has recently been demonstrated that the moderate rate of gonadotropin secretion is reduced by implants of testosterone in the hypothalamus (137). A similar decline in thyroid function was observed in animals with pituitary transplants when thyroxine was implanted in the hypothalamus or when lesions were produced in the ventral hypothalamus (87). This indicates that the control of the anterior pituitary is mediated via substances secreted by the hypothalamus into the bloodstream. They generally enter the portal circulation, but they can enter the general circulation, and when their secretion is inhibited, pituitary function declines to a low level. Substances increasing pituitary secretion of FSH (*116*) and ACTH (*14*) have been detected in the blood of hypophysectomized animals.

Additional proof of the correctness of the hypothesis that the anterior pituitary is controlled by blood-borne humoral agents is the extraction from hypothalamic and neurohypophyseal tissue of substances which modify anterior pituitary secretion. Those identified to date include at least one substance modifying the secretion of each of the six established anterior pituitary hormones. They have been partially separated and purified to differing degrees from the hypothalamic tissue of several species by acetic acid extraction, separation by Sephadex and carboxymethyl cellulose chro-

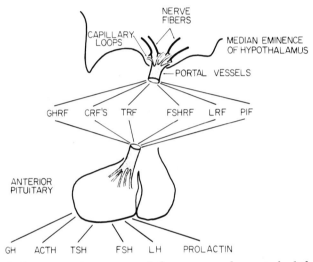

FIG. 2. Diagrammatic summary of the neurovascular control of the anterior pituitary. Control is exerted by releasing factors and PIF secreted from nerve endings in the hypothalamus into the bloodstream and carried via the portal vessels to the anterior pituitary.

matography and preparative electrophoresis (*104*). A follicle stimulating hormone releasing factor (FSHRF) and a luteinizing hormone releasing factor (LRF) have been extracted. FSHRF stimulates anterior pituitary release of FSH *in vitro* and *in vivo*, and LRF stimulates release of LH. A thyrotropin releasing factor (TRF), a growth hormone releasing factor (GHRF), and several corticotropin releasing factors (CRF's) have also been extracted (Fig. 2). A factor which inhibits the release of prolactin from the pituitary (prolactin inhibitory factor, PIF) has been extracted as well. These substances are presumably secreted from nerve endings into the capillary loops that are the origin of the hypophyseal portal vessels.

The bulk of experimental evidence indicates that the releasing factors and PIF are polypeptides of small molecular weight (*104*). However, there is currently considerable debate about the possibility that some of the factors are cyclic compounds or polyamines or other nonpeptide substances, and additional research is necessary before any firm conclusions can be drawn.

B. Control of Gonadotropin Secretion in the Male

When considering the regulation of gonadotropin secretion, the difference in the pattern of secretion between the two sexes makes it necessary to discuss the male and female separately. In adult males, the rates of FSH and LH secretion are more or less constant (33). In females, there is also a steady secretion, but superimposed on this is a sharp increase, or burst, of LH secretion, and, in all probability, a lesser burst of FSH secretion at

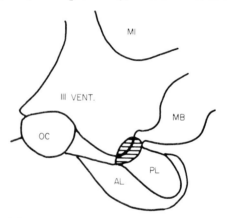

FIG. 3. Site of lesions which produce testicular atrophy and, presumably, inhibition of FSH and LH secretion in males. The striped area is the area common to lesions producing testicular atrophy in a series of male dogs. MI, mass intermedia; MB, mammillary bodies; PL, posterior lobe; AL, anterior lobe; OC, optic chiasma; III VENT., third ventricle. Davidson and Ganong (34), reproduced with permission.

the time of ovulation. There is no known function for prolactin in males, but in females of all mammalian species studied, prolactin plays a role in lactation. It is also luteotropic in the rat and the mouse, and in females, unlike males, there is a fair amount known about the mechanisms regulating its rate of secretion.

Lesions in the posterior tuberal region (Fig. 3) near the infundibulum have been shown to produce testicular atrophy in a number of different species (33). This atrophy is diffuse, is associated with atrophy of the prostate and decreased sperm counts, and is accompanied by a decrease in the pituitary content of LH and FSH (34). Thus, it appears that the secretion of both LH and FSH is reduced. The arcuate nucleus is located in the area where lesions produce testicular atrophy, and it is of interest that, in rats, large quantities of FSHRF can be extracted (*146*) from this general area of the hypothalamus.

Lesions which selectively inhibit FSH secretion might be expected to produce selective atrophy of the seminiferous tubules and inhibition of spermatogenesis without any change in the Leydig cells. Tubular atrophy with apparent maintenance of the Leydig cells has been reported in a few dogs (*34*) and rats (*11*) with lesions, but this combination has not been a consistent or reproducible one. Androgen secretion in response to LH stimulation of the Leydig cells is said to be capable of maintaining spermatogenesis in the absence of the pituitary (*145*), and this may explain the lack of consistent results. No increases in FSH secretion in response to brain stimulation have been reported, but this is not surprising in view of the absence until very recently of a method for measuring FSH in small quantities of blood. Thus, there is no clear-cut evidence for a center in the brain in males that affects FSH secretion without affecting LH secretion.

There is also no good evidence for a discrete brain center concerned with the selective regulation of LH secretion in males. In females, there is no established center with selective effects on FSH secretion, but there appears to be a region in the anterior hypothalamus and the preoptic area which is responsible for the ovulation-producing bursts of LH secretion. Indeed, the main difference between the brains of males and females as far as gonadotropin secretion is concerned is the presence in the latter of the separate LH-regulating region.

It has been known for many years that a major regulatory influence on gonadotropin secretion is the negative feedback effect of gonadal steroids. In appropriate doses, both androgens and estrogens are capable of inhibiting FSH and LH secretion in males and females. An additional negative feedback of the gonadotropins on their own secretion, presumably via their RF's, must also be considered. There is currently little evidence for such an "internal feedback" in males, but there is some evidence for its existence in females.

In males, castration leads to an increase in circulating FSH, and to an increase in pituitary FSH content in some species (*33, 60*). An increase has not been observed in male rats, but the FSH content is very high to start with in this species, 15–20 times that in adult female rats (Kragt, unpublished), and it may be difficult to elevate this level further. Pituitary LH content is increased by castration in rats and dogs, and most of the evidence indicates that circulating LH levels are also increased (*33*).

Androgens do not decrease pituitary FSH content and may actually increase it, but the evidence seems clear that this increase is associated with decreased secretion (*33*). Androgens in doses producing blood levels in the physiological range decrease circulating LH levels and also decrease pituitary LH content. However, there is evidence suggesting that androgens can augment the effects of hypothalamic extracts on gonadotropin secretion in males (85).

Data are beginning to accumulate on the effects of castration and steroid administration on the hypothalamic content of releasing factors. In male rats castration leads to an increase in the LRF content of the hypothalamus, and this increase can be inhibited by injections of testosterone (124).

Estrogens inhibit the secretion of FSH and LH in males (33). In certain humans with marked atrophy of the seminiferous tubules but normal Leydig cells, gonadotropin secretion has been found to be elevated. On the basis of this observation, there has been speculation that the seminiferous tubules secrete estrogen by this means, inhibiting gonadotropin secretion. However, the existence of "inhibin," another hormonal factor from the seminiferous tubules has also been postulated, and the whole subject of the feedback functions of substances other than androgens in males remains unsettled.

The site at which androgens act to inhibit FSH and LH secretion appears to be the median eminence of the hypothalamus. Lesions in the posterior tubular region of the median eminence in male dogs prevent the increase in pituitary FSH and LH content normally produced by castration (37), although this observation is, of course, subject to other possible interpretations. More direct supporting evidence is the observation that local implantations of androgens in the median eminence of male dogs produce testicular atrophy (36). Bogdanove has argued that in this and other implantation experiments, one cannot rule out diffusion of the implanted steroid into the portal vessels and consequent action on the pituitary itself (12). However, Smith and Davidson have recently presented evidence for a hypothalamic site of action which is difficult to refute (138). They studied hypophysectomized rats with pituitary transplants, in which testicular function had been maintained. When testosterone was implanted in the median eminence of these animals, testicular atrophy resulted. Control implants of cholesterol had no effect. The effect of the implants could not have been due to systemic absorption of the testosterone, since the accessory reproductive organs were not stimulated.

Support for the concept of a relatively autonomous gonadotropin-regulating center in the ventral hypothalamus in males has come from the studies of Halász and Pupp (73), who developed a technique for cutting all the nerve connections to the median eminence-arcuate region, leaving an isolated island of ventral hypothalamic tissue in an otherwise intact animal. Following this operation in adult male rats, testicular weight and histology were maintained at normal levels. The observations on the regulation of gonadotropin secretion in males are thus consistent with the view that there is a single hypothalamic regulatory area in or near the arcuate nucleus that is concerned with regulation of FSH and LH secretion. Androgens acting on this region inhibit FSH and LH secretion, and this negative feedback mechanism maintains the steady-state secretion in adults that is necessary for normal testicular function.

C. CONTROL OF GONADOTROPIN SECRETION IN THE FEMALE

1. FSH and LH

Lesions in the infundibular region produce diffuse ovarian atrophy in female guinea pigs (40) and rats (30). The sites of these lesions correspond to the site where lesions in males produce testicular atrophy. The presence of ovarian atrophy suggests decreased secretion of FSH and LH. It has also been reported that in ovariectomized rats with basal hypothalamic lesions, circulating LH levels are not as high as they are in ovariectomized controls (142). In female rats with isolation of the ventral hypothalamus by the technique of Halász and Pupp (73), there is some secretion of both FSH and LH. Thus, the basal secretion of FSH and LH in both sexes appears to be regulated by an area in the ventral hypothalamus in or near the arcuate nucleus.

Females, however, have a sudden increase in LH secretion that produces ovulation. This increase has recently been analyzed in women, using a radioimmunoassay to measure LH in plasma. There is a sharp, four-fold increase in the LH level at midcycle that lasts for about 1 day (119). There also appears to be a smaller burst of FSH secretion at this time (112). A prolonged decrease in pituitary FSH content begins at the time of ovulation in sheep (130), and there may be a decrease in pituitary FSH content at the time of ovulation in rats (105), but this does not occur in the rabbit (39). No data are available as yet to indicate whether the same mechanism that produces the burst of LH secretion is responsible for the increase in FSH secretion.

Dey and associates (41) first reported data suggesting that the burst of LH secretion responsible for ovulation was controlled by the anterior hypothalamus. They discovered that in the guinea pig, lesions located in the median eminence "just caudal to the optic chiasm" were associated with a state of constant estrus. Lesions in the suprachiasmatic and preoptic areas in rats have similar effects (51). The ovaries of these animals become full of follicles, but no ovulation occurs and no corpora lutea are seen. The vaginal epithelium becomes cornified and remains in this state. The condition produced by the lesions has been called the "constant estrus syndrome." This term is unfortunate, however, since the "estrus" is confined to the vagina; the rats do not mate. The term "constant vaginal cornification syndrome," therefore, seems more appropriate. Enough estrogen is being secreted to maintain the uterus and cornify the vaginal mucosa. FSH and LH are secreted, since FSH is necessary for follicular development and LH is necessary for the occurrence of estrogen secretion from the follicles (49). The follicles are capable of ovulation since injections of LH promptly bring about luteinization (143). However, endogenous LH is not secreted in sufficient amounts to produce ovulation.

One site of lesions that produce the constant vaginal cornification syndrome in rats is shown in Fig. 4. The area is considerably above and anterior to the ventral hypothalamic region concerned with the basal secretion of FSH and LH. However, it appears to exert its effects through the basal arcuate area, since basal lesions block ovulation even before ovarian atrophy has a chance to develop (51). Thus, the arcuate nucleus, the nerve endings that secrete releasing factors, and the portal vessels are a final common pathway to the pituitary from the hypothalamus. This pathway is separated from the anterior mechanism when the hypothalamus is isolated by the technique of Halász and Pupp (73), and, consequently, the constant vaginal cornification syndrome is produced.

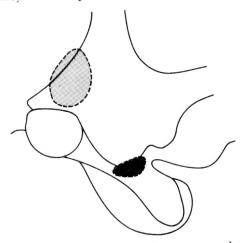

FIG. 4. Sites of lesions which produced changes in gonadotropin secretion in females. Lesions in the shaded area at the lower right produced diffuse ovarian atrophy and, presumably, inhibition of FSH and LH secretion. Lesions in the dotted area above the optic chiasma and adjacent areas cause inhibition of the burst of LH secretion which normally produces ovulation. Lesion location based on work of various authors in rats and guinea pigs, projected on the same diagram of the hypothalamus as that used in Fig. 3.

It is worth noting that a variety of other procedures produce the constant vaginal cornification syndrome, apparently by acting on the anterior LH-regulating region. It can be produced, for example, by constant exposure to light (28). It also appears when female rats reach adulthood if they are injected with androgen in infancy (see Section V).

LH secretion can be stimulated by the drug clomiphene, while the function of the LH-secreting mechanism responsible for ovulation can be inhibited by a variety of different CNS-active drugs (11). This is true not only in reflexly ovulating species such as the rabbit, in which the burst of LH secretion is initiated by impulses in afferent fibers from the sense organs (24), but also in spontaneously cycling species such as the rat. In the rat, the drug must be injected at a particular time of the cycle if it is to produce blockade. This "critical period" for injection is 2–4 PM on the day before expected estrus (65). Injection before 2 PM or after 4 PM is ineffective. The event inhibited by the drugs presumably lasts 20–35 minutes and precedes LH release by one-half hour. Injections during the critical period delay ovulation for 24 hours; repeated injections each day between 2 and 4 PM can delay ovulation for long periods.

The drugs known to inhibit ovulation in reflex and spontaneously ovulating species are summarized in Table I. The list includes tranquilizers,

TABLE I
DRUGS THAT INHIBIT OVULATION[a]

Drugs	Inhibiting ovulation in:		
	Spontaneously ovulating mammals	Reflexly ovulating mammals	Birds
Antiadrenergic agents			
Dibenamine	+	+	+
Dibenzyline	+		
SKF-501	+	+	+
Anticholinergic agents			
Atropine	+	+	+
Methantheline	+	+	
Pathilon	+		
Tranquilizers			
Reserpine	+		
Chlorpromazine	+		
Psychic energizers			
Iproniazid and other monoamine oxidase inhibitors	+		
Anticonvulsants			
Diphenylhydantoin	+		
Sedatives and Anesthetics			
Barbiturates	+	+	+
Ethanol	+	+	
Ether	+		
Analgesics			
Morphine	+	+	

[a] Data from Table V, Gold and Ganong (65).

sedatives, and compounds that depress brain norepinephrine content, as well as drugs such as morphine and diphenylhydantoin, which depress the brain stem. They also include cholinergic and adrenergic blocking agents, and the effects of these compounds may be due to inhibition of transmission at synapses in the chains of neurons responsible for the burst of LH secretion. Since it was observed that atropine had to be given within seconds after the copulatory stimulus to produce blockade in rabbits, while Dibenamine blocked if given up to 1 minute after copulation, Sawyer and his associates (132) suggested that a cholinergic followed by an adrenergic discharge was part of the chain of events culminating in reflex LH secretion. Injections of epinephrine into the third ventricle produce ovulation in the rabbit, but morphine and pentobarbital block this effect (C. H. Sawyer, personal communication). Consequently, the site of action of epinephrine is probably proximal to the final neural elements in the mechanism producing LH release.

There may be hypothalamic centers outside the arcuate nucleus that are concerned with the regulation of FSH and prolactin secretion in females, although their existence is certainly not established. Greer reported that prolonged diestrus without ovarian atrophy occurred in rats with lesions in the preoptic area (71), and Flérko and his associates believe that there is an anterior hypothalamic area which is acted upon by estrogens to produce inhibition of FSH secretion (51). Flérko has also reported that lesions of the thalamohypothalamic border produce prolonged periods of diestrus associated with hyperluteinization of the ovaries, and he suggests that this area normally regulates the secretion of PIF.

It is clear that impulses in afferent pathways converging on the hypothalamus trigger the ovulation-producing increases in secretion of gonadotropin(s) in animals that ovulate after copulation. In spontaneously ovulating species, the effects of light and other environmental stimuli on reproductive function (Chapter 17) indicate that in these animals impulses in afferents from the sense organs also affect gonadotropin secretion. In rabbits, ovulation can be produced by stimulation of the uterine cervix with a glass rod. However, genital stimulation is not essential for ovulation, since ovulation occurs following coitus after local anesthesia of the vagina and neighboring regions (48). Ovulation can also occur after a great variety of sensory receptors have been destroyed. Neither removal of the olfactory bulbs nor destruction of the vestibular apparatus and cochlea by themselves block copulation-induced ovulation (15). Blinding is also ineffective. In cats, which also ovulate only after coitus, complete sympathectomy does not alter the response (16). It appears probable, therefore, that many stimuli converge on the hypothalamus, and that no single afferent pathway is essential for LH release. In rats, lesions just above the optic chiasma block the production of constant vaginal cornification by exposure to constant light (28). This suggests that the inhibitory influence of light on the ovulation-producing release of LH might be mediated by pathways that leave the optic chiasma and enter the hypothalamus at this location. The effects of light on the ferret, which can be brought into estrus in the winter when exposed to extra light, have been studied in considerable detail. They appear to be mediated via the optic nerves as far as the hypothalamus, but interruption of the optic pathways beyond the hypothalamus has no effect on the response to light (23); this also suggests the existence of a direct retinohypothalamic pathway, although an effect via the accessory optic tracts is also a possibility. In birds, light not only acts by way of the eyes, it also penetrates the skull and appears to exert a direct effect on the diencephalon or the pituitary to increase gonadotropin secretion (8). The eyes are certainly the major receptors in mammals, but light does penetrate to the region of the diencephalon in rats, rabbits, dogs, and sheep (59).

The limbic system also sends afferents to the gonadotropin-regulating centers in the hypothalamus. Stimulation of the amygdala produces LH release and ovulation in two nonspontaneously ovulating species, the rabbit and the cat (77, 93, 136). It also produces ovulation in rats with the constant vaginal cornification syndrome produced by constant illumination, and stimulation of the septum has a similar effect (18). Lesions of the amygdala produce precocious puberty in immature rats, while prolonged stimulation of this structure inhibits the onset of puberty (29). However, Sawyer (131) has found that lesions of the septum and amygdala in rabbits do not affect reproductive behavior or copulation-induced ovulation, and the role of the amygdala in normal physiologic control of gonadotropin secretion remains uncertain.

Feedback effects on gonadotropin secretion are of great importance in the regulation of reproductive function in females as well as males, but the situation in females is much more complex. Estrogens and progesterone must both be considered, and there are demonstrated positive as well as negative feedback effects of both. In addition, gonadal steroids exert feedback effects on the secretion of prolactin; and in the rat and the mouse, although apparently not in other species, prolactin, in addition to its effects on the breast, maintains the corpus luteum.

A fundamental effect of estrogens is inhibition of FSH secretion. This action is probably due principally to an action of the hormone on the ventral hypothalamic region, where lesions produce inhibition of FSH secretion. Androgens have similar effects. Ovariectomy increases FSHRF content of the hypothalamus, and estrogens and androgens decrease the hypothalamic content of this releasing factor (32, 114). Ovarian atrophy is produced by implantation of estrogen in the median eminence (99). Estrogen also acts directly on the brain to produce estrous behavior in the female, but the locus of this estrogen action is more rostrally located in the suprachiasmatic region. The two separate loci of estrogen action on the brain are shown in Fig. 5.

The possibility that hormones implanted in the median eminence of the hypothalamus are carried to the pituitary via the portal vessels has been discussed in Section III, B. Implantation of androgen in the hypothalamus inhibits gonadotropin secretion in males with transplanted pituitaries (137), but no comparable experiment has been reported in females. However, estrogen implantation in the pituitary, unlike implantation in the median eminence, does not cause gonadal atrophy in female rabbits (35, 36). In addition, estrogen implants in the median eminence of rabbits have effects different from similar implants in the pituitary, and implantation in the median eminence but not in the pituitary inhibits the development of castration cells following ovariectomy (88, 89). This fact is of particular significance because castration changes develop in cells in close proximity to the implants in the pituitary. Thus, it seems likely that the main effect of estrogen is due to an action on the hypothalamus (51).

Estrogens also inhibit LH secretion, small doses causing the plasma level of this hormone to decrease in ovariectomized rats. In these experiments, the inhibitory effect of estrogen was promptly overcome by injections of LRF, evidence that the site of inhibition was the hypothalamus rather than the pituitary (103). Progesterone was found to synergize with estrogen in producing inhibition of LH secretion. Implantation of estrogen in the

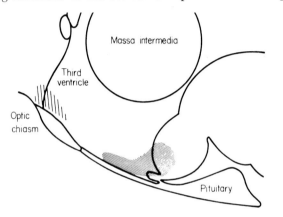

FIG. 5. Sites where estrogens act on the hypothalamus. Estradiol implants in the infundibular region inhibit gonadotropin secretion, producing ovarian atrophy (shaded area), while estradiol implants above the optic chiasma induce sexual behavior (striated area). From Ganong (58), reproduced with permission.

median eminence of the hypothalamus prevents copulation-induced ovulation in the rabbit (35). Following castration, the LRF content of the hypothalamus in female rats declines, but administration of estradiol to such an animal causes a further decline (124).

The effects of progesterone on gonadotropin secretion are both facilitory and inhibitory (51). No effect on FSH secretion has been reported, but there is an inhibitory effect on LH secretion. This effect is shared by a variety of synthetic derivatives of progesterone, and is the basis of the current worldwide use of orally active progestational agents as oral contraceptives. The inhibitory effect appears to be exerted on the hypothalamus, but an additional action directly on the pituitary is also a possibility. Enovid, a mixture of the oral progestational agent norethynodrel and a small amount of estrogen, has been shown to inhibit cycling and decrease pituitary LH and hypothalamic LRF content when administered to female rats (113). Norethindrone, another oral progestational compound, has been shown to prevent ovulation by blocking the copulation-induced increase in circulating

LH in rabbits. In this species, a direct action on the pituitary is suggested by the observation that norethindrone also blocks the LH release produced by infusion of hypothalamic extract directly into the pituitary (80). However, implantation of norethindrone in the ventral hypothalamus, but not in the pituitary, inhibits copulation-induced ovulation (90). Therefore, the agent may well act on both the pituitary and the hypothalamus.

Progesterone has been reported to reinitiate estrous cycles in rats with anterior hypothalamic lesions and the constant vaginal cornification syndrome (70). A similar reinitiation of cycles has been produced in rats with the constant vaginal cornification syndrome due to the administration of androgens in early life (2). The mechanism by which this effect of progesterone is exerted is unknown.

Positive feedback effects of estrogen are well documented. When administered in certain doses, estrogens facilitate LH secretion (45, 82), and it has been suggested that it is this positive feedback effect which is responsible for the increase in LH secretion which produces ovulation in spontaneously ovulating species. Estrogens cause release of LH from the pituitary *in vitro* (124) and may sensitize the pituitary to the action of LRF (42).

A possible positive feedback effect of estrogen on FSH secretion has been demonstrated in immature rats. Estrogen administration in these young animals causes not only vaginal canalization and cornification but also the onset of regular estrous cycles (127). LH plays a role in the onset of cycles, but FSH must be present as well. The effect of estrogen in this case is apparently exerted on the hypothalamus, since estrogen implants in the hypothalamus produce precocious puberty (138). However, estrogen implants in the pituitary also exert this effect, and so do control implants of inert substances in the pituitary, so the significance of these findings remains to be determined.

The existence of a "short loop" feedback by which LH itself feeds back has been postulated, since in animals with LH implanted in the hypothalamus, pituitary LH content is said to be decreased (26). Confirmation of this observation is needed, and the mechanism by which LH exerts the effect needs to be clarified. Sawyer has presented evidence that LH and several related gonadotropin preparations act on the brain (132) to lower the threshold of the EEG after-reaction. FSH, TSH, ACTH, and growth hormone did not have this effect. If a negative feedback of LH on LH secretion exists, its function is probably that of adding stability to the major feedbacks between LH and estrogen and progesterone.

2. Prolactin

Numerous physiological observations indicate that prolactin secretion is under the control of the nervous system. Nonlactating women, when suckled by infants, exhibit mammary gland development and lactation (63). Suckling of virgin female rats by foster litters results in the induction of lactation and pseudopregnancy (*134*). Pseudopregnancy has been induced by copulation with a sterile male and by mechanical or electrical stimulation of the cervix. Prolactin plays a major role in the development of pseudopregnancy, and there is depletion of pituitary prolactin after suckling or mechanical stimulation of the cervix (*79, 128*). The pituitary prolactin content of female rabbits and rats is reduced shortly after copulation (*79*). Visual and tactile stimulation such as seeing or touching eggs or young in the nest may lead to prolactin release and subsequent incubation, crop development, and broody behavior in ring doves (*98*) and domestic pigeons (*106*). Prolactin release in response to seasonal environmental changes has also been suggested to be responsible for premigratory deposition of fat in passerine species of birds (*107*).

Prolactin secretion in mammals increases after section of the pituitary stalk or transplantation of the pituitary to a site remote from the hypothalamus (see Section III, A). It is also increased by lesions in the median eminence that inhibit FSH and LH secretion (*46*). Initially, the data on the effects of hypothalamic lesions on prolactin secretion were misinterpreted; lactational performance was used as an end point, and since oxytocin secretion was reduced by the lesions, milk letdown was deficient. However, it has now been shown that median eminence lesions or pituitary stalk section cause increased prolactin release from the pituitary in female rats, male rats, rabbits, ferrets, cats, and women (*109*). Increased secretion, however, apparently does not occur when the hypothalamopituitary connections are severed in birds; at least Bayle and Assenmacher (*6*) could find no differences between crop weights and mucosal thickness in hypophysectomized pigeons with pituitary autotransplants and hypophysectomized pigeons without transplants. Thus, the control of prolactin secretion in avian species appears to differ from that in mammals (*95*).

Numerous CNS-active drugs and substances suspected of being synaptic mediators in the brain increase prolactin secretion. Epinephrine, norepinephrine, acetylcholine, serotonin, pilocarpine, and eserine all induce mammary gland development in estrogen-primed female rats (*111*). However, the action of these agents may be due to their stressful effects, since formalin injections are equally effective. Pseudopregnancy and mammary gland development occur in female rats treated with reserpine or chlorpromazine (*4, 110*), and these tranquilizers have been reported to produce galactorrhea in women (*139*). Oxytocin was once believed to stimulate prolactin release in the rat (*9*), but it has now been proved that oxytocin acts by promoting mammary gland evacuation, thereby preventing atrophy due to congestion (*108*). It is now generally held that the neural lobe hormones are not of primary importance in controlling the release of any of the anterior pituitary hormones.

Estrogens stimulate prolactin release *in vivo* and on incubation with pituitary tissue *in vitro* (*108*). Kanematsu and Sawyer (*88*) have presented evidence that suggests that estrogens may also act at the hypothalamic level to produce this effect. Progesterone, testosterone, and cortisol stimulate prolactin release *in vivo* when given in large doses, but have no direct effect on the pituitary *in vitro* (*108*).

PIF, the hypothalamic factor that inhibits prolactin release from the pituitary in mammals, has been discussed previously. The degree of inhibition of prolactin release *in vitro* is proportional to the logarithm of the amount of hypothalamic tissue added to the incubation medium (*96*). Suckling, estrogen administration, and reserpine injections, all of which induce prolactin release, decrease the PIF content of the hypothalamus (*108*). Hypothalamic extracts prevent the depletion of pituitary prolactin produced by suckling (*72*).

It is interesting that hypothalamic extracts from tricolored blackbirds (*117*), pigeons (*95*), and ducks (*67*) stimulate rather than inhibit the release of prolactin *in vitro*. This is additional evidence that in birds, the mechanism regulating prolactin secretion is different from that in mammals. Hypothalamic extracts from parent pigeons actively secreting crop milk have been shown to be more effective in stimulating prolactin release by pigeon pituitaries than extracts from young pigeons having no crop gland stimulation (*95*).

Several physiological observations in mammals suggest that prolactin and LH secretion fluctuate in a reciprocal manner (*46*). These observations led to the suggestion that a single neurohumor controlled both LH and prolactin release. However, selective effects on the secretion of LH or prolactin by hypothalamic lesions have been reported (*47*), and the LRF and PIF activities in hypothalamic extracts have been separated chromatographically (*104*). Chowers and McCann (*21*) have suggested that there may be a neuronal element sensitive to estrogen which can simultaneously decrease hypothalamic LRF and PIF, resulting in the reciprocal changes in LH and prolactin secretion.

There are some data on the pathways to the hypothalamus that mediate the increase in prolactin secretion produced by suckling. Since the only known prolactin-regulating factor in mammals is PIF, impulses in the afferent pathways presumably inhibit PIF secretion. The brain-stem reticular formation apparently contains ascending fibers that function to facilitate prolactin secretion, since lesions in this region block lactation (*46*). There is also evidence that olfactory nerve stimulation can inhibit prolactin secretion. This may be the basis of the "Bruce effect," the interruption of pregnancy that occurs in mice exposed to a cage recently occupied by a male mouse of another strain (*17*). However, studies in this field are in their infancy, and a great deal more work needs to be done.

IV. Regulation of the Onset of Puberty by the Nervous System

In addition to the part it plays in the endocrine and behavioral aspects of reproduction, there is evidence that the brain is involved in the initiation of puberty. Part of this evidence is the occurrence of precocious puberty in children with tumors or infections of the diencephalon (86, 147). The sexual development includes spermatogenesis in the male and ovulation in the female, and is normal in all respects except its timing. Thus, it is a "true" precocious puberty, and differs from "pseudoprecocious puberty," the condition in which secondary sexual characteristics develop without maturation of germ cells due to excessive secretion of gonadal steroids in children with conditions such as ovarian and adrenal tumors. True sexual precocity may occur in very young children, and cases of regular menstruation in 2-year-old girls have been reported.

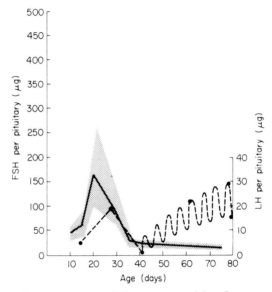

FIG. 6. Gonadotropin content of the pituitary of female rats at various ages. The solid line represents the mean FSH content and the shaded area represents the 95% confidence limits. Data from Kragt and Ganong (94). The dashed line represents the LH content, extrapolated from individual values (dots) reported in Matsuyama et al. (102).

Pineal tumors have also been reported to cause precocious puberty (92). For unknown reasons, precocity in association with such tumors is found almost exclusively in males. It is generally associated with lesions that destroy the pineal body, but pineal tumors, because of their anatomical position, also compress the hypothalamus early in their growth (147).

The most complete experimental studies of the mechanisms regulating the onset of puberty have been carried out in rats (see 29, 44). In this species the vaginal canal does not become patent until the time of puberty, and its opening is followed in about 2 days by the first estrous vaginal smear. The average normal age of vaginal opening is about 40 days. In

male rats, the testes become mature and sperm heads appear in the seminiferous tubules at about 40 days of age.

The failure of puberty to occur earlier in female rats is not due to unresponsiveness of the tissues to gonadal steroids, or to unresponsiveness of
the gonads to gonadotropins. Ovaries of immature animals function in the
adult manner when transplanted into adults (52), and injections of gonadotropins after the age of 20 days can cause ovulation and corpus luteum
formation. Precocious vaginal opening and cornification of the vaginal epithelium can also be produced. The pituitaries of immature animals contain
gonadotropins, and these can be released by appropriate hypothalamic
releasing factors, since precocious puberty can be produced by injection of

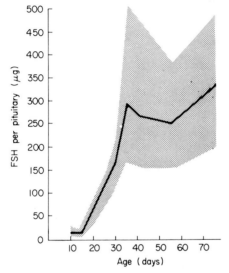

FIG. 7. FSH content of the pituitary of male rats at various ages. The solid
line represents mean values and the shaded area the 95% confidence limits. From
Kragt and Ganong (94a).

hypothalamic extracts (62). In addition, the pituitaries of immature animals
are capable of supporting normal estrous cycles when transplanted under
the hypothalamus in hypophysectomized adult female rats.

The FSH content of the pituitary in female rats (Fig. 6) is greatest
between 20 and 25 days of age, falls to low levels at the time of puberty,
and persists at low levels throughout adulthood (94). The pituitary FSH
content in male rats continues to rise during early life and reaches a plateau
at 35 days of age (Fig. 7). The LH content (100, 102) of the pituitary
in female rats reaches a peak at 25–30 days of age, declines between 30 and
40 days of age, and then increases to high levels during adulthood (Fig. 6).
The levels fluctuate during the estrous cycle, being high in proestrus and
low in diestrus. In males, the LH content at 25–30 days of age is about

half that in females. There is a moderate decline in content between 30 and 40 days of age and then an increase to levels higher than those seen in adult females (100).

The failure of puberty to occur at a younger age also appears not to be due to a deficiency of releasing factors or the pathway by which they are transported to the pituitary. The LRF concentration in the hypothalamic tissue of 25-day-old rats has been reported to be as great as that in adult female rats (127), and FSHRF is present in appreciable quantities as early as 10 days of age (93a). Hypothalamic portal vessels appear in fetal rats at about 21 days of gestation, and the median eminence capillary network is nearly complete by the fifth day after birth (64).

Evidence that the brain is involved in the control of the onset of puberty in female rats is provided by the observation that hypothalamic lesions accelerate its onset by 4–5 days. Anterior hypothalamic lesions were first reported to have this effect (29), but some of these lesions may have produced the precocious onset of the constant vaginal cornification syndrome (Section III, C, 1) rather than true precocious puberty with regular cycles (56). Gellert and Ganong (61) failed to observe precocious puberty in rats with anterior hypothalamic lesions, but did regularly observe precocity when the lesions were placed in the arcuate nucleus just above the infundibulum. The discrepancy between these results and those of other investigators may be more apparent than real; some of the anterior lesions in the early studies were large and may have involved the arcuate nucleus, while some of Gellert and Ganong's rats with anterior lesions did show precocity, even though there was no significant acceleration of vaginal opening and first estrus for the group as a whole. Recently, Schiavi (133) has reported precocious puberty following lesions in the anterior hypothalamus and in the tuberal region. Interestingly, despite a number of attempts to do so [(29) Lima-Ostos and Ganong, unpublished], no one has yet reported production of precocious puberty by placement of hypothalamic lesions in male rats.

Additional evidence for hypothalamic involvement in the regulation of puberty is the slowing of the onset of puberty produced by reserpine (20), a compound known to affect hypothalamic function. Decreased illumination also slows the onset of puberty, while increased light accelerates it (28). The limbic system also seems to play some role in the regulation of puberty. Electrical stimulation of the amygdala in immature female rats has been reported to delay puberty, while lesions in this structure hasten puberty (29). It has been claimed in the past that the effects of lesions are nonspecific and that any stress can produce acceleration of the onset of puberty (78). However, lesions in many portions of the nervous system other than the amygdala, the anterior hypothalamus, and the tuberal region have been reported to be without effect on the onset of puberty (44, 61).

The question of the role of the pineal body in the regulation of puberty has recently been reopened because of reports that melatonin, which is synthesized in the pineal body, decreases the frequency of estrous smears in rats exposed to constant light (22) and inhibits FSH release from the pituitary *in vitro* (115). However, melatonin has no effect on the onset of puberty when administered to immature female rats. Serotonin, which is also present in large quantities in the pineal, has recently been claimed to antagonize the action of exogenous gonadotropins on the ovaries of immature rats (121), but serotonin has also been claimed to slow the onset of puberty when injected directly into the hypothalamus (27). In addition, no consistent, reproducible acceleration of the onset of puberty has been produced by pinealectomy, and in the absence of such an effect, it is difficult to argue that the pineal has any important role in the regulation of sexual maturation.

The accelerating effects of hypothalamic lesions on puberty in rats suggest the presence of some sort of hypothalamic mechanism that tonically inhibits gonadotropin secretion in immature animals. However, no inhibitory substances could be identified in hypothalamic extracts prepared from the brains of immature animals (Gellert and Ganong, unpublished). Lesions in brain tissue have zones of irritation around them (129), and it is possible that the lesions produce stimulation of the surrounding normal arcuate nucleus with the premature discharge of releasing factors into the portal circulation. This explanation, however, cannot account for the effects of amygdaloid lesions, since stimulation of the amygdala has been demonstrated to delay puberty (29).

Currently, considerable attention is being focused on the role of feedback mechanisms in the control of the onset of puberty. There is some prepuberal secretion of estrogen in females and testosterone in males, and these gonadal steroids exert a greater inhibitory effect on gonadotropin secretion before puberty than they do after puberty (19, 29). It has therefore been suggested that the small amounts of secreted gonadal steroids hold gonadotropic hormone secretion in check before puberty, and that puberty is due to a decline in hypothalamic sensitivity to the negative feedback action of the steroids. Bloch and Davidson (10) have been able to produce precocious puberty in male rats by local implantation of an antiandrogen in the median eminence. Antiestrogens have been reported to produce accelerated vaginal opening, as well as precocious ovulation in 30-day-old rats (25). The data on hypothalamic lesions could be consistent with this hypothesis, since the lesions could be destroying the neural centers responsible for the negative feedback inhibition. The same explanation might even be advanced to explain the effects of amygdaloid lesions and stimulation, if estrogens act on the amygdala.

The results of several experiments which are somewhat difficult to fit into the negative feedback hypothesis suggest that other factors may be involved. The production of ovulation by injection of PMSG (pregnant mare serum gonadotropin) in immature rats, for instance, is apparently due to a direct effect of the gonadotropin on the brain (125). Currently, there is disagreement about the existence of a diurnal cycle in the sensitivity of the brain of immature rats to PMSG. Estrogen has a somewhat similar effect; it not only acts directly to produce vaginal opening, but it causes a true precocious puberty (126). This latter effect is apparently due to an action on the brain, since it can be produced by implantation of estrogens in the hypothalamus (138). However, the physiological significance of this presumed positive feedback effect of estrogen is currently uncertain.

V. Effects of Hormones on Development and Differentiation of the Brain

Current evidence indicates that the brain resembles the reproductive organs in that its development, like theirs, is determined by the hormonal environment early in life. The female pattern of gonadotropin secretion and sex behavior is innate, but the male pattern develops at puberty if the brain is briefly exposed to androgen during the fetal or neonatal period. Most of the expermients demonstrating these actions have been performed in rats, a species in which the young are particularly immature at birth (81). If testes are transplanted to infant female rats, they do not ovulate when they mature (2, 122). Instead, they develop the constant vaginal cornification syndrome (Section III, C, 1). Ovulation can be produced in such animals by injections of LH or, after progesterone priming, by hypothalamic stimulation (23). Thus, the rats are able to secrete LH at a steady level like the male, but they are unable to produce the peaks of LH secretion necessary for ovulation. Conversely, in males castrated at birth, transplanted ovaries show the female pattern of cyclic ovulation with luteinization of the ruptured follicles; but if the castrated rats with transplants are treated with androgens in early life, the male pattern of gonadotropin secretion develops (3, 75, 122).

Pfeiffer, who did much of the early work in this field, believed that the testes secrete a small amount of androgen which acts on the pituitary to make the pattern of pituitary secretion the male pattern (122). However, Harris and Jacobson (76) subsequently showed that pituitaries transplanted from male fetal rats to hypophysectomized female adult rats maintained normal estrous cycles. Thus, the sex of the pituitary is not fixed, but depends on the sex of the brain under which it is located.

A single dose of androgen as small as 10 μg of testosterone on the fifth day of life in a female is capable of producing the male pattern of gonadotropin secretion in adulthood (2). The LH content of the pituitary in androgen-treated female rats is low relative to normal females, but the FSH content is apparently unaltered (2). Estrogen administered to female rats in early life also causes failure to ovulate in adulthood. This failure to ovulate is associated with constant vaginal cornification or, in some instances, with prolonged periods of diestrus (2). Thus, it appears that the female pattern of cyclic gonadotropin secretion is the innate pattern irrespective of genetic sex, and that exposure of the brain to androgen during a critical period in the early days of life converts the cyclic female pattern into the steady male pattern.

The early exposure of the brain to hormones also determines the pattern of sexual behavior that develops in adulthood. Female rats treated with testosterone when 5 days of age do not behave sexually as females when they reach adulthood, but they attempt to mount other females with greater than normal frequency and show increased male sexual behavior. Males castrated at birth, however, show increased female sexual behavior, although they continue to act as males as well (75).

The similarity of the action of androgen on brain development and its action on the development of the external genitalia is striking. In many species, androgen from the fetal testes causes the undifferentiated genital anlage to develop into male external genitalia. In the absence of androgen, female external genitalia develop regardless of genetic sex (144). It is worth noting, however, that, at least in rats, the androgen effects on the genitalia occur earlier than the androgen effects on the brain. Therefore, it is possible to have normal genital development and abnormal brain development (75).

The effects of early exposure to steroids are most easily studied in the rat because in this species, the changes can be produced by treatment after birth. In other species, treatment must be given in utero, usually by treating the mother (3). For example, female pseudohermaphroditic offspring of rhesus monkeys treated during pregnancy with androgens have been shown to have abnormal sexual behavior in adulthood (123). Whether or not similar hormonal effects on the human brain occur in utero is unknown, but investigation of this possibility is clearly in order.

It is pertinent to note that early treatment of female rats with large doses of steroids other than androgens produce the constant vaginal cornification syndrome in adulthood. Estrogens, corticoids, and even cholesterol can also produce the syndrome (141). However, most steroids have the actions of other steroids if administered in sufficiently large doses—e.g., aldosterone has slight glucocorticoid activity, etc. (58). Consequently, it is unreasonable to expect complete specificity of the action of steroids on the brain.

It has also been reported that administration of reserpine, chlorpromazine, or suspensions of thymus cells at the same time as the androgen prevents the constant vaginal cornification syndrome from developing in adulthood (65, 91). The reasons for the blockade are unknown, but so, for that matter, is the exact mechanism by which the androgen exerts its masculinizing effect on the brain in the first place. However, the fundamental importance of the inductive effects of androgens on the brain is apparent, and unlocking the mechanisms by which the hormones exert their effects should provide invaluable leads to how other fundamental inductive changes take place.

VI. Summary

The nervous system, the great integrating system of the body, plays some role in almost every aspect of reproduction. Copulation is an act made up of a hierarchy of reflexes with their centers at various levels in the central nervous system. Sexual behavior is in large part under neuroendocrine control, especially in domestic animals and other nonprimates. Environmental variables affect reproduction via the nervous system, and parturition and lactation have prominent neural components. In addition, anterior pituitary secretion is controlled by the hypothalamus.

Brain control of anterior pituitary secretion is neurovascular; a group of substances, probably polypeptides, are secreted into the hypophyseal portal vessels in the ventral hypothalamus and pass in these vessels directly to the anterior pituitary, where they govern its secretion. Most of these brain substances are releasing factors which stimulate pituitary secretion; the CRF's stimulate ACTH secretion, TRF stimulates TSH secretion, LRF stimulates LH secretion, FSHRF stimulates FSH secretion, and GHRF stimulates growth hormone secretion. However, one factor, PIF, inhibits pituitary secretion of prolactin.

In adult males, there is a brain area in the arcuate nucleus of the ventral hypothalamus which appears to regulate FSH and LH secretion via FSHRF and LRF. It is acted upon in a negative feedback fashion by the gonadal steroids, thus providing a stable hormone output from day to day.

In adult females, the arcuate region controlling FSH and LH secretion is supplemented by a more anterior area in the preoptic region of the hypothalamus and its environs that is responsible for triggering the sudden increase in LH secretion that produces ovulation. Numerous afferent pathways converge on this area, including pathways from the eyes and the genitalia.

The gonadal steroids exert basic feedback effects in females that are analogous to those in the male, but there are in addition more complex feedback mechanisms. Hormonal and neural factors also combine to regulate prolactin secretion.

Not only is the regulation of gonadal secretion in adulthood under neural control via the pituitary and the brain, but sexual development and the onset of sexual activity at puberty is also governed by the brain. In addition, it now seems clear that in rats and probably in other species as well, exposure to androgens early in life causes "masculinization" of the brain mechanisms regulating gonadotropin secretion and sexual behavior. In the absence of androgens, the female patterns develop even in genetic males. Thus, the development of these aspects of brain function resemble the external genitalia in that they are primarily determined hormonally rather than genetically. The details and implications of these interrelationships and of other neuroendocrine interactions are fertile fields for future research.

REFERENCES

1. Bard, P., *Res. Publ., Assoc. Res. Nervous Mental Disease* **20**, 551 (1940).
2. Barraclough, C. A., *Recent Progr. Hormone Res.* **22**, 503 (1966).
3. Barraclough, C. A., *in* "Neuroendocrinology" (L. Martini and W. F. Ganong, eds.), Vol. II, p. 61. Academic Press, New York, 1967.
4. Barraclough, C. A., and Sawyer, C. H., *Endocrinology* **65**, 563 (1959).
5. Bauer, H. G., *J. Clin. Endocrinol. Metabol.* **14**, 13 (1954).
6. Bayle, J. D., and Assenmacher, I., *Compt. Rend. Acad. Sci.* **261**, 5667 (1965).
7. Beach, F. A., *Physiol. Rev.* **47**, 289 (1967).
8. Benoit, J., *Gen. Compt. Endocrinol. Suppl.* **1**, 254 (1962).
9. Benson, G. K., and Folley, S. J., *Nature* **177**, 700 (1956).
10. Bloch, G. J., and Davidson, J. M., *Science* **155**, 593 (1967).
11. Bogdanove, E. M., *Endocrinology* **60**, 689 (1957).
12. Bogdanove, E. M., *Endocrinology* **73**, 696 (1963).
13. Bogdanove, E. M., Spiritos, B. M., and Halmi, M. S., *Endocrinology* **57**, 302 (1955).
14. Brodish, A., and Long, C. N. H., *Endocrinology* **71**, 298 (1962).
15. Brooks, C. M., *Am. J. Physiol.* **120**, 544 (1937).
16. Brooks, C. M., *Res. Publ., Assoc. Res. Nervous Mental Disease* **20**, 525 (1940).
17. Bruce, H. M., and Parkes, A. S., *in* "Advances in Neuroendocrinology" (A. V. Nalbandov, ed.), p. 282. Univ. of Illinois Press, Urbana, Illinois, 1963.
18. Bunn, J. P., and Everett, J. W., *Proc. Soc. Exptl. Biol. Med.* **96**, 369 (1957).
19. Byrnes, W. W., and Meyer, R. K., *Endocrinology* **49**, 449 (1951).
20. Carraro, A., Corbin, A., Fraschini, F., and Martini, L., *J. Endocrinol.* **32**, 387 (1965).
21. Chowers, I., and McCann, S. M., *Proc. Soc. Exptl. Biol. Med.* **124**, 260 (1967).
22. Chu, E. W., Wurtman, R. J., and Axelrod, J., *Endocrinology* **75**, 238 (1964).
23. Clark, W. E. L., McKeown, T., and Zuckerman, S., *Proc. Roy. Soc.* **B126**, 449 (1949).
24. Clegg, M. T., and Doyle, L. L., *in* "Neuroendocrinology" (L. Martini and W. F. Ganong, eds.), Vol. II, p. 1. Academic Press, New York, 1967.
25. Coppola, J. A., and Perrine, J. W., *Endocrinology* **76**, 865 (1965).
26. Corbin, A., and Cohen, A. I., *Endocrinology* **78**, 41 (1966).
27. Corbin, A., and Schottelius, B. A., *Am. J. Physiol.* **201**, 1176 (1961).
28. Critchlow, B. V., *in* "Advances in Neuroendocrinology" (A. V. Nalbandov, ed.), p. 377. Univ. of Illinois Press, Urbana, Illinois, 1963.
29. Critchlow, B. V., and Bar-Sela, M. E., *in* "Neuroendocrinology" (L. Martini and W. F. Ganong, eds.), Vol. II, p. 101. Academic Press, New York, 1967.
30. D'Angelo, S. A., *Endocrinology* **64**, 685 (1959).
31. Daniel, P. M., *in* "Neuroendocrinology" (L. Martini and W. F. Ganong, eds.), Vol. I, p. 15. Academic Press, New York, 1966.

32. David, M. A., Fraschini, F., Motla, M., and Martini, L., *Abstr. 47th Meeting Endocrine Soc., New York, 1965*, p. 27.
33. Davidson, J. M., *in* "Neuroendocrinology" (L. Martini and W. F. Ganong, eds.), Vol. I, p. 565. Academic Press, New York, 1966.
34. Davidson, J. M., and Ganong, W. F., *Endocrinology* 66, 480 (1960).
35. Davidson, J. M., and Sawyer, C. H., *Acta Endocrinol.* 37, 385 (1961).
36. Davidson, J. M., and Sawyer, C. H., *Proc. Soc. Exptl. Biol. Med.* 107, 4 (1961).
37. Davidson, J. M., Contopoulos, A. N., and Ganong, W. F., *Endocrinology* 66, 735 (1960).
38. deGroot, J., *in* "Neuroendocrinology" (L. Martini and W. F. Ganong, eds.), Vol. I, p. 81. Academic Press, New York, 1966.
39. Desjardins, C., Kirton, K. T., and Hafs, H. D., *Federation Proc.* 26, 534 (1967).
40. Dey, F. L., *Endocrinology* 33, 75 (1943).
41. Dey, F. L., Fisher, C., Berry, C. M., and Ranson, S. W., *Am. J. Physiol.* 129, 39 (1940).
42. Döcke, F., and Dorner, G., *Acta Endocrinol.* 50 (Suppl. 100), 148 (1965).
43. Donovan, B. T., *in* "The Pituitary" (G. W. Harris and B. T. Donovan, eds.), Vol. II, p. 49. Univ. of California Press, Berkeley, California, 1966.
44. Donovan, B. T., and van der Werff ten Bosch, J. J., "Physiology of Puberty" Arnold, London, 1965.
45. Everett, J. W., *Physiol. Revs.* 44, 373 (1964).
46. Everett, J. W., *in* "The Pituitary" (G. W. Harris and B. T. Donovan, eds.), Vol. II, p. 166. Univ. California Press, Berkeley, California, 1966.
47. Everett, J. W., and Quinn, D. L., *Endocrinology* 78, 141 (1966).
48. Fee, A. R., and Barkes, A. S., *J. Physiol.* (*London*) 70, 385 (1930).
49. Fevold, H. L., *Endocrinology* 28, 33 (1941).
50. Fitzpatrick, R. J., *in* "The Pituitary" (G. W. Harris and B. T. Donovan, eds.), Vol. III, p. 453. Univ. of California Press, Berkeley, California, 1966.
51. Flerkó, B., *in* "Neuroendocrinology" (L. Martini and W. F. Ganong, eds.), Vol. I, p. 613. Academic Press, New York, 1966.
52. Foa, C., *Arch. Ital. Biol.* 34, 43 (1900).
53. Friedgood, H. B., *in* "Textbook of Endocrinology" (R. H. Williams, ed.), p. 635. Saunders, Philadelphia, Pennsylvania, 1950.
54. Fry, E. G., and Long, C. N. H., *Proc. Intern. Physiol. Congr., 20th Congr., Brussels, 1956*, p. 307.
55. Ganong, W. F., *in* "Reproduction in Domestic Animals" (H. Cole and P. T. Cupps, eds.), Vol. I, p. 185. Academic Press, New York, 1959.
56. Ganong, W. F., *in* "Control of Ovulation" (C. A. Villee, ed.), Discussion of paper by J. Hammond, Jr., p. 163, Pergamon, Oxford, 1961.
57. Ganong, W. F., *in* "Neuroendocrinology" (L. Martini and W. F. Ganong, eds.), Vol. I, p. 1. Academic Press, New York, 1966.
58. Ganong, W. F., "Review of Medical Physiology," 3rd ed. Lange, Los Altos, California, 1967.
59. Ganong, W. F., Shepherd, M. D., Wall, J. R., Van Brunt, E. E., and Clegg, M. T., *Endocrinology* 72, 962 (1963).
60. Gans, E., *Acta Endocrinol.* 32, 362 (1959).
61. Gellert, R. J., and Ganong, W. F., *Acta Endocrinol.* 33, 569 (1960).

62. Gellert, R. J., Bass, E., Jacobs, C., Smith, R., and Ganong, W. F., *Endocrinology* **75**, 861 (1964).
63. Gellhorn, G., *J. Am. Med. Assoc.* **51**, 1839 (1908).
64. Glydon, R. S. J., *J. Anat.* **91**, 237 (1957).
65. Gold, E. M., and Ganong, W. F., *in* "Neuroendocrinology" (L. Martini and W. F. Ganong, eds.), Vol. II, p. 377. Academic Press, New York, 1967.
66. Goldberg, R. C., and Knobil, E., *Endocrinology* **61**, 742 (1957).
67. Goudji, D., and Tixier-Vidal, A., *Compt. Rend. Acad. Sci.* **D263**, 162 (1966).
68. Green, J. D., *Am. J. Anat.* **88**, 225 (1952).
69. Green, J. D., and Harris, G. W., *J. Physiol. (London)* **108**, 359 (1949).
70. Greer, M. A., *Endocrinology* **53**, 380 (1953).
71. Greer, M. A., *Recent Progr. Hormone Res.* **13**, 67 (1957).
72. Grosvenor, C. E., McCann, S. M., and Nallar, R., *Abstr. 46th Meeting, Endocrine Soc., San Francisco, 1964*, p. 96.
73. Halász, B., and Pupp, L., *Endocrinology* **77**, 553 (1965).
74. Harris, G. W., "Neural Control of the Pituitary Gland" Williams & Wilkins, Baltimore, Maryland, 1955.
75. Harris, G. W., *Endocrinology* **75**, 627 (1964).
76. Harris, G. W., and Jacobsohn, D., *Proc. Roy. Soc.* **B139**, 263 (1952).
77. Hayward, J. N., Hilliard, J., and Sawyer, C. H., *Endocrinology* **74**, 108 (1964).
78. Herbert, J., and Zuckerman, S., *Nature* **180**, 547 (1957).
79. Herlyn, U., Geller, H. F., van Berswordt-Wallrabe, I., and van Berswordt-Wallrabe, R., *Acta Endocrinol.* **48**, 220 (1965).
80. Hilliard, J., Hayward, J. N., Croxatto, H. B., and Sawyer, C. H., *Endocrinology* **78**, 151 (1966).
81. Himwich, W. A., *Intern. Rev. Neurobiol.* **4**, 117 (1962).
82. Hohlweg, W., *Klin. Wochschr.* **13**, 92 (1934).
83. Houssay, B. K., Biasotti, A., and Sammartino, R., *Compt. Rend. Soc. Biol.* **120**, 725 (1935).
84. Jacobson, D., *in* "The Pituitary" (G. W. Harris and B. T. Donovan, eds.), Vol. II, p. 1. Univ. of California Press, Berkeley, California, 1966.
85. Johnson, D. C., *Proc. Soc. Exptl. Biol. Med.* **117**, 160 (1964).
86. Jolly, H., "Sexual Precocity." Thomas, Springfield, Illinois, 1955.
87. Kajihara, A., and Kendall, J. W., *Abstr. 49th Meeting, Endocrine Soc., Bal Harbour, 1969*, p. 90.
88. Kanematsu, S., and Sawyer, C. H., *Endocrinology* **72**, 243 (1963).
89. Kanematsu, S., and Sawyer, C. H., *Endocrinology* **73**, 687 (1963).
90. Kanematsu, S., and Sawyer, C. H., *Endocrinology* **76**, 691 (1965).
91. Kincl, F. A., *Recent Progr. Hormone Res.* **22**, 503 (1966).
92. Kitay, J. I., and Altschule, M. D., "The Pineal Gland." Harvard Univ. Press, Cambridge, Massachusetts, 1954.
93. Koikegami, H., Yamada, T., and Usei, K., *Folia Psychiat. Neurol. Japon.* **8**, 71 (1954).
93a. Kragt, C. L., Dahlgren, J., and Ganong, W. F., *Excerpta Med. Intern. Congr. Ser.* **157**, 138 (1968).
94. Kragt, C. L., and Ganong, W. F., *Endocrinology* **82**, 1241 (1968).
94a. Kragt, C. L., and Ganong, W. F., *Proc. Soc. Exptl. Biol. Med.* **128**, 965 (1968).

95. Kragt, C. L., and Meites, J., *Endocrinology* **76**, 1169 (1965).
96. Kragt, C. L., and Meites, J., *Endocrinology* **80**, 1170 (1967).
97. Kuntz, A., "The Autonomic Nervous System" Lea & Febiger, Philadelphia, Pennsylvania, 1953.
98. Lehrman, D. S., *Sci. Am.* **211**, 48 (1964).
99. Lisk, R. D., *J. Exptl. Zool.* **145**, 197 (1960).
100. Lisk, R. D., *Federation Proc.* **26**, 533 (1967).
101. Lisk, R. D., *in* "Neuroendocrinology" (L. Martini and W. F. Ganong, eds.), Vol. II, p. 197. Academic Press, New York, 1967.
102. Matsuyama, E., Weisz, J., and Lloyd, C. W., *Endocrinology* **79**, 261 (1966).
103. McCann, S. M., *Am. J. Physiol.* **202**, 395 (1962).
104. McCann, S. M., and Dhariwal, A. P. S., *in* "Neuroendocrinology" (L. Martini and W. F. Ganong, eds.), Vol. I, p. 261. Academic Press, New York, 1966.
105. McClintock, J. A., and Schwartz, N. B., *Federation Proc.* **26**, 366 (1967).
106. Medway, L., *J. Endocrinol.* **23**, 9 (1961).
107. Meier, A. H., and Farner, D. S., *Gen. Comp. Endocrinol.* **4**, 584 (1964).
108. Meites, J., *in* "Neuroendocrinology" (L. Martini and W. F. Ganong, eds.), Vol. I, p. 669. Academic Press, New York, 1966.
109. Meites, J., and Nicoll, C. S., *Ann. Rev. Physiol.* **28**, 57 (1966).
110. Meites, J., Nicoll, C. S., and Talwalker, P. K., *Proc. Soc. Exptl. Biol. Med.* **101**, 563 (1959).
111. Meites, J., Nicoll, C. S., and Talwalker, P. K., *in* "Advances in Neuroendocrinology" (A. V. Nalbandov, ed.), p. 238. Univ. of Illinois Press, Urbana, Illinois, 1963.
112. Midgley, A. R., *Abstr. 49th Meeting, Endocrine Soc., Bal Harbour, 1967,* p. 60.
113. Minaguchi, H., and Meites, J., *Abstr. 48th Meeting, Endocrine Soc., Chicago, 1966,* p. 34.
114. Mittler, J. C., and Meites, J., *Endocrinology* **78**, 500 (1966).
115. Moszkowska, A., *Ann. Endocrinol.* (*Paris*) **24**, 215 (1963).
116. Negro-Vilar, A., and Meites, J., *Abstr. 49th Meeting, Endocrine Soc., Bal Harbour, 1967,* p. 88.
117. Nicoll, C. S., *J. Exptl. Zool.* **158**, 203 (1965).
118. Nikitovitch-Winer, M. B., and Everett, J. W., *Endocrinology* **63**, 916 (1958).
119. Odell, W. D., Ross, G. T., and Rayford, P. L., *J. Clin. Invest.* **46**, 248 (1967).
120. Oppenheimer, J. H., *in* "Neuroendocrinology" (L. Martini and W. F. Ganong, eds.), Vol. II, p. 665. Academic Press, New York, 1967.
121. O'Steen, W. K., *Endocrinology* **77**, 937 (1966).
122. Pfeiffer, C. A., *Am. J. Anat.* **58**, 195 (1936).
123. Phoenix, C. H., Goy, R. W., and Young, W. C., *in* "Neuroendocrinology" (L. Martini and W. F. Ganong, eds.), Vol. II, p. 163. Academic Press, New York, 1967.
124. Piacsek, B. E., and Meites, J., *Endocrinology* **79**, 432 (1966).
125. Quinn, D. L., and Zarrow, M., *Endocrinology* **74**, 309 (1964).
126. Ramirez, V. D., and Sawyer, C. H., *Endocrinology* **76**, 1158 (1965).
127. Ramirez, V. D., and Sawyer, C. H., *Endocrinology* **78**, 958 (1966).
128. Reece, R. P., and Turner, C. W., *Proc. Soc. Exptl. Biol. Med.* **35**, 367 (1936).
129. Rowland, V., *in* "Neuroendocrinology" (L. Martini and W. F. Ganong, eds.), Vol. I, p. 107. Academic Press, New York, 1966.

130. Santolucito, J. A., Clegg, M. T., and Cole, H. H., *Endocrinology* **66**, 273 (1960).
131. Sawyer, C. H., *J. Exptl. Zool.* **142**, 227 (1959).
132. Sawyer, C. H., *in* "Advances in Neuroendocrinology" (A. V. Nalbandov, ed.), p. 444. Univ. of Illinois Press, Urbana, Illinois, 1963.
133. Schiavi, R. C., *Am. J. Physiol.* **206**, 805 (1964).
134. Selye, H., and McKeown, H., *Surg. Gynecol. Obst.* **59**, 886 (1934).
135. Semans, J. H., and Langworthy, O. R., *J. Urol.* **40**, 836 (1938).
136. Shealy, C. N., and Peele, T. L., *J. Neurophysiol.* **20**, 125 (1957).
137. Smith, E. R., and Davidson, J. M., *Endocrinology* **80**, 725 (1967).
138. Smith, E. R., and Davidson, J. M., *Federation Proc.* **26**, 366 (1967).
139. Sulman, F. G., and Winnik, H. Z., Lancet **i**, 161 (1956).
140. Szentagothai, J., Flerko, B., Mess, B., and Halasz, B., "Hypothalmic Control of the Anterior Pituitary." Publ. House Hung. Acad. Sci., Budapest, 1962.
141. Takewaki, K., *Experientia* **18**, 1 (1962).
142. Taleisnik, S., and McCann, S. M., *Endocrinology* **68**, 263 (1961).
143. Van Dyke, D. C., Simpson, M. E., Lepkovsky, S., Koneff, A. A., and Brobeck J. B., *Proc. Soc. Exptl. Biol. Med.* **95**, 1 (1957).
144. Van Wyk, J. J., *in* "Textbook of Endocrinology" (R. H. Williams, ed.), p. 515. Saunders, Philadelphia, Pennsylvania, 1962.
145. Walsh, E. L., Cuyler, W. F., and McCullagh, D. R., *Am. J. Physiol.* **107**, 508, (1934).
146. Watanabe, S., and McCann, S. M., *Federation Proc.* **26**, 365 (1967).
147. Weinberger, L. M., and Grant, F. C., *Arch. Internal Med.* **67**, 762 (1941).

8 OOGENESIS AND FOLLICULOGENESIS

P. MAULEON

I. General Characteristics of Female Gametogenesis

The whole cycle of gametogenesis in the mammalian female ends in ovulation, that is, in the liberation of the oocyte from the ovary; similarly, spermatogenesis terminates in the release of spermatozoa into the lumen of the seminiferous tubules. The oocyte is shed after extrusion of the first polar body—when the first maturation division is complete—while the male gamete is released after undergoing second maturation division and a series of changes in its cellular structure. Above all, female gametogenesis is not a continuous process like spermatogenesis; the oocyte pauses during meiotic prophase at the diplotene stage and only resumes development after transformations that characterize the female gamete—increase in size and

187

buildup of reserves. However, it does go through all the classical phases of gametogenesis: multiplication of germinal cells, preparation for haploidization: heterotypic prophase, gamete differentiation, and, finally, meiosis.

In terms of ovarian morphology, these processes are oogonial multiplication, formation of oocytes and primordial follicles, folliculogenesis and growth of the oocyte, maturation of the oocyte, and ovulation.

Oogenesis is a process which includes all these stages; the term "oogenetic period" is applied to the formation of the oocyte at the diplotene stage. The period that follows is particularly important for the follicle, and this period is called "folliculogenesis." The basic questions that arise concerning the formation of female gametes are:

Where do the gonocytes, which multiply soon after sexual differentiation of the gonad into the ovary, come from?

When are the oocytes contained in the primordial follicles formed?

How do the variations in number of primordial follicles, found in the ovaries of animals of the same species at different ages, arise?

Are the differences in oocyte production to be attributed to the duration of oogenesis or to the efficiency of oogonial mitoses?

Is the growth of the oocyte continuous during folliculogenesis? What is its duration, and how is it related to cyclic ovarian phenomena?

II. Formation of Primordial Follicles: Oogenesis

A. ORIGIN OF PRIMORDIAL GONOCYTES

1. Experimental Evidence for an Extragonadal Origin of the Primordial Germ Cells

Very early in embryonal development, cells termed "primordial germ cells," generally large in size, are identified in the region of the posterior extraembryonal entoblast. The stages in migration of these cells toward the genital ridges have been described (57, 176, 189); a particularly critical and detailed study was made by Wistchi (200) in man. These cells become primordial gonocytes in the differentiated gonad of both sexes, and experimental proof of this has been given by Everett (53) and Mintz (129–133) in the mouse.

Transplantation of the embryonic genital ridges under the renal capsule of an adult, before this epithelium is populated by migratory cells, does not lead to the formation of any germinal elements; this formation is produced only if the graft is performed when migration is already complete (53). Moreover, in mouse embryos homozygous for mutant alleles at locus W, the number of primordial germ cells is normal at the eighth day of gestation, but becomes smaller or nil by the tenth day (134). With such genotypes, the mice have few or no oocytes in their ovaries at birth (129, 135). No experimental evidence has yet come to light, however, which would suggest that the germinal epithelium can at any time form any of the cells capable of differentiating into primordial gonocytes.

2. Characteristics of the Primordial Germ Cells

The primordial germ cells of mammals possess histological characteristics which make them easily recognizable in certain species, particularly in man. The nucleus of these cells is large and weakly staining (200), but their cytoplasm has not the high concentration of vitellus which facilitates their identification in other vertebrates.

Fortunately, these primordial germ cells have a high alkaline phosphatase activity in man (111), in the mouse (33), in the rat (138), and in cattle (98). This cytoplasmic activity is asymmetrically distributed (98).

In the differentiated mouse gonad, this stainability by azo dyes after enzymic reaction is retained in the oogonia before meiosis (131). However, these are not the only embryonal cells (150) to possess alkaline phosphatase activity, and so this cannot be taken as an absolute criterion. Thus, Jost and Prepin (98) note that in the bovine embryo, between the 26th and 34th day of gestation, the number of cells showing positive alkaline phosphatase reaction increases considerably in the liver; the cells concerned are doubtless hemopoietic elements.

3. Migratory Pathways

It is generally accepted that in mammals these germinal cells migrate across the dorsal mesentery (200) as far as the primitive gonads, while in chick embryo these cells are mainly transported by the blood from the germinal crescent (181). In the younger bovine fetus, it is quite probable that a small number of germinal cells will pass into the aorta and circulatory apparatus (98).

4. Primordial Germ Cells of Domestic Mammals

The investigation of Jost and Prepin (98) recently conducted on cows confirms the usefulness of the alkaline phosphatase technique for following these cells. Their early migration has previously been described only very briefly (187).

At the 25th day of gestation, some cells with positive alkaline phosphatase reaction are already present in the future so-called germinal epithelium, in the dorsal mesentery and in the entoblast. Then in later stages, population of the presumptive gonadal region and dorsal mesentery by such cells increases. At 34 days, the number of extragonadal germ cells has greatly diminished.

B. Sex Differentiation of the Gonads and Genital Tract

1. Morphological Differentiation of the Gonads

It is generally accepted that two proliferations of the superficial epithelium of the undifferentiated gonad invade the underlying mesenchyme.

If the embryo is genetically male, the initial proliferation of the epithelium provides the sexual cords which differentiate into seminiferous tubules, and there is no further proliferation. In the female, the first proliferation provides the sex cords which will form the ovarian medulla. The second proliferation gives rise to the ovarian cortex, separated from the medulla by a layer of connective tissue. In the male, this layer is superficial and allows early morphological recognition of gonadal sex.

Before these structural modifications appear, the localization of germinal cells—peripheral in females, central in males (132)—permits differentiation of the future ovary from the future testis.

2. Factors Determining Sexual Differentiation of the Gonads

The idea most widely held is that of an antagonism between specific inductor substances, medullarine and cortexine (201), but the nature of these inducers is, in fact, unknown. When fetal testes and ovaries of the same age are grafted under the renal capsule of a castrated mouse, the fetal testis masculinizes the adjoining ovary, bringing about the formation of tubules and spermatocytes in the ovarian medulla (188). Conversely, if sexually indifferent gonads are grafted in close proximity to fetal ovaries of rats, the result is suppression of the testis rather than cortical differentiation (110).

With in vitro culture, the differentiation of just the ovary is slightly retarded by the presence of a testis. Structures suggestive of testicular cords develop in the medullary parts (78). These results are comparable to those obtained in birds, but are much less clear. In these animals, as in amphibia and reptiles, the inversion of ovarian germinal cells is itself a classic feature. Burns' (31) experiment in the opossum constitutes the only case of production of an ovotestis after estrogen injection.

3. Chronology and Factors Determining Sexual Differentiation of the Genital Tract

The differentiation of the genital tract (Table I) follows chronologically upon that of the gonad. The testis imposes male characteristics on the genital tract, developing the wolffian ducts and masculinizing the urogenital sinus and the external genitalia. The müllerian ducts regress either before or after this masculinization (96) and are also conditioned by the testis (93–95). The fetal testes thus produce two types of substance, one stimulatory and the other inhibitory.

Steroid 3-β-ol-dehydrogenase activity has been detected in the embryonic gonad (7, 140, 165). The embryonic testis is capable of converting such precursors as pregnenolone, progesterone, or sodium acetate into androgens, both in vitro and in vivo (192). The androgens induce a masculinizing effect, but cannot bring about the regression of the müllerian ducts (93–95). This is confirmed by the use of cyproteron acetate, an "antiandrogenic" substance which eliminates or reduces the masculinizing effects of the fetal

TABLE I
SEXUAL DIFFERENTIATION OF THE CALF FETUS[a]

Days	Males	Females
39–40	First sex differences in gonads	First sex differences in gonads
45	Testicular interstitial cells	Germinal epithelium thickening
	Low germinal epithelium	
40–48	Growing müllerian ducts	Growing müllerian ducts
45–47	First flexure of penile urethra	
49–52	Anogenital distance definitely increased	
52–56	Müllerian ducts: reduced diameter	
56	Prostatic buds and seminal vesicles appear	
58–60	Müllerian ducts: anterior part disappears; scrotum develops	
60	Penis opens under the umbilicus Balanopreputial fold in organization	
63	Müllerian ducts ± absent	Uterus increases in diameter
	Formation of epididymis	Retrogression of wolffian ducts begins

[a] From Jost (*96*).

testis, but does not interfere with its inhibitory effect on the müllerian ducts (*44, 96*).

4. Freemartinism in Cattle

In freemartin cattle the müllerian ducts are inhibited and the ovaries become sterile. Androgens injected into the mother masculinize only the external genitalia before the 49th day, but do not influence the regression of the müllerian ducts which, in males, occurs several days later (*95–97*).

Ovarian inhibition probably occurs between the 49th and 60th day, in other words, the ovaries of freemartins are not abnormal at the onset, and this inhibition takes place more or less simultaneously with regression of the müllerian ducts. During multiple gestations, the definitive anomalies of the freemartin appear only at 60 days (*96, 169, 170*). Jost considers that steroids cannot be involved in the inhibition of the müllerian ducts and of the ovarian cortex.

The fetal testis could act by secreting a substance whose nature is as yet unknown, acting on the female through vascular anastomoses between the chorions of the twins (*105*). There is, however, another possible explanation for freemartinism. Celllular exchanges by way of the bloodstream, particularly of primordial germ cells (*98*) have been confirmed by study of the freemartin karyotype and its twin brother, showing the genetic mosaic xx-xy (*145, 147*). The hypothesis that freemartinism is produced by this mosaicism rather than by hormonal influences must, therefore, be given consideration. The primordial germ cells would not only have a genetically determined potential but would also play an important role in gonad differentiation.

C. COURSE OF OOGENESIS

1. Oogonial Mitotic Divisions

In the male, a germinal cell becomes a primordial gonocyte when the gonad is differentiated. In the female, the primordial germinal cell becomes an oogonium when the gonad differentiates into an ovary; but does this cell possess the particular characteristics which distinguish it from the male gonocyte?

a. Periods of Multiplication of Germinal Cells. During their migration, the primordial germ cells divide mitotically (*33, 34, 98, 131, 200*). In the mouse, the germinal cells enter meiotic prophase (*23*) a little after the end of migration of the primordial germ cells, around the 12th day of embryonal life. By the 14th day, 40% of the cells are oogonia, and only 7% by the 15th day (*155*). In the rat and rabbit, mitosis of these cells continues after sexual differentiation until the appearance of meiotic prophase (*13, 34*). They then decrease rapidly. But in the guinea pig, ewe, cow, sow, monkey, and in woman, these divisions are numerous even after the appearance of meiotic prophase and persist for a long time after the appearance of the first primordial follicles (*8, 9, 49, 87, 120*) (see Fig. 3).

b. Morphological Types of Oogonia (Fig. 1). In addition to the stages of meiotic prophase, Winiwarter (*196*) distinguished three nuclear types in the rabbit ovary: protobrochal a, protobrochal b, and deutobrochal nuclei. After a study of the cat ovary, a new type was added, termed "dusty" nucleus by analogy with the "dusty" spermatogonia described by Regaud (*173*). According to Winiwarter, only the "protobrochal" types correspond to oogonia: the "deutobrochal" types are probably nuclei carrying out the last premeiotic synthesis of DNA, corresponding to the stage commonly called "preleptotene." Winiwarter's conclusions were complicated by the role which he attributed to the germinal epithelium; he described somatic cell nuclei under the heading of protobrochal a, and confused the supporting cells (destined to become follicular cells) with oogonia, classing both types of nuclei as "protobrochal b." The "dusty" nuclei also correspond to oogonia, although this nuclear differentiation obliged him to class them by definition as oocytes.

This extreme confusion has never been completely clarified, nor has the terminology ever been classically adopted. Only Van Beek (*14*) used it for oogonia of the bovine fetus.

c. Scheme of Oogonial Division. The use of the mitotic blocking agent colchicine (*119*), busulfan, which destroys cells at the time of division (*56, 75*), or tritiated thymidine, labeling nucleus during premitotic synthesis of DNA, has led to several hypotheses.

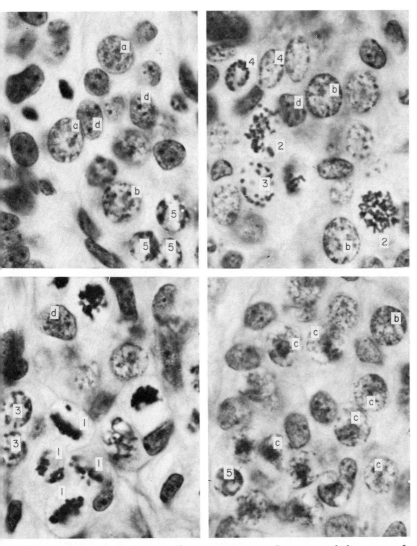

FIG. 1. Morphological types of oogonia in several sections of the ovary of the fetal ewe, 60 days' old. Several nuclear types (a, b, c) can be distinguished: type c with fine threads of chromatin, type a not very different from nuclei in somatic cells (d). Some synchronized mitotic divisions with chromosomes on metaphase spindle (*1*) or in metaphasic plate (*2*) and also mitotic prophase in oogonia (*3*) or in somatic cells (*4*) are near resting nuclei and cells in pycnosis (*5*).

In the rat, between days 12.5 and 16.5 of embryonic life, the same oogonium undergoes three divisions (122). The synchronization of oogonial multiplication is not perfect, for at any given instant—for example, at the instant of injection of tritiated thymidine—not all the oogonia are synthesizing DNA. Furthermore, those that are in the synthetic phase do not all belong to the same cell division cycle (99, 122). This entails a gradual appearance of meiotic prophase figures (23, 155, 196). Groups of germ cells undergoing a number of synchronized phenomena can be termed "waves."

The oogonoia do not disappear when the waves of meiotic prophase appear; on the contrary, in the ewe the number of oogonial mitoses increases (119) and the number of oogonia also increase in the guinea pig, in woman, and in the monkey (8, 9, 87). Even in the rat, oogonial divisions leading to oocyte formation still continue after the appearance of meiotic prophase figures. These later waves consist of oogonia that undergo a large number of divisions, since they give rise to oocytes lightly labeled after injection of tritiated thymidine on day 16.5 of embryonal life (122).

A knowledge of the scheme of oogonial divisions is necessary for an understanding of the possible interstrain and interspecies variations in the production of female gametes. Any interstrain difference in the length of ovogenetic period (90) cannot explain this high variability.

2. Meiotic Prophase

Winiwarter (196) makes reference to Van Beneden's work on oogenesis in *Ascaris*, and gives a precise definition of the whole series of nuclear modifications of the meiotic prophase; he created a terminology for the different stages which is still used today: leptotene, zygotene, pachytene, diplotene. These stages differ very little from one species to another (Fig. 2).

a. Variations in Chromosomal Configuration at the Dictyate Stage and Radiosensitivity. The oocytes are arrested at the same stage of meiotic prophase, termed "dictyate," but the chromosomal configuration of this stage of arrest varies between species.

It could permit the identification of ovaries of many species (human, mouse, guinea pig, goat, dog) (142). In cattle, this arrested stage of oogenesis might be the pachytene stage (76, 168). However, this stage very much resembles the so-called contracted stage observed in the guinea pig, and might, as in the guinea pig, be a modified diplotene stage (87). It is more frequent than the stage in which the chromosomes are distributed over the whole nuclear area, corresponding to the diplotene stage (167). This is the best explanation for the higher radioresistance of the oocyte of the primordial follicle in cattle (48), since the pachytene stage of meiotic prophase is the most sensitive stage to X-rays (11, 12, 114, 153, 154).

The differences between species in the radiosensitivity of primordial oocytes arise out of these variations in chromosomal configuration at the dictyate stage (9, 114, 142). It has been shown that oocytes with lampbrush chromosomal filaments are particularly radioresistant. This lampbrush struc-

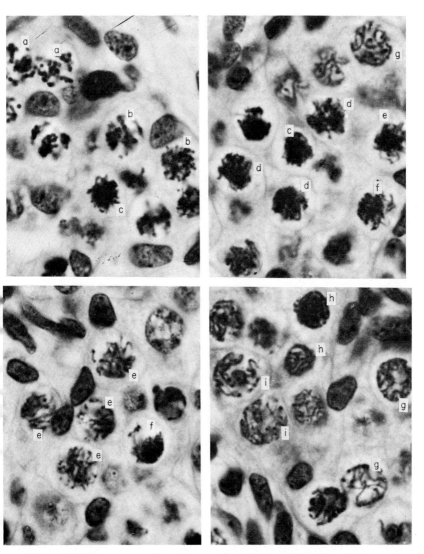

FIG. 2. Different stages of meiotic prophase in several sections of the ovary of the fetal ewe, (60 days' old): preleptotene stage with chromatin grains (a); fine threads joining these grains in an intermediate stage (b) with leptotene figure (c); different forms of zygotene stage (d, e) and particularly "bouquet" arrangement of chromosomes (f); pachytene stage (g) with degenerative forms (h); beginning of diplotene stage with large nuclei (i).

ture is found in the oocytes of human primordial follicles (10) and of the follicle at the start of its growth in the rat (9). In the same way, the "contracted" structure of the guinea pig oocyte corresponds to a higher radioresistance than the classic diplotene stage of the mouse oocyte (142).

b. Factors Determining the Arrest of Meiotic Prophase. The arrest of meiotic prophase after the diplotene stage is due to a nonhomologous association of bivalent chromosomes during oogenesis (144, mouse; 146, cattle). It is frequently observed in the oocytes, and only occasionally during prophase of somatic cells or during the pachytene stage of spermatogenesis. According to Ohno, it is the persistence of this association at the diplotene stage that leads the oocytes to the dictyate stage instead of their undergoing diakinesis and degenerating.

c. Duration of Meiotic Prophase. The precise duration of the stages of meiotic prophase in the female mouse has been established using radiotracers: the diplotene stage lasts 8 hours, the zygotene stage 40 hours, and the pachytene stage at least 60 hours (36), which is much shorter than in the male (155). Furthermore, a comparison of time intervals between the appearance of the first oocytes at leptotene stage, and that of the first oocytes at diplotene stage, shows that in females there are two large groups of species: rat and mouse, where the interval is around 4 to 5 days, and other species, where it is from 12 to 15 days (119).

3. Phenomena of Degeneration during Oogenesis

Intense degeneration phenomena in the germ cells have been observed in all species, and particularly in the cow, cat, and ewe (119, 198). These degenerations can effect oogonial mitoses and oocytes at the pachytene or diplotene stage (8, 13). They begin with the commencement of meiotic prophase and continue until the end of oogenesis, except in the rat. During oogenesis, in the midst of the isogenic groups, the cells that are retarded degenerate (13), but after oogenesis, degeneration of the earliest oocytes formed, i.e., those lying deepest in the cortical zone, takes place (99).

Very little is known about this phenomenon, which plays such an important part in determining the number of oocytes remaining after oogenesis; many authors have, in fact, been struck by its importance and have even wondered about the possibility of there being a different mode of formation of female gametes (199).

4. Arrest or Persistence of Oogenesis in the Adult

The essential fact is that, in most mammals, the oogonia and oocytes in the first stages of meiotic prophase disappear either during embryonal life or a little after birth (Fig. 3). There remain only oocytes at the diplotene or dictyate stages, isolated from each other by a layer of follicular cells, or sometimes grouped in nests, particularly in young pigs, lambs, and heifers.

Isolated figures of the beginning of meiotic prophase have sometimes been found in adults. However, in the guinea pig (4–6, 207) the nuclei of

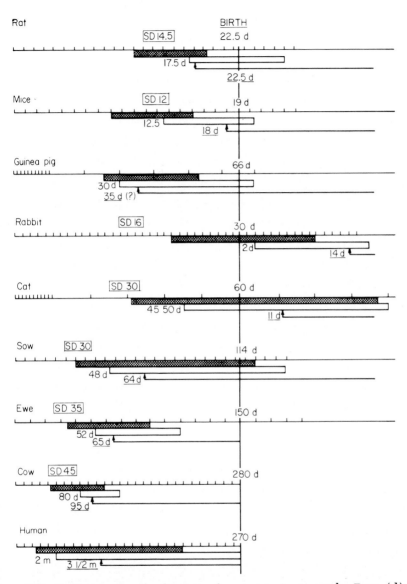

FIG. 3. Comparative development of oogenesis in mammals. Days (d);
months (m); sexual differentiation (sd). The first number gives the age of the
first heterotypic prophase stages, the second, underlined number corresponds to
the age of the first diplotene stages. The dotted strip represents the period of
oogonial mitoses and the clear strip shows the period when first meiotic prophase figures are present. The arrow points out the beginning of degenerative
phenomena. See reference (122).

oocytes described as being at the leptotene or zygotene stage are in reality in an early diplotene stage. But it is difficult, even if these rare findings (45, 197) do represent a true picture of heterotypic prophase, to regard them as proof of the formation of new oocytes in the adult; oogenesis is a process which involves oogonial divisions, a whole series of nuclear changes, and a progressive development of germinal cells which are no longer found, except in the ovaries of various lemurs or prosimian adults (58–60, 77, 88, 159, 160, 171).

Nevertheless, many authors believe that meiotic prophase plays no part in the formation of female gametes, and attribute an essential role to the germinal epithelium. They also have arguments for neoformation of oocytes, from the germinal epithelium after the arrest of classic oogenetic phenomena (2, 26, 30, 43, 50, 71, 72, 118, 191). Others rely on counts taken on samples of doubtful validity (50); still others calculate the rate or the time of destruction of oocytes in the adult ovary (29, 190) and deduce from this that there must be new oogenesis in order to explain their farfetched statistics.

In fact, the phenomena observed in the germinal epithelium are not connected with the neoformation of oocytes. Zuckerman (206, 207) has given many arguments for this point of view. However, in order to prove that the oocytes formed during the embryonic oogenetic period are the same as the oocytes ovulating in the adult ovary, it was necessary to label them. After intraperitoneal injections of tritiated thymidine to pregnant mice (13 or 14 days' gestation), a large number of labeled oocytes were found in the ovaries removed from the young mice, 12 days after birth (177, 178). The results just presented have been confirmed (106). After injecting tritiated thymidine into rabbits a little after birth, labeled ova were recovered from the fallopian tubes (99).

If the injection is given at a suitable time during the oogenetic period, then more than 90% of oocytes (Fig. 4) present in the adult ovary can be labeled (24, 99, 122); furthermore, oocyte nuclei cannot be labeled out of the period of oogonial mitoses (24, 36, 99, 122, 158, 183), especially in adult animals. It is therefore possible to affirm that the primordial follicles formed during the oogenetic period are "held in reserve" in the ovary, and that their number does not increase further, as there is no neoformation.

When figures of the beginning of meiotic prophase persist, as in lemurs mitotic divisions in oogonia also persist. If tritiated thymidine is injected into adults of these mammals, the oogonia in mitosis 24 hours later are found to be labeled (88). The new germ cells are not formed by transformation of somatic cells of the germinal epithelium as was thought (58–60, 171). In these mammalian species, oogenetic arrest is only retarded.

D. DEPENDENCE OF OOGENESIS ON HORMONAL FACTORS

Oogenesis can continue if the ovary is cultured in vitro (117, 179). Nevertheless, it cannot be concluded that oogenesis is independent of hormones since, in most cases, the ovaries cultivated *in vitro* were removed either at the time of, or very shortly before, the appearance of the pachytene stage, and no quantitative studies were made. The oogenetic processes *in vitro* seem to be slower; many oocytes at the zygotene stage remain at this stage for 6 or more days in culture (*117*).

In a 12-day-old mouse fetus, hypophysectomy by irradiation leads to the halving of the number of germ cells present in a median ovarian section

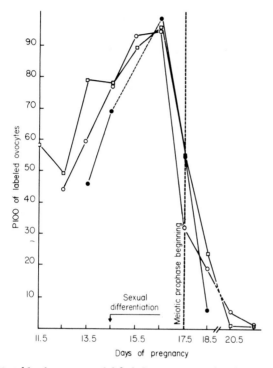

FIG. 4. Variable frequency of labeled oocytes on the day of tritiated thymidine injection in the fetus of the rat. Results are similar with different rat strains (as shown by the three different curves). Maximal percentage occurs just before the onset of meiotic prophase and decreases quickly. From Mauleon (*122*).

when examined at 18 days (*172*). In ewe embryos, the follicular stimulating hormone (FSH) and luteinizing hormone (LH) activities are biologically measurable at the time when these oogenetic phenomena are in progress, although this should not be regarded as proof that pituitary hormones have any effect on oogenesis. The level of hypophyseal FSH in the female fetus is much higher than that in the male fetus (*127*). The factors controlling oogenesis are present in the oocyte, and probably developed in the fetus from these eggs, as is shown by ovarian transplant (*92*). Differences in hypophyseal function (124) could determine the typical stock of oocytes in a strain.

III. Formation of Preovulatory Follicles: Folliculogenesis

A. RELATIONS BETWEEN OOCYTE AND FOLLICLE

1. Relationship between the Size of the Oocyte and of the Follicle

The growth of the oocyte can be divided into two phases, relative to that of the follicle (25). The first is the phase in which the oocyte grows to approach its maximum size. Simultaneously, the multiplication of follicular cells occurs. During the second phase, the oocyte increases very slowly in size, but the follicle grows rapidly in volume, mainly by development of the antrum, which collects the secretions from follicular cells that have become granulosa cells (69). This secretion commences at the beginning of follicular growth, during the first phase (70).

After hypophysectomy, the oocyte reaches its adult size in follicles persisting for 9 days, although these follicles are smaller than in the normal animal. This diminution is the result, first, of the disappearance of secretory function, and, second, of a lowering of the level of follicular cell multiplication.

2. Metabolism of the Oocyte during Growth and Maturation

The increase in size of the oocyte corresponds to an intense metabolic activity of the cell, but it exists only during the first phase of follicular growth. The level of RNA in the oocyte is low during this whole phase (37, 38, 74). It can be supposed that the follicular cells, which are rich in RNA, carry the brunt of protein synthesis, and these proteins are subsequently transferred into the oocyte. It is also probable that the rate of RNA turnover is high, so that active synthesis of proteins can take place during this phase; the incorporation of tritiated uridine is highest in the growing oocyte (141). The course of tritiated uridine incorporation follows that generally observed in other cells: successive labeling of the nucleolus, the nucleus, and then the cytoplasm. Fluorescence microscopical study of the nucleolus indicates a very high level of nucleolar RNA during this phase of oocyte growth; this level diminishes considerably at the time of oocyte atresia or before maturation (73).

In the preovulatory follicle, the nucleolus vacuolizes (113) and loses its affinity for both acid and basic stains, while the nucleolar envelope remains stainable (55). This shell gives the green fluorescence of DNA with acridine orange (73). The existence of an active synthesis of proteins does not exclude the possibility of macromolecular transfer during this phase of oocyte growth (61).

Exchanges between oocytes and perioocyte cells have not been clearly defined for the second phase of growth. However, the incorporation of ^{35}S-methionine (107, 136) and of ^{3}H-phenylalanine (175) by rabbit oocytes a little before meiosis is proof that such exchanges do take phase. This place of follicular growth is characterized by the secretion of follicular fluid, particularly of mucopolysaccharides by the granulosa cells, as shown by the sequence of ^{35}S-sulfate incorporation by the follicles (143). The rapid preovulatory growth is characterized by modification of the permeability of the follicular blood-fluid barrier (202, 203). Finally, RNA and protein synthesis by the follicle involve the release and action of proteolytic enzyme formed during the few hours after coitus in the rabbit (162–164). This enzyme could be responsible for a weakening of the follicle wall (47), which, in combination with the constant pressure inside the follicle (18, 46), would eventually result in rupture.

B. DEVELOPMENT OF DIFFERENT FOLLICULAR TYPES

1. Definition of Follicular Types

a. Morphological Criteria. Following Pincus and Enzmann (161), follicles have been classified according to histological criteria: thickness of the theca and granulosa, organization of the latter around the oocyte, degree of vascularity, quantity of muscle fibers and interstitial tissue, and position of the antral cavities. Today the classification most widely used is that of Mandl and Zuckerman (117): follicles with one layer of flattened cells, one layer of cuboid cells, two, three, or four layers of cells, and follicles with or without antra.

b. Dimensional Criteria. Follicles with an antrum can be differentiated by measuring their diameter and calculating their volume (19, 20, 41, 167). But it is also possible to measure effectively either the largest surface in section of the follicle at the site of the oocyte nucleus, or to calculate the volume from measurements of the surface in section at regular intervals; this procedure is used when the oocyte is no longer centrally situated in the follicle.

The utilization of this dimensional criterion gives a frequency curve whose shape, at least in immature animals, rats, and lambs, is constant. With reference to the shape of the frequency curve, it is possible to make a comparison between relative growth rates.

The phases of rapid growth correspond to classes with very low incidence; the phases of slow growth (or follicles held in reserve), however, are represented by the classes with high frequency. If this technique is compared with that of Mandl and Zuckerman (117), it is found that their classification gives a very large fraction constituted by the first phase of follicular growth, while the more important second phase of growth is only represented by a single category.

c. Normal and Atretic Follicles. The involution of a follicle can be defined by a series of morphological changes; these appear either in the granulosa somatic cells, or in the oocyte, and lead ultimately to the disappearance of the follicle. The characteristics of the granulosa cells during atresia of follicles with an antrum or with several cell layers are: pycnosis, replacement by cells with small fusiform nuclei, disruption of relations between granulosa cells, antrum or oocyte; this often coincides with the continuation of meiosis up to the second maturation spindle. But also, the chromosomes often dissolve into globules with weak staining power, dispersed in the cytoplasm, which is often fragmented.

These histological changes are preceded by histoenzymological changes. In the granulosa, the dissociation of cells bordering the antral cavity is accompanied (i) in the rat by the appearance of acid phosphatase and aminopeptidase activity (109); organophosphate resistant esterases (27, 28), enzymes probably connected with lysosomes; (ii) in the guinea pig by nucleoside polyphosphatase activity (both ADPase and ATPase) (1); or (iii) more generally by sudanophil lipids, or lipids stainable with red oils (39, 40, 68, 70). The increase in alkaline phosphatase activity in atretic follicles of the cow ovary (137) has not been confirmed in the rat.

2. Numerical Variations in Follicular Types

a. Variations in the Stock of Primordial Follicles. Few valid oocyte counts were carried out before Zuckerman (205), and his school developed a method of ovarian histological analysis. In fact, due to the heterogeneous structure of the ovary, a systematic sampling of the whole organ is necessary.

The number of oocytes is greatest toward the end of the period of their formation: 110–130 days' gestation in cattle (48, 49), 18.5–19.5 days' gestation in the rat (13), 45 days' gestation in the guinea pig (87), fifth to sixth month of pregnancy in women and in the rhesus monkey (9, 10), and 17th day of egg incubation in chicks (79).

The oocyte count falls off rapidly as the animal grows older (3, 21, 22, 86, 100, 184, 206, 207); in the rat, mouse, and in woman, the follicles can even totally disappear from the ovary before the end of life. The fall in the absolute number of follicles is sharpest at first: 50–60% disappear during the first weeks after birth in the rat and mouse (90) or during the first year in guinea pigs (87). The proportion of oocytes lost per unit time is constant (102). However, this decrease in the reserve of primordial follicles is difficult to demonstrate with certainty in the few months after birth in the ewe (125), and in the cow it only becomes apparent after the fourth year (48, 49). At a given age, this reserve appears to vary between individuals of the same species. The ratio of the numerical extremes ranges are 1:2 in the mouse (90) and the rat (126), 1:3 in the ewe (125), and 1:10 in the cow (48, 49, 122).

The ovaries of different strains of mice (90), or of rats selected for their sensitivity to gonadotropic hormones, contain reserves of primordial follicles (126) which differ significantly. Furthermore, within one of these strains of rats, differences between individuals of the maternal progeny suggest that the number of primordial follicles may be dependent on a genetic factor (*126*).

b. Variations in the Number of Follicles with an Antrum. In domestic mammals, the first follicles with an antrum appear 50–60 days after the end of the oogenetic period (*119*), thus, they are found in the fetal ovaries of the cow and the ewe. In the rat, mouse, and rabbit, the time of appearance of these follicles almost coincides with the appearance of ovarian sensitivity to gonadotropic hormones. However, the ovary of the lamb does not

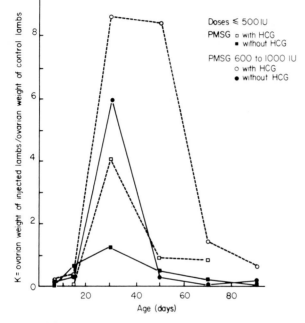

FIG. 5. Variability in ovarian response to pregnant mare serum gonadotropin (PMSG) and human chorionic gonadotropin (HCG) with the age of the ewe; the curve presents a peak at the 30th day and the first weight increase of the ovary is obtained about the 15th day. From Mauleon (unpublished data).

respond to pregnant mare serum gonadotropin (PMSG) and human chorionic gonadotropin (HCG) before the 20th day after birth (Fig. 5) i.e., well after the appearance of the first follicles with an antrum. Their number increases after birth, reaching a maximum at about the 60th day in the cow (*48, 49*) and at about the 18th day in the rat (*103, 156, 157*), i.e., before puberty.

In the adult cow, cyclic variations in the number of Graafian follicles have been demonstrated. There is an accumulation of follicles 5–8 mm in size during the third and fourth days of the cycle, while the formation of atretic follicles leaves only a single normal follicle 9–13 mm in diameter, remaining at the 13th day. This first wave of growth is followed by a second accumulation of follicles, 5–8 mm in size, between the 12th and 14th day of the cycle, with a second wave of atresia leaving a single large follicle of 12–16 mm at the 16th day (167). The follicle due to ovulate thus develops from a population of follicles with an average size of less than 5 mm in diameter. Except in humans (20), the diphasic growth during the cycle has not yet been demonstrated in other species. This growth of the "privileged" follicle is always accompanied by disappearance of the other follicles in the cow, the sow (128), the hamster (62–66), the guinea pig (1, 52, 139), and in the ewe (80).

c. *Numerical Relationship between the Different Categories of Follicle.* In prepubertal rats belonging to three strains and possessing different stock of primordial follicles, the number of follicles constituting the second peak in the analytical curve for the follicular population is related to the number of primordial follicles. The number of these that develop after an injection of FSH depends on the number of follicles in the second peak. Quantitatively speaking, each of the follicular categories that develops does not do so independently of the one acting as its reserve (126).

In the ovaries of prepubertal mice, the number of growing oocytes decreases in parallel with the number of primordial follicles (89) and represents a constant proportion (11%) of the total number of oocytes (156, 157). The same may be true of adults, since after the fourth year in the cow, the growing follicles diminish in the same way as the primordial follicles (48, 49). Similarly, in the rat, the number of follicles larger than 20 μ is related to the number of smaller follicles (3), and in women up to 35 years this relationship exists between follicles smaller than 100 μ and primordial follicles (21). This is important because it indicates that the number of follicles developing is determined by the number of primordial follicles (161).

3. *Duration of Development and Regression of Follicular Types*

The general tendency of the distribution curve of the follicles, as a function of their size, is logarithmic, as has already been noted (54, 148, 149). This could perhaps be explained by an identical degree of atresia for each follicular category. It is also possible that follicular size increases geometrically, and from this derives the idea of representing the frequency as a semilogarithmic curve, revealing polymodality. The appearance of several peaks implies temporary changes in the level of growth (123, 148, 149).

In the female rabbit, a primordial follicle would require 10 days to become a preovulatory follicle (41, 42); this is a shorter interval than that of an ovarian cycle, defined in this species as being the interval of time between two stages of equilibrium of the follicular population, and between which ovulation takes place. Using flash labeling with tritiated thymidine at the time of estrus, Peters and Levy (158) showed that in the mouse the follicles starting to form a large antrum are those that ovulate in the succeeding cycle; those not yet having an antrum, or having one that is still growing, ovulate during the four subsequent cycles. However, the follicles with a single layer of cells, some of which were found to be labeled on the day following injection, have the same intensity of labeling 5 cycles after the injection of tritiated thymidine.

Not enough is known about these basic concepts of the continuity of follicular growth, of variability in the growth rate, and of the duration of each growth phase. Thus, in the ewe, it is supposed that the ovulatory follicle starts to grow between 4 hours and 5 days after the start of the cycle. It then pauses, and ends up with a last phase of rapid growth lasting a few hours, at the beginning of estrus (80). In the cow, the follicle about to ovulate only begins its growth from the 12th day of the cycle (167). All these studies, which were based on the maximum diameter of the follicles present at a given moment, and on the distribution of follicles of different sizes during the cycle, imply that it is always the same follicles that are encountered at different times in the cycle. This, however, has not been demonstrated conclusively.

C. Dependence of the Phases of Follicular Growth on Hormonal Factors

1. Effect of Hypophysectomy

The number of oocytes diminishes during life. After hypophysectomy, a slowing down in the rate of decrease is observed (81, 91), and the largest follicles with an antrum decrease in number, then follicular secretion immediately disappears, whatever the size of the follicles; this clearly demonstrates the dependence of this secretion on gonadotropic hormones (15, 81, 104, 149, 152, 185, 186).

The fate of growing follicles can only be established by a quantitative study (Fig. 6). In the immature rat, 27 days after hypophysectomy, the class of growing follicles has almost totally disappeared (15, 104). At the end of 9 days, the class of growing follicles still persists; it consists of a single, isolated, large oocyte and also of multilayered follicles, but without antral secretion. The persistence of a few follicles where the cells are still multiplying 81 days after hypophysectomy suggests continuing presence of a few LH-secreting cells along the stalk or at the base of the median eminence after hypophysectomy; it could also imply continuance of estrogenic secretion in the ovary (85).

2. Effect of Inhibitors of Hypophyseal Release

In the immature rat, injection for 27 days of fluorogestone acetate (17α-acetoxy-9α-fluoro-11β-hydroxypregn-4-en-3,20-dione) which acts on hypophyseal release via the hypothalamus, causes intense diminution of the growing follicles (follicles of the second peak), while the Graafian follicle population is unaffected (174). The follicle distribution curve, classified according to size, resembles that of an adult rat after ovulation.

3. Effects of Gonadotropic Hormone Injection

By definition, follicular growth is dependent on follicular stimulating
hormone (FSH). Evans *et al.* (*51*) have proposed a technique for FSH
assay, determining the minimum effective dose capable of inducing average-
sized follicles in the ovary of an immature hypophysectomized rat 6–8 days
after operation. Numerous studies have been made using nonpurified or
insufficiently purified pituitary extracts, or nonpituitary hormones (PMSG,
HCG) with both FSH and LH activities. Furthermore, injection of hor-

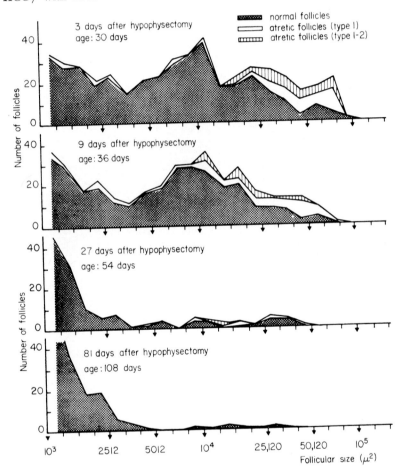

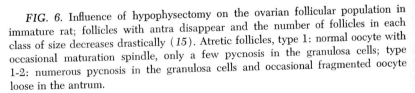

FIG. 6. Influence of hypophysectomy on the ovarian follicular population in
immature rat; follicles with antra disappear and the number of follicles in each
class of size decreases drastically (*15*). Atretic follicles, type 1: normal oocyte with
occasional maturation spindle, only a few pycnosis in the granulosa cells; type
1-2: numerous pycnosis in the granulosa cells and occasional fragmented oocyte
loose in the antrum.

mones into a nonhypophysectomized animal does not give a clear picture of the action of the injected hormone, since it induces an endogenous discharge of pituitary hormones (166, 204). Experiments using purified pituitary hormones in hypophysectomized animals must surely, therefore, yield more precise information concerning the action of these hormones on each phase of follicular growth leading to ovulation.

Preliminary trials have been made using purified FSH and LH (FSH-NIH-S1 and LH-NIH-S9) in immature hypophysectomized rats (Fig. 7). The injection of FSH over a limited 84-hour period will insure the survival of the existing follicular population after hypophysectomy, and even stimulate follicles with an antrum. Under the same conditions of injection, FSH stimulates follicles with an antrum in a rat hypophysectomized 25 days previously, but the sensitivity is only half that seen 10 days after hypophysectomy. There is no restoration of any other follicular categories; luteinizing hormone, under the same conditions of injection, has no action on the various follicular categories (174). Thus, FSH does not act on all stages together. It is possible, however, that the injections were continued for too short a time; the durations of follicular development must be known in order to understand hormonal dependence. It also seems certain that the hormonal balance permitting growth of the different follicular classes is complex, since ovulation in the hypophysectomized rat is facilitated by the simultaneous injection of FSH and LH; a ratio of LH to FSH of 4:1 facilitate follicular growth (32).

4. Effects of Estrogen Injection

The estrogens act on the ovary via the hypothalamohypophyseal complex. They do, in addition, have a direct action which can be demonstrated in the hypophysectomized animal. In an immature or adult rat (83, 84), the ovarian response to the injection of serum gonadotropin (193–195), chorionic gonadotropin (151, 182), or pituitary FSH (182) is increased if follicular regression is attenuated by estrogen treatment on the day of hypophysectomy.

Estrogen hormones not only reduce the intense follicular atresia in an immature rat (83, 84) but also ensure a development of the growing follicles in the hypophysectomized animal (35).

IV. Importance of the Quantitative Production of Female Gametes

The variations in primordial follicular reserve from one individual to another, and the major "wastage" of oocytes observed during life, at least suggest the possibility that gross deficiencies in female gametes can affect the individual's fecundity.

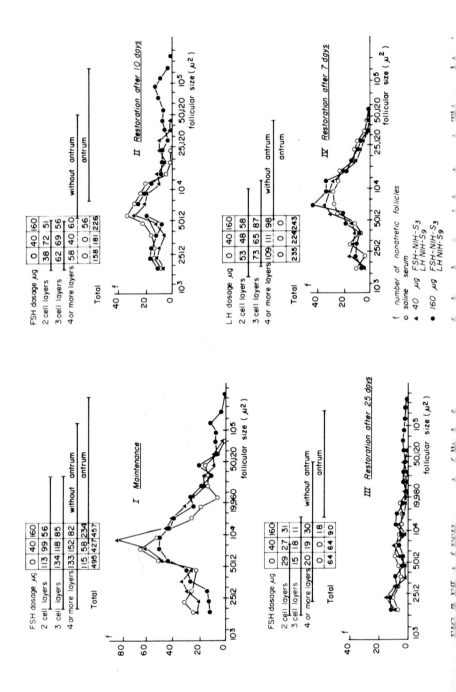

A. Variations in the Stock of Primordial Follicles as a Function of Reproductive Rhythm

In both the senile nulliparous and multiparous rat and mouse (90, 180), the number of oocytes decreases in an identical manner. The inhibition of ovulation during gestation and lactation do not influence this decline of the stock of primordial follicles. But, during pregnancy, there is constant and sizeable follicular development (67) even greater in the hamster (66) which is capable of "wasting" doubtless more oocytes than are required for ovulation. From the results, one may conclude that the number of oocytes is unaffected by ovulation.

B. Relations between Ovarian Sensitivity to Gonadotropic Hormones and Follicular Population

A given number of mature follicles develops at each estrous cycle, independently of the quantity of ovarian tissue left after partial ablation, according to Lipschutz's "law of the follicular constant" (108). However, the selection of strains of rats for ovarian sensitivity to FSH, i.e., essentially for the number of Graafian follicles, enables strains possessing a greater number of primordial follicles and growing follicles in their ovaries to be isolated (126). In cattle, cows showing a strong response at weak doses of exogenous gonadotrophic hormone always have a large number of primordial follicles in reserve; those that do not react to strong doses by superovulation or by intense follicular development usually have only small follicular reserves (121). The correlation is only clear with low amounts of gonadotrophic hormone. Thus, with three strains of mice selected for their fertility, the largest number of induced ovulations is obtained in animals from the strain with the largest number of spontaneous ovulations, but this order of sensitivity is altered by the injection of high doses (112).

C. Relationship between Ovarian Follicular Population and Fertility

It has been suggested that the decrease in fertility that occurs with age, and the reduction of reproductive life by half in hemicastrated animals (16, 17, 89) are related to the size of the oocyte population. It is certain that uterine factors, resulting from overcrowding of one horn after hemicastration (16, 17) or a change in pituitary hormonal balance (101), as shown by a diminished level of atresia in growing follicles of senile rats (115), play an important part. However, the presence of oocytes in the ovary when reproduction stops, in hemicastrated or senile rats, does not necessarily mean that fertility is independent of ovarian follicular characteristics.

After irradiation of an adult rat or cow, a relation is found to exist between the size of the last litter or the fertility and the total number of remaining oocytes (*48, 82, 157*); the number of animals giving birth at each pairing being only 50% (after the first litter) for those having the smallest number of remaining oocytes (*82*). The size of the litter also shrinks with age earlier in females having only a single ovary (*16, 17*). Nevertheless, Jones and Krohn (*90*) concluded that the different levels of fertility between mouse strains cannot be related to the number of oocytes. It is sure that the number of primordial follicles does not influence the fertility as a primary factor. When mice are irradiated between 21 and 42 days, the reproductive capacity depends upon the number of growing follicles preserved (*156, 157*). The number of growing follicles is related to the number of primordial follicles at sexual maturity. Also, the primordial follicles would play a role through the growing ones.

Our ignorance about the dynamics of follicular growth constitutes the main limiting factor in elucidating the part played by the ovarian characteristic—number of primordial growing follicles—in female fertility and in ovarian sensitivity to gonadotropic hormones.

REFERENCES

1. Adams, E. C., Hertig, A. T., and Foster, S., *Am. J. Anat.* **119**, 303 (1966).
2. Allen, E., *Am. J. Anat.* **31**, 439 (1923).
3. Arai, H., *Am. J. Anat.* **27**, 405 (1920).
4. Aron, C., Marescaux, J., and Petrovic, A., *Compt. Rend. Assoc. Anat.* **74**, 421 (1953).
5. Aron, C., Marescaux, J., and Petrovic, A., *Arch. Anat. Histol. Embryol.* **36–37**, 3 (1953–1954).
6. Aron, C., Marescaux, J., and Petrovic, A., *Compt. Rend. Soc. Biol.* **148**, 388 (1954).
7. Baillie, A. H., and Griffiths, K., *J. Endocrinol.* **31**, 63 (1964).
8. Baker, T. G., *Proc. Roy. Soc.* **B158**, 417 (1963).
9. Baker, T. G., *J. Reprod. Fertility* **12**, 183 (1966).
10. Baker, T. G., and Franchi, L. L., *J. Anat.* **100**, 697 (1966).
11. Beaumont, H. M., *Intern. J. Radiation Biol.* **3**, 59 (1961).
12. Beaumont, H. M., *Intern. J. Radiation Biol.* **4**, 580 (1962).
13. Beaumont, H. M., and Mandl, A. M., *Proc. Roy. Soc.* **B155**, 557 (1962).
14. Beek, W. F. Van, Ph.D. Thesis, Koch et Knuttel, Utrecht Gaida, 1921.
15. Benoit, M., and Mauleon, P., *Ann. Biol. Animale Biochim. Biophys.* (in press) (1969).
16. Biggers, J. D., Finn, C., and McLaren, A., *Proc. Intern. Congr. Animal Reprod., 4th, The Hague* **2**, 342 (1961).
17. Biggers, J. D., Finn, C., and McLaren, A., *J. Reprod. Fertility* **3**, 303 and 313 (1962).
18. Blandau, R. J., and Rumery, R. I., *Fertility Sterility* **14**, 330 (1963).
19. Block, E., *Acta Anat.* **12**, 267 (1951).
20. Block, E., *Acta Endocrinol.* **8**, 33 (1951).
21. Block, E., *Acta Anat.* **14**, 108 (1952).
22. Block, E., *Acta Anat.* **17**, 201 (1953).
23. Borum, K., *Exptl. Cell Res.* **24**, 495 (1961).
24. Borum, K., *Exptl. Cell Res.* **45**, 39 (1967).

25. Brambell, F. W. R., *Proc. Roy. Soc.* **B101**, 391 (1928).
26. Bullough, W. S., *J. Endocrinol.* **3**, 141 (1942).
27. Bulmer, D., *J. Anat.* **98**, 27 (1964).
28. Bulmer, D., *J. Roy. Microscop. Soc.* **84**, 189 (1965).
29. Burkl, W., and Kellner, G., *Z. Zellforsch. Mikroskop. Anat.* **41**, 172 (1954).
30. Burkl, W., *Z. Zellforsch. Mikroskop. Anat.* **41**, 121 (1955).
31. Burns, R. K., *J. Exptl. Zool.* **142**, 353 (1959).
32. Carter, T. C., Woods, M. C., and Simpson, M. E., *in* "Control of Ovulation" (C. A. Villee, ed.), p. 1. Pergamon, Oxford, 1961.
33. Chiquoine, A. D., *Anat. Record* **118**, 135 (1954).
34. Chretien, F., *J. Embryol. Exptl. Morphol.* **16**, 591 (1966).
35. Croes-Buth, J., Paesi, F. S. A., and de Jongh, S. E., *Acta Endocrinol.* **32**, 399 (1959).
36. Crone, M., Levy, E., and Peters, H., *Exptl. Cell. Res.* **39**, (1965).
37. Dalcq, A. M., *Compt. Rend. Soc. Biol.* **147**, 1259 (1953).
38. Dalcq, A. M., *Proc. Soc. Study Fertility* **7**, 113 (1955).
39. Deane, H. W., and Barker, W. L., *in* "Testis and Ovary, Eggs and Sperm" (E. T. Engle, ed.), p. 176. Thomas, Springfield, Illinois, 1952.
40. Deane, H. W., *Am. J. Anat.* **91**, 363 (1952).
41. Desaive, P., *Arch. Biol.* **58**, 331 (1947).
42. Desaive, P., *Arch. Biol.* **59**, 34 (1948).
43. Duke, K. L., *J. Morphol.* **69**, 51 (1941).
44. Elger, W., Cited in Jost (*96*).
45. Enders, A. C., *Anat. Record* **134**, 491 (1959).
46. Epsey, L. L., and Lipner, H., *Am. J. Physiol.* **205**, 1 067 (1963).
47. Epsey, L. L., and Lipner, H., *Am. J. Physiol.* **208**, 380 (1965).
48. Erickson, B. H., *J. Animal Sci.* **25**, 800 (1966).
49. Erickson, B. H., *J. Reprod. Fertility* **10**, 97 (1966).
50. Evans, H. M., and Swezy, O., *Mem. Univ. Calif.* **9**, 119 (1931).
51. Evans, H. M., Simpson, M. E., Tolksdorf, S., and Jensen, H., *Endocrinology* **25**, 529 (1939).
52. Everett, J. W., *in* "Sex and Internal Secretions" (William and Young, eds.), 3rd ed., Vol. I, pp. 497–555, 1961.
53. Everett, N. B., *J. Exptl. Zool.* **92**, 49 (1943).
54. Faure-Fremiet, E., and Kaufman, L., *Ann. Physiol. Physicochim. Biol.* **4**, 64 (1928).
55. Flax, M. H., Ph.D. Thesis, Columbia University, New York, 1953.
56. Forsberg, J. G., and Olivecrona, H., *Biol. Neonatorum* **10**, 180 (1966).
57. Fuss, A., *Arch. Mikroskop. Anat.* **81**, 1 (1912).
58. Gerard, P., *Arch. Biol.* **30**, 357 (1920).
59. Gerard, P., *Arch. Biol.* **43**, 94 (1932).
60. Gerard, P., and Herlant, M., *Arch. Biol.* **64**, 97 (1953).
61. Glass, L. E., *Develop. Biol.* **3**, 787 (1961).
62. Greenwald, G. S., *Endocrinology* **66**, 89 (1960).
63. Greenwald, G. S., *J. Reprod. Fertility* **2**, 351 (1961).
64. Greenwald, G. S., *Endocrinology* **71**, 378 (1962).
65. Greenwald, G. S., *Endocrinology* **73**, 436 (1963).
66. Greenwald, G. S., *Anat. Record* **148**, 605 (1964).
67. Greenwald, G. S., *Endocrinology* **79**, 572 (1966).
68. Guraya, S., and Greenwald, G. S., *Am. J. Anat.* **114**, 495 (1964).

69. Hadek, R., *Am. J. Vet. Res.* **19**, 873 (1958).
70. Hadek, R., *J. Ultrastruct. Res.* **9**, 445 (1963).
71. Hargitt, G. T., *J. Morphol.* **49**, 277 (1930).
72. Hargitt, G. T., *J. Morphol.* **49**, 333 (1930).
73. Heck, F., and Mauleon, P., *Ann. Biol. Animale Biochim. Biophys.* (in press) (1969).
74. Hedberg, E., *Acta Endocrinol.* **14**, 1 (1953).
75. Hemsworth, B. M., and Jackson, M., *J. Reprod. Fertility* **6**, 229 (1963).
76. Henricson, B., and Rajakoski, E., *Cornell Vet.* **49**, 494 (1959).
77. Herlant, M., *Ann. Soc. Roy. Zool. Belg.* **91**, 1 (1961).
78. Holyoke, E. A., and Beber, B. A., *Science* **128**, 1082 (1958).
79. Hugues, G. C., *J. Embryol. Exptl. Morphol.* **11**, 513 (1963).
80. Hutchinson, J. S. M., and Robertson, H. A., *Res. Vet. Sci.* **7**, 17 (1966).
81. Ingram, D. L., *J. Endocrinol.* **9**, 307 (1953).
82. Ingram, D. L., *J. Reprod. Fertility* **17**, 81 (1958).
83. Ingram, D. L., *J. Endocrinol.* **19**, 123 (1959).
84. Ingram, D. L., *J. Endocrinol.* **19**, 117 (1959).
85. Ingram, D. L., and Mandl, A. M., *J. Endocrinol.* **17**, 13 (1957).
86. Ingram, D. L., Mandl, A. M., and Zuckerman, S., *J. Endocrinol.* **17**, 280 (1958).
87. Ioannou, J. M., *J. Embryol. Exptl. Morphol.* **12**, 673 (1964).
88. Ioannou, J. M., *J. Embryol. Exptl. Morphol.* **17**, 139 (1967).
89. Jones, E. C., and Krohn, P. L., *J. Endocrinol.* **20**, 129 (1960).
90. Jones, E. C., and Krohn, P. L., *J. Endocrinol.* **21**, 469 (1961).
91. Jones, E. C., and Krohn, P. L., *J. Endocrinol.* **21**, 497 (1961).
92. Jones, E. C., and Krohn, P. L., *Nature* **195**, 1064 (1962).
93. Jost, A., *Arch. Anat. Microscop. Morphol. Exptl.* **36**, 271 (1947).
94. Jost, A., *Recent Progr. Hormone Res.* **8**, 379 (1953).
95. Jost, A., *in* "Organogenesis" (R. L. de Haan and H. Rusprung, eds.), Chapter 24. Holt, New York, 1965.
96. Jost, A., *Intern. Congr. Hormonal Steroids, 2nd Congr., Milano, 1966, Excerpta Med. Intern. Congr. Ser.* **132**, 24 (1967).
97. Jost, A., Chodkiewicz, M., and Mauleon, P., *Compt. Rend. Acad. Sci.* **256**, (1963).
98. Jost, A., and Prepin, J., *Arch. Anat. Microscop. Morphol. Exptl.* **55**, 161 (1966).
99. Kennelly, J. J., and Foote, R. H., *Am. J. Anat.* **118**, 573 (1966).
100. Krohn, P. L., *Lectures Sci. Basis Med.* **7**, 285 (1957–1958).
101. Krohn, P. L., *Proc. Roy. Soc.* **B157**, 128 (1962).
102. Krohn, P. L., *Arch. Anat. Microscop. Morphol. Exptl.* **56**, 151 (1967).
103. Lane, C. E., *Anat. Record* **61**, 141 (1935).
104. Lane, C. E., and Greep, R. O., *Anat. Record* **63**, 139 (1935).
105. Lillie, F. R., *Science* **43**, 611 (1916).
106. Lima-de-Faria, A., and Borum, K., *J. Cell Biol.* **14**, 381 (1962).
107. Lin, T. P., *Nature* **178**, 1175 (1956).
108. Lipschutz, A., *Brit. J. Exptl. Biol.* **5**, 19 (1928).
109. Lobel, B. L., Rosenbaum, R. M., and Deane, H. W., *Endocrinology* **68**, 232 (1961).
110. MacIntyre, M. N., Baker, L., and Wykoff, T., Jr., *Arch. Anat. Microscop. Morphol. Exptl.* **48** *bis* (1959).

111. MacKay, D. G., Hertig, A. T., Adams, E. C., and Danziger, S., *Anat. Record* **117**, 201 (1953).
112. McLaren, A., *J. Endocrinol.* **25**, 137 (1962).
113. Mandl, A. M., *Proc. Roy. Soc.* **B158**, 105 (1963).
114. Mandl, A. M., *Biol. Rev.* **39**, 288 (1964).
115. Mandl, A. M., and Shelton, M., *J. Endocrinol.* **18**, 444 (1959).
116. Mandl, A. M., and Zuckerman, S., *J. Anat.* **83**, 315 (1949).
117. Martinowitch, P. V., *Proc. Roy. Soc.* **13**, 125–232–249 (1938).
118. Marx L., *Anat. Record* **79**, 115 (1941).
119. Mauleon, P., *Ann. Biol. Animale Biochim. Biophys.* **1**, 1 (1961).
120. Mauleon, P., *Proc. Intern. Congr. Animal Reprod., 4th, The Hague* **2**, 348 (1961).
121. Mauleon, P., *Proc. 5th World Congr. Fertility Sterility No. 133, Excerpta Med. Intern. Congr. Ser.* **708** (1966).
122. Mauleon, P., *Arch. Anat. Microscop. Morphol. Exptl.* **56**, 125 (1967).
123. Mauleon, P., and Benoit, M., *Proc. Intern. Congr. Physiol. Pathol. Reprod. Artificial Insemination, 5th, Trento* **2**, 432 (1964).
124. Mauleon, P., and Pelletier, J., *Ann. Biol. Animal Biochim. Biophys.* **4**, 105 (1964).
125. Mauleon, P., and Pinot, R., unpublished data (1967).
126. Mauleon, P., and Rao, H. K., *Ann. Biol. Animal Biochim. Biophys.* **3**, 21 (1963).
127. Mauleon, P., and Reviers, M. M. de, unpublished data (1967).
128. Mauleon, P., and Signoret, J. P., *Proc. Intern. Congr. Physiol. Pathol. Reprod. Artificial Insemination, 5th, Trento* **2**, 432 (1964).
129. Mintz, B., *J. Embryol. Exptl. Morphol.* **5**, 396 (1957).
130. Mintz, B., *Anat. Record* **130**, 341 (1958).
131. Mintz, B., *Arch. Anat. Microscop. Morphol. Exptl.* **48**, *bis*, 155 (1959).
132. Mintz, B., *J. Cellular Comp. Physiol.* **56**, Suppl. 1, 31 (1960).
133. Mintz, B., *Symp. Germ Cells Develop.* p. 1 (1960).
134. Mintz, B., and Russell, E. S., *Anat. Record* **122**, 443 (1955).
135. Mintz, B., and Russell, E. S., *J. Exptl. Zool.* **134**, 207 (1957).
136. Moricard, R., and Gothie, S., *Compt. Rend. Soc. Biol.* **149**, 1918 (1955).
137. Moss, S., Wrenn, R., and Sykes, J. F., *Anat. Record* **120**, 409 (1954).
138. Mulnard, J., *Arch. Biol.* **66**, 525 (1955).
139. Myers, H. I., Young, W. C., and Dempsey, E. W., *Anat. Record* **65**, 381 (1936).
140. Niemi, M., and Ikonen, M., *Nature* **189**, 592 (1961).
141. Oakberg, E. F., *Arch. Anat. Microscop. Morphol. Exptl.* **56**, 171 (1967).
142. Oakberg, E. F., and Clark, E., *in* "Effects of Ionizing Radiation on the Reproductive System" (W. D. Carlson and F. X. Gassner, eds.), pp. 11–24, New York, 1964.
143. Odeblad, E., and Boström, H., *Acta Radiol.* **39**, 137 (1953).
144. Ohno, S., Christian, L. C., and Stenius, C., *Exptl. Cell Res.* **32**, 590 (1963).
145. Ohno, S., and Gropp, A., *Cytogenetics* **4**, 251 (1965).
146. Ohno, S., and Smith, J. B., *Cytogenetics* **3**, 324 (1964).
147. Ohno, S., Trujillo, J. M., Stenius, C., Christian, L. C., and Teplitz, R. L., *Cytogenetics* **1**, 258 (1962).
148. Paesi, F. J. A., *Acta Endocrinol.* **3**, 173 (1949).
149. Paesi, F. J. A., *Acta Endocrinol.* **3**, 89 (1949).

150. Pasteels, J. J., *in* "L'Origine de la lignée germinale," pp. 223–280, Hermann, Paris, 1962.
151. Pencharz, R. I., *Science* **91**, 554 (1940).
152. Perry, J. S., and Rowlands, I. W., *J. Reprod. Fertility* **6**, 393 (1963).
153. Peters, H., *Radiation Res.* **15**, 582 (1961).
154. Peters, H., and Borum, K., *Intern. J. Radiation Biol.* **3**, 1 (1961).
155. Peters, H., and Crone, M., *Arch. Anat. Microscop. Morphol. Exptl.* **56**, 160 (1967).
156. Peters, H., and Levy, E., *Fertility Sterility* **15**, 407 (1964).
157. Peters, H., and Levy, E., *J. Reprod. Fertility* **7**, 37 (1964).
158. Peters, H., and Levy, E., *J. Reprod. Fertility* **11**, 227 (1966).
159. Petter-Rousseaux, A., *Mammalia* **26**, 1 (1962).
160. Petter-Rousseaux, A., and Bourliere, F., *Folia Primatologica* **3**, 241 (1965).
161. Pincus, G., and Enzmann, E. V., *J. Morphol.* **61**, 351 (1937).
162. Pool, W. R., and Lipner, H., *Endocrinology* **79**, 858 (1966).
163. Pool, W. R. and Lipner, H., *Federation Proc.* **25**, 443 (1966).
164. Pool, W. R., and Lipner, H., *Federation Proc.* **26**, 535 (1967).
165. Price, D., and Ortiz, E., *in* "Organogenesis" (R. L. de Haan and H. Ursprung, eds.), Chapter 25. Holt, New York, 1965.
166. Quinn, D. L., and Zarrow, M. X., *Endocrinology* **74**, 309 (1964).
167. Rajakoski, E., *Acta Endocrinol. Suppl.* **52**, 7 (1960).
168. Rajakoski, E., *Nord. Veterinarmed.* **17**, 285 (1965).
169. Rajakoski, E., and Hafez, E. S. E., *Anat. Record* **147**, 457 (1964).
170. Rajakoski, E., and Hafez, E. S. E., *Cytogenetics* **3**, 193 (1964).
171. Rao, C. R. N., *Quart. J. Microscop. Soc.* **71**, 57 (1927).
172. Raynaud, A., *Arch. Anat. Microscop. Morphol. Exptl.* **39**, 518 (1950).
173. Regaud, C., *Arch. Anat. Microscop.* **4**, 231 (1901).
174. Reviers, M. M. de, and Mauleon, P., unpublished data, 1966.
175. Roversi, G. D., and Silvestrini, R., *Exptl. Cell Res.* **31**, 484 (1963).
176. Rubaschkin, W., *Anat. Anz.* **32**, 222 (1908).
177. Rudkin, G. T., and Griech, H. A., *J. Histochem. Cytochem.* **9**, 621 (1961).
178. Rudkin, G. T., and Griech, H. A., *J. Cell Biol.* **12**, 169 (1962).
179. Salzgeber, B., *Arch. Anat. Microscop. Morphol. Exptl.* **51**, 1 (1962).
180. Shelton, M., *J. Endocrinol.* **18**, 451 (1959).
181. Simon, D., *Arch. Anat. Microsc. Morphol. Exptl.* **49**, 94 (1960).
182. Simpson, M. E., Evans, H. M., Fraenkel-Conrat, H. L., and Li, C. H., *Endocrinology* **28**, 37 (1941).
183. Sirlin, J. L., and Edwards, R. G., *Exptl. Cell Res.* **18**, 190 (1959).
184. Slater, D. W., and Dornfeld, E. S., *Am. J. Anat.* **76**, 253 (1945).
185. Smith, P. E., *J. Am. Med. Assoc.* **88**, 280 (1927).
186. Talbert, G. B., Meyer, R. K., and McShan, W. N., *Endocrinology* **49**, 687 (1951).
187. Thomson, J. D., *Proc. Iowa Acad. Sci.* **49**, 475 (1942).
188. Turner, C. D., and Asakawa, H., *Science* **143**, 1344 (1964).
189. Vanneman, A. S., *Am. J. Anat.* **22**, 341 (1917).
190. Vermande-Van-Eck G. J. V., *Anat. Record* **121**, 378 (1955).
191. Watzka, M., *in* "Handbuch der mikroskopischen Anatomie des Menschen," Vol. 7/3. Springer, Berlin, 1957.
192. Weniger, J. P., Ehrhardt, J. D., and Fritig, B., *Compt. Rend. Acad. Sci. Ser. D* **264**, 1069 (1967).

193. Williams, P. C., *Nature* **145**, 388 (1940).
194. Williams, P. C., *Proc. Roy. Soc.* **B132**, 189 (1944).
195. Williams, P. C., *J. Endocrinol.* **4**, 131 (1945).
196. Winiwarter, H. (Von), *Arch. Biol.* **17**, 33 (1901).
197. Winiwarter, H. (Von), *Compt. Rend. Soc. Biol.* **83**, 1403 (1920).
198. Winiwarter, H. (Von), and Sainmont, G., *Anat. Anz.* **32**, 613 (1908).
199. Winiwarter, H. (Von), and Sainmont, G., *Arch. Biol.* **24**, 1 (1909).
200. Witschi, E., *Carnegie Inst. Wash. Contribs. Embryol.* **209**, 67 (1948).
201. Witschi, E., *in* "Colloque sur la differenciation sexuelle chez les vertébrés,"
pp. 33–64. C. N. R. S., Paris, 1951.
202. Zachariae, F., *Acta Endocrinol.* **26**, 215 (1957).
203. Zachariae, F., *Acta Endocrinol.* **27**, 339 (1958).
204. Zarrow, M. X., and Quinn, D. L., *J. Endocrinol.* **26**, 181 (1963).
205. Zuckerman, S., Lancet **i**, 1031 (1949).
206. Zuckerman, S., *Recent Progr. Horm. Res.* **6**, 63 (1951).
207. Zuckerman, S., *Ciba Found. Colloq. Ageing* **2**, 31 (1956).

9 THE ESTROUS CYCLE

P. T. CUPPS, L. L. ANDERSON,
AND H. H. COLE

I. Introduction

The estrous cycle in the female mammal is characterized by cyclic changes in the morphology of the reproductive organs and in the behavior of the animal. In domestic animals the estrous cycle is divided into various phases which are referred to as "proestrus," "estrus," "metestrus," and "diestrus." As these terms have evolved, the suffix "um" has been replaced by "us," and this terminology will be used in the present chapter. In spite of the general usage of these terms, their meanings have not been standardized and they will be used in the manner suggested by Asdell (11a). Proestrus pertains to that phase of the cycle when secretory activity of the

217

corpus luteum is declining and the reproductive organs are coming under the dominant influence of the intermediate-sized definitive follicles and the gonadal hormones produced by them. Estrus is defined as that phase of the cycle when the female will accept coitus. Metestrus is the short transitional stage following ovulation in which the effects of the estrogen are declining, the recently ruptured follicle is reorganized, and the secretion of progesterone is rising. Diestrus is that phase of the cycle during which progesterone exerts a dominant influence on the accessory organs. Anestrus designates a period of variable length in which the reproductive organs are relatively quiescent.

As defined here, the estrous cycles of the various species would be classified in different groups as follows. In cycles without a functional corpus luteum, as in the rat, the cycle would be composed of proestrus, estrus, and metestrus merging into proestrus. In polyestrous animals with a functional corpus luteum the cycle would be proestrus, estrus, metestrus, and, finally, diestrus merging into proestrus. In the seasonally polyestrous animals with a functional corpus luteum the cycles would be the same as for the polyestrous animals except that the last diestrus of the season would proceed to anestrus. In the monestrous species such as the dog the cycle would be proestrus, estrus, metestrus, diestrus, and anestrus.

The patterns of the estrous cycles in the domestic animals are quite diverse, ranging from the constant estrus pattern exhibited by the rabbit to long cycles including a period of anestrus, as exhibited by the bitch. This wide diversity reflects the difference in the inherent patterns of reproduction in the different species, but the cycles, when compared on the basis of the physiological mechanisms involved, are quite similar.

II. Puberty

Puberty is defined as the age at which reproduction becomes possible. In the female this is usually considered to be the age at first estrus. A compilation of the data (11, 28) suggests that the average age at puberty in the females of the common domestic species is as follows: cow (Holstein) 9–18 months; ewe 7–10 months; sow 6–8 months; mare 8–20 months; doe (goat) 7–10 months; bitch 8–24 months; cat 7–12 months; and the doe (rabbit) 5.5–8.5 months. The average body weight at puberty in some of these species is as follows: cow (Holstein) 260 kg; ewe 30–35 kg; sow 70–80 kg; bitch (Beagle) 10 kg; and cat 2.5 kg. The weight at puberty is quite variable and is dependent on the breed and on the nutrients available to the animal. Within a given nutrient level, individual animal variation is large. Under different nutritional regimes, height at withers and body length seem to be the most constant parameters associated with puberty in cattle (131a). In animals showing a sexual season, the age at puberty becomes more variable because animals which do not reach puberty during the first sexual season following birth will not show cycles until the next. Genetic factors are important in determining the age at which puberty is attained (27). Variability in individual animals associated with environmental factors, however, may tend to obscure the genetic effects.

III. The Sexual Season

Among the common domestic species the cow and the sow are polyestrus, showing diestrous cycles throughout the year. The mare, ewe, and doe (goat) are seasonally polyestrus, showing diestrous cycles during a defined sexual season. In the ewe and the doe the sexual season is confined largely to the fall and winter, whereas the mare and the jenny show activity during the spring and summer. Thus, the diurnal change in the photoperiod appears to be an important factor governing the sexual season. The relation between the light cycle and the sexual season appears to be related to the length of the gestation period inasmuch as the young are usually born at the season of the year which is most favorable for their survival.

Breed differences exist with respect to the length of the sexual season. Breeds of animals originating in areas of higher latitude usually show a more pronounced and a shorter season than those originating in areas nearer the equator. Thus, the black-faced British breeds have a shorter sexual season than does the Merino (28). The data available also suggest that the sexual season of the seasonally polyestrous animals is more distinct in areas of the largest diurnal variation in light, i.e., at the higher latitudes. Within the Merino breed (53) the proportion of ewes showing a pronounced anestrus was greater at the high latitudes than at the equator. The depth of anestrus is closely associated with the length of the sexual season, and animals with a shorter season show deeper anestrus. Other environmental factors affecting the length of the sexual season are discussed in Chapter 16. Braden and Moule (20) reported that transport of aged Merino ewes during anestrus caused ovulation in 48 of 77 ewes within the subsequent period of 6 days.

During the transitional stage between anestrus and the sexual season, introduction of the male appears to influence the onset of sexual activity. In Angora goats (126) the grouping of the young at birth indicated a concentration of matings approximately 10 days after exposure to the buck. Further experiments showed that ovulation was also concentrated around the tenth day after exposure. In one of the groups studied there was evidence that estrus and mating occurred very quickly in a majority of does following introduction of the buck. Several reports (108, 113, 124, 134) indicate that the introduction of the ram during the transitional period causes ovulation without estrus in a high proportion of ewes. In one experiment (124), introduction of a ram caused 44% of a group of ewes to ovulate within a 6-day period as compared to an 8.3% rate in the same period in ewes that had been with a ram continually. The first ovulation at the onset of the breeding season in the ewe is not accompanied by the normal behavioral patterns of estrus.

In contrast to the ewe, the transition from anestrus to the sexual season in the mare is characterized by long periods of estrus (sometimes designated as pseudoestrus) and lowered fertility (28).

IV. The Cycle

A. LENGTH OF CYCLE

The length of the estrous cycle, duration of estrus, and the time of ovulation are recorded in Table I. The data presented here represent a modified compilation of the information reported for the various domestic species from Asdell (12) and Cole and Cupps (28). Some of the information was recalculated to eliminate very short cycles and those which appear to represent two or three cycles since most investigators are in agreement that these cycles are not really representative of the normal cycles for the various species.

Generally speaking, negligible differences dependent upon time of year, age, and breed have been found, and thus we have made no attempt to provide values for these different groups. This is not to say that carefully controlled studies might not reveal small but nonetheless statistically significant differences.

The domestic species show a large variation with respect to the length of the cycle, ranging from 16 to 17 days in the ewe to about 200 days in the bitch. Many different investigators have reported on the length of the cycle in the ewe, with the average length being from 16.5 days to 17.5 days. The variation around the mean length is small with more than 90% of the cycles falling within 4 days of the average. Slight breed differences may exist, with the Scottish and Navajo breeds tending to have the shortest cycles, the medium-wool breeds being intermediate, and the fine- and long-wool breeds tending to be the longest (12). Cycles of multiparous cows average slightly longer than those of heifers; the modal length for the cows being 21 days and for the heifers 20 days. When cycles shorter than 17 days and longer than 23 days are eliminated, the mean and the mode are quite similar, suggesting a normal variation in the length of the cycles. Apparently, shorter than average cycles in the cow tend to be concentrated between 8 and 10 days. Limited data suggest that these short cycles account for approximately 2% of the total. Recent data (90) show that a rise in estrogen secretion occurs at this time in the cow, and the estrus manifested concurrently may reflect this change in estrogen titer. Cycles longer

TABLE I

LENGTH OF THE ESTROUS CYCLE, DURATION OF ESTRUS, AND TIME
OF OVULATION IN VARIOUS SPECIES OF DOMESTIC ANIMALS[a]

Breed, class, or species	Estrous cycle length (days)		Length of estrus (hours)		Time of ovulation
	Mean	Range	Mean	Range	Mean (hours)
Dairy cattle	21.3	18–24 84%	19.3	13–27 93%	10.7 after end of estrus
Merino sheep	17.0	16–19 85%	38.0	36–48 70%	36–40 after beginning of estrus
Angora goats	19.4	12–24	39.2	24–96	—
Swine	20.7	18–23 75%	59.3	—	36 after beginning of estrus
Thoroughbred horse	20.3	13–25 78%	120.0	—	24 before end of estrus
Dog	235	120–390	216	168–312	Within 24 after beginning of estrus
Cat	18	—	96[b] 228	—	24–30 after coitus
Rabbit	—	—	Constant[c]	—	10–12 after coitus

[a] Adapted from Asdell (12).

[b] In presence of male, estrus is reported to be 4 days in length; in absence of male, 9–10 days.

[c] Following infertile mating, the doe goes through a period of pseudopregnancy. There may be a rest period (anestrus) during very hot weather.

than 22–23 days tend to be grouped between 40 and 44 days and 60–66 days. In the older literature these abnormally long cycles were thought to be caused by the prolongation of the secretion of progesterone by the corpus luteum, but recent studies indicate that in most cases the longer cycles represent multiples of the normal cycle. The apparent long interval represents either a short estrus which is not detected or an ovulation unaccompanied by the normal behavior patterns associated with estrus, i.e., "silent estrus." McEntee et al. (81) found a high incidence of long cycles, approximately 30 days, in dairy heifers infected with vibrio fetus.

In contrast to the cow and ewe, only a few data are available for the doe (goat). For dairy goats the average length of the cycle has been reported as being 17.8 days (105). An abnormally high proportion of cycles were very short, less than 5 days. A recalculation of the observations eliminating the abnormally long and the abnormally short cycles gives an average length of about 20 days and probably represents a better estimate of the usual length of the cycle. In addition to the cycles less than 5 days in length, a few cycles approximately 7 days in length were also evident in these data, suggesting that the mechanisms controlling the cycle length in this species are not as constant as in some of the others; estrogen excretion has not been measured in the goat, but the high incidence of estrus at this time strongly suggests that it occurs.

Short cycles comparable to those found in the cow and doe have not been reported in swine. The length of the cycle in the mare and jenny is dependent upon the season and is more variable than the cycles reported for the other large domestic species, with the means for the various breeds ranging from 19 to 23 days. The seasonal variation in the length of estrus and "pseudoestrus" in these species probably accounts for the major part of the variability found. The length of the estrous cycle in the bitch as reported in Table I includes anestrus. The average length of the cycle, excluding anestrus, appears to be somewhere between 48 and 78 days. Thus, the interval between two periods of proestrus is composed mainly of the anestrous period. On the basis of histological evidence the corpus luteum begins to degenerate about the 30th day after the end of estrus, but, unfortunately, progesterone secretion studies have not been done in order to establish the length of the life of the functional corpus luteum.

B. Proestrus

Proestrus is an ill-defined phase of the cycle and its duration is variable, depending on the species involved and the method used to define it. As estimated from the early histological degenerative changes in the corpus luteum, proestrus would begin about the 14th day in the ewe (107) and the 16th to 18th day in the cow (34) and the sow (32).

The urinary excretion of estrogen (19, 78, 109), which begins to rise at the 17th or 18th day in the sow, heralds the arrival of proestrus. Mellin and Erb (90) reported a similar rise in estrogen excretion beginning on the 16th day of the cycle in the cow. Changes in the flow elasticity (18) and in arborization of the cervical mucus of the sow (17), cow (1, 2), and the ewe (110) are indicators of estrogen secretion and coincide with the early degenerative changes which occur in the corpus luteum. Secretion of progesterone (106) in the cow and sow begins to decrease at similar times, but a precipitous decrease does not occur until late in the proestrous period. Proestrus in the bitch is quite prolonged, averaging 9 days, and is accompanied by high blood titers of estrogen (91).

C. Estrus

As shown in Table I, length of estrus varies from about 20 hours in the cow to more than 200 hours in the bitch and cat. In some species, such as the ewe and cow, the onset occurs abruptly, while in others, such as the bitch and cat, it appears to be more gradual and may be preceded by varying lengths of time in which the male and female are attracted to each other, but mating does not occur.

Seasonal variations in length of estrus occur in the mare and jenny. Trum (135) reported a change in the length of estrus in mares from early spring to summer. For example, estrus of less than 4 days' duration was found in only 44% of the cycles recorded in March and in more than 70% in July. Periods of more than 10 days were recorded in about one-fifth of the periods in March, but none were that long in June and July. These prolonged periods of estrus in the early spring may not be accompanied by ovulation.

Undisclosed climatic factors apparently influence the length of estrus in cattle. For example, under Louisiana conditions the average duration of estrus for dairy cattle checked at 2 and 6 hour intervals was 11.9 hours (54). This duration is shorter than that reported in Table I, from data collected primarily in northern US (28). A short duration of estrus, 6–8 hours, also has been reported for beef cattle under range conditions in Arizona. Hall and co-workers consider the subtropical climate to be one of the factors causing the shortened duration of estrus. However, the climatic effect was complicated by a suboptimal forage feeding program which also may have affected the length of estrus. Monthly variations in the duration of estrus were reported by Hall and co-workers, with an average length of estrus of 10.7 hours for April and May and 13.8 hours for September and December. Since weight loss was more severe in the fall and winter when the duration of estrus was longer, they suggested that nutritional effects appeared to be of secondary importance.

Data concerning the relationship between age and duration of estrus are conflicting. In cattle and sheep most investigators have reported that the young animals have a shorter estrus than older animals. In swine, the differences in the average duration of estrus ranged from 1.5 to 25 hours shorter in gilts than in sows. Other reports, however, indicate that the duration of estrus in heifers is longer than in parous cows (54).

Estrus may begin at any time of the day or night. McKenzie and Terrill (83) did not find any difference in the number of ewes coming into estrus during the different times of the day. Hulet et al. (64) found that 15% of the ewes showed the first signs of estrus between midnight and 6 AM; 36% between 6 AM and 12 noon; 33% between noon and 6 PM and 16% between 6 PM and midnight. They believed the daily variation was related to the management of the experimental animals. Conversely, Joubert and Louw (70) found that 54% of the ewes showed first signs of estrus during the night. It has been reported that the peak activity in Welch Mountain ewes occurred immediately after first light (65). Robertson and Rakha (116), observing a group of ewes continuously, found two peak periods for the onset of estrus as measured by first acceptance of the ram. The two peaks of activity were centered around sunrise and sunset. Some diurnal variation in the onset of estrus was found in cattle checked four times daily at 6 AM and 12 noon; 6 PM, and midnight. These observers found that 54.8% began during the day, with peak activity centered around 6 AM.

The interval between parturition and first estrus is quite variable among the domestic species and apparently several factors affect it. The average interval between parturition and first estrus in dairy cattle was 33 days (SD 18.7 days) following normal calving and 36 days following abnormal calving (21, 121). In beef cattle, Warnick (141) found a postpartum interval of 62.7 days. Wiltbank and Cook (148) reported an interval of 84 days (SD 41.2 days) from parturition to first estrus in nursed cows and a 54-day interval (SD 25.2 days) in cows milked twice daily. In this study corpora lutea were present in some instances before estrus was detected. Clapp (24) reported that nursing and frequent milking prolonged the postpartum interval in cows.

The mare, jenny, and sow may show estrus shortly after parturition. In the mare, Trum (135) found that 77% of mares were in estrus between the seventh and tenth day after foaling. Although ovulation occurs during this "foal heat," fertility is low and is accompanied by an increased abortion rate. A variable number of sows may show estrus approximately 2 days after parturition. In one study (142) postpartum estrus was found in 18 of 36 sows. Ovulation did not occur during this estrus in sows which were suckling pigs, but did occur in two animals that did not nurse the young. Burger (22) found that 85 of 88 sows showed a postpartum estrus. Animals bred at this estrus did not conceive, indicating a failure of ovulation. Estrus does not occur in the sow during lactation, but sows begin to cycle shortly after lactation ceases. Barker and Wiggans (15) reported that 8% of Rambouillet ewes and 44% of Dorset ewes showed an anovulatory estrus immediately after parturition.

The time of ovulation with respect to estrus is reported in Table I. Ovulation is spontaneous in all of the domestic species except the cat and the rabbit and occurs during estrus in all species except the cow, in which it occurs, on the average, 10 hours after the cessation of estrus. As with the other characteristics of the cycle the time of ovulation is not constant and individual differences may be large. In species in which multiple ovulations occur, a period of several hours may intervene between the time of rupture of the first follicle and the last. McKenzie and Terrill (83) found an interval of 7.5 hours between twin ovulations in the ewe. In the sow, Burger (22) estimated that complete ovulation of all the mature follicles required between 6 and 7 hours. The preovulatory changes in the follicle appear to be similar in those species studied. Within a few hours of the time of rupture a small circular area on the surface of the follicle becomes very thin, tends to become avascular, and may form a slight cone-shaped protrusion in the area where rupture will occur.

D. METESTRUS

Metestrus is a rather poorly defined phase of the cycle. From the standpoint of the changes occurring in the reproductive organs the time usually given for metestrus roughly corresponds to the interval between ovulation and the time that is required for the fertilized ovum to traverse the oviduct. Although behavioral estrus continues for a variable period following ovulation in most species, the secretion of estrogen appears to decrease shortly after the follicle collapses and the secretion of progesterone is low during the early development of the corpus luteum. Although variable, this developmental process continues for about 3 days, at which time the secretion of progesterone increases rapidly. These changes are very characteristic of the domestic species having diestrous cycles and probably afford the most valid way to measure the length of metestrus. Voluminous sloughing of the vaginal epithelium occurs during this period in some species. The changes occurring in the other reproductive organs will be discussed further under the individual organs.

E. DIESTRUS

The length of diestrus primarily determines the length of the estrous cycle and is variable in the different species. Significant amounts of progesterone are secreted from the fourth day onward in the ewe (43), the cow (106), and the sow (87). Ovarian plasma levels of progesterone began to drop on the 16th day in the sow, approximately 1–2 days before estrus in the cow, and on the 15th or 16th day in the ewe, suggesting a period of 10–13 days for the diestrus in these species.

V. Cyclic Changes in the Reproductive and Endocrine Organs

A. OVARY

The ovaries are paired organs attached to the broad ligament in the lumbar region of the abdominal cavity in close proximity to the oviducts and horns of the uterus. Their position within the body is quite variable, depending on the species, age, and reproductive condition of the animal. In the ewe and cow they are oval in shape. In the bitch and the mare they are bean-shaped, and in the sow they are lobulated. They are surrounded by bursae in the bitch and sow and are held in close proximity to the infundibulum of the oviduct by a short ovarian ligament. In most of the domestic species follicles are found over the entire surface of the ovary and ovulation can occur from any portion of the surface. The ovary of the mare, particularly in older animals, has a specialized area on the surface called the ovulation fossa from which ovulation occurs. During anestrus and before puberty the ovary from the domestic species is characterized by the presence of oocytes and of follicles of different degrees of maturity. With the establishment of estrous cycles changes in the character of the ovary occur and it becomes quite complex. During the cycle the size and, to a certain extent, the shape of the ovary is determined by the number, size, and condition of the large follicles and corpora lutea.

Histologically, the ovary is an intricate organ composed of an outer surface layer of either cuboidal or squamous cells called the germinal epithelium. Just beneath this serosal surface a layer of dense connective tissue, the tunica albuginea, is found, and next to it a cellular connective tissue, the cortical layer, which contains the primordial follicles and the oocytes. The medulla, or central zone of the ovary is a richly vascular network surrounded by a loose connective tissue. The vascular supply enters the ovary through the hilus, and in most species the larger vessels are highly coiled.

The first stages of oogenesis occur rather early in the fetal period (62), and the germ cells are present as primary oocytes at the time of birth. At puberty, some of the ovarian follicles begin to grow, and in the cow (111) and the ewe (66) the cyclic growth occurs in two phases. In heifers the largest follicles present in the ovary after ovulation have a diameter of approximately 6 mm. One and sometimes two of these follicles begin to enlarge and reach a diameter of 10–12 mm by the sixth or seventh day of the cycle. In most of the animals studied one follicle of approximately this size could be found in the ovary until late proestrus or early estrus. At this time the follicle starts to grow again, and this growth results in ovulation. Rajakoski believes that the follicle which reaches its maximum diameter at the middle of the cycle undergoes atresia and that another follicle grows to take its place. He believes that this second follicle is the one which will ovulate at the next estrus. Studies on multiparous cows, however, indicate that the intermediate sized follicle does not undergo atresia in most cases and that it is the follicle which ovulates at the next estrus. Changes in the volume of the largest follicle in the ewe (66) show the same growth pattern as those recorded in cattle, and the preovulatory growth of the intermediate-sized follicle begins early in estrus (Fig. 1). The two phases of the growth are very closely associated with the release of the PAS-positive material from the small basophilic cells of the pituitary and its disappearance from the acini (34). The preovulatory growth of the intermediate-sized follicles coincides very closely with the release of gonadotropins from the pituitary as indicated by changes in hormone levels in the gland (see Section VI, B). The cyclic growth is accompanied by changes in the granulosa and thecal cells of the follicles. During estrus some of the cells of the theca interna become epithelioid (11, 34), and the granulosa cells become widely separated, but are connected by cytoplasmic bridges. Mitoses appear more frequently in both cell layers during the middle of the cycle. The increased mitotic activity of the small tertiary follicles seen at this time closely coincides with a rise in the secretion of estrogen.

Detailed studies (*111*) indicate that approximately half of the follicles present in the ovary are in some stage of atresia. Rajakoski (*111*) describes four types of atresia. In the first type, which occurs primarily in the primordial follicles, the oocyte degenerates mainly by autolysis and disappears without leaving any structures in the stroma of the ovary. This kind of atresia is uncommon. In the second type the oocytes in follicles up to 1–2 mm in diameter degenerate with hyalinization of the zona pellucida. The

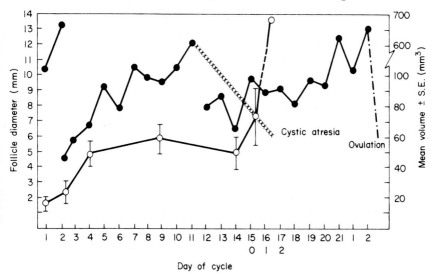

FIG. 1. Changes in the size of follicle during the estrous cycle in the cow (●) (*111*) and ewe (○) (*66*). In the cow follicle size is represented by changes in diameter and in the ewe by changes in volume.

follicular cells then degenerate and disappear. The third type of atresia affects the follicular wall first and occurs in follicles from 2–6 mm in diameter. The granulosa degenerates first; the epithelioid cells disappear from the theca, and the thecal connective tissue elements extend inward to fill the lumen. The cumulus and the oocyte then degenerate, leaving the zona pellucida, and the collagen fibers coalesce to form a glassy membrane. The fourth type, also called "cystic atresia," follows a course similar to that just described, except that a glassy membrane is not formed and the theca undergoes fibrotic changes. The mechanisms causing the different types of atresia and the significance of atresia in relation to ovarian functions are unknown. Late preovulatory changes in the mature follicle resemble in some respects the early atretic changes in the third and fourth types, and partial atresia in a mature follicle theoretically could contribute to the formation of the "cystic" corpora lutea described in the cow.

When the follicle ruptures, its walls collapse and the granulosa and thecal layers are thrown into folds. At the point of rupture a slight eversion of the layers may occur which, with further development, becomes a prominent protuberance on the surface of the ovary. The amount of hemorrhage which accompanies ovulation is variable in the different species, ranging from no bleeding to very slight bleeding in the ewe, the cow, and the sow, and being rather extensive in the mare. Eosinophils are found in the stroma of the ovary surrounding the mature follicle, and large numbers infiltrate both cellular layers as the corpus luteum begins to develop. As the corpus luteum develops, small blood vessels from the theca invade the granulosa and the granulosa cells begin to hypertrophy or luteinize. The corpus luteum is formed from cells of both granulosa and thecal origin, with the granulosa cells showing hypertrophy in the earlier stages of development. There is some evidence (34) indicating that the thecal cells tend to regress during the early stages of development and then to undergo a hypertrophy beginning about the eighth day of the cycle in the cow. The corpus luteum develops rapidly, reaching its maximum size between the 12th and 15th days of the cycle in the cow and sow and the tenth day in the ewe. Growth is rapid during the first 4–5 days following ovulation and then proceeds at a slower rate until the maximum size is reached. Histologically, some of the luteal cells begin to show degenerative changes several days before progesterone secretion declines, but these degenerative processes are not extensive until the late proestrus and early estrus of the ensuing cycle. Deane et al. (36) have described the physiological degenerative changes of the corpus luteum in the ewe. According to them, the earliest regressive changes were increased size and decreased density of the mitochondria in the luteal cells occurring on days 12 and 13 of the cycle. Lipid droplets were evident on the 14th day. On the 15th day many of the luteal cells were shrunken with pycnotic nuclei and some cells were beginning to fragment. These extensive regressive changes were associated with a reduction in Δ^5-3β-hydroxysteroid dehydrogenase and diaphorase activity. The relation of these changes to progesterone secretion may be found in Section VI, A.

B. Oviduct

The oviducts are typical tubular organs consisting of an external serous coat, muscular layers, and a mucous membrane (Fig. 2). The epithelial cells lining the oviduct have cilia which (114) are more numerous in the ampulla and infundibulum. The height of the epithelium varies with the stage of the cycle, being highest shortly after estrus and lowest during the middle of the cycle. Cellular changes in the isthmus are less pronounced. Under the influence of estrogen, a physiological block is formed at the uterotubal junction (42) which prevents the oviduct fluids from passing to the uterus. These authors suggested that this might be the mechanism

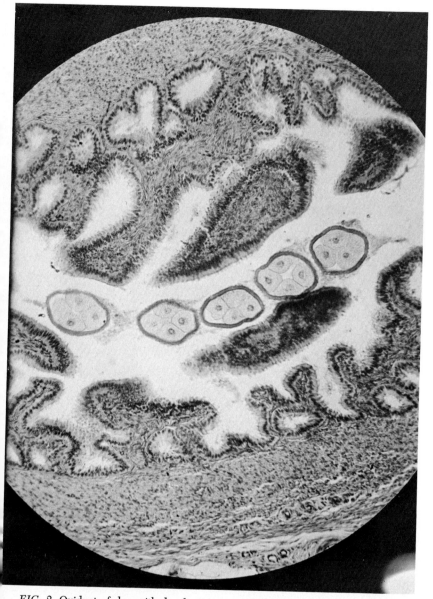

FIG. 2. Oviduct of dog with developing zygotes. From Evans and Cole (*44*).

which controls the entry of the zygote into the uterus. During diestrus small cells migrate into the lumen of the oviduct in large numbers, reaching a maximum at about 9 days. These cells appear to be derived from the wandering lymphoid cells of the connective tissue (*98*), and migration through the epithelium can be induced in castrate animals with progestins. Globular cytoplasmic droplets also appear to be present in the secretions. An analysis of fluid from the oviducts of ewes (104) gave the following average values: protein 3.02 gm/100 ml; lactic acid 44.13 mg/100 ml; alkaline phosphatase 32.9 units/ml. Volume of fluid secreted and the phosphatase activity were increased during estrus and reducing sugars were found only in trace amounts. The composition of the oviduct fluid from rabbits was quite different (57), containing much less protein and lactic acid. Calcium and zinc appeared to be present in rather high concentrations.

C. UTERUS

The uterus is a tubular muscular organ which is composed of a serous coat, the perimetrium, a layer of longitudinal muscle, a vascular bed, a layer of circular muscle, and an endometrium. The connective tissue of the endometrium is composed of a loose layer lying adjacent to the muscular layer and of a rather dense cellular layer next to the surface epithelium (see Fig. 3). Uterine glands penetrate the connective tissue of the endometrium and terminate adjacent to the circular muscle layer. In the cow and the ewe specialized areas (cotyledons) are found in the endometrium in which the density of the compact layer is increased and uterine glands are not present. These are very vascular areas, and following pregnancy, the blood vessels do not regress to the virginal conditions but remain heavily walled and highly coiled. In black-faced ewes these cotyledonary areas frequently contain a pigment, melanin (52, 86), and occasionally in white-faced ewes a red pigment is present.

Before puberty and during anestrus the entire wall of the uterus is thin and only partially developed. The endometrium is thin; the uterine glands are sparse and have a simple tubular structure. The surface epithelium is cuboidal and the nuclei tend to be in a basal position. When estrous cycles begin, the uterus increases in size and undergoes cyclic changes. The luminal epithelial cells are tall and columnar during proestrus and estrus. They tend to regress slightly during metestrus and reach their maximum height about the middle of the cycle (8, 32, 44, 82, 96, 114, 143). In the late stages of diestrus they regress. The uterine glands are relatively straight during the follicular phase, but shortly after ovulation they begin to show coiling, which reaches its maximum during diestrus. They show their maximum secretory activity during the stages of maximal coiling. Changes in the endometrium are dramatically illustrated in the bitch (Fig. 3), in which glandular regression begins about the 20th day, but it proceeds slowly and requires approximately 80 days to return to the anestrous condition.

During proestrus and estrus the vascularity and edema in the connective tissue of the endometrium are increased. The edema is greatest at estrus. It tends to separate the cellular elements of the stroma, giving it an open appearance. During metestrus and diestrus the edema disappears, giving the stroma a greater density, but the vascularity, particularly that in the dense layer of the stroma, remains abundant, and at the eighth to tenth day the endometrium may appear to be more vascular than during estrus. Lymphoid wandering cells, mast cells, and leukocytes are present in the endometrium at all stages of the cycle. Concentrations of some of these cells appear to vary at different stages of the cycle (99), and the rate of movement of leukocytes into the mucosa and lumen of the uterus

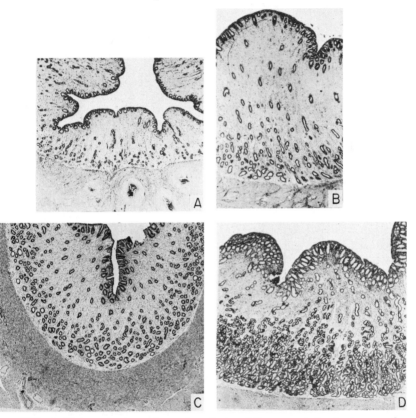

FIG. 3. Changes in the endometrium during different periods of estrous cycle in the bitch. A, anestrus; B, proestrus; C, estrus; D, diestrus. From Evans and Cole (44).

in response to inoculation of bacteria into the uterus was found to be faster during estrus than during the luteal phase (60).

In cattle (28, 119, 143) cyclic changes of alkaline phosphatase activity occur in the uterine epithelium. Maximum activity occurs during the middle of the cycle and is inversely related to the glycogen content of the tissues. Similar changes in phosphatase activity occur in the ewe (52) and the sow (13), but appear to reach a maximum earlier in the cycle in these animals than in the cow. Glycogen was not found in the uterine mucosa of the ewe. Hadek (52) found that cyclic changes in the secretion of iron, mucoprotein, ribonucleic acid, and lipid occurred in the ewe. Fitch (46) found glycogen in both the endometrium and myometrium of the bitch. Gupta (51) reported the uterine fluid in the cow contained 372 mg of Na, 77 mg K, 17 mg Ca, 2.4 mg Mg, and 6.6 mg inorganic phosphorus per 100 ml. The pH was 7.91; the reducing sugars and protein nitrogen were 41.8 and 497.0 mg per 100 ml, respectively.

Changes in the myometrium are also evident during the cycle (33), with the individual muscle cells being longest during the estrogenic phase. Changes in the spontaneous motility of the myometrium have been associated with the morphological alterations of this tissue. During proestrus, estrus, and metestrus excised strips of longitudinal muscle (33) showed slow, even contractions of high amplitude. As the corpus luteum developed, the even, rhythmical contractions were replaced by small, rapid contractions and very slow changes in tone. With intrauterine balloons in intact cows, Hays and VanDemark (61) found small rapid contractions during estrus followed by slower, larger, more irregular contractions during the interestrus intervals. The marked differences in motility obtained by the *in vivo* as compared to the *in vitro* approach at comparable stages of the cycle are unexplained. These workers also found that the uterus from the castrate was inactive and that both estrogen and progesterone increased the spontaneous motility. VanDemark and Hays (137) reported that the motility patterns of the myometrium could be modified by oxytocin.

Bleeding occurs from the endometrium of the cow during metestrus (58). Any portion of the endometrium will bleed, but bleeding tends to occur more frequently from the cotyledons. Bleeding is more frequent in heifers than in multiparous cows, occurring with a frequency of about 80–90% in heifers, compared with 50–60% in the older animals. Bane and Rajakowski (14) reported that bleeding occurred on any of the first 5 days of the cycle. Counting estrus as day 1, the incidence of the metestrous bleeding was as follows: 2% on day 1, 28% on day 2, 65% on day 3, 58% on day 4, and 10% on day 5. Bleeding was evident on more than 1 day in more than one-half of these instances. It usually occurs within 24 hours after ovulation, but this is not constant because it sometimes precedes ovulation. Removal of the ovaries during estrus or at other times during the cycle does not precipitate bleeding. Neither estrogen and progesterone given to castrates nor their withdrawal causes bleeding, indicating other factors may be responsible for bleeding in the cow. It does not appear to be related to fertility. Bleeding may also occur from the vagina in the cow. When present, it is small in amount, accompanied by thin mucus, and is seen most frequently during estrus. In the cow bleeding is frequently observed between the tenth and 14th day following parturition, but no studies have been conducted on the sites from which the bleeding occurs. In the bitch bleeding from the uterus occurs during proestrus. It is associated with increased secretion of mucus and can be produced in the castrate by supplemental estrogens. As in the cow, bleeding occurs in small areas. The blood vessels do not rupture so that most of the red cells escape by diapedesis. Pigments from the extravasated cells may accumulate in the superficial layers of the endometrium.

D. Cervix

Anatomically, the cervix is considered to be a part of the uterus, but its structure and function are distinctly different. The mucous membrane is composed of an epithelium of mucoid-secreting cells and the stroma is a dense connective tissue composed primarily of collagenous fibers, fibroblasts, and cement substance. Complex folding occurs in the luminal portion of the stroma, giving the impression of a highly regular series of tubular glands. Cyclic changes in the secretory epithelium of the cervix have been described in the cow (26, 55, 63, 114), mare (56), ewe (83), and the bitch (9). The amount and the nature of the mucus change during the estrous cycle. During proestrus and estrus the amount of mucus increases and becomes thin, stringy, and clear. Following ovulation, the mucus decreases in amount and is thick. During estrus, Gupta (51) reports the following biochemical properties of bovine cervical mucus; density 0.952; pH 7.81; Na 316 mg/100 ml; K 76 mg/100 ml; Ca 11 mg/100 ml; Mg 2.7 mg/100 ml; inorganic phosphorus 3.1 mg/100 ml; reducing sugars 44 mg/100 ml; and protein 97 mg/100 ml. The physical properties of the mucus are characterized by its "flow-elasticity" (18) and by its ability to form definite morphological patterns when smeared on glass slides (1, 17). Both of these characteristics have been used to identify the follicular phase of the cycle.

E. Vagina

The wall of the vagina consists of three layers: a mucous membrane, an ill-defined muscular coat, and a loose connective tissue which binds it to the surrounding organs. The lamina propria underlying the epithelium is a dense connective tissue characterized by an abundant vascular supply, the presence of numerous lymph nodules, and many cells of the leukocyte series. The epithelium shows marked variations within the different areas of the vagina; it is thinner in the anterior region than in the vestibule.

Cyclic changes occur in the vaginal epithelium. During proestrus and early estrus there is a marked growth and increased thickness of the epithelium. The growth occurs by cellular division in the basal layers, and these cells tend to hypertrophy and become polygonal as they extend toward the surface. In the bitch (Fig. 4) and in rodents the stratified squamous epithelium thickens to 15 to 25 layers and there is extensive cornification of the superficial layers, but in most of the domestic animals cornification is limited in extent. The cells near the lumen are flattened, but

234   P. T. CUPPS, L. L. ANDERSON, AND H. H. COLE

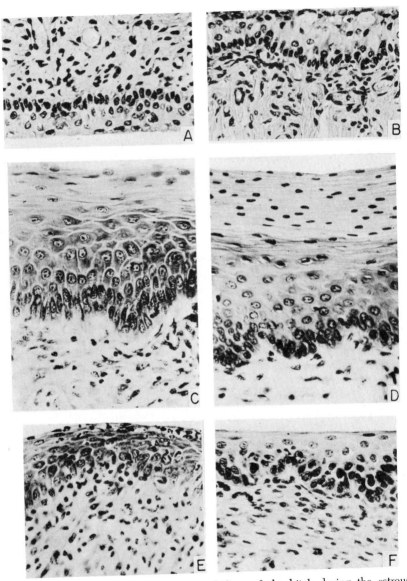

FIG. 4. Changes in the vaginal epithelium of the bitch during the estrous cycle; A and B, anestrus; C, proestrus; D, early estrus; E, metestrus; F, diestrus (44).

retain their nuclei. In the cow (Fig. 5) there is an extensive formation of goblet-type cells in the cervical region of the vagina, which secrete mucus. The growth of the vaginal epithelium is under the influence of estrogen and is an excellent indicator of estrogen secretion. Upon withdrawal of the estrogenic stimulus during late estrus or metestrus the superficial layers of the epithelium slough extensively. Desquamation is accompanied by a massive infiltration of leukocytes and disintegration of the epithelial cells. During diestrus, vaginal smears indicate that the superficial cells are cuboidal and that leukocytes migrate continuously through the epithelium into the

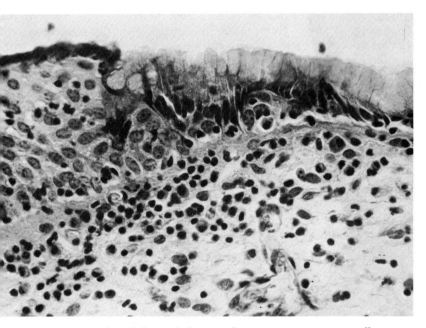

FIG. 5. Vaginal epithelium of the cow showing mucus-secreting cells.

lumen. Some growth may occur during the diestrous phase of the cycle. The cyclic changes in the epithelial cells of the vaginal smear in most domestic animals are not as precise as those seen in rodents. Many investigators have used secretory patterns of the mucus as indicators for determining the stage of the cycle. Two to three days before estrus the vaginal mucus becomes thinner and shows a fern pattern. During late proestrus and early estrus the amount of mucus increases. It becomes clear and very thin, forming long, fine threads, and the fern pattern is very distinct. In the late stages of estrus the amount is decreased and slightly thickened and the fern patterns are quite distinct. During metestrus the mucus is decreased in quantity. It becomes thick and usually has a whitish or yellowish opaque appearance which is caused by the presence of large amounts of the slough- ing epithelium. Details of the changes in the vaginal epithelium during the estrous cycle have been published for the cow (52, 55, 59), ewe (30, 118), mare (8), sow (82, 146), and bitch (44).

F. Pituitary Gland

The morphological changes in the pituitary gland in relation to the estrous cycle have been described in the sow (25), cow (34, 71), ewe (140), bitch (149), and rabbit (150). Although minor species differences in the changes in the pituitary gland with respect to the estrous cycle have been reported, the relationship of the changes in the basophilic cells to those occurring in the ovaries are remarkably similar. In early proestrus, beginning about the 16th day in the cow (Fig. 6) and the 14th day in the ewe, the small basophilic or delta cells begin to synthesize granular material. These granules increase rapidly and then during late proestrus or early estrus in the species which ovulate spontaneously they are released from the cells. A similar degranulation occurs rapidly following coitus in species which do not ovulate spontaneously. This degranulation is accompanied by the accumula- tion of a colloid in the acini of the gland. In the cow the amount of colloid material is maximum about the time of ovulation and then gradually dis- appears during the next 4 or 5 days. The granulation and degranulation of these cells and the accumulation and disappearance of the colloid material are closely associated with the preovulatory growth of the follicle and with the growth of one or more small tertiary follicles to an intermediate size. Whether either the granules within the cells or the colloid is a hormone is not known. Catchpole (23) presented data suggesting that a part of this material is the follicle stimulating principle, but Ross et al. (119) concluded that the colloid was a glycolipid containing no gonadotropic activity.

VI. Hormonal Changes during the Estrous Cycle

A. Steroids

Intensive investigations during the last few years have shown that the ovary synthesizes and secretes many steroids during the estrous cycle. Short (129) found that the follicular fluid from the cow contained pregnenolone, progesterone, 20β-hydroxy-Δ^4-pregnene-3-one, 17α-hydroxyprogesterone, androstenedione, testosterone, estrone, and 17β-estradiol. Progesterone and 17β-estradiol were the two major components. In follicular fluid from the mare, he (127, 128) reported the presence of 17β-estradiol, estrone, cortisol, progesterone, 17α-hydroxyprogesterone, epitestosterone, androstenedione, 19-norandrostenedione, 6α-hydroxyestradiol, 20α-hydroxy-Δ^4-pregnene-3-

one, and dehydroepiandrosterone. Concentrations of estrogens and some of the steroids just mentioned in the ovary and follicular fluids during the estrous cycles have been measured in the mare (73, 128, 138), in the cow (80), and in the sow (79). The range in concentration of the estrogens is very large within the individual ovaries, but in general the concentrations are highest in the ovaries and the follicular fluid when large normal follicles

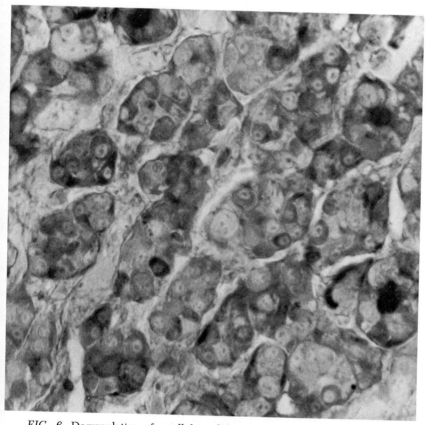

FIG. 6. Degranulation of small basophils and accumulation of PAS-positive material in the pituitary gland. From cow in estrus.

are present. In some instances, however, large follicles may contain very small amounts of estrogen.

Detailed studies of the urinary excretion of estrogen during the estrous cycle have been reported for the sow (19, 78, 109), and the cow (90, 139). Blood levels of free estrogens during the estrous cycle and pregnancy have been measured in the dog (91). The major urinary estrogen metabolite is 17α-estradiol, in the cow, and estrone, in the sow. Estrogens do not appear to be stored within the body, and their excretory rate is an excellent index for their secretion. Although daily variations in excretion rate are large, differences found at the various stages of the estrous cycle are distinct and are in good general agreement between the species which have been studied in detail. The urinary titers begin to rise in early proestrus and reach their highest levels during late proestrus or early estrus. They then decrease slightly in late estrus and before ovulation, reaching their lowest levels shortly after ovulation occurs. At variable periods during the diestrus a secondary rise in estrogen occurs. It has been shown, on the basis of studies from a few individuals, that this rise occurs between the seventh and tenth days in the sow and on the seventh or eighth day in the cow. In both spe-

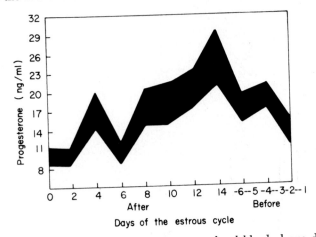

FIG. 7. Concentration of progesterone in peripheral blood plasma during the estrous cycle in the cow. The width of the line represents the subgroup mean ± 1 standard error Plotka *et al.* (*106*).

cies, this diestrous rise is of rather short duration, with the amounts of estrogen decreasing again before the 15th day. In the bitch with a long proestrus the peak excretion occurs very early in proestrus and declines to intermediate levels during late proestrus, with a further decrease during estrus which apparently is related to the time of ovulation.

The secretion of progesterone has been measured during the different stages of the estrous cycle in several domestic species. Using concentrations in the effluent ovarian venous blood, Edgar and Ronaldson (*43*) demonstrated that low levels were present during estrus and the first 3 days of the cycle in the ewe. Beginning on the fourth day, the titers began to rise, reaching a maximum concentration by the seventh day and remaining high through the 15th day. The levels began to drop on the 15th day of a 17-day cycle and decreased abruptly during the 24 hours before the next estrus. Concentrations from individual ewes on any given day of the cycle were quite variable. More closely timed studies (*36*) indicate that the inhibition of the secretion and the release from the corpus luteum occurred suddenly, probably within a few hours on the 15th day in ewes having cycles that averaged 16.5 days.

The abruptness of the change suggested an active inhibition of the secretion. Their studies also suggest that slight degeneration of the luteal cells occurs before the secretion rate is inhibited and that widespread degeneration accompanies the cessation of secretion. Progesterone concentration in the venous blood draining the ovary in the sow was low the first day following estrus. On the fourth day following estrus the average concentration had increased fourfold. It reached a maximum on the eighth day, started to decline by the 14th day, and reached low levels on the 16th and 18th days (49, 87). Schomberg et al. (125) found high correlations between ovarian secretion rates and levels of metabolites in the urine. Plotka et al. (106)

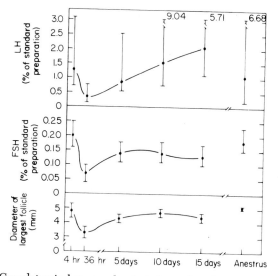

FIG. 8. Gonadotropic hormone levels in hypophysial glands and diameters of ovarian follicles in Welsh Mountain ewes. Standard preparations were Armour ovine FSH and Armour ovine LH. Mean values and their 95% fiducial limits are shown for each period. Adapted from Robertson and Hutchinson (115).

reported the following levels of progesterone in nanograms per milliliter in the peripheral blood of cattle during the estrous cycle (Fig. 7): estrus 10.1; 2 days 9.9; 4 days 17.7; 6 days 10.6; 8 days 17.7; 10 days 18.4; 12 days 20.4; 14 days 25.8; 5–6 days before estrus 17.1; 3–4 days before estrus 19.4; and 1–2 days before estrus 13.3. The relative changes in the peripheral blood reported by these investigators appear to be consonant with the total amounts of progesterone and progestins found in the corpora lutea at similar stages of the cycle by Mares et al. (85). Cyclic changes in other steroids which have been isolated from ovarian tissue have not been reported.

B. GONADOTROPINS

Development of assays for FSH and LH—the Steelman–Pohley method (133) for FSH; the Greep ventral prostate method (50) and the Parlow

OAAD method (*102*) for LH—has made it possible to study the changes in the levels of these hormones in the pituitary gland during the various stages of the estrous cycle. Since the amount of the hormone in the gland represents a balance between synthesis and release and since the rate of release may not be constant, the levels of hormone reported have been quite variable and sometimes difficult to interpret. Using various combinations of the assays just mentioned, pituitary levels of the gonadotropins have been measured in the ewe (*115, 117, 123*), the sow (*35, 103*), and the cow (*7, 112*). In cycling ewes, both pituitary gonadotropins decreased between 4 and 35 hours after the onset of behavioral estrus and then returned to pro-

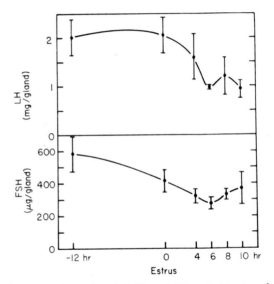

FIG. 9. Changes in hypophysial FSH and LH activities in relation to estrus and ovulation in the ewe. FSH or LH are expressed as microgram-equivalents of NIH-FSH-S1 or NIH-LH-S1 per gland. Mean values and their 95% fiducial limits are shown. From Robertson and Rakha (*117*).

estrous levels by the 15th day (Fig. 8). More closely timed studies (*117*) showed a significant drop in pituitary FSH sometime during the 12 hours before the onset of estrus, with a further decline during the first 6 hours after the onset of estrus. A disturbing aspect of this carefully controlled study is the large individual variations in both FSH and LH potencies reported at given stages of the cycle (Fig. 9). Is it true that the pituitary content of one individual will be 3 or 4 times greater than that of another in a comparable physiological state? Dierschke and Clegg (*37*) did not study FSH or LH pituitary levels prior to estrus, but did obtain evidence of a decline in concentration of both hormones after first acceptance of the male. Parlow *et al.* (*103*) and Melampy *et al.* (*89*) found a steady increase in the FSH and LH content between days 1 and 16 of the estrous cycle in the sow with a slight decline on the 18th day. These gonadotropins declined to lowest levels during early estrus, indicating a further release at this time. Hypophysial levels of FSH and LH (112) declined significantly during the first 18 hours of estrus in the cow (Fig. 10).

Using an ovarian cholesterol depletion assay, Liptrap and Raeside (76) reported a brief elevation in LH activity in the blood of the sow 16–24 hours before the onset of estrus, which coincided with the maximal secretion of urinary estrogen. It was suggested that this peak of LH activity represented

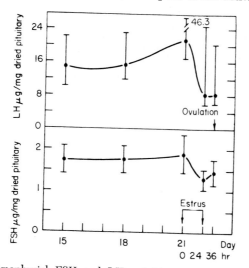

FIG. 10. Hypophysial FSH and LH activities in cows at ovulation. Gland concentrations of FSH and LH are expressed in microgram-equivalents of NIH-FSH-S1 or NIH-LH-B1 per milligram of dried pituitary gland. Mean values and their 95% fiducial limits are shown. From Rakha and Robertson (112).

the ovulatory surge of this hormone. In preliminary experiments, Anderson and McShan (7) reported a high level of LH activity in porcine plasma at day 1 of the estrous cycle, with minimal levels at days 13 to 19. They also reported rises in LH concentration in the blood of cows 6–17 hours before ovulation.

VII. Mechanisms Controlling the Estrous Cycle

The physiological mechanisms controlling the various events of the estrous cycle are complex and, at present, not fully understood. Some of the interactions between the central nervous system, the pituitary gland, the gonads, and the accessory reproductive organs in the cow, sow, and ewe are schematically presented in Fig. 11. As depicted in this figure, gonadotropins from the anterior pituitary gland stimulate ovarian follicular and luteal function. The steroids produced by the ovaries stimulate or inhibit the central nervous system to affect sexual behavior responses as well as regulate, probably indirectly, through the hypothalamus, the production of tropic hormones by the pituitary gland. They also stimulate endometrial and myometrial function.

Very little information is available on the levels of LH and FSH in the blood of domestic animals at different stages of the cycle. Anderson and McShan (7) have reported values for LH in the sow and cow based on the ovarian ascorbic acid depletion assay. In both species about 11 μg/100 ml were found on the first day of estrus as compared with levels of less than 1 μg/100 ml at other phases of the cycle. Dierschke and Clegg (37) ob-

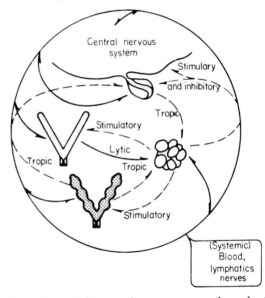

FIG. 11. Relationships of the central nervous system, hypophysis, ovaries, and uterus in the cow, sow, and ewe.

tained values in ewe serum by the OAAD method which, in some instances, were 100-fold greater than that obtained by Geschwind (47) on the same sera using radioimmunoassay. Snook and Cole (131) found no correlation between values of LH in the serum of mares immunized with FSH as an antigen by the OAAD method as compared with the ventral prostate assay. Thus, it seems clear that the OAAD method cannnot be used successfully for blood values of LH in all circumstances.

In polyestrous animals the length of the estrous cycle is controlled by the length of the functional life of the corpus luteum and the secretion of progesterone. Early work (55, 145) showed that removal of the corpus luteum shortened the estrous cycle. Interference with the development of the corpus luteum and the secretion of progesterone also shortens the cycle.

Experimentally, the injection of oxytocin (10) in the early stages of the cycle prevents the normal development of the corpus luteum and shortens the cycle in the cow. Supplementary oxytocin is not effective if injected after the corpus luteum is formed and depends on the presence of an intact uterus (5, 10). Uterine distention shortens the cycle in the ewe (69, 95), but has no effect on the length of the cycle in the gilt (3).

Exogenous progesterone (16, 40, 136, 144) inhibits estrus and thus prolongs the estrous cycle if it is supplied before the functional activity of the corpus luteum is impaired.

The role of the uterus in controlling ovarian function and, thus, sexual behavior is now well established in domestic animals. Secretory activity of the corpus luteum is altered by the adenohypophysial gonadotropins (luteotropin) as well as by local and systemic effects of the uterus. Some reviews on the relationships of the uterus to ovarian and hypophysial functions include those by Rothchild (120), Eckstein (41), Anderson and Melampy (6), Melampy and Anderson (88), and Short (130).

In the pig, ewe, and cow the development and beginning of regression of the corpus luteum during the estrous cycle require 2–3 weeks.

After hysterectomy the secretory function of the corpus luteum is maintained for a period greater than that for gestation. In partially hysterectomized animals the corpus luteum fails, though the cyclical intervals are usually slightly longer than found in unoperated or sham operated ones. A local effect of the uterus is found in partially hysterectomized animals, with persistence of corpora lutea in the ovary opposite the retained uterus, the luteal regression occurring in the ovary adjacent to the uterine fragment.

The luteolytic effect of the nongravid uterus, whether acting locally or systemically, is mediated by the vascular system, since estrous cycles continue after autotransplantation of the uterus. Experimental evidence also indicates the luteolytic action of injected oxytocin in the cow is through the uterus (10, 48, 61a). The interrelationships of the uterus and the functional life-span of the corpus luteum are shown in Fig. 12.

The behavioral patterns associated with estrus in the normal cycling female are complex and depend upon steroids secreted by the ovary; these secretions, in turn, involve the closely integrated activity of the central nervous system and the pituitary gland. In the normal cycling female, estrus is associated with a high titer of estrogen and a decreasing titer of progesterone, suggesting that the changing levels of these steroids are of primary importance in its production. In spayed ewes the behavioral patterns of estrus can be produced experimentally by exogenous progesterone for periods of several days, followed by withdrawal and the injection of exogenous estrogen (118). Exogenous estrogen alone in the spayed ewe resulted in a rather erratic response and, possibly, inhibition. Treatment with the progesterone apparently removed the inhibition and lowered the threshold for the response to estrogen. Exogenous testosterone (29, 75) can potentiate behavioral estrus in the ewe, but the patterns may not be identical with those shown by the normal cycling female. Changes in androgen secretion and its effects on the estrous cycle have not been studied in detail. The effects of the steroid hormones on the behavioral patterns of estrus are mediated through the central nervous system. At the present time, the pathways involved are not known, but the hypothalamus appears to be of primary importance.

The important roles of the gonadotropins in the development of the follicle, ovulation, and corpus luteum formation have been recognized since Fevold et al. (45) reported that certain pituitary extracts produced follicular growth and others produced ovulation and corpus luteum formation after the follicles had reached a certain stage of development. This view con-

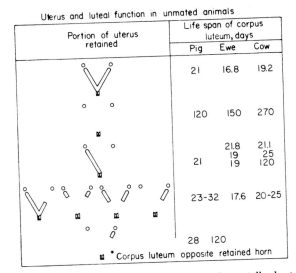

Uterus and luteal function in unmated animals

Portion of uterus retained	Life span of corpus luteum, days		
	Pig	Ewe	Cow
	21	16.8	19.2
	120	150	270
	21	21.8 19 19	21.1 25 120
	23-32	17.6	20-25
	28	120	

⋈ *Corpus luteum opposite retained horn

FIG. 12. Luteal function in hysterectomized and partially hysterectomized pigs, ewes, and cows (4, 38, 39, 48, 68, 72, 84, 93, 94, 97, 122, 132, 147).

sidered that follicle stimulating hormone was responsible for follicular growth to the preovulatory stage and then an abrupt increase in luteinizing hormone caused further growth, ovulation, and corpus luteum formation. Robertson and Rakha (117) have reported the following sequence of events in relation to estrus and ovulation in the ewe. Follicle stimulating hormone concentration in the pituitary gland showed a significant drop sometime during the 12 hours before the onset of estrus, with a further decline during the first 6 hours. Luteinizing hormone content of the pituitary did not decrease until after the onset of estrus, but declined very rapidly during the first 6 hours. These changes suggest that the release of gonadotropins from the pituitary occurs approximately 24–30 hours before ovulation in the cow and the ewe. This time interval is very similar to that reported for the cat, which does not ovulate spontaneously, but is somewhat longer than that reported for the rabbit. The normal variation between the onset of estrus and the time of ovulation suggests that the time of release of the gonadotropins may also be variable with respect to the onset of estrus.

Though, no doubt, surges of FSH and LH secretion do occur at slightly different times, too much emphasis has probably been placed upon the sequential action of these hormones. None of the recent radioimmunoassay studies of FSH and LH activities in the plasma of women (92, 100) indicate that the plasma becomes devoid of either of these hormones at any stage of the normal menstrual cycle. Also, studies on relatively pure FSH extracts (77) or on FSH extracts in which LH has been neutralized by LH antibodies (31, 74) may be interpreted as indicating that both FSH and LH are essential for every step in follicular development beyond the stage of development reached in the hypophysectomized animal up to the ovulation stage and for the secretion of estrogen. Lostroh and Johnson (77) found that neither FSH nor LH injected alone into hypophysectomized female rats produced estrogen secretion or follicular growth in the doses employed. They did find that if FSH and LH were injected together for 3 days, the injection of either FSH or LH 8 hours after the third injection induced ovulation in 100% of the hypophysectomized rats. Imamichi (67) has also reported that ovulation can be induced with FSH. Contrary to these findings, Papkoff (101) reported that highly purified preparations of ovine FSH stimulated both follicular growth and estrogen secretion. Thus, nearly 35 years after the report that the anterior lobe secreted two hormones, FSH and LH, the role which each plays in controlling ovarian activity remains obscure.

On the basis of the present evidence, the interactions between the pituitary, central nervous system, ovaries, and uterus to produce the diestrous cycle in polyestrous animals may be summarized as follows. During the latter part of the diestrous phase the progesterone levels decline slightly from the maximum secretion rate and the pituitary begins to increase the synthesis of gonadotropin(s). This is associated with an increased secretion of estrogen. As the estrogen titers rise during the late proestrus, progesterone secretion is inhibited abruptly by factors from the uterus allowing the full effects of estrogen to be exerted. The precipitous fall in progesterone secretion is followed shortly by the behavioral patterns characteristic of estrus, and releasing factor(s) from the hypothalamus cause an increased secretion of gonadotropin(s), which results in ovulation. Continued secretion of one or more of the gonadotropins causes the formation of a new corpus luteum and the preliminary growth of one or more small tertiary follicles. As the corpus luteum forms, the secretion of progesterone increases and a new cycle is initiated. A second rise in the secretion of estrogen occurs in some cycles in the cow, but its frequency and extent have not been fully evaluated. Further research will probably reveal variations of this basic pattern in the different species, particularly in the time relationships and, probably, in the number of hormones involved.

REFERENCES

1. Abusineina, M. E., *Vet. Record* **74**, 619 (1962).
2. Alliston, C. W., Patterson, T. B., and Ulberg, L. C., *J. Animal Sci.* **17**, 322 (1958).
3. Anderson, L. L., *J. Animal Sci.* **21**, 597 (1962).
4. Anderson, L. L., Bowerman, A. M., and Melampy, R. M., *in* "Advances in Neuroendocrinology" (A. V. Nalbandov, ed.), p. 345. Univ. of Illinois Press, Urbana, Illinois, 1963.
5. Anderson, L. L., Bowerman, A. M., and Melampy, R. M., *J. Animal Sci.* **24**, 964 (1965).
6. Anderson, L. L., and Melampy, R. M., *U.S. Dept. Agr. Misc. Publ.* **1005**, 64 (1964).
7. Anderson, R. R., and McShan, W. H., *Endocrinology* **78**, 976 (1966).
8. Andrews, F. N., and McKenzie, F. F., *Missouri Univ. Agr. Expt. Sta. Res. Bull.* **329** (1941).
9. Arenas, N., and Sammartino, R., "Estudio experimental sobre los organos genitales de la perra." Aniceto Lopez, Buenos Aires, 1938.
10. Armstrong, D. T., and Hansel, W., *J. Dairy Sci.* **42**, 533 (1959).
11. Asdell, S. A., *Cornell Vet.* **50**, 3 (1960).
11a. Asdell, S. A., "Patterns of Mammalian Reproduction," 1st ed., p. 20. Cornell Univ. Press (Comstock), Ithaca, New York, 1946.
12. Asdell, S. A., "Patterns of Mammalian Reproduction," 2nd ed., pp. 518, 539, 585, 635. Cornell Univ. Press (Comstock), Ithaca, New York, 1964.
13. Austad, R., and Garm, O., *Nature* **184**, 999 (1959).
14. Bane, A., and Rajakoski, E., *Cornell Vet.* **51**, 77 (1961).
15. Barker, H. B., and Wiggins, E. L., *J. Animal Sci.* **23**, 967 (1964).
16. Becker, L. N., Ulberg, L. C., Grummer, R. H., and Casida, L. E., *J. Animal Sci.* **13**, 648 (1954).
17. Betteridge, K. J., and Raeside, J. I., *J. Reprod. Fertility* **3**, 410 (1962).
18. Blackburn, P. S., and Castle, M. E., *Brit. Vet. J.* **115**, 399 (1959).
19. Bowerman, A. M., Anderson, L. L., and Melampy, R. M., *Iowa State J. Sci.* **38**, 437 (1964).
20. Braden, A. W. H., and Moule, G. R., *Australian J. Agr. Res.* **15**, 937 (1964).
21. Buch, N. C., Tyler, W. J., and Casida, L. E., *J. Dairy Sci.* **38**, 73 (1955).
22. Burger, J. F., *Onderstepoort J. Vet. Res.* **25**, Suppl. 2, 218 (1952).
23. Catchpole, H. R., *J. Endocrinol.* **6**, 218 (1949).
24. Clapp, H., *Proc. Am. Soc. Animal Production*, p. 259 (1937).
25. Cleveland, R., and Wolfe, J. M., *Am. J. Anat.* **53**, 191 (1933).
26. Cole, H. H., *Am. J. Anat.* **46**, 261 (1930).
27. Cole, H. H., and Casady, R. B., *Endocrinology* **41**, 119 (1947).
28. Cole, H. H., and Cupps, P. T. (eds.), "Reproduction in Domestic Animals," 1st ed., Vol. I, pp. 225, 295. Academic Press, New York, 1959.
29. Cole, H. H., Hart, G. H., and Miller, R. F., *Endocrinology* **36**, 370 (1945).
30. Cole, H. H., and Miller, R. F., *Proc. Soc. Exptl. Biol. Med.* **28**, 841 (1931).
31. Cole, H. H., and Snook, R. B., *Proc. 5th Intern. Congr. Animal Reproduction, Trento* **II**, 143 (1964).
32. Corner, G. W., *Carnegie Inst. Wash. Contribs. Embryol.* **13**, 117 (1921).

33. Cupps, P. T., and Asdell, S. A., *J. Animal Sci.* **3**, 351 (1944).
34. Cupps, P. T., Laben, R. C., and Mead, S. W., *Hilgardia* **29**, 383 (1959).
35. Day, B. N., Anderson, L. L., Hazel, L. N., and Melampy, R. M., *J. Animal Sci.* **18**, 675 (1959).
36. Deane, H. W., Hay, M. F., Moor, R. M., Rowson, L. E. A., and Short, R. V. *Acta Endocrinol.* **51**, 245 (1966).
37. Dierschke, D. J., and Clegg, M. T., *J. Reprod. Fertility* **15**, 321 (1968).
38. du Mesnil du Buisson, F., Thesis, Doct. Sci., University of Paris, 1966.
39. du Mesnil du Buisson, F., and Dauzier, L., *Ann. Zootech. Suppl.* **8**, 147 (1959).
40. Dutt, R. H., and Casida, L. E., *Endocrinology* **43**, 208 (1948).
41. Eckstein, P., *Trans. 2nd Meeting Intern. Study Group Steroid Hormones, Rome*, p. 337 (1965).
42. Edgar, D. G., and Asdell, S. A., *J. Endocrinol.* **21**, 315 (1960).
43. Edgar, D. G., and Ronaldson, J. W., *J. Endocrinol.* **16**, 378 (1958).
44. Evans, H. M., and Cole, H. H., *Mem. Univ. Calif.* **9** (1931).
45. Fevold, H. L., Hisaw, F. L., and Leonard, S. L., *Am. J. Physiol.* **97**, 291 (1931).
46. Fitch, K. L., *J. Morphol.* **113**, 331 (1963).
47. Geschwind, I. I., personal communication, 1967.
48. Ginther, O. J., *J. Animal Sci.* **26**, 578 (1967).
49. Gomes, W. R., Herschler, R. C., and Erb, R. E., *J. Animal Sci.* **24**, 722 (1965).
50. Greep, R. O., Van Dyke, H. B., and Chow, B. F., *Endocrinology* **30**, 635 (1942).
51. Gupta, H. C., *Dissertation Abstr.* **23**, 803 (1962).
52. Hadek, R., *Am. J. Vet. Res.* **19**, 882 (1958).
53. Hafez, E. S. E., *J. Agr. Sci.* **42**, 189 (1952).
54. Hall, J. G., Branton, C., and Stone, E. J., *J. Dairy Sci.* **42**, 1086 (1959).
55. Hammond, J., "The Physiology of Reproduction in the Cow." Cambridge Univ. Press, London and New York, 1927.
56. Hammond, J., and Wodzicka, K., *Proc. Roy. Soc.* **B130**, 1 (1941).
57. Hamner, C. E., and Williams, W. L., *Fertility Sterility* **16**, 170 (1965).
58. Hansel, W., and Asdell, S. A., *J. Animal Sci.* **11**, 346 (1952).
59. Hansel, W., Asdell, S. A., and Roberts, S. J., *Am. J. Vet. Res.* **10**, 221 (1949).
60. Hawk, H. W., Turner, G. D., and Sykes, J. E., *Am. J. Vet. Res.* **22**, 689 (1961).
61. Hays, R. L., and VanDemark, N. L., *Am. J. Physiol.* **172**, 553 (1953).
61a. Henricks, D. M., Oxenreider, S. L., Anderson, L. L., and Guthrie, H. D., *Federation Proc.* **26**, 366 (1967).
62. Henricson, B., and Rajakoski, E., *Cornell Vet.* **49**, 494 (1959).
63. Herrick, J. B., *Am. J. Vet. Res.* **12**, 276 (1951).
64. Hulet, C. V., Blackwell, R. L., Ercanbrack, S. K., Price, D. A., and Wilson, L. O., *J. Animal Sci.* **21**, 870 (1962).
65. Hutchinson, J. S. M., O'Conner, P. J., and Robertson, H. A., *J. Agr. Sci* **63**, 59 (1964).
66. Hutchinson, J. S. M., and Robertson, H. A., *Res. Vet. Sci.* **7**, 17 (1966).
67. Imamichi, T., *Saishin Igaku* **18**, 1207 (1963).
68. Inskeep, E. K., and Butcher, R. L., *J. Animal Sci.* **25**, 1164 (1966).

248   P. T. CUPPS, L. L. ANDERSON, AND H. H. COLE

69. Inskeep, E. K., Oloufa, M. M., Howland, B. E., Pope, A. L., and Casida, L. E., *J. Animal Sci.* **21**, 331 (1962).
70. Joubert, D. M., and Louw, D. F. J., *Proc. S. African Soc. Animal Production* **3**, 139 (1964).
71. Jubb, K. V., and McEntee, K., *Cornell Vet.* **45**, 593 (1955).
72. Kiracofe, G. H., and Spies, H. G., *J. Reprod. Fertility* **11**, 275 (1966).
73. Knudson, O., and Velle, W., *J. Reprod. Fertility* **2**, 130 (1961).
74. Li, C. H., Moudgal, N. R., Trenkle, A., Bourdel, G., and Sadri, K., *Ciba Found. Colloq. Endocrinol.* **14**, 20 (1962).
75. Lindsay, D. R., and Robinson, T. J., *Nature* **192**, 761 (1961).
76. Liptrap, R. M., and Raeside, J. I., *J. Reprod. Fertility* **11**, 439 (1966).
77. Lostroh, A. J., and Johnson, R. E., *Endocrinology* **79**, 991 (1966).
78. Lunaas, T., *J. Reprod. Fertility* **4**, 13 (1962).
79. Lunaas, T., *Acta Endocrinol.* **44**, 529 (1963).
80. Lunaas, T., *Acta Vet. Scand.* **5**, 35 (1964).
81. McEntee, K., Hughes, D. E., and Gilman, H. L., *Cornell Vet.* **44**, 376 (1954).
82. McKenzie, F. F., *Missouri Univ. Agr. Expt. Sta. Res. Bull.* **86** (1926).
83. McKenzie, F. F., and Terrill, C. E., *Missouri Univ. Agr. Expt. Sta. Res. Bull.* **264** (1937).
84. Malven, P. V., and Hansel, W., *J. Dairy Sci.* **47**, 1388 (1964).
85. Mares, S. E., Zimbelman, R. G., and Casida, L. E., *J. Animal Sci.* **21**, 266 (1962).
86. Marshall, F. H. A., *Phil. Trans. Roy. Soc. London, Ser. B* **196**, 47 (1903).
87. Masuda, H., Anderson, L. L., Henricks, D. M., and Melampy, R. M., *Endocrinology* **80**, 240 (1967).
88. Melampy, R. M., and Anderson, L. L., *J. Animal Sci.* **28**, Suppl. 77 (1968).
89. Melampy, R. M., Henricks, D. M., Anderson, L. L., Chen, C. L., and Schultz, J. R., *Endocrinology* **78**, 801 (1966).
90. Mellin, T. N., and Erb, R. E., *Steroids* **7**, 589 (1966).
91. Metzler, F., Jr., Eleftheriou, B. E., and Fox, M., *Proc. Soc. Exptl. Biol. Med.* **121**, 374 (1966).
92. Midgley, A. R., Jr., *Proc. 49th Meeting Endocrine Soc., Miami Beach,* p. 60 (1967).
93. Moor, R. M., *J. Animal Sci.* **26**, 1499 (1967).
94. Moor, R. M., and Rowson, L. E. A., *J. Reprod. Fertility* **11**, 307 (1966).
95. Moore, W. W., and Nalbandov, A. V., *Endocrinology* **53**, 1 (1953).
96. Mulligan, R. M., *J. Morph.* **71**, 431 (1942).
97. Neill, J. D., and Day, B. N., *Endocrinology* **74**, 355 (1964).
98. Nellor, J. E., *Anat. Record* **151**, 171 (1965).
99. Nellor, J. E., and Brown, J. E., *Anat. Record* **155**, 591 (1966).
100. Odell, W. D., and Parlow, A. F., *Proc. 49th Meeting Endocrine Soc., Miami Beach,* p. 61 (1967).
101. Papkoff, H., *Acta Endocrinol.* **48**, 439 (1965).
102. Parlow, A. F., in "Human Pituitary Gonadotropins" (A. Albert, ed.), p. 300. Thomas, Springfield, Illinois, 1961.
103. Parlow, A. F., Anderson, L. L., and Melampy, R. M., *Endocrinology* **75**, 365 (1964).
104. Perkins, J. L., and Goode, L., *J. Animal Sci.* **25**, 465 (1966).

105. Phillips, R. W., Simmons, V. L., and Schott, R. G., *Am. J. Vet. Res.* **4**, 360 (1943).
106. Plotka, E. D., Erb, R. E., Callahan, C. J., and Gomes, W. R., *J. Dairy Sci.* **50**, 1158 (1967).
107. Quinlin, J., and Mare, G., *Vet. Res. S. Africa* **17**, 663 (1931).
108. Radford, H. M., and Watson, R. H., *Australian J. Agr. Res.* **8**, 460 (1957).
109. Raeside, J. I., *J. Reprod. Fertility* **6**, 421 (1963).
110. Raeside, J. I., and McDonald, M. F., *J. Endocrinol.* **18**, 350 (1959).
111. Rajakoski, E., *Acta Endocrinol. Suppl.* **52** (1960).
112. Rakha, A. M., and Robertson, H. A., *J. Endocrinol.* **31**, 245 (1965).
113. Riches, J. H., and Watson, R. H., *Australian J. Agr. Res.* **5**, 141 (1954).
114. Roark, D. B., and Herman, H. A., *Missouri Univ. Agr. Expt. Sta. Res. Bull.* **455** (1950).
115. Robertson, H. A., and Hutchinson, J. S. M., *J. Endocrinol.* **24**, 143 (1962).
116. Robertson, H. A., and Rakha, A. M., *J. Reprod. Fertility* **10**, 271 (1965).
117. Robertson, H. A., and Rakha, A. M., *J. Endocrinol.* **35**, 177 (1966).
118. Robinson, T. J., *in* "Reproduction in Domestic Animals" (H. H. Cole and P. T. Cupps, eds.), 1st ed., Vol. I, p. 312. Academic Press, New York, 1959.
119. Ross, G. T., Bahn, R. C., and Schmidt, R. W., *Program 40th Meeting, San Francisco, Endocrine Soc. Paper No.* **48** (1958).
120. Rothchild, I., *Vitamins Hormones* **23**, 209 (1965).
121. Rottensten, K., *Beretn. Forsøgslab.* **306**, 1 (1958).
122. Rowson, L. E. A., and Moor, R., *Proc. 5th Intern. Congr. Animal Reproduction Artificial Insemination, Trento* **2**, 394 (1954).
123. Santolucito, J. A., Clegg, M. T., and Cole, H. H., *Endocrinology* **66**, 273 (1960).
124. Schinckle, P. G., *Australian J. Agr. Res.* **5**, 465 (1954).
125. Schomberg, D. W., Jones, P. H., Erb, R. E., and Gomes, W. R., *J. Animal Sci.* **25**, 1181 (1966).
126. Shelton, M., *J. Animal Sci.* **19**, 368 (1960).
127. Short, R. V., *J. Endocrinol.* **20**, 147 (1960).
128. Short, R. V., *J. Endocrinol.* **22**, 153 (1962).
129. Short, R. V., *J. Endocrinol.* **23**, 401 (1962).
130. Short, R. V., *Ann. Rev. Physiol.* **29**, 373 (1967).
131. Snook, R., Cole, H. H., and Geschwind, I. I., *J. Reprod. Fertility* **15**, 239 (1968).
131a. Sorenson, A. M., Hansel, W., Hough, W. H., Armstrong, D. T., McEntee, K., and Bratton, R. W., *Cornell Agr. Expt. Sta. Bull.* **936** (1959).
132. Spies, H. G., Zimmerman, D. R., Self, H. L., and Casida, L. E., *J. Animal Sci.* **19**, 101 (1960).
133. Steelman, S. L., and Pohley, F. M., *Endocrinology* **53**, 604 (1953).
134. Torell, D. T., *Sheep Day/Beef Day Bull.* p. 19, Univ. of Calif., Davis, California (1965).
135. Trum, B. F., *Cornell Vet.* **40**, 17 (1950).
136. Ulberg, L. C., Christian, R. E., and Casida, L. E., *J. Animal Sci.* **10**, 752 (1951).
137. VanDemark, N. L., and Hays, R. L., *Fertility Sterility* **5**, 131 (1954).
138. van der Horst, C. J. G., and de Bois, C. H. W., *Tijdschr. Diergeneesk.* **91**, 1002 (1966).

139. Varman, P. N., and Smith, E. P., *J. Dairy Sci.* **47**, 687 (1964).
140. Warbritton, V., and McKenzie, F. F., *Missouri Univ. Agr. Expt. Sta. Res. Bull.* **257** (1937).
141. Warnick, A. C., *J. Animal Sci.* **14**, 1003 (1955).
142. Warnick, A. C., Casida, L. E., and Grummer, R. H., *J. Animal Sci.* **9**, 66 (1950).
143. Weeth, H. J., and Herman, H. A., *Missouri Univ. Agr. Expt. Sta. Res. Bull.* **501** (1952).
144. Willett, E. L., *J. Dairy Sci.* **33**, 381 (1950).
145. Williams, W. L., and Williams, W. W., "The Diseases of the Genital Organs of Domestic Animals." W. L. Williams, Ithaca, New York, 1921.
146. Wilson, K. M., *Am. J. Anat.* **37**, 417 (1926).
147. Wiltbank, J. N., and Casida, L. E., *J. Animal Sci.* **15**, 134 (1956).
148. Wiltbank, J. N., and Cook, A. C., *J. Animal Sci.* **17**, 640 (1958).
149. Wolfe, J. M., Cleveland, R., and Campbell, M., *Z. Zellforsch Mikroskop. Anat.* **17**, 420 (1933).
150. Wolfe, J. M., Phelps, D., and Cleveland, R., *Am. J. Anat.* **55**, 363 (1934).

10 SPERMATOGENESIS AND MORPHOLOGY OF THE SPERMATOZOON

R. ORTAVANT, M. COUROT,
AND M. T. HOCHEREAU

I. Introduction

Spermatozoa represent only the final step in a series of complex changes (spermatogenesis) that govern their number and properties. We will try to clarify the phenomenon of spermatogenesis in the bull (*63, 68, 71*), the ram (*33, 94*), the boar (*60, 66*), and the rabbit (*4, 114*).

1. The primordial germ cells migrate from germinal crests and occupy gonadal space sometime before sexual differentiation. In the fetus and young male the *gonocytes* are contained inside the seminiferous tubules.

2. Gonocytes multiply and, some months after birth, give rise to *sper-*

matogonia. The quantitative efficiency of spermatogenesis depends to a great extent on the manner in which these divisions take place.

3. The cells originating from the last spermatogonial division are the *primary spermatocytes*. Meiotic division of these spermatocytes results in the production of daughter cells, the *secondary spermatocytes*.

4. The metamorphosis of the *spermatids* (products of the division of the secondary spermatocytes) into spermatozoa (spermiogenesis) constitutes the fourth point of interest. The quality of the spermatozoa produced depends to a great extent on this metamorphosis, which occurs in the seminiferous epithelium, but undergoes completion in the epididymis.

5. The various germ cells are located in the seminiferous epithelium, whose structure is maintained by the Sertoli cells.

II. Description of the Spermatogenic and Seminiferous Epithelial Cycles

The spermatogenic cycle begins with a stem cell or A-type spermatogonium, which provides the starting point of a spermatogenic series. Before this series has completed its evolution, several new ones are produced on the same site of the seminiferous tubule. Thus, any section of a seminiferous tubule shows several superimposed generations of germ cells. They develop in close relation one to another such that in any given area of the seminiferous epithelium there is a constant succession of cellular associations that takes place with a cyclic regularity.

"The cycle of the seminiferous epithelium is formed by the series of changes occurring in a given area of the seminiferous epithelium between two successive appearances of the same cellular association" (76, 77). *The duration of the spermatogenic cycle is the interval between the appearance of the stem spermatogonium and the release of spermatozoa which are produced from it.* It thus represents the length of time necessary for the formation of the spermatogenic series.

A. THE STAGES OF THE CYCLE OF THE SEMINIFEROUS EPITHELIUM

The cellular associations which may be recognized during a cycle of the seminiferous epithelium permit distinguishing the various stages.

Two principal methods of classification may be used. One is based on the development of the acrosomic system (32, 77), the other on meiotic divisions, the shape of spermatid nucleus, and the release of spermatozoa into the lumen of the seminiferous tubule (94, 105).

Clermont and Leblond (33) defined twelve stages in the cycle of the seminiferous epithelium of the ram and of the bull. In the uniformly stained idiosome (stage 1) of the young spermatids, two or three proacrosomic granules appear (stage 2) which fuse into one single acrosomic granule (stage 3) during the "Golgi phase." The "cap phase" is characterized by a slight flattening of the granule on the nuclear surface (stage 4), then by the appearance of a head cap (stage 5), which gradually covers, first, a third (stage 6), then half (stage 7) of the nuclear surface. At the beginning of the "acrosome phase" the acrosomic granule and the cap migrate toward the basement membrane (stage 8), then, the acrosomic granule, which is now known as the acrosome, protrudes at the tip of the nucleus (stage 9) and changes from an elongated rod (stage 10) into a triangle (stage 11) and finally into a crescent (stage 12). The "maturation phase," therefore, succeeds the "acrosome phase."

According to Roosen-Runge and Giesel (105) and Ortavant (94), eight stages may be defined in the seminiferous epithelial cycle of the ram (Table I), bull, and boar, which are described as follows:

Stage 1: From the disappearance of spermatozoa from the seminiferous epithelium to the onset of elongation and increase in stainability of the spermatid nuclei (Fig. 1).

Stage 2: From the beginning of elongation and increase in stainability of the nuclei to the bundle formation of the spermatids (Fig. 2).

Stage 3: From the beginning of the bundle formation of the spermatids to the appearance of the first maturation division of the primary spermatocytes (Fig. 3).

Stage 4: From the beginning of the first maturation division to the end of the second maturation division (Fig. 4).

Stage 5: Begins immediately after the second maturation division and ends when the chromatin of the nuclei in the new spermatids shows a dusty appearance. The nuclei of these spermatids contain karyosomes bound together by a loose network (Fig. 5).

Stage 6: From the beginning of the dusty appearance of the nuclear chromatin in the new spermatids to the point when *all* the bundles of old spermatids have separated from the nuclei of the Sertoli cells.

Stage 7: From the beginning to the end of the migration of old spermatids toward the lumen of the seminiferous tubules.

Stage 8: From the end of the centripetal movement of the spermatozoa to their complete release into the lumen of the seminiferous tubule (Fig. 6).

This last method permits a rapid identification of variations in the principal events of spermatogenesis, but certain stages have been subdivided for a more comprehensive analysis (65).

B. FREQUENCY OF THE STAGES OF THE SEMINIFEROUS EPITHELIAL CYCLE

Seminiferous epithelial cycles are similar in the bull, the ram, and the rabbit; in the boar there are differences, and they tend to resemble the pattern of the cycle in the rat (Table II). The rate of occurrence of the first three stages decreases from the bull to the rat (62.2–23%), while that

TABLE I

SEMINIFEROUS EPITHELIAL CYCLE IN THE RAM WITH CELLS OF THE SPERMATOGENIC SERIES CHARACTERISTIC OF EACH STAGE[a]

Stage 1	Stage 2	Stage 3	Stage 4	Stage 5	Stage 6	Stage 7	Stage 8
A_1	x A_1	1 Spg A_1	A_1	A_1	A_1	A_1	A_1
x 16 Spcl	16 L	1 A_2	x A_2	2 In	x In	4 B_1	x -- 8 B_2
16 P	16 D	16 (L + Z)	16 Z	16 (Z + P)	16 P	16 P	16 P
		16 D	x 32 SpcI x	64 Spi R	64 R	64 R	64 R
64 R	64 Spi L	64 L	64 L	64 L	64 L	64 L	64-0 Spz

[a] Arrows indicate the direction of evolution of the spermatogenic series.

Key: Spg = spermatogonia; SpcI = primary spermatocyte; L = leptotene; Z = zygotene; P = pachytene; D = diplotene; SpcII = secondary spermatocyte; Spi R = round spermatid; Spi L = elongated spermatid; Spz = spermatozoa; x = division.

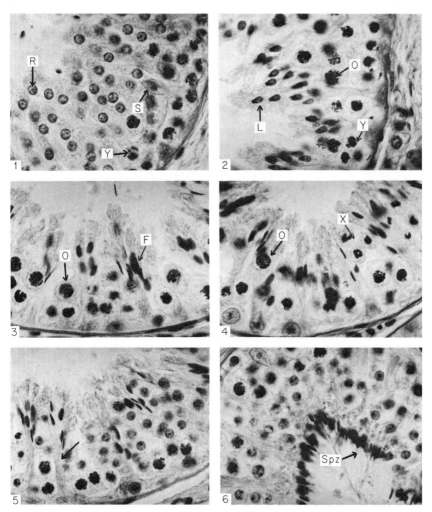

FIGS. 1–6. Cross section of seminiferous tubules at different stages of the cycle in the bull (alcian blue Feulgen) × 500.

FIG. 1. Stage 1 of the cycle: spermatid nuclei are round (R). Sertoli cell nucleus (S); young primary spermatocytes (Y).

FIG. 2. Stage 2 of the cycle: spermatid nuclei are beginning to elongate (L). Old primary spermatocytes (O).

FIG. 3. Stage 3 of the cycle: bundle formation of spermatids (F).

FIG. 4. Stage 4 of the cycle: meiotic divisions of primary spermatocytes (X).

FIG. 5. End of stage 4 of the cycle: two generations of spermatids—one round, newly formed, and the other of the previous generation, which are elongated (above the arrow). Three secondary spermatocytes can be seen (right).

FIG. 6. Stage 8 of the cycle: the heads of immature spermatozoa (Spz) line up on the inner surface of the seminiferous epithelium. When the spermatozoa have been released, the seminiferous epithelium is found again at stage 1 of the cycle.

TABLE II
FREQUENCY OF THE STAGES OF THE SEMINIFEROUS EPITHELIAL CYCLES

Stage	Bull	Ram	Boar	Rabbit	Rat
1	30.8 ± 0.3	21.7 ± 0.9	12.7 ± 1.3	30.2	3.7
2	9.1 ± 0.2	10.6 ± 0.6	16.7 ± 1.4	12.3	4.8
3	20.1 ± 0.2	18.4 ± 0.6	5.0 ± 0.5	7.2	14.5
4	12.8 ± 0.2	10.5 ± 0.5	13.8 ± 1.0	9.0	4.8
5	1.6 ± 0.1	4.2 ± 0.4	9.7 ± 1.2	5.5	3.4
6	5.9 ± 0.1	13.1 ± 0.8	19.0 ± 1.0	16.7	33.6
7	8.1 ± 0.1	10.8 ± 0.7	12.6 ± 1.6	11.2	11.6
8	11.6 ± 0.2	10.3 ± 0.6	9.5 ± 2.0	8.3	17.6

of the last four stages increases (26.2–72.2%). It therefore appears that the relative frequency of spermiogenesis increases from the bull to the boar.

Even though the rate of occurrence of the various stages in the seminiferous epithelial cycle varies between species, it is constant for one species (63).

C. THE SPERMATOGENIC WAVE

The succession of cellular associations takes place, not only in a cross section but along the length of the seminiferous tubule (62, 98) as well. Therefore, a portion of tubule displaying one type of cellular association is followed by a portion of tubule displaying the stage immediately preceding or following in the seminiferous epithelial cycle. There is a "continuity of the segmental order" (98). Each complete spatial series of cellular associations is called "spermatogenic wave." In some places the spermatogenic wave displays local reversal in the order of the consecutive stages. These irregularities are called "modulations" (62, 98).

The tubular length occupied by one stage of the seminiferous epithelial cycle is not constant; the consequence is a variation in the length of the spermatogenic wave. Its average length is 10 mm in the bull. Nevertheless, it has been observed that for each stage the relative ratio of its mean segmental length corresponds to its relative frequency determined on cross-sectioned tubules, i.e., to their duration (62, 98). So well-defined a wave does not exist in man (29).

III. The Cellular Elements of the Spermatogenic Cycle in Domestic Animals

A. THE SPERMATOGONIA

Spermatogonia may be defined as the germ cells contained in the parietal layer of the seminiferous epithelium, the last generation of which gives rise to primary spermatocytes.

1. Morphology of the Different Classes of Spermatogonia

Several types of spermatogonia may be distinguished: the dustlike (103) or A-type spermatogonia (2); the intermediate-type spermatogonia (32), originating from the former type; and finally, the crustlike (103) or B-type spermatogonia resulting from the multiplication of the intermediate type.

These three types of spermatogonia are present in the bull, ram, boar, and rabbit (3, 60, 94, 114). Besides, in the rat and bull, large A_0-type spermatogonia have been found. Their place in the spermatogenic cycle is unknown (30, 65).

The A-type spermatogonia (Fig. 7) are large cells, more or less flattened against the wall of the seminiferous tubule. The nuclei, each surrounded by a thin envelope, are ellipsoid in shape with very fine chromatin granules and a large nucleolus.

The nucleus of the intermediate-type spermatogonia contains a coarser chromatin (Fig. 8).

The B-type spermatogonia nucleus (Fig. 9) is smaller and increasingly spherical. The chromatin granules, which are abundant in the ram, but scarcer in the bull and the boar, tend to adhere to the nuclear envelope.

The duration of DNA synthesis increases progressively from A-type spermatogonia ($S = 10$ hours) to In-type spermatogonia ($S = 16$ hours) and B-type spermatogonia ($S = 20$ hours) (61, 65, 83), S being the phase of DNA synthesis.

The chromosomes differ in appearance in each spermatogonial division. They are elongated during the prophase of the A-type spermatogonia and are shorter and contracted during the prophase of the B-type spermatogonia. The chromosomes may most easily be counted during the prophase of spermatogonial divisions: $2n = 60$ in the bull (82); $2n = 54$ in the ram (15); $2n = 44$ in the rabbit (116); $2n = 38$ in the boar (15).

2. Number of Spermatogonial Divisions

In the bull the study of the mitotic index and frequency of labeled cells —tritiated thymidine—show six peaks of DNA synthesis and mitosis: three are A-type spermatogonia, one is intermediate-type spermatogonia, and two are B-type spermatogonia (Fig. 11).

A few A_0-type spermatogonia are also labeled and divide at various stages of the seminiferous epithelium. They could represent the mechanism by which the stem cell stock increases long after puberty (8).

In the ram, five spermatogonial populations have been observed up to now (94) (Fig. 12); only two are A-type spermatogonial generations.

3. Spermatogonial Renewal

During each cycle, new spermatogonia must appear to replace those which develop into spermatogenic series. The problem is to define the origin of these new spermatogonia.

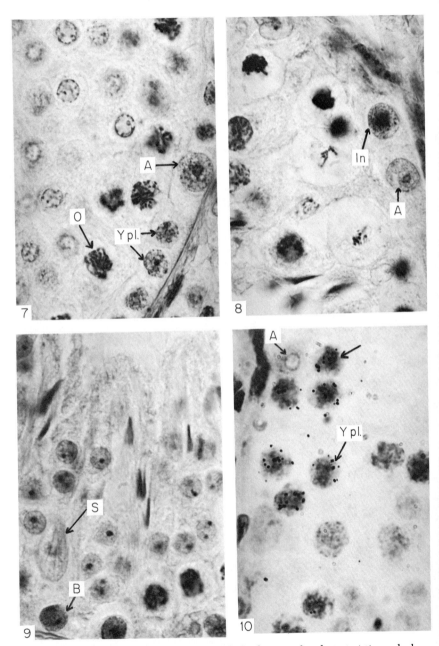

FIGS. 7–10. A₁-type spermatogonium (A), showing the characteristic nucleolus in the bull. Young primary spermatocytes (Ypl.) are at the preleptotene stage (stage 1 of the cycle). Old primary spermatocytes (O) × 1000.

The A-type spermatogonia at stages 6, 7, and 8 can be considered as stem cells. These divide at stages 1–3 and the new stem cells arise from these divisions. Up to the present, it seems that, in the bull, they originate partly after the second spermatogonial division by an equivalent mitosis (65b) like in the rat (28, 30). In the ram, it seems that the new stem cell arises from the first spermatogonial division (94) (Tables III and IV).

TABLE III

VARIATIONS OF THE AVERAGE (CORRECTED) NUMBER OF SPERMATOGONIA
PER CROSS SECTION OF SEMINIFEROUS TUBULE IN THE RAM

| Stage | Number of spermatogonia per cross section of seminiferous tubule | | Number of tubules |
	Spermatogonia A	Spermatogonia B and young spermatocytes	
1	2.3 ± 0.2	—	68
2	3.9 ± 0.3	—	22
3	5.4 ± 0.3	—	67
4	6.6 ± 0.4	—	31
5	2.3 ± 0.2	5.2 ± 0.4	41
6	2.2 ± 0.2	7.8 ± 0.5	43
7	2.4 ± 0.2	10.9 ± 0.4	33
8	2.1 ± 0.2	20.5 ± 0.8	47
1	2.3 ± 0.2	37.1 ± 1.4 (spc)	68

TABLE IV

VARIATIONS OF THE AVERAGE NUMBER OF SPERMATOGONIA PER CROSS SECTION
OF SEMINIFEROUS TUBULE IN THE BULL (10 μ)

Stages	Classes of spermatogonia	Number of spermatogonia	Number of tubules
8–1a	A_1	4.15 ± 0.27	73
2	A_2	8.18 ± 0.97	16
3a	$In + A$	12.00 ± 1.13	13
6–7	B_1	17.85 ± 1.02	27
8b	B_2	36.54 ± 1.27	24
1–2–3	Spermatocytes	67.38 ± 1.39	103

This model of spermatogonial division governs the quantitative production of primary spermatocytes.

FIG. 8. Intermediate-type spermatogonium (In) in the bull, with granules of chromatin (stage 4 of the cycle) × 1000.

FIG. 9. B-type spermatogonium (B) in the bull with chromatin crusts under the nuclear membrane. Sertoli cell nucleus (S) × 1000.

FIG. 10. Autoradiograph of a seminiferous tubule from a bull castrated 1 hour after intra-arterial injection of tritiated thymidine in the testis. The young primary spermatocytes are labeled.

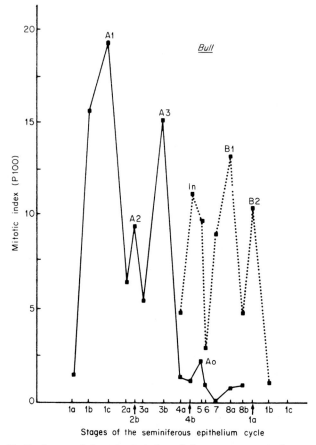

FIG. 11. Evolution of the mitotic index of the spermatogonia during the seminiferous epithelial cycle. Six peaks of mitosis are seen. A-type spermatogonia, (A_1, A_2, A_3, and A_0); intermediate-type spermatogonia (In); B-type spermatogonia (B_1, B_2).

The mean coefficient of efficiency of spermatogonial mitoses is 16 for the ram and bull, but 28 for the rat (28) and possibly for the boar also (Ortavant, unpublished). In man, it is 4 (29).

It is particularly interesting to notice that this efficiency coefficient in a bull with a subnormal spermatogenesis can decrease to 10, and in rams submitted to long daylight, it is reduced to 10 or even less (93). The principal critical stage is the intermediate-type spermatogonia.

B. The Spermatocytes

The primary spermatocytes, products of mitosis of the last generation of spermatogonia, represent germ cells which undergo meiotic division.

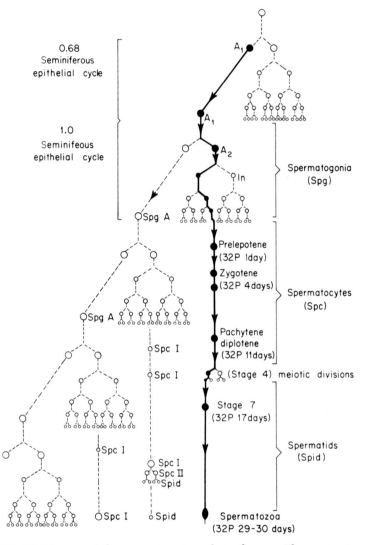

FIG. 12. Diagram of the spermatogenic cycle in the ram. The progression of a spermatogenic series from the spermatogonium stem cell A₁ to the liberation of spermatozoa is illustrated in this figure (thick line). A new spermatogenic series is arising after each division of stem cell.

1. The Different Phases of Meiotic Prophase

The young primary spermatocytes originate at the beginning of stage 8 in the cycle of the seminiferous epithelium (boar) or at the beginning of stage 1 (bull and ram). Immediately after their formation the nuclei of the primary spermatocytes show such a great resemblance to those of the mother cells that they have often been mistaken for B-type sperma· togonia (see Fig. 7).

Some authors have called these cells "resting spermatocytes," but this is quite incorrect since an active synthesis of DNA occurs during this phase (S = 28 hours) (65) (see Fig. 10). Most workers now agree on the use of the term "preleptotene" for this phase.

The chromatin crusts distributed under the nuclear membrane of the primary spermatocytes become dispersed in the nucleus and give rise to thin chromatin filaments, (*leptotene phase*). At the end of this phase in the bull these filaments contract strongly and the chromosome spirals are reduced to only a few coils (82). Thereafter, the tension of the chromo- some spiral diminishes, and long, slender chromosomes are obtained, as in other domestic animals.

At the *zygotene* phase homologous chromosomes pair off and their bouquet arrangement becomes still more apparent (stages 3, 4, and 5 of the seminiferous epithelium cycle in the ram and bull).

At the pachytene phase each chromosome divides longitudinally into 2 chromatids, the chromosomes thus appearing thicker. This phase may be observed at stages 6, 7, 8, and 1.

The *diplotene* phase is characterized by the formation of chiasma be- tween the homologous chromosomes so that they are less easily distinguish- able one from another (stages 2 and 3).

Finally, in *diakinesis,* the last and very short stage of the meiotic prophase, the contraction of the chromosomes is greatest, and each bivalent shows various arrangements.

The end of the meiotic prophase coincides with stages 4 of the semi- niferous epithelium, during which the metaphase, anaphase, and telo- phase occur rapidly. Secondary spermatocytes are now present. They have a spherical nucleus containing 5–6 particles of DNA joined together by a network of filaments. This interphase lasts only a few hours, then each secondary spermatocyte divides to give rise to two spermatids.

Meiosis also plays a part in governing the quantitative and qualitative efficiency of spermatogenesis. A certain number of primary spermatocytes do not pass the zygotene stage; for example, in rams submitted to long day- light, they give rise to pycnotic nuclei (93).

The genetic consequences, resulting from the particular behavior of the chromosomes during meiosis, will not be developed here. However, an examination of the behavior of the X-Y bivalent may be interesting. The X-Y bivalent is represented in the bull by a long chromosome, X, and a very short chromosome, Y. In any case, two categories of spermatozoa are obtained. Many authors have tried to take advantage, with reports of varying success, of the properties of these two categories of spermatozoa with the aim of controlling the sex ratio, either by electrophoresis, or by countercurrent centrifuging or density gradient (*10, 55, 80, 109, 110*).

C. The Spermatids

Spermiogenesis, the sum of the nuclear and cytoplasmic changes in the spermatids, is certainly the part of the spermatogenic cycle which has been the most intensively studied. These changes govern, to a great extent, the quality of the final product: the spermatozoa. For that reason, we shall now study the development of each component of the spermatid in order to understand the structure of the spermatozoa.

1. Development of the Spermatid Nucleus

The nuclear envelope of the spermatid is double, and contains few if any communicating pores between the karyoplasm and the cytoplasm, even though pores of this type are frequent in the spermatogonia (23). The nucleus of the young spermatid (see Fig. 5), although smaller, is similar to that of the secondary spermatocytes. It contains several large granules of DNA of various sizes scattered on a filamentous network. These granules, which after a while disintegrate into dustlike granulations, become very homogeneous during stages 8 and 1 of the seminiferous epithelial cycle. In this phase the spermatid nuclei contain nucleoli. At stage 2, the nucleus elongates and flattens dorsoventrally. During this metamorphosis, the nucleic acid molecules gather to form lines parallel to the longitudinal axis (53) producing birefringence (100) or X-ray diffraction (121) phenomena.

It is important to notice that the base of the spermatid nucleus of the bull contracts during stage 2 of the seminiferous epithelial cycle. Without doubt, the primary abnormality of spermatozoa described in the literature are formed at this stage.

The incorporation of tritiated arginine in the nuclear histone takes place at the end of spermiogenesis (stage 4 to 7) (84).

2. The Cytoplasmic Components

The cytoplasm is moderately dense and finely granular in appearance; the endoplasmic reticulum is abundant with smooth vesicles or canaliculi. The ribosomes are scattered individually or in clusters throughout the cytoplasm of the spermatid. As studied by André (6) the mitochondria exhibit unusual structure: their cristae are swollen, occupying most of the organelles as a pseudomatrix.

a. The Acrosomic System. The formation of the acrosomic system is very similar in various domestic animals. A remarkable description of the evolution of this system was given in ultrastructural studies on the cat, human, and guinea pig made by Fawcett and co-workers (23, 47, 50).

In the young spermatid, the Golgi complex is composed of numerous small vacuoles surrounded by flattened vesicles with parallel limiting membranes (23, 27). This complex assumes a U-shape, and it has been observed in living cells as established by studies on the rat (9).

Inside this complex 2 or 3 granules appear immersed in a substance.

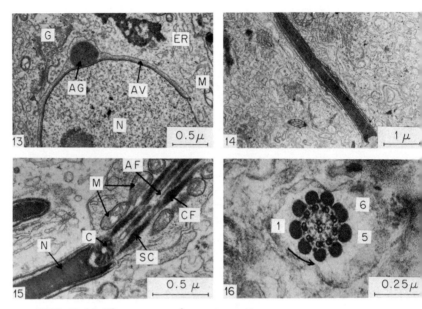

FIGS. 13–16. Ultrastructure of spermiogenesis.

FIG. 13. Round spermatid during the spermiogenesis in the ram, showing: nucleus (N); golgi apparatus (G); acrosomic granule (AG); acrosomic vesicle (AV); mitochondria (M); endoplasmic reticulum (ER).

FIG. 14. Spermiogenesis in the bull. Elongated spermatid, showing, outward from the nucleus: nuclear membrane, inner acrosomic membrane, acrosomic material, outer acrosomic membrane, cellular membrane, Sertoli cell membrane.

FIG. 15. Spermiogenesis in the bull. Elongated spermatid, showing: nucleus (N); proximal centriole in cross section (C); mitochondria (M); coarse fibers (CF); axial filament (AF); segmented column of the connecting piece (SC).

FIG. 16. Cross section of a sperm tail in elongated spermatid of the bull. According to Bradfield (19) and Fawcett (48), this is a polar view backward from the head; fibers are numbered according to the dense fibers.

These are the proacrosomic granules. Both the granules and the substance are stainable with PAS. The name *idiosome* is often given to this system.

Soon the proacrosomic granules gather to form a single *acrosomic granule,* which appears to be contained in a vesicle (stage 6 of the cycle). They move toward the anterior part of the nucleus, and the inner membrane of the vesicle adheres to the nuclear membrane, which appears thicker (Fig. 13). Shortly after the remnant of the Golgi complex leaves the acrosomic vesicle and migrates into the caudal part of the cell, often disintegrating during this process.

The acrosomic vesicle, flattened onto the nucleus, encompasses the acrosomic granule between its outer and inner membrane. It grows and finally covers nearly two-thirds of the nucleus in the ram and boar and a little less in the bull. Meanwhile, the acrosomic granule flattens gradually onto the nucleus, giving rise to the *acrosome* (Fig. 14). The combination of the acrosome and the acrosomic vesicle forms the acrosomic system (*76*), generally referred to as the acrosome (*47*).

b. *The Caudal Sheath or Manchette.* During stage 2, a tubule, the *caudal sheath,* appears in the cytoplasm of the spermatid. It consists of a layer of related microtubules parallel to the long axis of the cell around the posterior part of the nucleus and the beginning of the flagellum. It appears to be differentiated from the cytoplasmic, ringlike structure at the base of the acrosome (*23, 38*).

The manchette is a transient structure which disappears in the final stages of spermiogenesis. Its role is not yet clearly understood; it could serve as a structural framework within the cell.

c. *The Locomotory Apparatus.* It consists of the neck, the axial filament, and the middle piece. The axial filament is formed when the acrosomic vesicles appear (*119*). The joint between the tail and the head, and the formation of the middle piece, can be observed at the stage of the elongating spermatid nucleus (stages 2 and 3).

The neck (Fig. 15): It consists of a proximal centriole and 9 crossstriated fibers; 4 of them fuse 2 by 2 to form the "implantation plate" (*49, 89, 106, 122*).

The tail (Fig. 16): The filament seems to originate from the centriole when the latter is moving toward the posterior part of the nucleus. It is initially formed of 9 fibrils arranged in a circle around 1 central fibril and surrounded by a tubular membrane. Toward the end of spermiogenesis the structure is more complex.

In the proximal section, the central part is now constituted of 2 tubular fibrils surrounded by 9 "doublets." Each doublet consists of 1 dense fibril, A-fiber, and 1 tubule, B-fiber (*48*). Nine coarse fibers run close to the fibrillar doublet. Three of them (numbers 1, 5, and 6) originate from the fusion of 2 fibers and appear larger than the others (*19, 25*).

In the distal section the two circles of fibers and fibrils are less distinct: the outer fibers become thinner and more closely pressed against the corresponding inner fibrils.

The middle piece: During stages 5 and 7, mitochondria assemble in a spiral around the axial filament to form the mitochondrial sheath of the middle piece between the proximal centriole and the terminal ring.

D. MORPHOLOGY OF THE SPERMATOZOON

The mature spermatozoon consists of three principal parts: the head, the neck, the tail, which is composed of the middle piece, the main piece, and the end of the axial filament.

The dimensions of each of these component parts are given in Table V.

TABLE V

COMPARATIVE SIZE OF SPERMATOZOA (μ)

Species (animal)	Head		Middle piece		Main tail piece		References
	Length	Width	Length	Width	Length	Width	
Bull	9.15	4.25	14.84	0.670	45–50	0.51	(17)
Ram	8.2	4.25	14	0.800	40–45	0.500	(100)
Boar	8.5	4.25	10	—	30	—	(59)
Stallion	7.0	3.91	9.83	—	43	—	(90)
Stallion	5	2.4	8	0.500	30	0.490	(16)

1. The Head

The nucleus forms most of the head of the spermatozoon. The chromatin consists of 43% DNA and 57% arginine-rich proteins (78).

In spermatozoa, the amount of DNA corresponds to half that of the diploid nuclei (79). Variations in form, size, and DNA content often result in subfertility (21, 46, 54, 79).

The anterior part of the nucleus in the spermatozoa of domestic animals (100) is covered by the acrosome in such a way that the following elements must be found in mature spermatozoa, successively from the exterior inwards: the cytoplasmic membrane of the spermatozoa, the outer membrane of the spermatozoa, the outer membrane of the acrosomic vesicle, the acrosomic material (derived from the acrosomic granule), and the inner membrane of the acrosomic vesicle thickened and pressed against the nuclear membrane.

It may be mentioned here that an hereditary anomaly in the acrosomic system causes sterility in the bull (58) or quasisterility in the mouse (99).

The acrosomic system is composed of mucopolysaccharides containing galactose, mannose, fucose, and hexosamine (34), and acid and alkaline phosphatases (52, 81). It also contains a lipoglycoprotein, which acts on egg envelopes (113) and hyaluronidase.

The base of the nucleus is surrounded by the postnuclear cap, and also by the cytoplasmic membrane, which is very sensitive to alkali (56). The postnuclear cap is formed of fibrous proteins rich in sulfur. It is easily impregnated with silver (59) and, in dead spermatozoa, is very permeable to some dyes such as eosin (75), bromophenol blue, and bromocresol green (18). This property is useful in recognizing dead spermatozoa. The structure of the neck is similar to that described for spermatids.

2. The Tail

The axial filament of the tail is made up of 2 axial fibrils surrounded by two concentric circles of 9 fibrils; the structure of the axial filament is of type $9 + 9 + 2$, derived from the general type $9 + 2$ found in flagellates (19, 111).

a. The Middle Piece. This constitutes the proximal part of the tail. Due to the arrangement of the coarse fibers, there exists only one plane of symmetry, which is perpendicular to the central pair of fibrils (*19*). The fibril bundles are enclosed by a spiral of mitochondria (*19, 21, 25*). The outer membrane is derived from the cytoplasmic membrane of the spermatid (*23, 26*).

In the anterior part of the epididymis, the neck of most spermatozoa has a cytoplasmic droplet that migrates toward the distal end of the middle piece, from which it is later eliminated (*20, 58, 87, 101, 102*). This droplet contains elements from the disintegrating Golgi apparatus and endoplasmic reticulum (*13, 69*), but its actual role is not understood. The droplet in a proximal position signifies a defect in the maturation of the sperm in the epididymis (*57, 74*).

b. The Main Piece. In all spermatozoa of domestic animals, the axial bundle of $9 + 9 + 2$ fibrils contains two longitudinal ribs situated on the same diameter as the central pair of fibrils and surrounded by a helix of structural proteins (*19, 25, 88, 115*). This whole structure is surrounded by a membrane.

The contraction mechanism of the flagellum has been discussed in detail by Bradfield (*19*) and Bishop (*11, 12*), the contractions are excited by rhythmic impulses which occur first in the neck and are then transferred to each fibril in turn. Due to the arrangement of the fibrils in the outer bundle, the movement of the tail is governed by three-dimensional waves.

c. The End of the Axial Filament. The end piece consists only of the axial fibril bundle except for the double-layer cell membrane, which covers the entire spermatozoon (*70*).

IV. The Sertoli Cells

The Sertoli cells are the somatic elements of the seminiferous epithelium. It is currently assumed that in the adult, they do not divide and their number does not vary.

The name of these cells originates from the fundamental discovery of Sertoli, who first described the branched cells. Electron microscope observations show that Sertoli cells do not form a syncytium, but that each of them is limited by a distinct membrane (*49, 119*). Long, thin cytoplasmic processes surround all the germ cells in the tubule, except the spermatogonia stem cells, which are in close contact with the basement membrane (*117*). The relationship between the cytoplasm of the Sertoli cells and the germ cells undergoes cyclic variations (*43, 44, 45*).

Their cytoplasm in the bull and the ram contains small aggregates of ribosomes and a smooth endoplasmic reticulum, often organized into a network around the nucleus (49). These cells are rich in glycogen, glyco-proteins (40, 49), and lipids, with cyclic variations (72, 73).

It has been shown, by means of radioactive acetate (104), that the turnover of these lipids is very rapid. In addition, the Sertoli cells contain some steroids (7).

The *nucleus* of the Sertoli cells contains a large nucleolus. The shape of the nucleus is irregular, having very deep indentations, and its triangular or elongate shape varies during the cycle of the seminiferous epithelium (76).

The role played by the Sertoli cells is not clearly understood (104a). Their structural role seems to be incontestable in the prepuberal testis as well as in the adult one. It is also possible that they have a protective and nutritional role for certain germ cells. In addition, they are concerned in the release of the spermatozoa (22, 76) and the resorption of the residual bodies (39, 51, 72, 103). Their secretory role, particularly concerned with the production of estrogens, seems to be questionable (73). They could be, also an intermediate in the action of gonadotropins on the germ cells (36, 37, 85).

V. Establishment of Spermatogenesis in the Young Male

As sexual differentiation is considered in Chapter 8, it will not be discussed here.

The growth curve of the testis has the same appearance in the lamb and the calf (Fig. 17) (1, 8, 24, 35, 108). There is a slow growth rate in the first 2 or 3 months after birth and a more rapid one thereafter when spermatogenesis commences. At the end of this period, the eighth or ninth month after birth in the calf, and the fifth in the lamb, the testicular growth slows down again.

During the first period only two types of cells are present in the sex cords: the *supporting cells*, which have a small, highly stainable nucleus and are located along the basement membrane, and the *gonocytes*, whose large and lightly stained nuclei are found in the central part of the sex cords (Fig. 18).

After long controversy about the fate of these cells (107), it is now currently accepted that the supporting cells are transformed into Sertoli cells and the gonocytes into spermatogonia. The supporting cells prolif-erate during 4 to 6 months after birth in the lamb and in the calf, then they stop dividing and begin to take on the aspect of Sertoli cells.

The number of gonocytes increases progressively until adulthood. In the lamb many of them give rise to A-type spermatogonia, followed, about the 105th day, by primary spermatocytes, and, about the 120–125th day, by spermatids. The last stages of the cycle of the seminiferous epithelium occur only toward the 140–150th day (35, 108). In the calf a similar de-

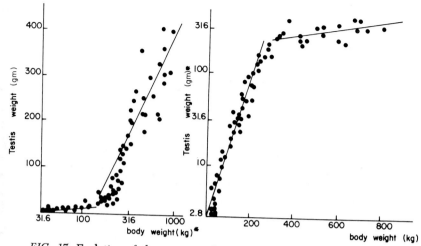

FIG. 17. Evolution of the testis weight in relation to the body weight in the calf. Logarithmic scale (*).

velopment takes place, but spermatogenesis does not commence until after 4 months, and the first spermatozoa appear at about the seventh month (1, 8).

The reported variations in the initiation dates of spermatogenesis are largely due to two factors: that initiation of spermatogenesis is dependent more on the development of the animal than on its age (35, 67, 120), and that certain authors have mistaken the supporting cells for spermatogonia and the gonocytes for primary spermatocytes.

It is important to notice that, even at its commencement, spermatogenesis develops with similar cyclic changes of the seminiferous epithelium as it does in the adult, but its maximal efficiency is attained only after several months (8, 35).

VI. Duration of the Spermatogenic Processes

The total number of spermatozoa produced per day depends upon the rate of development of the spermatogenic processes. It is also necessary to know when the effect of a stimulatory or noxious factor acting on a given stage of the spermatogenic cycle is detected in the ejaculate.

The duration of the spermatogenic cycle is determined by labeling germ cells with radioactive precursors of DNA, i.e., tritiated thymidine. Generally, however, results are expressed in terms of the duration of the seminiferous epithelial cycle. This duration varies according to species (Table VI). One can also calculate the duration of different spermatogenic

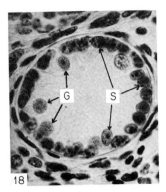

FIG. 18. Sex cord from a young calf in which numerous gonocytes (G) and supporting cells (S) are present.

processes. For example, meiotic prophase takes 15 and 19 days, and spermiogenesis 14 or 20 days in the ram (94) and the bull, respectively (65a).

Neither gonadotropic hormones, nor testosterone propionate modify the rate of spermatogenic processes (31, 41).

Thus, it is possible to conclude that when spermatogenesis is disturbed, a certain number of cells degenerate, but those that continue their development until the end do so at the same rate of speed. The spermatogenic cycle, therefore, seems to be a biological constant.

The time taken for the spermatozoa to pass along the ductus epididymis is about 11–14 days in the collected ram (5), 6–11 days in the bull (91), 14 days in the boar (112), and 9–10 days in the rabbit (4, 92).

TABLE VI

DURATION OF THE SEMINIFEROUS EPITHELIAL CYCLE

Species	Duration (days)	References
Man	16	(59a)
Bull	13.5	(64)
Rat	12.3	(33a)
Ram	10	(94)
Mouse	8.6	(90a)
Boar	8	(96a)

VII. Control of Spermatogenesis

A. ENDOCRINE FACTORS

In the impuberal testis the supporting cells are under gonadotropic control. The gonocytes are more independent. In the lamb (37) (Fig. 19)

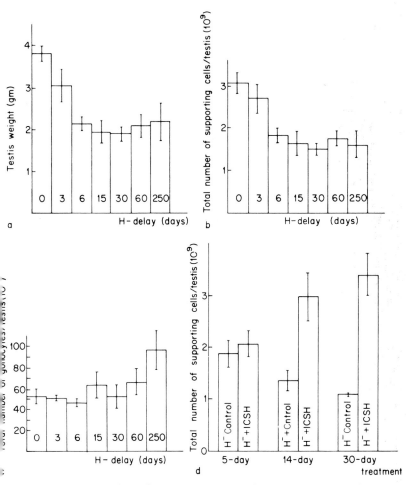

FIG. 19. Action of hypophysectomy in the lamb: (a) evolution of the testis weight after hypophysectomy; (b) evolution of the total number of supporting cells after hypophysectomy; (c) evolution of total number of gonocytes after hypophysectomy; (d) action of ICSH treatment after hypophysectomy. ICSH treatment increases the total number of supporting cells.

the testis weight and the number of supporting cells greatly decrease after hypophysectomy; the number of gonocytes increases. However, this increase is slower than in a normal animal. Injection of ICSH into the hypophysectomized lamb increases the testis weight (Fig. 20) and the total number of supporting cells (Fig. 19d). In addition, there are no spermatocytes without gonadotropins (37).

In the adult rat both FSH and ICSH are gametokinetic, but their respective importance is unequal. Even though both act on spermatogonial

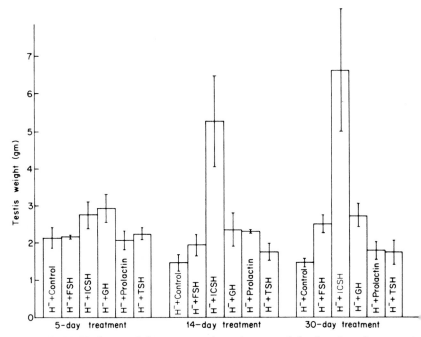

FIG. 20. Evolution of the testis weight in function of the duration of treatment and hormonal supplementation in the hypophysectomized lamb. Only ICSH treatment increases testis weight.

divisions, only ICSH influences meiotic prophase and spermiogenesis to a great extent (95, 96). ICSH acts either directly or by androgenic secretion. Results obtained in maintaining or repairing spermatogenesis after hypophysectomy with testosterone propionate have shown that this pathway is partly used (14, 86).

In conclusion, although the rate of speed of spermatogenesis cannot be affected by hormones such as gonadotropins or androgens, the yield of spermatogenesis is influenced by ICSH.

B. EXTERNAL FACTORS

The principal external factors which have been studied are photoperiodism and temperature.

In the ram, when daylight duration increases from 8 hours to 16 hours, spermatogenic activity decreases. Intermediate spermatogonia, pachytene spermatocytes, meiotic divisions, and elongating nucleus spermatid stages are particularly affected (93, 97).

It is known that high summer temperatures decrease fertility in sheep and cattle (42, 57). In the ram, when scrotal temperature is artificially increased to 41°C for 3 hours, the pachytene spermatocytes are rapidly destroyed (stage 8 of the seminiferous epithelial cycle). There is also a transient effect on spermatogonial divisions with an increase of prophases and metaphases. Other germ cells are apparently not modified (*118*).

REFERENCES

1. Abdel-Raouf, M., *Acta Endocrinol. Suppl.* **49**, 109 pp. (1960).
2. Allen, E., *J. Morphol.* **31**, 133 (1918).
3. Amann, R. P., *Am. J. Anat.* **110**, 69 (1962).
4. Amann, R. P., Koefoed-Johnsen, H. H., and Levy, H., *J. Reprod. Fertility* **10**, 169 (1965).
5. Amir, D., and Ortavant, R., *Ann. Biol. Animale Biochim. Biophys.* **8**, 195 (1968).
6. André, J., *J. Ultrastruct. Res., Suppl.* **3**, 185 pp. (1962).
7. Ashbel, R., Cohen, R. B., and Seligman, A. M., *Endocrinology* **49**, 265 (1951).
8. Attal, J., and Courot, M., *Ann. Biol. Animale Biochim. Biophys.* **3**, 219 (1963).
9. Austin, C. R., and Sapsford, C. S., *J. Roy Microscop. Soc.* **71**, 397 (1951).
10. Bangham, A. D., *Proc. Roy. Soc.* **B155**, 292 (1961).
11. Bishop, M. W. H., *Physiol. Rev.* **42**, 1 (1962).
12. Bishop, M. W. H., and Smiles, J., *J. Reprod. Fertility* **6**, 297 (1963).
13. Bloom, G., and Nicander, L., *Z. Zellforsch. Mikroskop. Anat.* **55**, 833 (1961).
14. Boccabella, A. V., *Endocrinology* **72**, 787 (1963).
15. Bomsel, O., Thesis Doct. Sci., Paris, 1967.
16. Bonadonna, T., and Caretta, A., *Zootec. Vet.* **9**, 65 (1954).
17. Bonadonna, T., Caretta, A., and Corrias, A., *Zootec. Vet.* **8**, 369 (1953).
18. Bonadonna, T., and Olgiati, L., *Zootec. Vet.* **8**, 195 (1953).
19. Bradfield, J. R. G., *Soc. Exptl. Biol.* **9**, 306 (1955).
20. Branton, C., and Salisbury, R. W., *J. Animal Sci.* **6**, 154 (1947).
21. Bretschneider, L. H., *Koninkl. Ned. Akad. Wetenschap. Proc.* **53**, 531 (1950).
22. Burgos, M. H., and Vitale, R. E., *Proc. 2nd Intern. Congr. Endocrinol., Part II* **83**, 1299 (1964).
23. Burgos, M. H., and Fawcett, D. W., *J. Biophys. Biochem. Cytol.* **1**, 287 (1955).
24. Carmon, J. L., and Green, W. W., *J. Animal Sci.* **11**, 674 (1952).
25. Challice, C. E., *Proc. Soc. Study Fertility* **4**, 2 (1952).
26. Challice, C. E., *J. Roy. Microscop. Soc.* **73**, 115 (1953).
27. Clermont, Y., *J. Biophys. Biochem. Cytol.* **2**, Suppl., p. 119 (1956).
28. Clermont, Y., *Am. J. Anat.* **111**, 111 (1962).
29. Clermont, Y., *Am. J. Anat.* **118**, 509 (1966).
30. Clermont, Y., and Bustos, E., *Anat. Record* **154**, 332 (1966).
31. Clermont, Y., and Harvey, S. C., *Endocrinology* **76**, 80 (1965).
32. Clermont, Y., and Leblond, C. P., *Am. J. Anat.* **93**, 475 (1953).
33. Clermont, Y., and Leblond, C. P., *Am. J. Anat.* **96**, 229 (1955).
33a. Clermont, Y., Leblond, C. P., and Messier, B., *Arch. Anat. Microscop. Morphol. Exptl.* **4**, bis, 37 (1959).

34. Clermont, Y., Clegg, R. C., and Leblond, C. P., *Exptl. Cell Res.* **8**, 453 (1955).
35. Courot, M., *Ann. Biol. Animale Biochim. Biophys.* **2**, 21 (1962).
36. Courot, M., *Ann. Biol. Animale Biochim. Biophys.* **2**, 157 (1962).
37. Courot, M., *Arch. Anat. Microscop. Morphol. Exptl.* **56**, 97 (1967).
38. Courot, M., and Flechon, J., *Ann. Biol. Animale Biochim. Biophys.* **6**, 479 (1966).
39. Daled, H. J., *Arch. Anat. Microscop. Morphol. Exptl.* **40**, 183 (1951).
40. Daoust, R., and Clermont, Y., *Am. J. Anat.* **96**, 255 (1955).
41. Desclin, J., and Ortavant, R., *Ann. Biol. Animale Biochim. Biophys.* **3**, 329 (1963).
42. Dutt, R. H., *J. Dairy Sci.* **43**, *Suppl.*, 123 (1960).
43. Elftman, H., *Anat. Record* **106**, 381 (1950).
44. Elftman, H., *in* "Studies on Testis and Ovary, Eggs and Sperm" (E. T. Engle, ed.), pp. 26. Thomas, Springfield, Illinois, 1952.
45. Elftman, H., *Am. J. Anat.* **113**, 25 (1963).
46. Esnault, C., and Ortavant, R., *Ann. Biol. Animale Biochim. Biophys.* **7**, 25 (1967).
47. Fawcett, D. W., *Z. Zellforsch.* **67**, 279 (1965).
48. Fawcett, D. W., *Am. Assoc. Advan. Sci., Publ.* **72**, 147 (1962).
49. Fawcett, D. W., and Burgos, M. H., *Ciba Found. Colloq. Ageing* **2**, 86 (1956).
50. Fawcett, D. W., and Hollenberg, R. D., *Z. Zellforsch.* **60**, 276 (1963).
51. Firlit, C. F., and Davis, J. R., *Quart. Microscop. Sci.* **106**, 93 (1965).
52. Friedlander, M. H. G., and Fraser, M. J., *Exptl. Cell Res.* **3**, 462 (1952).
53. Gibbons, I. R., and Bradfield, J. R. G., *J. Biophys. Biochem. Cytol.* **3**, 133 (1957).
54. Gledhill, B. L., *Acta Vet. Scand.* **7**, 166 (1966).
55. Gordon, M. J., *Proc. Natl. Acad. Sci. U.S.* **43**, 913 (1957).
56. Green, W. W., *Anat. Record* **76**, 455 (1940).
57. Gunn, R. M. C., Sanders, R. N., and Granger, W., *Australia CSIRO* **148**, 140 pp. (1942).
58. Hancock, J. L., *J. Exptl. Biol.* **30**, 50 (1953).
59. Hancock, J. L., *J. Roy. Microscop. Soc.* **76**, 84 (1957).
59a. Heller, C. G., and Clermont, Y., *Science* **140**, 184 (1963).
60. Henricson, B., and Backström, L., *Acta Anat.* **53**, 278 (1963).
61. Hilscher, W., *Beitr. Pathol. Anat. Allgem. Pathol.* **130**, 69 (1964).
62. Hochereau, M. T., *Ann. Biol. Animale Biochim. Biophys.* **3**, 5 (1963).
63. Hochereau, M. T., *Ann. Biol. Animale Biochim. Biophys.* **3**, 93 (1963).
64. Hochereau, M. T., Courot, M., and Ortavant, R., *Ann. Biol. Animale Biochim. Biophys.* **4**, 157 (1964).
65. Hochereau, M. T., *Arch. Anat. Microscop. Morphol. Exptl.* **56**, 85 (1967).
65a. Hochereau, M. T., Unpublished data (1967).
65b. Hochereau, M. T., *6th Congr. Intern. Rept. Animale Inst. Artif., Paris*, 33 (1968).
66. Kennelly, J. J., Thesis Master Sci., Cornell Univ. Ithaca, New York, 81 pp., (1960).
67. Kibler, H. H., Bergman, A. J., and Turner, C. W., *Endocrinology* **33**, 250 (1943).

68. Knudsen, O., *Acta Pathol. Microbiol. Scand. Suppl.* **101**, 79 pp. (1954).
69. Kojima, Y., and Ishikawa, T., *Jap. J. Vet. Res.* **11**, 157 (1963).
70. Kojima, Y., *Jap. J. Vet. Res.* **14**, 1 (1966).
71. Kramer, M. F., Dr. Diergeneesk. Rijskuniv. te Utrecht, 183 pp., 1960.
72. Lacy, D., *Brit. Med. Bull.* **18**, 205 (1962).
73. Lacy, D., and Lofts, B., *J. Physiol.* (*London*) **161** (1), 23 (1961).
74. Lagerlof, N., *Acta Pathol. Microbiol. Scand. Suppl.* **19** (1934).
75. Lasley, J. F., Easley, G. T., and McKenzie, F. F., *Anat. Record* **82**, 167 (1942).
76. Leblond, C. P., and Clermont, Y., *Am. J. Anat.* **90**, 167 (1952).
77. Leblond, C. P., and Clermont, Y., *Ann. N.Y. Acad. Sci.* **55**, 548 (1952).
78. Leuchtenberger, C., *J. Histochem. Cytochem.* **4**, 435 (1956).
79. Leuchtenberger, C., Murmanis, I., Murmanis, L., Ito, S., and Weir, D. R., *Chromosoma* **8**, 73 (1956).
80. Lindahl, P. E., *Nature* **181**, 784 (1958).
81. Melampy, R. M., Cavazos, L. F., and Porter, J. C., *J. Dairy Sci.* **35**, 140 (1952).
82. Melander, R., and Knudsen, O., *Hereditas* **39**, 305 (1953).
83. Monesi, V., *J. Cell Biol.* **14**, 1 (1962).
84. Monesi, V., *Exptl. Cell Res.* **36**, 683 (1964).
85. Murphy, H. D., *Proc. Soc. Exptl. Biol. Med.* **118**, 1202 (1965).
86. Nelson, W. O., *Cold Spring Harbor Symp. Quant. Biol.* **5**, 123 (1937).
87. Nicander, L., *Acta Zool.* **38**, 1 (1957).
88. Nicander, L., *Congr. Electron Microscop., 5th, Philadelphia* **2**, M4 (1962).
89. Nicander, L., and Bane, A., *Intern. J. Fertility* **7**, 339 (1962).
90. Nishikawa, Y., Waide, Y., and Onuma, H., *Nogyo Gijutsu Kenkyusho Hokoku Chikusan* (Bull. Natl. Inst. Agr. Sci.) **1**, 129 (1951).
90a. Oakberg, *Am. J. Anat.* **99**, 507 (1956).
91. Orgebin-Crist, M. C., *Ann. Biol. Animale Biochim. Biophys.* **2**, 51 (1962).
92. Orgebin-Crist, M. C., *J. Reprod. Fertility* **10** (2), 241 (1965).
93. Ortavant, R., *Compt. Rend. Soc. Biol.* **150**, 471 (1956).
94. Ortavant, R., Thesis Doct. Sci., Paris, 127 pp. 1958.
95. Ortavant, R., and Courot, M., *Arch. Biol.* **75**, 623 (1964).
96. Ortavant, R., and Courot, M., *Arch. Anat. Microscop. Morphol. Exptl.* **56**, 111 (1967).
96a. Ortavant, R., Orgebin-Crist, M. C., and Singh, G., *Proc. Conf. Mexico City* **1**, 312. Acad. Pr. Publ. (1962).
97. Ortavant, R., Thibault, C., and Mauleon, P., *Ann. N. Y. Acad. Sci.* **117**, 157 (1964).
98. Perey, B., Clermont, Y., and Leblond, C. P., *Am. J. Anat.* **108**, 47 (1961).
99. Rajasekarasetty, M. R., *Fertility Sterility* **5**, 68 (1954).
100. Randall, J. T., and Friedlander, M. H. G., *Exptl. Cell Res.* **1**, 1 (1950).
101. Rao, C. K., and Hart, G. H., *Am. J. Vet. Res.* **9**, 117 (1948).
102. Rao, C. K., and Berry, R. O., *Am. J. Vet. Res.* **10**, 357 (1949).
103. Regaud, C., *Arch. Anat. Microscop.* **4**, 101 (1901).
104. Roosen-Runge, E. C., *Anat. Record* **121**, 358 (1955).
104a. Roosen-Runge, E. C., *Biol. Rev.* **37**, 343 (1962).
105. Roosen-Runge, E. C., and Giesel, L. O., *Am. J. Anat.* **87**, 1 (1950).

106. Saacke, R. G., and Almquist, J. O., *Am. J. Anat.* **115**, 163 (1964).
107. Santamarina, E., and Reece, R., *Am. J. Vet. Res.* **18**, 261 (1957).
108. Sapsford, C. S., *Australian J. Agr. Res.* **13**, 487 (1962).
109. Schroder, V., *Dokl. Akad. Nauk. SSSR* **26**, 692 (1940).
110. Schilling, E., *Z. Säugetierk.* **31**, 314 (1966).
111. Serra, J. A., *Exptl. Cell Res.* **20**, 395 (1960).
112. Singh, G., *Ann. Biol. Animale Bioch. Biophys.* **2**, 43 (1962).
113. Srivastava, P. N., Adams, C. E., and Hartree, E. F., *Nature* **205**, 498 (1965).
114. Swierstra, E. E., and Foote, R. A., *J. Animal Sci.* **20**, 980 (1961).
115. Telkkä, A., Fawcett, D. W., and Christensen, A. K., *Anat. Record* **141**, 231 (1961).
116. Venge, O., *Kgl. Lantbruks—Högskol. Ann.* **19**, 233 (1952).
117. Vilar, O., Perez Del Cerro, M. I., and Mancini, R. E., *Exptl. Cell Res.* **27**, 158 (1962).
118. Waites, G. M. H., and Ortavant, R., *Ann. Biol. Animale Biochim.* (in press) (1968).
119. Watson, M. L., *Biochim. Biophys. Acta* **8**, 369 (1952).
120. Watson, R. H., Sapsford, C. S., and McCance, I., *Australian J. Agr. Res.* **7**, 574 (1956).
121. Wilkins, M. H. F., and Randall, J. T., *Biochim. Biophys. Acta* **10**, 192 (1953).
122. Wu, S. H., and Newstead, J. D., *J. Animal Sci.* **25**, 1186 (1966).

11 PHYSIOLOGY OF SEMEN AND OF THE MALE REPRODUCTIVE TRACT

T. MANN

I. Introduction

It is proposed to discuss in this chapter mainly those aspects of the physiology and biochemistry of semen and male reproductive organs which are related to problems in the large domestic animals such as the bull, stallion, boar, and ram, with an occasional reference to other species, so as to underline certain comparative aspects of reproduction in the male. In line with the practice adopted when writing a similar chapter for the previous edition of this book, special emphasis will be given to the chemical and metabolic aspects, without too much detail, however, because the subject of the biochemistry of semen and of the male reproductive tract has been extensively reviewed in 1964 in the form of a monograph (136).

II. General: Composition and Properties of Semen and Secretions of Male Accessory Glands

When discussing the physiology of semen, one must always bear in mind the composite nature of semen due to the fact that a number of separate glandular structures are involved in its elaboration. The two main parts of semen as ejaculated are the *spermatozoa* and *seminal plasma*. The spermatozoa, which are the carriers of paternal chromatin, are concerned with the process of fertilization; the seminal plasma, which is a mixture of the accessory secretions, acts as a fluid medium for the spermatozoa, and a source of nutrients supporting sperm motility and metabolism. The spermatozoa are formed in the testes and stored in the epididymides, the seminal plasma is secreted in various male accessory organs of reproduction, which include the epididymides, ductus deferentes, prostate, seminal vesicles, and the bulbourethral and urethral glands. The secretory activity of these organs is subject to strict and intricate control by testosterone produced in the testis, and the testicular androgen production in turn is dependent on gonadotropic stimulation provided by the anterior pituitary gland.

The investigator of semen is confronted by a very wide range of variability in the composition of semen, which differs not only from one species to another but between individuals belonging to the same species as well. Even in the same individual the composition of semen is by no means constant, but is subject to considerable day-to-day fluctuations. Therefore, analyses of semen will yield variable results, even if they are restricted to the same animal and carried out under identical experimental conditions. The fluctuations in semen composition of a given individual are conditioned by a host of factors, among which the male sex-hormone function ranks high in importance. A seasonally conditioned hormone-dependent "male sex cycle" occurs in most domesticated animals, including the bull, stallion, ram, and billy goat (*86, 136*). It finds expression in certain cyclic phenomena evident in sexual functions such as libido, fertility, the secretory output of the accessory organs, and, ultimately, the composition of semen. However, in the domesticated species these cyclic phenomena are not nearly as pronounced as they are in the wild animals. Thus, for example, in the roebuck (*Capreolus capreolus*) the ratios between the highest and lowest value for testicular testosterone, or vesicular fructose, can be as high as 50:1, whereas in the farm animals such ratios are nearer 5:1 (*186*).

Another factor with an important bearing on the physiology of semen is linked to the changes which occur normally in spermatozoa during their passage, first in the male, and next in the female, reproductive tract. The changes which occur in the male tract, chiefly in the epididymis, are collectively referred to as the "ripening" or "maturation" process. They involve morphological as well as functional alterations, such as the migration, and finally shedding, of the kinoplasmic droplet, structural changes in the acrosome, alterations in the chemical composition of sperm lipids, and progressive loss of water, associated with a corresponding increase in the specific gravity of the sperm cell (*9, 42, 52, 103, 113*). The process of maturation does not end at ejaculation, but continues in the female reproductive tract, where the spermatozoa undergo a further change, called "capacitation," as a result of which the sperm cell acquires its full fertilizing capacity and power to penetrate the female gamete (5, 29). Experiments with rabbit sperm have shown that capacitated spermatozoa, when brought in contact with seminal plasma, can be "decapacitated" by a nondialyzable and heat-stable constituent named "decapacitation factor," and that such decapacitated spermatozoa can be recapacitated, that is, again rendered fertile, in the female reproductive tract (10, 45).

A. SPERMATOZOA

The spermatozoa possess two highly specialized functions, motility and fertilizing capacity, which are located in two different parts of the sperm structure. The sperm head, which incorporates the nucleus, carries the deoxyribonucleoprotein, which is the most important constituent insofar as the fertilizing capacity of spermatozoa is concerned. The sperm flagellum, which comprises the middlepiece and tail, is the organ of motility and carries all the enzymes and coenzymes needed for metabolic activity. Fertilizing capacity and motility occasionally become dissociated. In the semen from certain sterile bulls which ejaculate "decapitated" spermatozoa, the free sperm heads are incapable of penetrating the eggs, but the flagella remain perfectly motile and show undiminished metabolic activity. There are other instances where the fertilizing ability and motility of spermatozoa do not coincide, as, for example, in semen subjected to heavy irradiation by X-rays, which destroy fertility without affecting motility. Under normal circumstances, however, a male's fertility and the concentration of motile spermatozoa in his semen ejaculate are closely interrelated, to such an extent that on the basis of these relationships certain so-called fertility indices have been proposed (198).

As a result of chromatin reduction which takes place in the testes during the process of spermatogenesis, ejaculated spermatozoa contain only half the amount of chromatin and, therefore, only half the amount of deoxyribonucleic acid present in somatic cells. The sperm cells carrying the X chromosome are female producing, and those with the Y chromosome are male producing. Assuming that these two kinds of spermatozoa traverse the female reproductive tract at an equal speed, one would normally expect a primary sex ratio of 1:1. In recent years there have been several attempts to segregate these two kinds of spermatozoa by various physicochemical methods, so as to achieve some degree of "sex predetermination." Counterstreaming centrifugation (111), electrophoresis (63), differential sedimentation (16, 17, 182), all these and other methods have been applied to semen in order to separate male- and female-determining spermatozoa. Occasionally, success has been reported, but a vast amount of work remains to be done before we can claim to have solved the problem of controlling the sex ratio of progeny by sperm segregation.

Sperm deoxyribonucleic acid, when separated from the nuclear protein, is composed chiefly of four nucleotides, each consisting of one molecule of phosphoric acid; one molecule of the sugar, deoxyribose; and one molecule of a purine or a pyrimidine base: adenine, guanine, cytosine, or thymine. Within any one species all normal spermatozoa appear to contain a constant amount of deoxyribonucleic acid (200). Ribonucleic acid is virtually absent from mature spermatozoa (131). The proteins conjugated with deoxyribonucleic acid in sperm nuclei are of the basic type and have been shown to be either protamines or histones. There are indications that some deviations from the normal content of deoxyribonucleic acid may occur in spermatozoa from subfertile individuals or as a result of senescence changes (12, 107, 108, 164, 175, 213). The relevant evidence is based largely on results obtained by microspectrophotometric methods, which permit determinations of nucleic acid in individual spermatozoa. In analyses of this kind the degree of absorption by an individual sperm nucleus is determined either in unstained microscopic preparations, by utilizing the absorption in the ultraviolet region by nucleic acid (at about 257 mμ), or in microscopic preparations stained with the Feulgen fuchsinsulfurous acid reagent, by determining the absorption of visible light (at about 546 mμ). However, as regards the latter method, "Feulgen stainability" does not represent an absolutely reliable criterion for assessing nucleic acid, since the ability of spermatozoa to take up the Feulgen stain depends not only on the content of nucleic acid but also on the nature of the basic nuclear proteins, the state of the nucleic acid-protein linkages, as well as on other as yet not fully understood factors (24, 57, 136).

In addition to deoxyribonucleoprotein, the sperm head carries several other important constituents, including some carbohydrate material in the acrosome, which yields a positive PAS-reaction with the periodic acid-Schiff reagent. There are at least two methods available now by means of which the acrosomes can be satisfactorily detached from the sperm heads. One depends on the use of weak sodium hydroxide, sodium carbonate, or hexadecyltrimethylammonium bromide solutions, and the other involves mechanical shaking with small glass beads. From such detached acrosomes (Fig. 1), a well-defined lipoglycoprotein has been isolated, composed of a phospholipid and a glycoprotein. In the glycoprotein seventeen amino acids are present (including particularly large concentrations of glutamic acid, aspartic acid, leucine, alanine, serine, glycine, and proline), and at least six carbohydrate components: mannose, galactose, fucose, glucosamine, galactosamine, and sialic acid. The entire lipoglycoprotein complex as prepared from ram or bull spermatozoa, exhibits characteristic proteolytic and hyaluronidase activity, and is capable of dispersing the cumulus oophorus and corona radiata of newly ovulated rabbit eggs, and occasionally, dissolving the zona pellucida as well. There are indications that the acrosomal lipoglycoprotein may play an important physiological role in the process of denudation and penetration of the mammalian eggs by the spermatozoa (192).

In addition, in the sperm head several other so-called residual proteins are present. Within that category is a soluble nonbasic nuclear protein which, unlike protamines and histones, contains tryptophan; and another, much less soluble, sulfur-rich, keratin-like protein which is believed to constitute the sperm membrane.

The middle piece and tail, which together constitute the sperm flagellum, are the main organ of motility and also the site of some interesting proteins, located mainly in the contractile fibrils, which form part of the so-called axial filament complex. Early investigators of sperm motility depended largely on microscopic observations for the appraisal of the various types of sperm movement, but recently, there have been many attempts to replace the subjectively biased microscopic methods by cinematographic, photoelectric, and other physical techniques (20, 136, 170, 197). The average rate of progressive movements of bull spermatozoa, swimming in a physiological saline solution, at a dilution of 20,000 spermatozoa/μliter, is 156 μ/second (range of means 107–203). However, in the mucus from the uterine cervix of the cow, the mean swimming rate is reduced to about 60 μ/second (194).

In the region of the middle piece, the axial filament complex is sur-

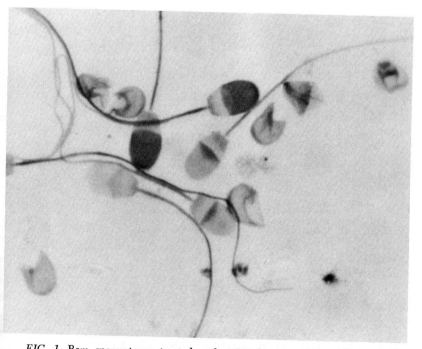

FIG. 1. Ram spermatozoa treated with 0.05% hyamine for 90 minutes, pH 5.8, at 37°, and acrosomes detached by that treatment. From Hartree and Srivastava (75).

rounded by the "mitochondrial sheath," a structure which is particularly rich in phospholipid, most of it bound to protein; some phospholipid, however, is also present in other parts of the spermatozoon. Much of that phospholipid occurs in the form of choline plasmalogen (phosphatidal choline) (73, 120). The structure attributed to plasmalogen is shown below (I):

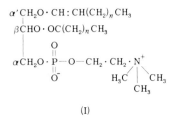

(I)

However, both the content and composition of lipids in spermatozoa are subject to considerable species variations (74, 90, 91, 149). Furthermore, both qualitative and quantitative changes occur in sperm phospholipids during the passage of spermatozoa in the epididymis (42, 65).

Other important components of the mitochondrial sheath are the complete cytochrome system, and a number of enzymes. Cytochemical methods, and in particular a procedure based on the reduction of tetrazolium salts to formazan, have contributed greatly to the present knowledge of various sperm dehydrogenases, including the succinic, malic, isocitric, 6-phosphoglucose, and lactic enzyme (7, 47, 66, 78, 218). Some of the oxidizing enzymes have also been studied in sperm homogenates (155), and at least one, namely, the sorbitol dehyrogenase, has been obtained in a purified state (88). In general, most of the dehydrogenases so far studied seem to bear some similarity to analogous enzymes in other animal tissues. But this rule is not without some notable exceptions. Thus, for example, most animal tissues contain five distinct isozymes of lactate dehydrogenase, whereas the testis and spermatozoa are distinguished by the presence of at least one other isozyme, designated as "LDH IV" because it appears as band number IV during electrophoretic separation (61, 62).

The sperm flagellum is, moreover, the locus of other enzymes and coenzymes necessary for respiration and glycolysis, including adenosinetriphosphatase, the enzyme held to be responsible for generating the energy required for motility, through its action on adenosine triphosphoric acid.

B. SEMINAL PLASMA

The seminal plasma, i.e., the fluid medium in which spermatozoa are normally ejaculated, represents the combined secretions of the male accessory organs and differs in several ways from other body fluids. It is distinguished by a high content of choline (both free and bound), citric acid, fructose, inositol, ergothioneine, and certain other chemical substances not found elsewhere, at least not in large quantities, in the animal body. Chemical determinations of the content of any of these substances, either in the semen as ejaculated or in the secretions of the accessory glands directly, can serve as a most useful and quantitative index of the accessory gland function. A great advantage of these chemical methods over the older anatomical and histological tests that were necessarily made on dissected accessory organs is that they enable one to assess the functional state of such organs as the prostate, seminal vesicles, or epididymides in *live* animals, at frequent time intervals, and, if desired, over a period of months or years. It is possible, by analyzing chemically either the seminal plasma or the individual accessory secretions, to give prompt and unequivocal answers concerning the effects of gonadectomy or hypophysectomy on the accessory gland function. Similarly, the chemical approach is convenient for investigations of the effects which diseases, nutritional deficiencies, and endocrine dysfunctions exert on the male accessory system (*134, 137*).

The high choline content of seminal plasma in domestic animals is due not to free choline, but mostly to glycerylphosphorylcholine (II). Ram

$$H_2C-OH$$
$$HC-OH \quad O$$
$$H_2C-O-\overset{\overset{\displaystyle \|}{}}{P}-O-CH_2-CH_2-\overset{+}{N}$$
$$\overset{\displaystyle |}{O^-} \qquad H_3C \overset{|}{\underset{CH_3}{\diagup}} \diagdown CH_3$$

(II)

seminal plasma in particular represents an exceedingly rich source of glycerylphosphorylcholine, while that of the bull, boar, and stallion has a lower concentration. This substance is derived mainly from the epididymal secretion (*41*). Human semen, however owes its high content of choline partly to phosphorylcholine and partly to free choline.

Most higher mammals, including man, bull, ram, boar, stallion, goat, rat, rabbit, and guinea pig, possess a high concentration of citric acid in semen (*81, 181*). In man citric acid originates chiefly in the prostate, whereas in the bull, ram, boar, and stallion it is derived mainly from the seminal vesicle secretion. Insofar as its nutrient role is concerned, citric acid

$$CH_2COOH$$
$$C \cdot OH \cdot COOH$$
$$CH_2COOH$$

(III)

(III) would seem to be of little use to spermatozoa. Conceivably, however, it may play some role in the process of coagulation of semen, or its function may be linked with the calcium-binding ability of seminal plasma (79).

That the seminal plasma of several mammalian species, including man, contains a reducing sugar in a concentration exceeding by far that of glucose in blood, has been known since early biochemical research on semen. Not until 1945, however, was the seminal sugar identified chemically as fructose (IV) (127, 128).

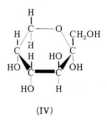

(IV)

At the site of their origin, in the testis and in the epididymis, the spermatozoa, still hardly motile, have no fructose at their disposal. When they traverse the male genital tract, however, they mix with the seminal vesicle secretion, containing fructose in most, though by no means all, mammalian species. Once in contact with spermatozoa, fructose diffuses readily into the cells and enters a characteristic chain of enzymic reactions leading to the formation of lactic acid (fructolysis).

Inositol (V) occurs as a major chemical constituent only in the semen of the boar, but smaller quantities of it are also found in other species

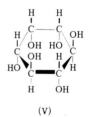

(V)

(71, 132). Practically the whole of the inositol secreted in the boar seminal plasma occurs in a free, and not a phosphorylated, form, and it originates almost exclusively in the seminal vesicle. The concentration of inositol in the secretion of the boar seminal vesicles is so high that by using a few simple chemical manipulations it is possible to obtain 2 gm of this substance in a crystalline form from 100 ml of the secretory fluid.

Another peculiarity of the boar vesicular secretion is the presence, in a high concentration, of the sulfur-containing base ergothioneine (VI) (140).

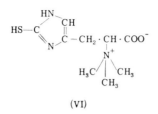

(VI)

Ergothioneine occurs also in the semen of stallion and jackass. Whereas in the boar it is formed chiefly in the seminal vesicles, in the stallion and jackass it is contributed mainly by the ampullae (*106, 144*). Owing to the presence of a sulfhydryl group, ergothioneine exhibits a high reducing power toward certain reagents, such as silver nitrate, iodine, and dichlorophenol-indophenol. In semen it presumably exerts a protective influence on spermatozoa through the reducing action of its sulfhydryl group on the protein-bound, intracellular sulfhydryl groups occurring in spermatozoa.

In addition to glycerylphosphorylcholine, citric acid, fructose, inositol, and ergothioneine, the seminal plasma contains some other unusual constituents. Thus, human and ram seminal plasma, for example, are renowned for their high content of so-called prostaglandins. This is a group of unsaturated C_{20}-fatty acids containing a cyclopentanone ring, and endowed with two outstanding pharmacodynamic properties, namely, the ability to stimulate smooth-muscle organs such as the uterus and to lower pressure in blood vessels. A large number of prostaglandins have been identified in recent years, mostly in human and ram semen, and ram seminal vesicles (*13, 14, 27, 180*). Another unusual feature which distinguishes the seminal plasma from other body fluids is the presence of a wide range of highly active enzymes (*136*) such as proteolytic enzymes (*80, 124, 169*), phosphatases (*11, 122, 123, 130, 173*), nucleases, nucleotidases and nucleosidases (*109, 110, 136, 204*), and glycosidases (*31, 32*). The latter group includes a particularly powerful β-N-acetylglucosaminidase; this enzyme has been recently purified from ram testis (*28*). Yet another peculiarity of seminal plasma worth mentioning is the high content of certain mineral constituents, particularly calcium and potassium.

C. Metabolism of Semen

The two important metabolic processes of semen are fructolysis and respiration. The rates of both these processes are determined largely by sperm density and the degree of sperm motility (*53, 130, 138, 177*). Among the various environmental factors which influence sperm metabolism, those that have been studied with particular attention include different substrates, of which some occur in the female reproductive tract (*48, 67,*

159, 162, 207); sperm concentration (*3*); oxygen and carbon dioxide tension (*64, 112, 154, 157, 176, 206*); ion concentration (*44, 118, 205, 211*); effects of light (*216*).

In the absence of oxygen the spermatozoa depend on fructose as the chief source of metabolic energy. Spermatozoa of bull and ram metabolize fructose to lactic acid at a rate of about 2 mg/10^9 motile cells/hour at 37°C. Boar and stallion spermatozoa, however, have a much lower rate of anaerobic fructolysis (*1, 145*). Fructose is not utilized, or at most poorly utilized, either by azoospermic semen (i.e., ejaculates which contain no spermatozoa) or by necrospermic semen (that is, containing only immotile sperm cells). The correlation between fructolysis and motility is so close that chemical determinations of the amount of fructose disappearing from semen during anaerobic incubation form a convenient and quantitative measure of sperm motility (*21, 129*). The existence, however, of a similar correlation between fructolysis and fertility is a matter of dispute (*21, 54*). One may mention here again the observations made with infertile bulls which consistently produce ejaculates with "decapitated" spermatozoa, that is, with sperm heads separated from the midpiece-tail portions. Although separated from the heads, the midpiece-tail portions in the semen of such bulls are perfectly motile and capable of metabolizing fructose at the normal rate (*135, 148*).

In species that contain fructose as a normal constituent of the seminal plasma, anaerobic fructolysis in whole semen enables the spermatozoa to survive without oxygen. When, however, the spermatozoa are separated from the seminal plasma, e.g., by centrifugation and washing, they cannot carry on anerobically unless the seminal plasma is restored or replaced by glycolyzable sugars, such as fructose, glucose, or mannose. Under anaerobic conditions, the final product of sperm glycolysis, namely, lactic acid, is not further oxidized. In the presence of oxygen the situation differs, however, in that the rate of sugar utilization ("aerobic glycolysis") diminishes; moreover lactic acid undergoes further oxidation, thus providing an additional source of metabolic energy. The "Pasteur-Meyerhof oxidation quotient," which measures the extent to which sperm glycolysis is inhibited by oxygen, is believed to depend on the presence in spermatozoa of a "metabolic regulator," an agent which occurs in the epididymal sperm in a "bound form" but is released in an "active form" after ejaculation (*56, 98*).

The ability of washed spermatozoa to convert not only fructose but glucose and mannose as well into lactic acid is due in all probability to the fact that the metabolic degradation of these three sugars is initiated by the same enzymic reaction, namely, the hexokinase-catalyzed transfer of a phosphoric acid group from adenosine triphosphate to the sugar (*136, 171*). Adenosine triphosphate is a normal constituent of spermatozoa, and a coenzyme of considerable importance in the economy of the sperm cell. Any interference with the normal process of breakdown or resynthesis of adenosine triphosphate, such as "cold shock," leads to a decrease in both glycolysis and motility (*141*).

Aerobically, even after all fructose has been removed from semen by centrifugation and washing, the spermatozoa still remain motile and consume oxygen, at a rate of approximately 100–200 μliters $O_2/10^9$ sperm cells/hour at 37°C. This rate of oxygen consumption can be increased by the addition of a number of substances, including fructose, glucose, mannose, lactic acid, pyruvic acid, acetic acid, glycerol, and sorbitol. The latter substance is of particular interest since, when added to respiring spermatozoa, it produces fructose as the primary oxidation product. Fructose thus formed is subsequently metabolized by spermatozoa to lactic acid, and the lactic acid in turn oxidized to carbon dioxide and water. Glycerol itself does not occur in semen, except perhaps in traces. It could, however, arise in the female reproductive tract as a result of the action of an enzyme (diesterase) on seminal glycerylphosphorylcholine (*212, 215*).

There is good evidence that sperm respiration, like fructolysis, is correlated with motility. However, the existence of a similar correlation with fertilizing capacity still remains questionable (*21, 55*). As regards the chemical nature of the intracellular substrate which is oxidized by the spermatozoa during their endogenous respiration, that is, following their separation from the seminal plasma by washing, all the available evidence points to phospholipids as the main source of oxidizable material (*73, 74, 99, 100*). In washed suspensions of ram spermatozoa the intracellular plasmalogen has been shown to break down during aerobic incubation, the oxidative degradation of the liberated fatty acid serving as the ultimate source of energy.

Apart from direct manometric determination of oxygen consumption, which is the standard procedure for measuring the respiration of spermatozoa (*30*), certain other tests are sometimes used in the evaluation of semen. One group of such tests is based on the dehydrogenase activity of semen, which is assessed by measuring the time required by a semen sample to change the color of standard amounts of certain dyes such as methylene blue, resazurin, or triphenyltetrazolium chloride (*22, 26, 190, 195*). Another test depends on measuring the oxygen uptake of washed spermatozoa in a system made up of pyruvate, fluoride, and dinitrophenol (*58, 151*).

III. Species Characteristics

A. BULL

The reproductive tract of the bull is shown in Fig. 2. The testes (including the epididymides) which in an adult may reach 1 kg in weight,

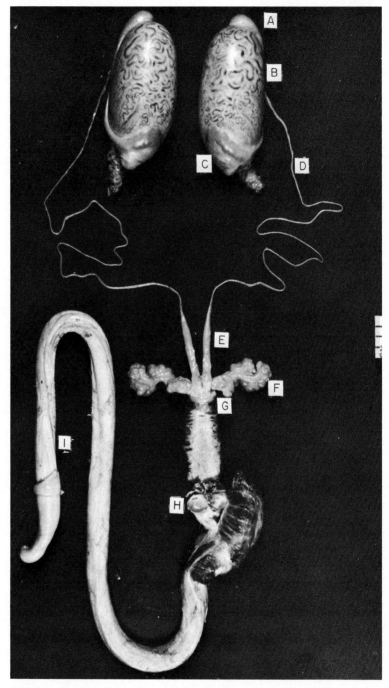

FIG. 2. Reproductive tract of the bull, showing: cauda epididymidis (A); testis (B); caput epididymidis (C); ductus deferens (D); ampulla (E); seminal vesicle (F); prostate (G); bulbourethral gland (H); penis (I).

are supposedly capable of releasing daily up to 10,000,000,000 spermatozoa and up to 100 mg testosterone. Bull testis, it may be recalled, was, in fact, the organ from which, in 1935, testosterone was first isolated in a pure state (36). In addition to testosterone, the adult bull testis contains small amounts of other steroids, notably, androstenedione. In bull calves, however, the ratio between the androgenically active testosterone and the androgenically inactive androstenedione is much lower; up to 4 months of age, androstenedione predominates over testosterone.

In the bull, as in other animal species, the appearance of testosterone precedes considerably the formation of spermatozoa (76, 116). The occurrence of a small androgenic activity has been reported in extracts of fetal bull testes. In the testes of pubescent bull calves testosterone can be chemically detected at the age of 1 month, i.e., about half a year before the appearance of first spermatozoa; at that age the sex cords do not as yet show a lumen, and contain gonocytes, but no spermatogonia. Spermatogenesis sets in at about 3 months of age, and the appearance of the first spermatogonia coincides with the onset of the testosterone-dependent secretory function of the seminal vesicles, reflected in the production of fructose and citric acid; but appreciable quantities of fructose and citric acid appear in the seminal vesicles only about a month later, and in electro ejaculates, at about 5–6 months of age. Such ejaculates are, of course, completely devoid of spermatozoa and remain sperm free for several more months. At the age of 5–6 months the seminiferous tubules of the bull calf begin to acquire a lumen, and contain some primary spermatocytes, but no spermatids or spermatozoa. This is the time when the testosterone/androstenedione ratio reaches approximate unity. From then onward the concentration of testosterone exceeds that of androstenedione. At 9 months of age testosterone becomes the predominant steroid of the bull testis, which now also produces large numbers of mature spermatozoa.

Although spermatozoa appear in the pubescent calf several months later than testosterone, the two basic functions of the testis, that is, the gametogenic and androgenic activity, are, nevertheless, interdependent. This is shown by the existence of a highly significant correlation between two seemingly unrelated parameters of reproductive activity in the bull calf, such as the increase in the diameter of the seminiferous tubules and the simultaneous rise in the weight of seminal vesicles (76). The weight, as well as the fructose and citric acid contents, of the seminal vesicles, are closely correlated with the testosterone content of the testes, this correlation holding good both in pubescent bull calves and in sexually mature bulls (116). Moreover, there exists in the bull a remarkably close proportionality between the level of testosterone in the testes and the rate at which these organs release the hormone into the spermatic vein blood (114).

Castration deprives the animal of its source of testosterone and, consequently, it arrests the process of fructose and citric acid secretion in the seminal vesicles. Implantation or injection of testosterone, however, readily restores the secretory function of the seminal vesicles in castrated bulls (54, 143). Restriction of food in young growing bull calves has a marked delaying influence on the appearance of testosterone in the testes and on the onset of fructose and citric acid secretion in the seminal vesicles (38, 146). This delaying effect of underfeeding on the bovine testis, which influences much more the androgenic activity of the gonad than its sperm-producing capacity, is due not so much to the inability of the testes to generate the male sex hormone as to inadequate stimulation of the testes by gonadotropin. Injections of gonadotropin given to the calf elicit a rapid rise in the androgen production of the testes and a prompt response from the seminal vesicles in the form of abundant secretion of fructose and citric acid.

On leaving the seminiferous tubules, bovine spermatozoa progress along the series of collecting ducts which comprise the rete testis and ductuli efferentes to the caput epididymidis, and from there, along the corpus to the cauda epididymidis. The testicular fluid, in which the spermatozoa are carried from the testis to the epididymis, originates within the seminiferous tubules, and is chemically distinct from the testicular lymph, which is confined to the interstitial tissue (115, 202). As the fluid passes through the epididymis, there is a general decrease in total electrolytes and an increase in organic constituents, such as protein, carbohydrate (nonreducing), and glycerylphosphorylcholine; at the same time a large proportion of sodium ions is replaced by potassium ions (34, 35, 209).

From the epididymis, the spermatozoa and the epididymal fluid pass along the ductus deferens (vas deferens), the ampulla ductus deferentis, moving, finally, to the urethral canal. In the bull, the ampullae, which histologically, and also chemically, resemble the seminal vesicles (glandulae vesiculares) open into the urethra medially to the vesicles and under the body of the relatively small prostate, one on each side of the colliculus seminalis. This is also the point of entry for the secretion of the seminal vesicles, which are more correctly described as vesicular "glands," since they consist of multiple lobes of glandular tissue. Lower down in the urethral canal, the spermatozoa, which emerge from the ampullae, and the secretion voided by the seminal vesicles, both merge with the fluids secreted by the bulbourethral and urethral glands.

The total period of time required for the generation of a spermatozoon in the seminiferous tubule and its passage through the whole length of the epididymis and seminal duct is something like 50 days. When a bull is injected with inorganic phosphate-^{32}P and the radioactivity measured separately in spermatozoa and seminal plasma, high counts will be recorded in the seminal plasma within a week or so of treatment, but in the spermatozoa much later. Deoxyribonucleic acid in epididymal spermatozoa becomes radioactive some 41 days after isotope administration, and measurable radioactivity in ejaculated spermatozoa becomes evident at about 50 days. As regards epididymal passage of spermatozoa, this can be shortened to less than 10 days by increased frequency of semen collections (40, 89, 160, 161).

The basic fact that spermatozoa appear in bull semen nearly 2 months after their generation in the testis must be fully taken into account in the practical evaluation of the quality of bull ejaculates. It means that an abnormality noted in semen on the day of collection can be the outcome of events that have taken place in the testis something like 2 months earlier, and not necessarily on the day of collection.

As the practice of artificial insemination in cattle expands, the need for improved morphological and chemical methods of evaluation of semen also increases. The last three decades, in particular, have witnessed strikingly rapid advances in the chemical analysis of bull semen and its application to studies in the reproductive physiology of cattle (4, 23, 60, 93, 102, 136, 150, 153, 178). Along with these advances came important new developments concerning the use of artificial diluents and the technique of storage of bull semen for the purpose of artificial insemination.

Bull ejaculates can vary greatly in volume (1.7–9 ml) and in density (0.3–3.1 million cells/μliter) (21). An average ejaculate, with a volume of about 5 ml and a sperm density of about 1 million cells/μliter, would be expected to yield, on sharp centrifugation, at least 4.5 ml seminal plasma and up to 0.5 ml well-packed sperm. In bull semen, however, as in other species, not only the ratio between sperm and seminal plasma but also the composition of seminal plasma as such is subject to large fluctuations, depending on the contribution of the various accessory organs, particularly the seminal vesicles. The fluid secreted in the seminal vesicles of the bull is distinguished by a high concentration of potassium ions, citric acid, and fructose, and it is often distinctly yellow in color because of its high flavin content. It is also rich in several enzymes, including alkaline phosphatase and 5-nucleotidase. The contribution of the bull prostate toward the makeup of the whole ejaculate appears to be small. The ampullary secretion, however, contributes some fructose as well as citric acid, while the epididymal secretion has a markedly high content of glycerylphosphorylcholine. A number of chemical constituents of bull semen are listed in Table I; more detailed information concerning the chemical composition of bull semen will be found in papers to which reference is made in Table I.

Although, in the bull, ejaculation under physiological conditions appears to be instantaneous, the "split-ejaculate method," when applied with the aid of electric stimulation, makes it possible to obtain and analyze separately several fractions (121). The early portion of the electroejaculate is sperm free, colorless, of urethral origin, and contains little fructose or citric acid; the later portion is sperm rich, sometimes yellow-colored, and has a considerable admixture of seminal vesicle secretion, as reflected in the high content of fructose and citric acid. Table II records the analysis of an

TABLE I
COMPOSITION OF BULL SEMEN

		Value, average or range (mg/100 ml)	S.E., average or range (mg/100 ml)	Reference
Dry weight		9486		(133)
Hydrogen ion concentration (pH)		6.48–6.99		(92)
Freezing point (°C)	WS[a]	−0.587	0.54–0.73	(179)
	SP[a]	−0.533	0.50–0.71	(112)
Chloride (Cl)	WS	371	309–433	(15)
	SP	174.8	110–293	(172)
Sodium	WS	109	57–201	(15)
	SP	258.2	152–370	(172)
	WS	233	±15.7	(168)
	S[a]	150	±9.3	(168)
	SP	225	±12.9	(168)
Potassium	WS	288	150–415	(15)
	SP	171.6	50–387	(172)
	WS	142	±12.0	(168)
	S	194	±15.3	(168)
	SP	155	±6.4	(168)
Calcium	WS	34	24–45	(15)
	SP	37.3	24–60	(172)
	WS	44.1	±2.55	(168)
	S	27.2	±1.8	(168)
	SP	39.6	±1.7	(168)
Magnesium	WS	12		(133)
	WS	8.4	0.1–18	(172)
	WS	8.8	±0.18	(168)
	S	13.8	±0.86	(168)
	SP	8.1	±0.25	(168)
Iron	SP	2.1	1–4	(172)
Inorganic phosphorus	WS	9		(133)
CO_2(ml/100 ml)	WS	16		(185)
Total nitrogen	WS	756		(133)
	SP	876.9	441–1169	(172)
Nonprotein nitrogen	WS	48		(133)
Urea	WS	5		(196)
Uric acid	SP	2.46	0.82–4.4	(105)
Ammonia	WS	2		(184)
Adenosine triphosphate-NH_2-N	WS	0.41		(126)
Creatine	WS	3		(82)
Creatinine	WS	12.1		(82)
Adrenaline	WS	0.1		(25)
Glycerylphosphorylcholine	WS	232		(41)
	SP	350	110–496	(41)
Ergothioneine	SP	Trace		(140)

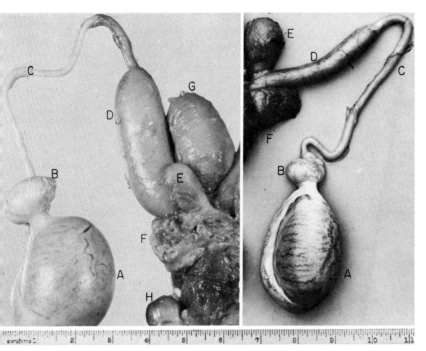

FIG. 3. Part of the reproductive tract of jackass (left) and stallion, (right) showing: testis (A); epididymis (B); vas deferens (C); ampulla (D); seminal vesicle (E); prostate (F); bladder (G); Cowper's gland (H). Scale in inches. From Mann *et al.* (*145*).

the endocrine activity of the testis, as assessed by steroid assays of testicular tissue, appears to be completely normal (*87*).

A most striking feature of the reproductive tract of the stallion, and of the jackass, is the occurrence of large ampullae (Fig. 3). The ampullary secretion, when separated from spermatozoa by centrifugation, appears as a yellowish-colored fluid with a high content of ergothioneine. It is also marked by a high level of glycerylphosphorylcholine which, however, is derived from the epididymides, and not from the ampullary glands as such. The absence of fructose in the stallion's ampullae contrasts with the occurrence of this sugar in the ampullae of the bull (*144, 145, 147*).

Close to the ampullae lie the seminal vesicles, shaped like ovoid sacs, and filled with a colorless but often gelatinous secretion, rich in citric acid and lactic acid (*145*). Lower down the tract are located the prostate and bulbourethral glands.

The ejaculate of the stallion is whitish, opaque, and often of a characteristic gelatinous consistency. The volume varies from 18 to 320 ml (*43, 97, 144*). Of the whole ejaculate, only a small portion, usually less than

3%, is represented by the sperm, the rest is seminal plasma (217). The concentration of spermatozoa varies in the stallion within a very wide range: 30,000–800,000 sperm/μliter semen (97). The results of chemical investigations on the composition of stallion semen are summarized in Tables III and IV. As can be seen from Table IV, which gives the results of analyses carried out in several ejaculates of the same stallion, the composition of semen, even in the same stallion, is subject to considerable variations. Points which deserve particular attention are the extremely low content of fructose and the rather high content of ergothioneine and citric acid.

In addition to the differences between whole ejaculates collected from the same stallion on various occasions, there is a marked difference between various portions of the same ejaculate. This difference occurs because stallion semen is not ejaculated all at once and different portions of semen follow one another in a definite sequence. Usually, it is possible to distinguish at least three fractions, called "presperm," "sperm rich," and "postsperm," respectively, each of entirely different origin. While the presperm fraction is mostly of a watery appearance and contains no sper-

TABLE III
COMPOSITION OF STALLION SEMEN[a]

	Whole semen, average or range	Sperm, average	Seminal plasma, average or range
Specific gravity	1.0117–1.0149	1.0975	1.0116
Freezing point (°C)	−0.5570	—	0.615
Dry material (gm/100 ml)	4.295	20.225	2.541
Ash (gm/100 ml)	0.915	1.760	0.914
	2.238	—	—
Protein (gm/100 ml)	1.043	—	—
Nonprotein nitrogen (mg/100 ml)	55	—	—
Sodium (mg/100 ml)	68	—	257
Potassium (mg/100 ml)	62	—	103
Calcium (mg/100 ml)	20	122	26
Magnesium (mg/100 ml)	3	43	9
Sulfur (mg/100 ml)	3	32	8
Chloride (mg/100 ml)	86–443	11	
Bicarbonate (ml CO_2/100 ml)	24		
Creatine (mg/100 ml)	3		
Creatinine (mg/100 ml)	12.1		
Lipid (gm/100 gm dry weight)		14	2
Cholesterol (mg/100 ml)	4.2		
Acid phosphatase (units/100 ml)			7–86
Alkaline phosphatase (units/100 ml)			25–255

[a] Data taken from papers given in references (15, 82, 91, 152, 189, 193, 217).

TABLE IV

FURTHER DATA ON THE COMPOSITION OF STALLION SEMEN BASED ON ANALYSES
OF EJACULATES COLLECTED FROM THE SAME PONY ON DIFFERENT OCCASIONS[a]

	Average	Range
Volume of ejaculate (12)[b] (ml)	56	27–100
Dry weight (9) (mg/ml)	30.7	22.7–37.5
Ethanol-soluble material (4) (mg/ml)	19.6	13.2–26.2
Sperm density (11) (million cells/ml)	113	40–172
Citric acid (15) (mg/100 ml)	26.1	8.1–53.0
Ergothioneine (15) (mg/100 ml)	7.6	3.5–13.7
Phosphorus, total (3) (mg/100 ml)	17.3	12.0–27.8
Phosphorus, acid-soluble (3) (mg/100 ml)	14.2	11.5–22.1
Carbohydrate, ethanol-soluble and anthrone-reactive (5) (mg/100 ml)	32.7	16.9–42.1
Carbohydrate, ketose-reactive (8) (mg/100 ml) (in terms of fructose)	8.4	4.9–16.2
Carbohydrate, fructose, i.e., ketose-reactive and yeast-fermentable (8) (mg/100 ml)	2.1	0.3–6.3
Lactic acid (3) (mg/100 ml)	12.1	9.2–15.3
Urea (1) (mg/100 ml)	3	
Ammonia (4) (mg/100 ml)	1.3	0.3–2.4
Glycerylphosphorylcholine (2) (mg/100 ml)	76	38–113
Inositol (6) (mg/100 ml)	31.2	19.0–47.3

[a] Data taken from papers given in references (41, 71, 133, 144).
[b] Figures in parentheses refer to the number of ejaculates analyzed.

matozoa, ergothioneine, or citric acid, the sperm-rich fraction, collected a
few seconds after the first, has a high sperm concentration and a high
ergothioneine content, but a low concentration of citric acid. A few seconds
later, the gelatinous, postsperm fraction follows, usually exhibiting a very
low concentration of spermatozoa and ergothioneine, but at the same time
a high concentration of citric acid. This indicates its derivation, chiefly
from the seminal vesicles. Near the end of ejaculation the postsperm fraction is followed by yet another fraction, of watery appearance, and containing little sperm, ergothioneine, or citric acid. This fourth or terminal
fraction, often discharged by the stallion when it dismounts from the mare
on completing the service, constitutes the postcoital penis drip or "tail-
end sample." In some thoroughbred studs it is still a common practice to
"strip" the tail-end sample and "inseminate" the mare with it in the belief
that the sample is a valuable and integral portion of the ejaculate. This
practice is presumed to increase the probability of conception. A view has
been expressed that the tail-end sample has a composition which is representative of the whole ejaculate and, in particular, that a one-to-one
relationship exists between the sulfhydryl content of this sample and that
of the whole ejaculate (214). A more recent study has shown, however,
that, as the sperm and sulfhydryl content of the tail-end samples collected

from different stallions is generally very low, and as the volume and composition of such samples collected from the same stallion on different occasions vary considerably, it is unlikely that tail-end samples form an integral or valuable portion of the stallion's ejaculate (147).

Jackass semen and reproductive tract (see Fig. 3) share many characteristics with the stallion, but the daily sperm output of the jackass is distinctly higher (19, 158). The two species also resemble each other as regards the presence of certain seminal constituents such as ergothioneine and citric acid. Jackass, like stallion, spermatozoa are highly effective "aerobes," i.e., their respiration rate is high. In fact, the rate of aerobic sperm metabolism is higher in the jackass than in the stallion; as regards sperm survival under storage conditions *in vitro*, the resistence of jackass spermatozoa to deleterious environmental factors is markedly better than that of the stallion (145).

C. Ram and Billy Goat

Except for the relatively large size of the testes, the reproductive tract of the ram resembles that of the bull. The epididymides secrete glycerylphosphorylcholine. The seminal vesicles produce fructose and citric acid.

The close proximity of the spermatic veins to the artery in the region of the pampiniform plexus provides in the ram an efficient mechanism for a rapid exchange of heat between arterial and venous blood. The peculiar vascular anatomy of the ram testis and its large size and good accessibility, have made it possible to use the ram for extensive studies in testicular physiology, especially in problems such as measurements of blood and lymph flow, arteriovenous differences of glucose and oxygen, composition of testicular lymph, and metabolism of the testis under *in vivo* conditions (33, 115, 183, 203, 210).

The sperm output and fertilizing ability of the ram are prodigious. As an example, one may mention here the Caucasian ram, which when 5 years old, is reputed to have yielded enough semen during a single breeding season to inseminate 17,681 ewes, and, thus, to sire 18,414 lambs (163). The daily sperm production of the ram, as estimated by exhaustive ejaculation, is probably of the order of 4–8×10^9. Experiments with phosphate-^{32}P injected into rams indicate that about 30 days elapse before spermatozoa with labeled deoxyribonucleic acid appear in the head of the epididymis, and an additional 20 days or so before they emerge from this organ (161). In another series of experiments with rams involving injections of both phosphate-^{32}P and carboxy-^{14}C-stearic acid, spermatozoa with labeled deoxyribonucleic acid first appeared in ejaculated semen 42 days after injections, but radioactivity reached a peak at 50–52 days (39). The rate of sperm pasage in the epididymis and seminal duct is influenced by muscular contractions; it can be speeded up by administration of oxytocin (51).

Much of what is known about the fate of nonejaculated spermatozoa in the male body has been gained by the study of rams. The two mechanisms for sperm disposal that have been proposed are: resorption of aged spermatozoa from the epididymides and seminal ducts, and voidance in the urine. Resorption has been favored by the early investigators. However, more recent quantitative estimates of the number of spermatozoa voided daily in the urine support the view that, in the ram, resorption from the epididymis, vas deferens, or ampulla plays a relatively minor role, and that the bulk of "surplus" sperm is eliminated in the urine (18, 117).

A ram ejaculate generally amounts to little more than 1 ml, but because of the high sperm concentration (2–5 million cells/μliter), ram semen lends itself extremely well to biochemical studies on spermatozoa.

TABLE V
COMPOSITION OF RAM SEMEN[a]

	Average
Dry weight	14820
Chloride (Cl)	87
Sodium	
In whole semen	192
In seminal plasma	178
In spermatozoa	111
Potassium	
In whole semen	92
In seminal plasma	89
In spermatozoa	132
Magnesium	
In whole semen	8.8
In seminal plasma	5.8
In spermatozoa	13.3
Calcium	9
Inorganic phosphorus	12
Total nitrogen	875
Nonprotein nitrogen	57
Urea	44
Uric acid	11
Ammonia	2
Fructose	247
Lactic acid	36
Citric acid	137
CO_2 content (ml/100 ml)	16
Ascorbic acid	5

[a] Results are average values expressed, unless otherwise stated, in milligrams/100 ml of whole semen. Data taken from the following references: sodium, potassium, and magnesium (168); uric acid (105); CO_2 (185); remaining data (136) are based on analysis of material pooled from ejaculates of 10 rams (average volume of single ejaculate, 1.2 ml; average density, 2,940,000 sperm/μliter).

TABLE VI
DISTRIBUTION OF TRACE ELEMENTS AND CERTAIN ORGANIC COMPOUNDS
AND ENZYMES IN RAM SPERMATOZOA AND SEMINAL PLASMA[a]

	Ram semen (100 ml) contains:	
	In spermatozoa (mg)	In seminal plasma (mg)
Iron	0.68	0.16
Hematin iron	0.58	0.01
Zinc	0.70	0.28
Copper	0.12	0.05
Total phosphorus	186.7	141.8
Acid-soluble phosphorus	27.4	132.0
Phospholipid phosphorus	27.9	2.9
Nucleic acid phosphorus	111.0	0.0
Adenosine triphosphate-NH_2-N	0.7	0.0
Plasmalogen	128	15.5
Glycerylphosphorylcholine	Trace	1,281.0
Inositol (free)	0.0	14.8
Fructose	2.0	372.0
Citric acid	1.0	174.0
α-Mannosidase	32,000	5,000
β-N-Acetylglucosaminidase	400,000	1,600,000

[a] Results expressed in milligrams/100 ml except for α-mannosidase and β-acetyl-glucosaminidase [units/100 ml as defined in reference (*32*)].

Much of our present knowledge concerning the intracellular constituents of mammalian spermatozoa, such as cytochrome, trace elements, coenzymes, phospholipids, and nucleic acid, has, in fact, been gained largely by experiments with ram sperm. When subjected to high-speed centrifugation, ram semen separates, on the average, into about one-third well-packed sperm and two-thirds seminal plasma. The latter is distinguished by a high content of fructose, citric acid, and glycerylphosphorylcholine. Results of chemical examination of ram semen, including those which were obtained by separate analyses of spermatozoa and seminal plasma, are given in Tables V and VI. The following differences in chemical composition between the sperm and seminal plasma are noteworthy: Ram spermatozoa have a much higher content of iron, zinc, copper, hematin (most of it present as cytochrome), and plasmalogen, than the seminal plasma. Both sperm and seminal plasma contain a large proportion of phosphorus in the form of acid-soluble compounds, i.e., extractable with trichloroacetic acid. The acid-soluble phosphorus of sperm is due largely to adenosine triphosphate, while that of seminal plasma is derived mainly from glycerylphosphoryl-choline. Nucleic acid, all in the form of deoxyribonucleoprotein is confined entirely to spermatozoa. The actual amount of nucleic acid phosphorus present in each sperm cell is 0.36×10^{-9} mg P; this corresponds to a content of 3.2×10^{-9} mg deoxyribonucleic acid/spermotozoon. The two glycosidases listed at the end of Table VI behave differently from other enzymes of the same group in that they occur not only in the seminal plasma but in the spermatozoa as well. In contrast to α-mannosidase and β-N-acetylglucosaminidase, other glycosidases, including glucuronidase, are confined mainly to seminal plasma (32).

Goat semen shares several characteristics with ram semen. The average volume of the ejaculate is about 1 ml, and sperm concentration 1–5 million/μliter. The seminal plasma of the goat, like that of the ram, is characterized by a high content of fructose, citric acid, and glycerylphosphorylcholine, and by absence of ergothioneine. It also contains a peculiar "egg-yolk coagulating enzyme," which is said to be secreted mainly in the Cowper's glands (83, 174). The seminal vesicles of the goat resemble closely the analogous organs in the ram, and act, together with the ampullae, as a source of fructose. The output of fructose, however, is subject to considerable seasonal variations, dependent, in all probability, on the level of androgenic activity of the testes; it reaches peak values during the early autumn, when sexual activity is highest (104).

D. Boar

Among the peculiarities of the boar's reproductive tract, the following deserve special mention: absence of ampullae; presence of large, baglike seminal vesicles filled with a milky, highly viscous, but not gelifying fluid; and presence of large and cylindrically shaped bulbourethral glands, filled with an extremely viscous, almost rubberlike, white secretion which plays an essential role in the process of "gelation" of ejaculated semen.

A striking feature of the boar's ejaculate is its extraordinarily large volume, amounting occasionally to as much as half a liter. This volume chiefly consists not of spermatozoa but of seminal plasma generated in the accessory organs, including the seminal vesicles, prostate, bulbourethral, and urethral glands.

Sperm density in boar ejaculates may vary from as little as 2500 to 250,000 cells/μliter. Boar spermatozoa differ in several respects from those of other domestic animals. Under storage conditions *in vitro* they become immotile when cooled from body temperature to 15–20°C, but regain motility on rewarming. Even after 3–4 days' storage at 15°C, it is possible to restore motility by rewarming. That is why boar semen used for the purpose of artificial insemination is frequently stored at 15°C and not at lower temperatures, particularly so since, in contrast to bull and ram, cooling of boar semen to 2–5°C, even if done slowly so as to avoid the "cold shock," appears to damage permanently sperm motility. The metabolism of boar sperm is also different from that of bull or ram. Boar spermatozoa are comparatively ineffective "anaerobes," that is, their ability to metabolize carbohydrates anaerobically is negligible. They

TABLE VII
COMPOSITION OF BOAR SEMEN[a]

	Average (mg/100 ml)	Range (mg/100 ml)
Dry weight	4600	2200–6200
Chloride (Cl)	328	258–428
Sodium	646	280–837
Potassium	243	83–382
Calcium	5	2–6
Magnesium	11	5–14
Inorganic phosphorus	17	
CO_2 content (mg/100 ml)	50	
Total nitrogen	613	334–765
Nonprotein nitrogen	22	15–31
Urea	5	
Uric acid	3	
Ammonia	1.5	0.5–2
Fructose	12.6	2.5–48.5
Lactic acid	27	
Citric acid	129	36–325
Total phosphorus	357	
Acid-soluble phosphorus	171	
Lipid phosphorus	6	
Ergothioneine	15.2	5.7–29.5
Inositol	532	382–625
Glycerylphosphorylcholine	171	
Ascorbic acid	3.5	2–5

[a] Data on dry weight, electrolytes, and total nitrogen: reference (125), inositol: (59, 71); glycerylphosphorylcholine: (41); ascorbic acid (84, 85). Boar semen contains 12 gm lipid/100 gm dry wt. (90); it is composed of phospholipids (74.7%), cholesterol (12.6%), diglycerides (5.7%), triglycerides (4.5%), and wax esters (2.4%); only a small portion of the dry matter of seminal plasma is made up of lipid (0.23%).

are capable, however, of functioning effectively as "aerobes," their respiratory coefficient being equal to that of ram and bull sperm (1).

As in the bull and ram, the endogenous respiration of boar spermatozoa depends in all probability mainly on intracellular phospholipids. The average lipid content (12%) and the general distribution pattern of the major phospholipid components is similar in boar and bull spermatozoa (90). Recent analyses of ejaculated boar spermatozoa and of sperm removed from different portions of the epididymis indicate that the concentration of at least two phospholipids, namely, phosphatidyl choline and phosphatidyl ethanolamine, decreases progressively as the spermatozoa pass along the epididymis, and becomes lowest in ejaculated semen (65). The period of time required by a boar spermatozoon to undergo complete development in the testis and epididymal passage, is certainly more than a month. One month after a boar had been injected with phosphate-^{32}P, the deoxyribonucleic acid in ejaculated spermatozoa still remains unlabeled, and a period of 46 days has been found to be necessary for maximum labeling (188).

The chemical composition of boar seminal plasma also differs in several respects from that of other domestic animals. Of special interest is the high content of ergothioneine (59, 140), citric acid (81, 181), and inositol (132), and the comparatively low content of fructose (59, 128). All four substances are generated in the seminal vesicles and characterize boar seminal vesicle secretion. Therefore, the determination of any one of these substances can be used to evaluate quantitatively the contribution of the

TABLE VIII

COMPOSITION OF THE VESICULAR AND EPIDIDYMAL SECRETIONS OF THE BOAR[a]

	Seminal vesicle secretion (mg/100 ml)	Epididymal fluid (mg/100 ml)
Dry weight	17,225	6,520
Dialyzable	5,975	4,150
Nondialyzable	11,250	2,370
Soluble in 66% ethanol	4,795	3,750
Ash	432	694
Chloride	12	12
Sodium	62	88
Potassium	212	188
Calcium	12	6
Total nitrogen	1,396	357
Nonprotein nitrogen after precipitation with:		
Zn(OH)$_2$	61	173
Trichloracetic acid	72	198
Ethanol 66%	60	157
Urea nitrogen	9	9
Total phosphorus	37	292
Nonprotein phosphorus after precipitation with:		
Zn(OH)$_2$	34	290
Trichloracetic acid	35	291
Ethanol 66%	34	292
Inorganic phosphorus	7	15
Total anthrone-reactive carbohydrate	139	184
Total amino sugar	—	128
Fructose	59	4
Inositol	2,150	95
Ergothioneine	57	3
Citric acid	635	12
Glycerylphosphorylcholine	190	3,060

[a] For further data on the composition of epididymal contents in boars see reference (34).

seminal vesicles to the final composition of the boar's ejaculate (139). Another characteristic constituent of boar semen is glycerylphosphorylcholine. The seminal vesicle secretion contains little of this substance; its highest concentration occurs in the epididymal secretion (41). Yet another peculiarity of boar semen is the high content of sialic acid in the seminal gel. This comes mainly from the sialoprotein secreted by the bulbourethral glands. The secretion, as obtained directly from these glands, has been shown to contain 26.6% of sialic acid, mainly in the form of N-acetylneuraminic acid, and 13.3% of galactosamine (almost equimolar with sialic acid), besides small amounts of other carbohydrates and some estersulfate (72). Chemical data on the composition of boar semen are summarized in Table VII, and the distinctive properties of the vesicular, epididymal, and bulbourethral secretions of the boar semen are illustrated by data in Table VIII.

Under physiological conditions, boar semen, like stallion semen, but unlike bull semen, is not ejaculated all at once, but is emitted in fractions. Usually, one may observe, during the protracted emission process, three distinct phases, corresponding to the presperm, sperm-rich, and postsperm fractions. The results of analysis of boar semen obtained by the fractional collection procedure are given in Table IX. It can be seen that there is a clear difference in sperm concentration between fractions 1–3, the highest sperm density being associated with fraction 2. It will also be noticed that fructose, ergothioneine, and citric acid, derived from the seminal vesicles, are distributed among all the fractions, but reach a maximum only in fraction 3. There is, in other words, a considerable degree of overlapping between the three fractions, at least insofar as content in them of the vesicular secretion is concerned. Table IX shows that following the delivery of the three fractions 1–3, two more fractions, 4 and 5, are produced. Fraction 4 represents probably the terminal portion of fraction 3,

TABLE IX
ANALYSIS OF BOAR SEMEN OBTAINED BY FRACTIONAL COLLECTION[a]

	Fractions				
	1	2	3	4	5
Time of delivery from the beginning of ejaculation (minutes)	1	4	7	8	13
Characteristic features	Clear	Creamy	Gel	Gel	Creamy
Volume (ml)	46	100	175	125	140
Sperm (thousands/μliter)	0	327	18	4	88
Fructose (mg/100 ml)	2.9	4.5	6.5	4.6	5.5
Ergothioneine (mg/100 ml)	6.3	12.4	23.0	17.8	21.7
Citric acid (mg/100 ml)	31	50	84	56	69
Chloride (mg Cl/100 ml)	360	350	280	330	340

[a] For details see reference (59).

while fraction 5, because of its high sperm density, may be regarded as a separate, second ejaculate. The occurrence of two ejaculatory waves following one another closely is by no means an infrequent phenomenon in the boar.

Chemical methods of semen analysis in the boar have been successfully applied also for the purpose of studying the effects of certain pharmacodynamic agents on the male reproductive performance. When, for example, 25 mg atropine sulfate is injected into a boar, and semen collected 30 minutes later, the volume of the ejaculate as well as its gel and chloride content are greatly reduced, but sperm density as well as the levels of fructose, citric acid, ergothioneine, and glycerylphosphorylcholine are all greatly increased. This effect of atropine was shown to be principally due to an arrest of the secretory activity in the bulbourethral and urethral gland. In spite of that, however, the atropine-treated boar still remains capable of ejaculating those portions of semen which come from the epididymides, seminal ducts, and seminal vesicles (46). Similar experiments, with both atropine and pilocarpine, have been carried out on bulls (6, 187).

E. Other Species

Dog semen is of particular biochemical interest, as it is almost completely devoid of both fructose and citric acid. The absence of these two substances from dog semen coincides with the lack of seminal vesicles in this species (70, 136). Bulbourethral glands are also absent. The epididymis in the dog, as in other species, is probably the main source of seminal glycerylphosphorylcholine (208). Although dog semen is devoid of fructose, canine spermatozoa are, nevertheless, endowed with the ability of utilizing added fructose, both anaerobically and aerobically (8).

Dog spermatozoa, in common with those of bull, ram, and rabbit, oxidize glucose and fructose at approximately the same rate. However, while ram and bull spermatozoa oxidize sugars at a rate which, if anything, is lower than acetate oxidation, dog and rabbit spermatozoa oxidize sugars faster than acetate (156).

The prostate of the dog is a particularly well-developed organ, and its secretion represents a substantial portion of the whole ejaculate. This secretion, usually of a watery, colorless appearance, is distinguished by the presence of certain proteolytic enzymes, and it contains, though in concentrations which are below those found in the prostatic fluid of man, some phosphatases and glucuronidase. The ionic composition of the canine prostatic secretion is made up chiefly of sodium and chloride ions, and, to a small extent only, of potassium, magnesium, calcium, bicarbonate, and phosphate (79). Sperm density of dog semen can vary from 60 to 600 thousand sperm/μliter, depending on the content of prostatic secretion and other accessory secretions in the whole ejaculate (68, 69).

Rabbit semen is distinguished by a high content of fructose (40–400 mg/100 ml), citric acid (50–600 mg/100 ml) and glycerylphosphoryl-choline (215–370 mg/100 ml); occasionally, it contains, in addition, a small quantity of glucose (142). A single rabbit ejaculate may vary in volume from less than 1 ml to as much as 6 ml, but this variation is due mainly to seminal gel; the fluid portion of the rabbit seminal plasma fluctuates much less. Fructose, originating in the rabbit partly in the prostate and partly in the glandula vesicularis, is associated chiefly with the fluid portion of the seminal plasma, while citric acid, derived mainly from the glandula vesicularis, is associated to a large extent with the seminal gel (37). Spermatozoa are found mostly in the fluid portion of the seminal plasma in a concentration of about 50–250 thousand/μliter (201).

Cock semen, with its high sperm concentration (averaging 3,500,000 sperm/μliter) and turkey semen, usually even more concentrated (7,000,000 sperm/μliter), both contain very little fructose, and hardly any citric acid. The low carbohydrate content of cock seminal plasma appears to consist partly of bound mucopolysaccharide (94) and partly of glucose, inositol, and glycerol (2, 136). The cock has no glands corresponding to the mammalian vesicles or prostate, but the vascular bodies in the cloaca bear some resemblance to the mammalian bulbourethral glands inasmuch as they secrete abundant mucopolysaccharide. The nonprotein nitrogen content of cock seminal plasma, like that of the mammals, is due, at least partly, to free amino acids, chiefly, glutamic acid (95). Cock spermatozoa, in spite of the paucity of fructose in whole semen, are capable of utilizing added fructose and of converting it to lactic acid in a manner resembling that of mammalian sperm cells; they have also been shown to be able to form fructose from glucose (96, 119).

REFERENCES

1. Aalbers, J. G., Mann, T., and Polge, C., J. Reprod. Fertility 2, 42 (1961).
2. Ahluwalia, B. S., and Graham, E. F., J. Reprod. Fertility 12, 359 (1966).
3. Amir, D., and Schindler, H., J. Reprod. Fertility 13, 93 (1967).
4. Anderson, J., "The Semen of Animals and Its Use for Artificial Insemination." Imp. Bur. Animal Breeding Genet., Edinburgh, 1945.
5. Austin, C. R., Australian J. Sci. Res. Ser. B 4, 581 (1951).
6. Baker, R. D., Vandemark, N. L., Graves, C. N., and Norton, H. W., J. Reprod. Fertility 8, 297 (1964).
7. Balogh, K., and Cohen, R. B., Fertility Sterility 15, 35 (1964).
8. Bartlett, D. J., J. Reprod. Fertility 3, 190 (1962).
9. Bedford, J. M., J. Anat. 99, 891 (1965).
10. Bedford, J. M., and Chang, M. C., Am. J. Physiol. 202, 179 (1962).
11. Bell, D. J., and Lake, P. E., J. Reprod. Fertility 3, 363 (1962).
12. Berchtold, M., Zuchthygiene 1, 22 (1966).
13. Bergström, S., Krabisch, L., and Sjövall, J., Acta Chem. Scand. 14, 1706 (1960).
14. Bergström, S., Ryhage, R., Samuelsson, B., and Sjövall, J., Acta Chem. Scand. 16, 501 (1962).

15. Bernstein, A. D., *Trans. Vet. Pathol. Orenburg Vet. Inst.* 1, 9, 63, 116 (1933).
16. Bhattacharya, B. C., *Z. Wiss. Zool.* 166, 203 (1962).
17. Bhattacharya, B. C., Bangham, A. D., Cro, R. J., Keynes, R. D., and Rowson, L. E. A., *Nature* 211, 863 (1966).
18. Bielański, and Wierzbowski, S., *Proc. 4th Intern. Congr. Animal Reprod., The Hague* 2, 274 (1961).
19. Bielański, W., and Wierzbowski, S., *Acta Biol. Cracoviensa* 5, 117 (1962).
20. Bishop, D. W., *Am. Assoc. Advan. Sci. Publ.* 72 (1962).
21. Bishop, M. W. H., Campbell, R. C., Hancock, J. L., and Walton, A., *J. Agr. Sci.* 44, 227 (1954).
22. Blackshaw, A. W., *Australian J. Biol. Sci.* 13, 371 (1960).
23. Bonadonna, T., "Nozioni di Tecnica della Fecondazione Artificiale degli Animali." Istituto Editoriale Cisalpino, Milano-Varese, 1945.
24. Bouters, R., Esnault, C., Ortavant, R., and Salisbury, G. W., *Nature* 213, 181 (1967).
25. Brochart, M., *Compt. Rend. Soc. Biol.* 142, 646 (1948).
26. Brochart, M., *Rec. Med. Vet.* 124(2), 64 (1948).
27. Bygdeman, M., and Samuelsson, B., *Clin. Chim. Acta* 10, 566 (1964).
28. Caygill, J. C., Roston, C. P., and Jevons, F. R., *Biochem. J.* 98, 405 (1966).
29. Chang, M. C., *Nature* 168, 697 (1951).
30. Chang, M. C., and Walton, A., *Proc. Roy. Soc.* B129, 517 (1940).
31. Conchie, J., and Findlay, J., *Endocrinol.* 18, 132 (1959).
32. Conchie, J., and Mann, T., *Nature* 179, 1190 (1957).
33. Cowie, A. T., Lascelles, A. K., and Wallace, J. C., *J. Physiol.* (*London*) 171, 176 (1964).
34. Crabo, B., *Acta Vet. Scand.* 6, Suppl. 5 (1965).
35. Crabo, B., and Gustafson, B., *J. Reprod. Fertility* 7, 337 (1964).
36. David, K., Dingemanse, E., Freud, J., and Lacqueur, E., *Z. Physiol. Chem.* 233, 281 (1935).
37. Davies, D. V., and Mann, T., *Nature* 160, 295 (1947).
38. Davies, D. V., Mann, T., and Rowson, L. E. A., *Proc. Roy. Soc.* B147, 332 (1957).
39. Dawson, R. M. C., *Biochem. J.* 68, 512 (1958).
40. Dawson, R. M. C., *Nature* 181, 1014 (1958).
41. Dawson, R. M. C., Mann, T., and White, I. G., *Biochem. J.* 65, 627 (1957).
42. Dawson, R. M. C., and Scott, T. W., *Nature* 202, 292 (1964).
43. Day, F. T., *Vet. Record* 52, 597 (1940).
44. Dott, H. M., and White, I. G., *J. Reprod. Fertility* 7, 127 (1964).
45. Dukelow, W. R., Chernoff, H. N., and Williams, W. L., *Am. J. Physiol.* 211, 826 (1966).
46. Dziuk, P. J., and Mann, T., *J. Reprod. Fertility* 5, 101 (1963).
47. Edwards, R. G., and Valentine, R. C., *Exptl. Cell Res.* 31, 508 (1963).
48. Ehlers, M. H., and Chiriboga, J., *J. Reprod. Fertility* 10, 303 (1965).
49. Ehlers, M. H., Dixon, J., and Erb, R. E., *J. Dairy Sci.* 44, 1679 (1961).
50. Ehlers, M. H., Flerchinger, F. H., and Erb, R. E., *J. Dairy Sci.* 36, 1021 (1953).
51. Ewy, Z., Bielański, W., and Zapletal, Z., *Bull. Acad. Polon. Ser. Sci. Tech.* [2] 11, 145 (1963).
52. Fawcett, D. W., and Hollenberg, R. D., *Z. Zellforsch.* 60, 276, (1963).

53. Flipse, R. J., *Publ. Am. Assoc. Advan. Sci.* **72**, 133 (1962).
54. Gassner, F. X., Hill, H. J., and Sulzberger, L., *Fertility Sterility* **3**, 121 (1952).
55. Ghosh, D., Casida, L. E., and Lardy, H. A., *J. Animal Sci.* **8**, 205 (1958).
56. Ghosh, D., and Lardy, H. A., *J. Animal Sci.* **11**, 545 (1952).
57. Gledhill, B. L., *Acta Vet. Scand.* **7**, 1 (1966).
58. Glew, G., *Proc. 3rd Intern. Congr. Animal Reprod. Cambridge, Engl., Sect. I Physiol.* p. 36 (1956).
59. Glover, T., and Mann, T., *J. Agr. Sci.* **44**, 355 (1954).
60. Goetze, R., "Besamung und Unfruchtbarkeit der Haussaugetiere." Schaper, Hannover, 1949.
61. Goldberg, E., *Science* **139**, 602 (1963).
62. Goldberg, E., *Arch. Biochem. Biophys.* **109**, 134 (1965).
63. Gordon, M. J., *Proc. Natl. Acad. Sci. U.S.* **43**, 913 (1957).
64. Graves, C. N., Lodge, J. R., and Salisbury, G. W., *Nature* **211**, 308 (1966).
65. Grogan, D. E., Mayer, D. T., and Sikes, J. D., *J. Reprod. Fertility* **12**, 431 (1966).
66. Gupta, B. L., and Kamboj, V. P., *Nature* **193**, 788 (1962).
67. Hamner, C. E., and Williams, W. W., *J. Reprod. Fertility* **5**, 143 (1963).
68. Hancock, J. L., and Rowlands, I. W., *Vet. Record* **61**, 771 (1949).
69. Harrop, A. E., *Vet. Record* **67**, 494 (1955).
70. Harrop, A. E., "Reproduction in the Dog." Baillière, London, 1960.
71. Hartree, E. F., *Biochem. J.* **66**, 131 (1957).
72. Hartree, E. F., *Nature* **196**, 483 (1962).
73. Hartree, E. F., and Mann, T., *Biochem. J.* **71**, 423 (1958).
74. Hartree, E. F., and Mann, T., *Biochem. J.* **80**, 464 (1961).
75. Hartree, E. F., and Srivastava, P. N., *J. Reprod. Fertility* **9**, 47 (1965).
76. Hay, M. F., Lindner, H. R., and Mann, T., *Proc. Roy. Soc.* **B154**, 433 (1961).
77. Heppel, L. A., and Hilmoe, R. J., *J. Biol. Chem.* **200**, 217 (1953).
78. Hrudka, F., *J. Reprod. Fertility* **10**, 15 (1965).
79. Huggins, O., *Physiol. Revs.* **25**, 281 (1945).
80. Huggins, C., and Neal, W., *J. Exptl. Med.* **76**, 527 (1942).
81. Humphrey, F. G., and Mann, T., *Biochem. J.* **44**, 97 (1949).
82. Ilyasov, I., *Trans. Vet. Pathol. Orenburg Vet. Inst.* **1**, 48 (1933).
83. Iritani, A., and Nishikawa, Y., *Japan. J. Animal Reprod.* **10** (2), 44 (1964).
84. Karg, H., and Gassner, F. X., *Proc. 4th Intern. Congr. Animal Reprod. The Hague,* p. 256 (1961).
85. Karg, H., and Leidl, W., *Zuchthygiene* **3**, 232 (1959).
86. Kihlström, J. E., *Experientia* **22**, 630 (1966).
87. King, J. M., Short, R. V., Mutton, D. E., and Hamerton, J. L., *in* "Comparative Biology of Reproduction in Mammals" (I. W. Rowlands, ed.), Symp. Zool. Soc. 15, p. 151. Academic Press, New York, 1966.
88. King, T. E., and Mann, T., *Proc. Roy. Soc.* **B151**, 226 (1959).
89. Koefoed-Johnsen, H. H., *Nature* **185**, 49 (1960).
90. Komarek, R. J., Pickett, B. W., Gibson, E. W., and Jensen, R. G., *J. Reprod. Fertility* **9**, 131 (1965).
91. Komarek, R. J., Pickett, B. W., Gibson, E. W., and Lanz, R. N., *J. Reprod. Fertility* **10**, 337 (1965).

92. Laing, J. A., *J. Agr. Sci.* **35**, 1 (1945).
93. Laing, J. A., "Fertility and Infertility in the Domestic Animals." Baillière, London, 1955.
94. Lake, P. E., *J. Anat.* **91**, 116 (1957).
95. Lake, P. E., and W. M. McIndoe, *Biochem. J.* **71**, 303 (1959).
96. Lake, P. E., Lorenz, F. W., and Reiman, W. D., *Nature* **194**, 545 (1962).
97. Lambert, W. V., and McKenzie, F. F., *U.S. Dept. Agr. Circ.* **567** (1940).
98. Lardy, H. A., *in* "Studies on Testis and Ovary, Eggs and Sperm" (E. T. Engle, ed.), p. 111. Thomas, Springfield, Illinois, 1952.
99. Lardy, H. A., Hansen, R. G., and Phillips, P. H., *Arch. Biochem.* **6**, 41 (1945).
100. Lardy, H. A., and Phillips, P. H., *Arch. Biochem.* **6**, 53 (1945).
101. Larson, B. L., and Salisbury, G. W., *J. Biol. Chem.* **201**, 601 (1953).
102. Lasley, J. F., and Bogart, R., *Missouri Univ. Agr. Expt. Sta. Res. Bull* **376** (1943).
103. Lavon, U., Volcani, R., Amir, D., and Danon, D., *J. Reprod. Fertility* **12**, 597 (1966).
104. Leidl, W., "Klima und Sexualfunktion männlicher Haustiere." Schaper, Hannover, 1958.
105. Leone, E., *Quaderni Sez. Perugina Soc. Ital. Biol. Sper.* **10**, 1 (1953).
106. Leone, E., *Nature* **174**, 404 (1954).
107. Leuchtenberger, C., *J. Dairy Sci.* **43**, 31 (1960).
108. Leuchtenberger, C., Weir, D. R., Schrader, F., and Leuchtenberger, R., *Acta Genet. Statist. Med.* **6**, 272 (1956).
109. Levin, S. J., and Bodansky, O., *J. Biol. Chem.* **241**, 51 (1966).
110. Libonati, M., and Leone, E., *Ital. J. Biochem.* **11**, 135 (1962).
111. Lindahl, P. E., *Nature* **181**, 784 (1958).
112. Lindahl, P. E., and Thunqvist, L. O., *Arkiv Zool.* **16**, 367 (1964).
113. Lindahl, P. E., and Thunqvist, L. O., *Experientia* **21**, 94 (1965).
114. Lindner, H. R., *J. Endocrinol.* **23**, 139 (1961).
115. Lindner, H. R., *J. Endocrinol.* **25**, 483 (1963).
116. Lindner, H. R., and Mann, T., *J. Endocrinol.* **21**, 341 (1960).
117. Lino, B. F., Braden, A. W. H., and Thurnbull, K. E., *Nature* **213**, 594 (1967).
118. Lodge, J. R., Salisbury, G. W., Schmidt, R. P., and Graves, C. N., *J. Dairy Sci.* **46**, 473 (1963).
119. Lorenz, F. W., *Nature* **182**, 397 (1958).
120. Lovern, J. A., Olley, J., Hartree, E. F., and Mann, T., *Biochem. J.* **67**, 630 (1957).
121. Lutwak-Mann, C., and Rowson, L. E. A., *J. Agr. Sci.* **43**, 131 (1953).
122. Lundquist, F., *Acta Physiol. Scand.* **13**, 322 (1947).
123. Lundquist, F., *Acta Physiol. Scand.* **14**, 263 (1947).
124. Lundquist, F., Thorsteinsson, T., and Buus, O., *Biochem. J.* **59**, 69 (1955).
125. McKenzie, F. F., Miller, J. S., and Bauguess, L. C., *Missouri Univ. Agr. Expt. Sta. Res. Bull.* **279** (1938).
126. Mann, T., *Biochem. J.* **39**, 451 (1945).
127. Mann, T., *Biochem. J.* **39**, 458 (1945).
128. Mann, T., *Biochem. J.* **40**, 481 (1946).
129. Mann, T., *J. Agr. Sci.* **38**, 323 (1948).
130. Mann, T., *Advan. Enzymol.* **9**, 329 (1949).

131. Mann, T., *Biochem. Soc. Symp.* (*Cambridge, Engl.*) **7**, 11 (1951).
132. Mann, T., *Proc. Roy. Soc.* **B142**, 21 (1954).
133. Mann, T., "The Biochemistry of Semen." Methuen, London, 1954.
134. Mann, T., *Recent Progr. Hormone Res.* **12**, 353 (1956).
135. Mann, T., *Proc. Soc. Study Fertility* **9**, 3 (1958).
136. Mann, T., "The Biochemistry of Semen and of the Male Reproductive Tract." Methuen, London; Wiley, New York, 1964.
137. Mann, T., *Ciba Found. Colloq. Endocrinol. Testis* **16**, 233 (1967).
138. Mann, T., *in* "Fertilization. Comparative Morphology, Biochemistry, and Immunology," (C. B. Metz and A. Monroy, eds.), Vol. 1, p. 99. Academic Press, New York, 1967.
139. Mann, T., and Glover, T., *J. Endocrinol.* **10**, iv (1954).
140. Mann, T., and Leone, E., *Biochem. J.* **53**, 140 (1953).
141. Mann, T., and Lutwak-Mann, C., *Arch. Sci. Biol.* (*Bologna*) **39**, 578 (1955).
142. Mann, T., and Parsons, U., *Biochem. J.* **46**, 440 (1950).
143. Mann, T., Davies, D. V., and Humphrey, F. G., *J. Endocrinol.* **6**, 75 (1949).
144. Mann, T., Leone, E., and Polge, C., *J. Endocrinol.* **13**, 279 (1956).
145. Mann, T., Minotakis, C. S., and Polge, C., *J. Reprod. Fertility* **5**, 109 (1963).
146. Mann, T., Rowson, L. E. A., Short, R. V., and Skinner, J. D., *J. Endocrinol.* **38**, 455 (1967).
147. Mann, T., Short, R. V., Walton, A., Archer, R. K., and Miller, W. C., *J. Agr. Sci.* **49**, 301 (1957).
148. Masaki, J., and Hartree, E. F., *Biochem. J.* **84**, 347 (1962).
149. Masaki, J., Tomizuka, T., and Hiroe, K., *Nippon Chikusangaku Kaiho* (*Japan. J. Zootech. Sci.*) **35**, 67 (1964).
150. Melrose, D. R., *in* "The Semen of Animals and Artificial Insemination" (J. P. Maule, ed.), p. 2. Commonwealth Agr. Bur., Farnham Royal, Bucks., England, 1962.
151. Melrose, D. R., and Terner, C., *Biochem. J.* **53**, 296 (1953).
152. Milovanov, V. K., "Iskusstvennoe Osemenenie Seljskohozjaistvennyh Zhivotnyh," 4th ed. Seljhozgiz, Moscow, 1938.
153. Milovanov, V. K., and Sokolovskaya, I. I., "Stockbreeding and the Artificial Insemination of Livestock." Hutchinson, London, 1947.
154. Mohri, H., and Yasumasu, I., *J. Exptl. Biol.* **40**, 573 (1963).
155. Mohri, H., Mohri, T., and Ernster, L., *Exptl. Cell Res.* **38**, 217 (1965).
156. Murdoch, R. N., and White, I. G., *J. Reprod. Fertility* **12**, 271 (1966).
157. Nevo, A. C., *J. Reprod. Fertility* **9**, 103 (1965).
158. Nishikawa, Y., "Studies on Reproduction in Horses." Japan Racing Assoc. Shiba Temuracho Minotoku, Tokyo, 1959.
159. Ogasawara, F. X., and Lorenz, F. W., *J. Reprod. Fertility* **7**, 281 (1964).
160. Orgebin, M. C., *Ann. Biol. Animale Biochim. Biophys.* **1**, 117 (1961).
161. Orgebin-Crist, M. C., *Ann. Biol. Animale Biochim. Biophys.* **2**, 51 (1962).
162. O'Shea, T., and Wales, R. G., *J. Reprod. Fertility* **11**, 263 (1966).
163. Oshin, W. F., *in* "Die künstliche Besamung bei den Haustieren." Fischer, Jena, 1963.
164. Parez, M., Petel, J.-P., and Vendrely, C., *Compt. Rend. Acad. Sci.* **251**, 2581 (1960).
165. Phillips, P. H., Lardy, H. A., Heiser, E. E., and Rupel, I. W., *J. Dairy Sci.* **23**, 873 (1940).

166. Pigoń, H., Lunaas, T., and Velle, W., *Acta Endocrinol.* **36**, 131 (1961).
167. Pigoń, H., Marchut, M., and Nestorov, N., *J. Reprod. Fertility* **11**, 221 (1966).
168. Quinn, P. J., White, I. G., and Wirrick, B. R., *J. Reprod. Fertility* **10**, 379 (1965).
169. Rasmussen, J., and Albrechtsen, O. K., *Fertility Sterility* **11**, 264 (1960).
170. Rikmenspoel, R., *Trans. N.Y. Acad. Sci.* [2], **26**, Suppl. 8, 1072 (1964).
171. Rikmenspoel, R., and Caputo, R., *J. Reprod. Fertility* **12**, 437 (1966).
172. Rothschild, (Lord), and Barnes, H., *J. Exptl. Biol.* **31**, 561 (1954).
173. Roussel, J. D., and Stallcup, O. T., *J. Reprod. Fertility* **12**, 423 (1966).
174. Roy, A., *Nature* **179**, 318 (1957).
175. Salisbury, G. W., de la Torre, L., Binge, W. J., and Lodge, J. R., *J. Biophys. Biochem. Cytol.* Abstr. **43**, 882 (1961).
176. Salisbury, G. W., and Graves, C. N., *J. Reprod. Fertility* **6**, 351 (1963).
177. Salisbury, G. W., and Lodge, J. R., *Advan. Enzymol.* **24**, 35 (1962).
178. Salisbury, G. W., and Vandemark, N. L., "Physiology of Reproduction and Artificial Insemination of Cattle." Freeman, San Francisco, California, 1961.
179. Salisbury, G. W., Knodt, C. B., and Bratton, R. W., *J. Animal Sci.* **7**, 283 (1948).
180. Samuelsson, B., *J. Biol. Chem.* **238**, 3229 (1963).
181. Scherstén, B., *Skand. Arch. Physiol.* **74**, Suppl. 9 (1936).
182. Schilling, E., *J. Reprod. Fertility* **11**, 469 (1966).
183. Setchell, B. P., and Waites, G. M. H., *J. Physiol. (London)* **171**, 411 (1964).
184. Shergin, N. P., *Trans. Vet. Pathol. Orenburg Vet. Inst.* **1**, 57 (1933).
185. Shergin, N. P., *Problemy Zhivotnovodstva* **13**, 100 (1935).
186. Short, R. V., and Mann, T., *J. Reprod. Fertility* **12**, 337 (1966).
187. Signoret, J. P., *Ann. Biol. Animale Biochim. Biophys.* **4**, 91 (1964).
188. Singh, G., *Ann. Biol. Animale Biochim. Biophys.* **1**, 403 (1961).
189. Slovtzov, B., *Compt. Rend. Soc. Biol.* **79**, 208 (1916).
190. Sørensen, E., *Skand. Vettidskr.* **32**, 358 (1942).
191. Spallanzani, L., "Opuscoli di Fisica Animale, e Vegetabile," Presso la Societa Tipographica, Modena, 1776; English translation: "Tracts on the Nature of Animals and Vegetables." Creech and White, Edinburgh, 1799.
192. Srivastava, P. N., Adams, C. E., and Hartree, E. F., *J. Reprod. Fertility* **10**, 61 (1965).
193. Szumowski, P., *Compt. Rend. Acad. Agr. France* **50**, 697 (1964).
194. Tampion, D., and Gibbons, R. A., *J. Reprod. Fertility* **5**, 259 (1963).
195. VanDemark, N. L., Mercier, E., and Salisbury, G. W., *J. Dairy Sci.* **28**, 121 (1945).
196. VanDemark, N. L., and Salisbury, G. W., *J. Biol. Chem.* **156**, 289 (1944).
197. van Duijn, C., Jr., *Proc. 5th Intern. Congr. Animal Reprod., Trento* **III**, 355 (1964).
198. van Duijn, C., Jr., *Ann. Biol. Animale Biochim. Biophys.* **5**, 419 (1965).
199. Velle, W., *J. Reprod. Fertility* **12**, 65 (1966).
200. Vendrely, C., *Bull. Biol. France Belg.* **86**, 1 (1952).
201. Venge, O., and Fröhlich, A., *Acta Agr. Scand.* **1**, 291 (1951).
202. Voglmayr, J. K., Scott, T. W., Setchell, P. B., and Waites, C. M. H., *J. Reprod. Fertility* **14**, 87 (1967).
203. Waites, G. M. H., and Setchell, B. P., *J. Reprod. Fertility* **8**, 339 (1964).

204. Waldschmidt, M., Karg, H., and Kinzler, M., *Naturwissenschaften* **51**, 364 (1964).
205. Wales, R. G., *J. Reprod. Fertility* **10**, 369 (1965).
206. Wales, R. G., and O'Shea, T., *J. Reprod. Fertility* **11**, 171 (1966).
207. Wales, R. G., and Restall, B. J., *Australian J. Biol. Sci.* **19**, 199 (1966).
208. Wales, R. G., and White, I. G., *J. Reprod. Fertility* **9**, 69 (1965).
209. Wales, R. G., Wallace, J. C., and White, I. G., *J. Reprod. Fertility* **12**, 139 (1966).
210. Wallace, J. C., and Lascelles, A. K., *J. Reprod. Fertility* **8**, 235 (1964).
211. Wallace, J. C., and Wales, R. G., *J. Reprod. Fertility* **8**, 187 (1964).
212. Wallace, J. C., and White, I. G., *J. Reprod. Fertility* **8**, 187 (1964).
213. Welch, R. M., Hanly, E. W., Guest, W., and Resch, K., *Texas Univ. Publ.* **6041** (1962).
214. Werthessen, N. T., Marden, W., Haag, F., and Goldzieher, J. W., *Proc. Soc. Study Fertility* **8**, 42 (1957).
215. White, I. G., Wallace, J. C., and Stone, G. M., *J. Reprod. Fertility* **5**, 298 (1963).
216. Williams, W. L., and Hamner, C. E., *J. Reprod. Fertility* **6**, 235 (1963).
217. Yamane, J., *J. Coll. Agr. Sapporo* **9**, 161 (1920).
218. Young, M. R., and Edwards, R. G., *J. Histochem. Cytochem.* **11**, 444 (1963).
219. Zondek, B., *Nature* **133**, 209, 494 (1934).

12 PHYSIOLOGICAL ASPECTS OF
ARTIFICIAL INSEMINATION

R. H. FOOTE

I. Introduction

In 1780 Spallanzani, an Italian physiologist, successfully inseminated a bitch, but these exploits aroused little interest in artificial insemination until the beginning of the twentieth century, when a serious effort was made in Russia to apply the technique to domestic animals. The greatest potential of artificial insemination is the genetic improvement possible through the widespread use of genetically superior sires. Artificial insemination is largely applied within breeds, but is well suited to crossbreeding. When it is desirable to introduce characteristics of another breed into an area in which the pure breed does not perform well, the preserved semen can be sent. The replacement of the act of copulation by artificial insemination also serves as a valuable prophylactic measure in the control of disease, particularly venereal diseases. Furthermore, it extends the service of superior males to small or remote units of breeding females. Also, intensive use of artificial insemination in dairy cattle normally has economic advantages and reduces the hazards of housing sires on farms.

Disadvantages of artificial insemination in dairy cattle arise primarily when the program of sire selection, semen processing, and field service is done improperly. In other farm animals research to improve semen preservation is needed before the full potential of this technique can be realized.

The first systematic studies on artificial insemination were initiated in the USSR by Ivanov and co-workers. They investigated artificial insemination techniques for horses and later for sheep and cattle. The work spread to Japan, the rest of Europe, and the United States. The first organized artificial insemination of dairy cattle in the USA was started in 1938. The USSR, United States, and France lead in number of cows inseminated, but Denmark, Japan, and Israel lead in the percentage of cows inseminated, all exceeding 95% (164). In Japan beef cattle operations are intensive and 600,000 cows (89%) are inseminated each year. Argentina

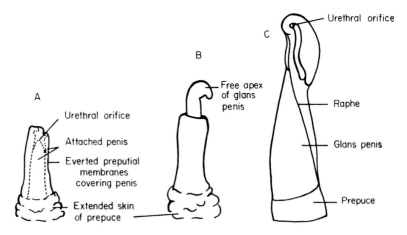

FIG. 1. Diagrammatic representation of the separation of the glans penis from the prepuce in the young bull. (A) Skin of prepuce (sheath) everted, showing all but the apex of the glans penis adherent within the preputial membranes. (B) Free apex of the glans penis, which may be protruded by males approaching sexual maturity. (C) Mature glans penis completely free from adhesions. Based on Ashdown (12, 13) and H. O. Dunn, PhD thesis, Cornell University, 1952.

has an important artificial insemination industry. In the United States about 650,000 beef cows are inseminated annually. Another 875,000 dairy cows are inseminated with beef semen. Fifty-million ewes are inseminated annually, nearly 40 million of which are in Russia. Artificial insemination practice in swine is growing in several countries, but the annual world total of 1 million is a small proportion of the total breeding females. Interest in breeding light horses artificially is increasing. Several million turkeys and other types of fowl are inseminated in large breeding operations.

In this chapter, the physiological aspects of semen collection, preservation, and insemination will be discussed for several domestic species, but emphasis will be placed on studies in cattle. Only a sample of important papers and reviews are cited, but many of these are recent ones which cite earlier work. Detailed procedural steps which vary with time and location, are well described in annual reports on artificial insemination published in different countries, and in textbooks on artificial insemination (*150, 180, 217*).

II. Development of Sexual Function

A. CHARACTERIZATION OF PUBERTY

Puberty has occurred when spermatogenesis is complete. Practically, this is measured by determining the age at which sperm are first ejaculated. Normal ejaculation cannot occur until the penis is completely free in the sheath. This requires that adhesions between the glans penis and the preputial mucosa, characteristic of the immature state, be eliminated (*12, 13, 168, 260*) before semen collection is initiated, or tearing and possible infection may result. Stages in this separation and in development of the glans are shown diagrammatically in Fig. 1. The separation is influenced by testosterone. Testosterone secretion is required to elicit normal libido and ejaculation. Thus, in its fullest sense puberty occurs when (1) spermatogenesis is complete, (2) libido is manifested, and (3) penile development permits normal ejaculation. Functionally, it is the earliest age at which males can impregnate females or serve the artificial vagina.

B. FACTORS AFFECTING PUBERTY AND POSTPUBERTAL DEVELOPMENT

1. Hormonal Involvement

The student of artificial insemination should become thoroughly familiar with the mechanisms responsible for sexual development and overt sexual behavior (Chapters 10, 11, and 20) in order to fully exploit the spermatogenic potential of the male. Gonadotropins play an important role in the development of the interstitial or Leydig cells and the seminiferous tubules. The interstitial cells produce androgens at an early age; the androgens initiate development of the accessory sex glands and secondary sex characteristics before spermatogenesis is complete (52, 105, 142). In the bull calf the ratio of androstenedione to testosterone production may shift in favor of testosterone during prepubertal development. This is accompanied by an increase in size of the seminal vesicles and their secretions, and in the diameter of the seminiferous tubules. However, evidence is incomplete and somewhat contradictory concerning the elaboration of these androgens and the direct effects of a shift in balance on reproductive development. The correlation between seminal vesicle weight and tubular diameter in calves 1–5.5 months old was +0.95 (52). Lindner (131) reported that testosterone was higher in testicular lymph than in arterial blood, which suggests that the tissue fluid of the testis could contain sufficient testosterone to affect the seminiferous tubules even though the systemic blood level was low.

2. Genetics

Both genetic and environmental factors influence the age at puberty. Clear-cut differences among species, breeds (1, 3, 135, 219, 253), and identical twin pairs (16) attest to the large genetic effects. For example, buffalo bulls mature much more slowly than bulls of European breeds. Also, studies with "pure" lines and crossbreds point out heritable differences in body development and sexual maturity.

3. Nutrition

Low energy intakes retard sexual development in young males and high energy intakes accelerate it. The differences become smaller as animals age (16, 33, 71, 174, 196). Both the endocrine and spermatogenic functions of the testes are affected (52). The secretion of fructose and citric acid is considerably delayed by underfeeding, and spermatogenesis, which appears subsequently, also is delayed.

Several extensive studies with Holstein bulls (32, 33, 71, 109, 250) clearly show that temporarily restricted intake delays puberty, but usually causes no permanent harm. Several effects reported by Flipse and Almquist (71) are shown in Table I. As the level of intake increased, the age to appearance of the first motile sperm decreased. Height was quite uniform and appeared to represent an approximate physiological size at puberty in Holsteins. Similar studies by Bratton et al. (33) showed that the total energy (TDN) consumed per group to puberty was not significantly different. Sperm output (see Table I) increased more rapidly in the high-intake group, but after 2 years of age there was no difference. The high-intake bulls showed reduced libido (prolonged reaction time). Weakness of the feet and legs was evident, suggesting damage after prolonged high

TABLE I

EFFECT OF FEEDING LEVEL ON SEXUAL DEVELOPMENT AND
SEMEN CHARACTERISTICS IN HOLSTEIN BULLS[a]

Item measured	% of recommended feed intake			
	70	100	115	130
Motile sperm first obtained:				
Age (weeks)	61	45	41	44
Withers height (centimeters)	114	114	117	119
Weight (pounds)	523	643	675	784
Billions of motile sperm/ejaculation:				
57–80 weeks	1.0	1.1	2.2	2.3
81–104 weeks	3.2	2.4	2.8	3.9
105–112 weeks	4.6	2.7	3.9	3.8
113–208 weeks	4.8	3.6	5.1	4.6
Reaction time to ejaculation				
After 3 years of age (minutes)	1.1	1.1	3.7	9.2

[a] Feed intake is expressed as per cent of the Morrison standard.

From Flipse and Almquist (71).

feeding. No difference in fertility was noted, which confirmed extensive fertility information on bulls raised differently for 80 weeks (33).

Bulls underfed for long periods may never achieve full sexual development. VanDemark et al. (248) fed two groups of bulls at 60% and 100% of the recommended allowances from 8 weeks to 46 months, and then reversed them for 1 additional year. The group underfed initially showed the expected reduced body, testicular, and accessory gland growth initially. However, after reversal this group did not recover appreciably in testicular or endocrine function, although body weight was near normal.

Nutrition studies with rams (196), boars (65, 167), and stallions (232), although less extensive, show the same trends (Chapter 18). Development of sexual function requires a certain energy input. High energy intake will advance puberty in males and permit them to be sampled and used in artificial insemination at an earlier age. Subsequent energy intake should be gauged to allow for normal growth, but to prevent fatness, which may reduce libido and accelerate aging.

Several beef bulls fed about 1.5% protein died, but they were still producing spermatozoa at the time of death (229). The reproductive system appears to be less affected than many other systems. Semen quality (72) was normal, with protein levels from 10–22%.

4. Temperature and Light

Unfavorable climatic conditions stress animals, decrease feed intake, retard puberty, and may reduce libido. Jersey bulls placed in chambers

at 35°–36°C and 80–90% relative humidity for 8 hours daily at 26 weeks
of age reached puberty at 55 weeks, 7 weeks later than controls (54).
Testicular size and spermatogenic activity were reduced. Part of the effect
of heat may be mediated via the thyroid. Thyroxine has been shown to
stimulate spermatogenesis and thiouracil to inhibit it (34, 143). Mild hy-
perthyroidism can hasten puberty. High environmental temperatures suppress the thyroid, and administration of thyroxin under such conditions
is not beneficial.

Light influences spermatogenesis in birds and many mammals (Chapter
17). Sexual maturity, activity, and testicular size in rams are affected by
the photoperiod (64, 173, 243), with long photoperiods being harmful.
Perfection of semen freezing techniques would permit semen collection
during periods when semen quality is high.

A summary of several features of sexual development, particularly as
they may relate to training and using young males in artificial insemination, is presented in Table II. The ranges given reflect nutritional, breed,
and individual differences.

TABLE II

APPROXIMATE AGES AT WHICH STAGES OF SEXUAL DEVELOPMENT
ARE FOUND IN DOMESTIC ANIMALS

Species	Age (weeks)	Criteria of development	References
Dairy	34–40	Penis-sheath separation complete	(12)
bulls	36–61	Motile sperm first ejaculated—	(32, 33, 54, 71, 72, 174, 248)
	52+	semen suitable for artificial insem-	
		ination 8 weeks after puberty	
Beef	34–42	Penis-sheath separation complete	(13)
bulls	41	Average age when first sperm	(265)
		collected	
	45	Average age when >50 million	(6)
		sperm collected	
	58+	Most semen freezes satisfactorily	(49)
Ram	15–30	Penis-sheath separation complete	(260)
	18–36	Age when sperm first collected	(See reference 134)
	22+	Good quality semen 4 weeks after	(134)
		puberty	
Goat	22	Age when sperm first collected	(134)
	28	Good semen 6 weeks later	(134)
Boar	15–26	Penis-sheath separation complete	(43, 168)
	19–31	Age when sperm first collected	(65, 104, 136, 168, 244, 261)
	25+	Good semen 6 weeks after puberty	(244)
Stallion	56–86	Age when sperm in testis and	(166)
		epididymis	
	104+	Good semen several months after	(166)
		puberty	

III. Sperm Production

Once a male has been selected for artificial insemination, it is important to harvest the maximum number of sperm cells at their optimum fertility. The other components of semen (Chapter 11) often are largely eliminated at some stage of semen collection or processing.

Sperm-producing capabilities of animals of different species can be obtained by measuring sperm output while ejaculating males frequently (Chapter 10). The maximum daily potential sperm production can be estimated from histological data. It has been estimated to be 12.8 billion in a group of mature Holstein bulls (9), 5.3 billion in a group of young Shorthorn bulls, (241) and 31.3 billion in 2-year-old Yorkshire boars (121). In carrying out these experimental studies information on (1) the cellular composition of each testis, (2) duration and kinetics of certain cellular proliferations, and (3) size of each testis was required. Items 1 and 2 are quite uniform in healthy animals, and once parameters are established for each species, testis size in individual animals affords an adequate estimate of potential sperm production. Testis size varies greatly. It can be estimated in the live animal with a high degree of accuracy from various linear measurements [$(r = 0.94)$; see references (28, 264)]. Then maximum sperm potential of each animal can be estimated, the males ranked accordingly, and sperm output determined when they are ejaculated frequently. Order of rank should be similar. Animals with large testis size which rank much lower than expected on the basis of sperm output should be studied carefully for testicular lesions and associated anomalies which may reduce sperm output (63). Behavioral characteristics should be checked to determine if the male is properly prepared sexually at the time of semen collection.

IV. Libido and Semen Collection

A. LIBIDO AND FACTORS AFFECTING IT

1. General Sources of Stimuli

The internal forces of sex drive (libido) accumulate until released by copulation, masturbation, or other forms of ejaculation. There is great individual variation in libido as measured by (a) various courtship patterns, (b) foreplay, (c) speed and vigor of mounting and thrusting, and (d) number of ejaculations over a given period of time. When collecting semen, it is very important to exploit all routes through which males may be sexually stimulated, i.e., by the senses of sight, smell, and hearing, and through tactile stimulation at the time of intromission and ejaculation (95).

Older, experienced males develop conditioned reflexes of the well-known Pavlovian type. These reflexes are not fixed and may increase or diminish with subsequent experience. For example, under the stimuli of a free-mating system libido may remain high. If semen is collected in a routine, stereotyped manner, libido may decline over a period of time. Negative or inhibitory factors, such as cruel treatment, injury, and pain may reduce sexual drive. Artificial insemination centers should employ a variety of techniques to maintain maximum libido of each male, as this will be reflected in the quality of the semen obtained (100).

In addition to genetic differences other factors affecting libido are age, nutrition, disease, season, temperature, and other stresses affecting the general health and condition of the animal (95, 99, 112). New surroundings tend to inhibit all males, but whether or not this causes any important physiological stress is controversial. In bulls adrenal anomalies (50) have been associated with poor semen quality, and spermatogenic degeneration was thought to be due to the "stress" of transport (153). However, extensive transport of bulls has no effect on sexual activity or fertility (263).

Many bulls, especially older animals, are removed from artificial insemination studs with arthritic and other debilitating conditions which may reduce libido (20, 201, 262). However, forced exercise does not seem to affect libido or semen quality (233). Both may be reduced by high temperature.

2. Species Characteristics

In the presence of a female or suitable teaser, courtship patterns of males, such as smelling, licking, and nudging in bulls and rams, biting in stallions, grunting, foaming at the mouth, and elevation of the female in boars, and more elaborate patterns in dogs are usually seen (95). Bulls and rams with high libido mount and copulate rapidly. Vision in the bull is not absolutely essential, but is probably an important factor normally involved in arousing sexual desire. Lack of vision has been shown to (a) delay onset of sexual activity, (b) impair initial orientation in mounting the teaser and (c), reduce ability of the male to discover and respond to a new teasing situation (100). Lighting may have a temporary effect on semen quality (205, 206). Smell is not essential. Bringing forth an estrous female as a teaser may help (137), but in large measure this is merely presenting a new situation (animal) as a source of stimulation (100). In the ram smell and sight appear to be important. Bilateral olfactory ablations eliminate the ability of rams to detect estrous ewes, but after locating such ewes mating is normal (132). Seasonal effects may be pronounced (64, 87), and libido is reduced in the nonbreeding season (95).

Sound plays an important role in courtship in boars (95, 230). The boar emits a series of soft grunts in approaching the female. He may mount the female or a dummy several times. Thereafter, proper tactile stimulation is required to initiate the long copulation period. Surroundings play an important role. Boars develop conditioned reflexes quickly and are stimulated by association with areas used previously for semen collection.

High sexual activity prior to mating is necessary in the stallion in order to stimulate erection. Both smell and sight appear to be important in eliciting normal mating behavior initially (95, 257). Young stallions show some response to a dummy, provided it is sprinkled with urine, but a higher proportion respond to a mare. However, neither smell nor sight is essential in the trained stallion, and they will mount dummies when blindfolded and, also when olfactory reception is inhibited.

In the dog the normal sexual behavioral pattern may be altered considerably by training.

B. Sexual Training and Preparation for Semen Collection

1. General Principles

Sexual preparation procedures to maintain high sexual activity of males with vigorous ejaculation into the artificial vagina at regular intervals is extremely important in insuring collection of high-quality semen. Training for semen collection should start shortly after puberty (see Table II) so that sires may be placed in service as soon as possible. Before puberty males may be kept in groups (51), but during training separate housing facilitates handling and avoids excessive stimulation among them. Pederasty is especially common among boars.

Young males often are awkward, hesitate to mount, or may attempt to mount from improper positions. They vary in the time required to adapt to the environment and handlers at the time of semen collection. Novel situations may be required to stimulate interest. Patience and ingenuity are required, and it is important to avoid rough handling and other forms of negative or inhibitory situations. Application of sexual stimuli should be intensive rather than intermittent and prolonged. Repetition of the conditions leading to successful ejaculation will soon condition the male reflexly to become partially aroused sexually when brought to the collection area.

2. Bull

During semen collection precautions should be taken to prevent contamination and possible disease spread by using sterile collection equipment and by cleaning bulls and disinfecting teasers. Collection techniques and practices designed to keep the libido of bulls high may be summarized as follows (6, 7, 94, 98, 100, 122, 189):

a. Provide a collection system with posts (217) so that the bull can be positively controlled by the handler without brutality, and so that live teasers are restrained.

b. Provide good footing so the male will not slip, as this will be an inhibitory stimulus and may cause injury.

c. Provide a teaser of proper height. This can be a well-padded dummy, or, more frequently, other bulls, steers, or females.

d. Avoid distractions such as loud strange noises, strangers, strange handlers, and rough treatment.

e. Provide novel stimuli such as new teasers, more than one teaser, and a change in position or location of the teasers (100) so as to reinforce the sex drive and maintain a high stimulus pressure. This often requires more ingenuity on the part of the handlers of European and Zebu-type beef bulls, because frequently they exhibit less libido than dairy bulls.

f. Encourage the bull to mount and dismount the teaser one to three times (depending upon the bull) under restrained conditions before permitting ejaculation into a properly prepared artificial vagina. This restraint and "false mounting" markedly increases the number of sperm per ejaculate (47, 98, 100, 247).

3. Other Domestic Animals

Less is known about the other domestic animals, but the same principles described for the bull can be applied, taking into account species differences previously discussed. Sperm output is increased in all by "teasing" prior to semen collection (38, 150, 258). Minimal restraining facilities are needed for the ram. Ewes, other rams, or dummies can be used to stimulate rams.

An active boar needs little assistance in reaching a high state of arousal during a period of foreplay and can be readily trained to mount dummies. If difficulty is encountered, different dummies, movement of the dummy to the boar's own pen (23), or live females may be beneficial (151).

Estrogenized mares that are hobbled to prevent kicking the stallion work well. Most experienced males can be trained to mount a dummy. Urine from an estrous female on the dummy may help.

The dog is easily distracted by strangers and collections should be made in familiar surroundings by someone the dog knows. An estrous female restrained to permit easy mounting by the male is helpful in causing an erection. Pressure by the hand on the posterior portion of the bulb at the time the male mounts the female usually evokes a strong thrusting action, complete erection, and subsequent ejaculation.

C. Physiology of Ejaculation and Collection Procedures

The copulatory-ejaculatory pattern is determined by the anatomy of the penis. Proper construction and use of the artificial vagina aid in harvesting a maximum number of spermatozoa (74).

1. Anatomy and Physiology of the Penis

The penis of the bull, ram, goat, and boar is the fibroelastic type (177). Therefore, it is relatively firm in the nonerect state. The corpora cavernosa and corpora spongiosum are relatively small and the walls between the interconnecting spaces are fibroelastic. This allows for little expansion at the time of erection, but the penis does become more rigid due to an increase in blood supply. Protrusion is accomplished by relaxation of the retractor muscles, which allows the sigmoid flexure to straighten (Fig. 2).

The penis in the stallion and dog contains much erectile tissue. The interconnecting corpora cavernosa are particularly large. The walls are smooth muscle which allow for considerable expansion as the corpora become engorged with blood. There is an increase in blood flow through the expansion of helicine arteries under nervous control. Corresponding contractions in venules and possible compression of the dorsal vein by the ischiocavernosus muscle produce rigidity of the penis as blood enters the

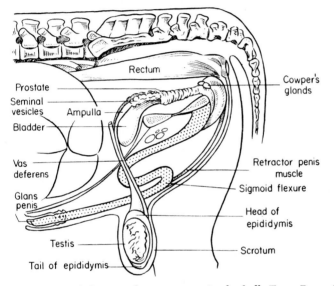

FIG. 2. Diagram of the reproductive organs in the bull. From Perry (180). Courtesy of the author.

spaces more rapidly than it leaves. In the dog the corpus cavernosum enlarges at the ischial arch to form the bulb.

The glans penis varies in size and shape in different species (Fig. 3). In the boar it is absent, but the tip is spiraled. The tip frequently spirals in bulls as much as 360° during semen emission (222), and may spiral abnormally prior to emission in some bulls (39). The sensory nerve endings (128) respond to temperature, pressure, and, possibly, friction. In bulls and rams, temperature is particularly important. The internal temperature of the artificial vagina should be slightly above body temperature (138). In species with longer copulation times (boar, stallion, dog) continuous or pulsating pressure on the glans penis is more important and temperature can vary somewhat. In the dog pressure on the bulb, simulating natural mating, assists in attaining complete erection. These facts are summarized in Table III.

2. Semen Collection with the Artificial Vagina

The artificial vagina for each species should (a) be of proper diameter and length, (b) provide appropriate pressure and temperature, (c) include a simple container to receive the semen, and (d) be flexible and noninjurious to the male. Some type of heavy rubber outer casing and a

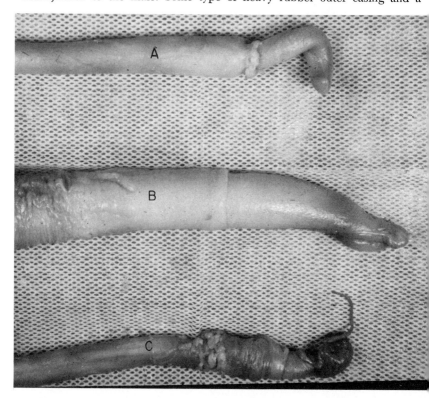

FIG. 3. Anterior portion of penes in the (A) boar, (B) bull, and (C) ram. Note the prominent urethral process (filiform appendage) in the ram.

flexible inner liner with warm water between form the basic components of most artificial vaginas. A collection vessel with a warm protecting cover can be connected at one end, and lubrication applied to the opposite end, which initially contacts the glans penis. The construction and use of artificial vaginas is adequately described in the literature (150, 180, 217).

The male usually thrusts as soon as the glans penis contacts the lubricated warm surface of the artificial vagina. Ejaculation in the bull and the ram is brought about by a rapid series of contractions propelling

TABLE III

CHARACTERISTICS OF THE PENIS AND STIMULI ASSOCIATED
WITH EJACULATION AND SEMEN COLLECTION

Species	Type of penis	Importance of tactile stimuli		Dummy or live teaser normally used	Duration of ejaculation
		Temperature	Pressure		
Bull	Fibroelastic	++	+	Live	<1 second
Ram	Fibroelastic	++	+	Live	<1 second
Boar	Fibroelastic	+	++	Dummy	2–10 minutes
Stallion	Vascular-muscular	+	++	Live	<1 minute
Dog	Vascular-muscular	+	++	Live	5–20 minutes[a]

[a] The sperm fraction is obtained within 1–2 minutes.

spermatozoa through the epididymis and ductus deferens (Fig. 2) and expelling fluids from the urethral and accessory sex glands. The final discharge of semen is brought about by contractions of the bulbocavernosus and ischiocavernosus muscles. Ejaculation lasts only a fraction of a second (24, 222). Thus, the collector must grasp the sheath lightly and coordinate his movements quickly to have the artificial vagina aligned with the penis properly when rams and bulls mount.

In the stallion, boar and dog various muscular contractions occur in separated sequences, producing an ejaculate which can be partially fractionated into contributions from the epididymis and accessory glands (see Chapter 11). Studies with atropine suggest that the parasympathetic nervous system partially controls the accessory sex glands (67). Continued pressure producing a penis-locking condition is essential during the prolonged ejaculation in the boar. The stallion should be allowed to thrust vigorously into the artificial vagina (11, 180), and, usually, pulsations and ejaculation will follow. In the dog either an artificial vagina or a glass funnel and tube may be used (27, 75, 103, 180). The latter is preferable because damage to the sperm, which may occur if it is deposited on the warm liner of the artificial vagina, is prevented.

3. Electroejaculation

Electrical stimulation of ejaculation can be used for most animals (1, 3, 38, 103, 135, 150). It is widely used in rams, but when rams are trained to serve the artificial vagina, more uniform ejaculates which are slightly higher in quality and fertility are obtained (149, 211). Hulet et al. (114) also found several characteristics of natural ejaculates to be more highly correlated with fertility. Electroejaculation is an effective technique for obtaining semen from beef bulls (14) not handled regularly, or when injury prevents serving the artificial vagina. This technique does not work well with boars.

4. Frequency of Ejaculation

Proper sexual preparation and frequent semen collection are the key factors in obtaining the maximum number of usable sperm per unit of time (100). Unfortunately, many investigators have thought frequent semen collections were harmful because fewer spermatozoa were obtained per ejaculate, and metabolic tests gave a lower value when sperm concentration was reduced. However, frequent semen collection is somwhat analogous to a water reservoir used sufficiently to prevent much water loss via the overflow. Likewise, fewer sperm are lost in the urine and by other means when semen is collected frequently. A practical schedule is one in which collections are frequent enough to obtain a majority of the sperm available, and in which each semen sample contains a significant number of sperm. Libido can be maintained with frequent ejaculation if a reasonable combination of novel stimuli are applied.

Carefully controlled studies with dairy bulls (7, 9, 28, 30, 97, 100, 126, 264) indicate that they may be ejaculated as often as once per day for long periods with high sperm output and ejaculates that can be used consistently in liquid and frozen semen programs. Sperm motility, morphology, and fertility are not affected. The 60- to 90-day nonreturn rate of bulls ejaculated daily for 32 weeks averaged 73% as compared to 70% for controls ejaculated weekly (97). Corresponding values for sperm output per week were 33.8 billion and 17.8 billion. Other studies (9, 100) indicate that after 2 years of age dairy bulls collected 6 times weekly ejaculate 25–35 billion sperm per week. This is similar to the number of sperm removed from the epididymis in depletion tests consisting of 10 to 20 successive ejaculates collected over a period of several hours (7, 100, 247). In practice, dairy bulls often are ejaculated 4 times weekly (68) by taking 2 ejaculates daily at 3- to 4-day intervals. Characteristics of semen and the effect of frequent collection on sperm output are shown in Table IV.

Hereford and Angus bulls also can be ejaculated successfully beginning at puberty as often as 6 times weekly (6), and the weekly yield of sperm at 2 years of age is about 15–20 billion. Swierstra (241) obtained 9.4 billion sperm per week from 18-month-old Shorthorns by electroejaculation every second day. Collections 4 times weekly have caused some reduction in the libido of Zebu-type bulls (231). Weekly sperm output, as measured by depletion tests, was about 17 billion (223).

Rams are capable of producing large numbers of sperm with a moderate number per ejaculate. Lunca (135) recommended collecting 2–3 or 3–4 ejaculates per day, depending on the capability of the ram. Bielanski (22) obtained 26 billion sperm per week from rams ejaculated an average of 3.8 times per day. During 5-day periods, rams can be ejaculated as often as 16 times per day (209, 210), and will produce about 70 billion sperm. The number of sperm obtained under these conditions probably reflects the large epididymal reserves. Fertility is not altered, but if sperm numbers decrease

TABLE IV

CHARACTERISTICS OF EJACULATED SEMEN FROM NORMAL MALES[a]

| Species | Infrequent ejaculation (once weekly) | | | | Optimum frequency of semen collections | |
	Volume (ml)	Motility (%)	Sperm concentration, (10^6/ml)	Total sperm per ejaculation, (10^9)	No. of ejaculations per week	Sperm per week (10^9)
Bull	8	65	1800	14	4	30
Ram	1.2	75	3000	3–4	20	25
Boar	200[b]	70	250	50	3	110
Stallion	100[b]	65	150	15	3–4	30
Dog	2[c]	85	300	0.6	3	2

[a] Averages for healthy mature males trained to serve the artificial vagina. Values for the ram and stallion are for the breeding season. Great variation in individual ejaculates may be expected.

[b] Gel-free basis.

[c] Small breed (Beagle), and omitting the third fraction, which would add 5–10 ml.

below 120–125 million per insemination, fertility decreases (209). Other effects of frequent ejaculation in rams are similar to those found in bulls.

Ejaculates from boars generally are the largest in volume and contain the most sperm of all the common domestic animals (see Table IV). Rested boars with large testes may ejaculate as many as 100 billion sperm in a single sample. Aamdal (1) reported that boars ejaculated at 2-, 3-, and 4-day intervals produced an average of 30, 43, and 45 billion sperm per ejaculate. Two-year-old Yorkshire boars produced 19.7 billion sperm per day when collected daily (121). Semen samples taken every second day from boars about 9 months of age averaged 22–23 billion per ejaculate (242). The effects of frequent ejaculation on properties of boar semen are similar to those mentioned for the bull and ram (167).

Stallions are intermediate between the bull and the boar in rate of depletion of sperm reserves and in sexual satiation. Frequent ejaculation is possible (22, 166, 256, 258), but collecting more often than every 2–3 days causes a reduction in sperm concentration and numbers per ejaculate. With daily ejaculation, about 5 billion sperm per day (35–40 billion sperm per week) can be obtained during the breeding season. Nearly as many sperm can be obtained (see Table IV) by collecting at 2-day intervals with little effect on libido.

Dogs have the smallest testes and produce the fewest sperm of any of the animals considered (see Table IV). The effects of frequent ejaculation, summarized by Boucher et al. (27), show that the same principles apply as in other species. Collection more often than once every 2 days reduces sperm numbers in the ejaculate, and collection less often reduces sperm output per week.

5. Measures of Semen Quality

Semen quality tests serve as a basis for initial selection or rejection of semen samples for use in artificial insemination. These tests must be rapid to prevent delays in processing. Frozen semen offers the possibility of further selection on the basis of subsequent tests that are sufficiently correlated with fertility to justify their use (86, 185). Single tests of semen quality generally have low correlations with fertility of individual semen samples (150, 217). Some improvement can be made by applying a combination of tests (31, 113). Correlations of average semen quality of bulls with average fertility usually are higher, but they are of limited value because the fertility of individual males usually is known as a result of previous information (190).

Low correlations between laboratory tests and fertility result from the failure (1) to standardize test conditions adequately and (2) to use semen to breed a large enough sample of randomly selected females to reliably measure fertility. Also, it appears from recent recalculations of published data (252) that certain transformations and other statistical considerations may increase the computed correlation coefficients.

Computers can facilitate more thorough evaluation of data collected and more thorough quality control checks. In large operations data from a combination of mechanized tests on a particular semen sample may be supplied directly to a computer for proper weighting and an estimate of semen quality based on these tests be made available immediately.

Several common characteristics of semen are listed for each species in Table IV. Many tests of quality have been described (69, 142, 150, 180, 217), and a discussion of the significance of several tests follows.

Volume and appearance can be determined quickly when semen is collected in a transparent calibrated vessel. Volume is important as one indication of the number of sperm present. Appearance is important in determining the presence of gross contaminating substances such as dirt, hair, urine, and blood. Urine contamination causes a characteristic odor. The semen from some bulls may contain yellow flavin pigments which should not be confused with urine contamination. Contamination is more common in stallion and boar semen. Special precautions to clean the preputial area and dummies or teasers should be taken. Filtration during collection removes debris and the gel.

Concentration of spermatozoa is extremely important. It varies greatly (96, 142), and an accurate determination, along with the volume, indicates how many sperm are available for processing. A rapid and accurate photoelectric procedure involving light-absorbing properties of sperm can be used for all species (79, 93, 217, 270). Initial calibration of the photoelectric colorimeter requires making simultaneous sperm counts with the aid of a hemocytometer or calibrated electronic counting equipment (*82, 89, 117*). Packed cell volume also is an indicator of sperm numbers, but care should be taken to control cell swelling (*82*).

Motility is one of the most widely used tests for semen quality. The test has a sound physiological basis, but it must be recognized that motility is only one indication of cell viability. The proportion of progressively motile cells, rate of movement, and gross abnormalities can be seen microscopically following dilution with physiological saline. The "swirl" of undiluted semen seen microscopically is an indication of motility and concentration. These microscopic methods are simple. They are subjective, and procedural details vary greatly (*69, 150, 217*). Electronic instruments and high speed cinemicrography, used in research work to objectively evaluate sperm motility, (*199, 217, 252*) have not been applied in artificial insemination.

Live and dead cells can be discriminated on the basis of their permeability to eosin, using a suitable background stain such as opal blue or nigrosin. Dead cells are permeable to the eosin stain, presumably as a result of membrane changes, but the mechanism of action has not been established. Careful control of pH and tonicity of the stain, and temperature and length of staining time are necessary to minimize effects of these variables on stainability. The increase in proportion of stained sperm on slides stored for some time (*37, 69*) can be prevented by making permanent mounts or by storing slides in a dry atmosphere.

Morphology of sperm can be examined at the same time that live-dead ratios are determined. Atypical sperm heads are considered to be primary abnormalities. Abnormalities of the midpiece and tail are secondary types. Highly fertile males usually produce semen with less than 20% abnormals, and fertility tends to decrease as the percentage of abnormals increases (*31, 69, 107, 150, 180, 217*). The acrosome has been given special attention in recent years (*37, 151, 158*) because it may play a special role in fertilization. The importance of maintaining membrane integrity has been clearly demonstrated by electron microscopy of sperm following freezing (*194, 208*). Other tests include evaluation of head or nuclear size and DNA content in fixed preparations (*179, 214, 215, 218*), or relative sperm sizes in living material (*82*).

Metabolic tests, such as oxygen consumption, pyruvate oxidation, fructose utilization, lactic acid production, change in inorganic phosphate, methylene blue reduction time, resazurin reduction time, and pH change, indicate functional activity of sperm cells. These biochemical tests are positively related to sperm concentration and motility.

The impedance test, which measures the conductivity between two electrodes as impeded by swirling spermatozoa, also is correlated with motility and concentration. Objective recordings of impedance changes can be made with a digital scaler (*147*). Correlations with fertility are similar to other tests of motility, concentration, and morphology.

Resistance to stress tests have met with limited success in predicting fertility. Sperm resistance to (a) incubation, (b) high dilution, (c) sudden chilling with ice water (cold shock), (d) acid titration, (e) hypertonic NaCl and other osmotic shocks, and (f) freezing or refreezing damage have been studied (86, 150, 185, 207, 217). These tests appear to have a sound physiological basis, particularly with frozen semen, where sperm are exposed to osmotic and thermal shock followed by the necessity for survival at body temperature in the female reproductive tract.

Biochemical and physical characteristics of semen hold many possibilities (Chapter 11). The availability of simple tests for important enzymes provides a challenging opportunity to study fundamental biochemical reactions and their possible disruption by stresses such as freezing. However, routine analyses of semen for pH, osmotic pressure, specific gravity, viscosity, and biochemical constituents are likely to be of more value for suggesting appropriate conditions to include in the fluids used for extending (diluting) semen for artificial insemination, or as indicators of androgen secretion than they are for predicting fertility.

V. Semen Preservation

A. Physiological Requirements of Spermatozoa

Although sperm cells are limited in function, their physiological requirements are complex. These requirements will be discussed. Lists of many extenders (diluters) have been summarized previously (150, 164, 180, 217). Many "recipes" preserve sperm fertility, but often by means not well understood.

Preservation of the sperm cell implies maintenance of both the genetic material of the head and the propulsion unit comprising the tail. Presumably, the whole cell is important up to the point of syngamy, and the survival of both parts is assumed to be related, although not equally measured, by most laboratory tests. Considerations in providing an optimum environment for sperm include (1) temperature, (2) osmotic pressure, (3) pH and appropriate buffering, (4) source of energy, (5) bacterial control, (6) exclusion of toxic materials and neutralization of toxic products, (7) dilution, and (8) components of the gas phase and external environment. Table V outlines several of the constituents and conditions commonly provided for sperm preservation.

1. Temperature

Refrigeration is the most effective means of sperm preservation. Metabolism and rate of aging can be markedly reduced (155, 213, 216, 217), although not totally inhibited. As the temperature of a medium is

TABLE V

PHYSIOLOGICAL CHARACTERISTICS OF SEMEN AND CONDITIONS AND CONSTITUENTS COMMONLY PROVIDED FOR SPERM PRESERVATION

Items	Species				
	Bull	Ram	Boar	Stallion	Dog
Common temperatures (°C)					
Ejaculated semen	38	39	39	37	38
Semen preservation	+5 to −195	+5	+15	+5 to −195	+5
Protectors against thermal shock					
Semen stored unfrozen	———————————— Yolk, milk[e] ————————————				
Additional for freezing[a]	———————————— Glycerol[e] ————————————				
Osmotic pressure: Δf.p., (°C)[b]	0.54	0.55	0.54	0.58	0.58
pH[c]	6.9	6.8	7.5	7.2	6.6
Buffers and extenders used	Yolk + citrate, phosphate, or Tris; milk[e]				
Added energy source	———————————— Fructose, glucose[e] ————————————				
Bacterial control	———————————— Penicillin, streptomycin[e] ————————————				
Extension (dilution) rate[d]	1:50–200	1:5	1:4	1:2	1:4

[a] Sperm from all species are motile after freezing, but only the bull and stallion have satisfactory fertility.

[b] Lower range of values for freezing point depression were selected from the literature as being more nearly physiological. See text.

[c] Average values determined immediately after semen collection. Value for the dog is with minimal prostatic fluid, which would increase the pH to about 7.0.

[d] Liquid bull semen can be extended more than frozen bull semen. Ram semen should be concentrated and inseminated in small volumes.

[e] For all species.

lowered, the solubility of gases in the liquid phase increases, solubilities of other components may change, pH may be altered, and intracellular reaction rates decrease. Sperm have little inherent resistance to these collective effects. Cooling to 5°C without protective agents causes cold shock, a condition characterized by coiled tails, reduced motility and fertility, and loss of ATP, lipoprotein, and other substances (142).

The remarkable protective action of glycerol discovered by Polge et al. (188) made freezing of sperm, blood, and other tissues practical. Egg yolk, milk, lipoproteins, lecithin, and other lipids help protect sperm during cooling and freezing (127, 145, 191). These substances and glycerol assist in maintaining the integrity of the membrane (high in lipoprotein) during chilling and freezing (194, 208), and probably minimize loss of lipids which occurs when unprotected sperm are frozen (184). Since high fertility can be attained with frozen semen (29, 66, 150, 186), stopping and starting of intracellular processes by freezing and thawing does not appear to have a major effect on fertility.

The mechanism of glycerol action is unknown. Attempts to demonstrate that intracellular glycerol is or is not essential for freezing have not given conclusive results (46, 228). In addition to altering ice crystal formation, it appears to act as a salt buffer, minimizing electrolyte damage as water freezes out. Even so, a compromise rate of freezing to balance thermal and osmotic shock may assist sperm in surviving freezing (35, 269). The problem of thermal shock (195) may be largely overcome by freezing sperm in small spheres or pellets, thus providing a large surface area to mass ratio (159–161). Thermal shock during rising temperatures is less critical, but generally, rapid thawing is desirable (182). Storage at −196°C in liquid nitrogen is preferable to the dry-ice temperature of −79°C (19, 186), because extensive changes, including crystal growth, occur at −79°C (194).

2. Osmotic Pressure

The osmotic pressure of semen or seminal plasma, as indicated by the freezing point depression in Table V, is similar to other physiological fluids (124, 213a, 217). Greater freezing point depressions reported (142) may have been determined on whole semen that had an opportunity to accumulate products of metabolism prior to estimating osmolarity.

It is generally assumed that osmolarity of seminal plasma represents the ideal physiological osmotic pressure and that isosmotic solutions prepared for suspending sperm are isotonic. This is not necessarily true. Sperm can tolerate a considerable deviation from isosmotic levels (69), and motility may be stimulated in hyposmotic solutions (166, 236). Fertility may be maximal nearer the isosmotic level (236). However, more extensive tests are needed, using carefully controlled pH and electrolyte balance to determine the effects of osmolarity on fertility (69, 213a, 235).

Pronounced osmotic shock produces a bending of sperm tails (8, 130, 235) and circular swimming patterns, as well as high mortality, particularly during freezing in hyperosmotic solutions high in electrolytes (268). A proper balance of electrolytes and the ratio of electrolytes to other components contributing to osmotic pressure also is important (213a, 217, 267). Sensitive indications of the tonicity of the medium can be measured by changes in cell size by electron microscopy (58), by packed cell volume, and by electronic sizing (82).

3. pH

Immediately after ejaculation, semen is slightly below the neutral point in most species, except in the boar and, possibly, in the stallion. Loss of CO_2 upon standing may initially increase the pH, whereas the production of lactic acid by sperm will decrease it. Rate of sperm movement and metabolism is inhibited when the pH of the medium is lowered from 7.5 to 5.7 (142). Sperm motility and fertility in egg yolk and milk extenders usually is well preserved near the neutral point, although there is a suggestion that the fertility of bull sperm is slightly better when preserved at a pH of 6.5 instead of 6.8 (76). Saturation of bicarbonate-containing media with CO_2 causes metabolic inhibition (18, 217, 249), and this system developed by VanDemark and co-workers has been widely applied (150, 164). Part of the inhibition may be due to reduction of the pH to about 6.3. Thus, the optimum pH may vary with other conditions in the preserving environment (18, 69, 77, 142, 171, 217, 235). Buffers to maintain a suitable pH during storage is especially important when sperm concentration in the extender and storage temperatures are high enough to permit autotoxication through acid products of metabolism.

4. Energy Source

Semen contains a variety of constituents, particularly fructose in most species, which can be utilized by sperm as a source of energy. Preferentially, sperm utilize glucose (142), and a small amount of either glucose or fructose is supplied in all extenders. In the absence of other substrate, sperm may oxidatively utilize intracellular phospholipid. This would appear to be undesirable for sperm cells, and generally they should be preserved under anaerobic conditions.

5. Bacterial Control

Semen extenders are good culture media for many organisms which may produce products toxic to sperm and infect the female inseminated. Therefore, bacterial contamination should be minimized by using healthy bulls and aseptic collection procedures, and bacterial growth should be controlled by refrigeration and antibacterial agents. Addition of 500–1000 IU of penicillin and 500–1000 μg/ml of streptomycin to the extender, as first reported by Almquist and co-workers (40), has been instrumental in maintaining a high level of fertility in breeding cattle artificially. These antibiotics, along with polymyxin, neomycin, certain tetracyclines, and sulfa drugs, have been recommended for semen treatment of all species (88, 133, 156, 176, 239, 254).

6. Exclusion of Toxic Materials

Solutions for suspending spermatozoa should be prepared with distilled water and pure reagents. Otherwise, harmful contaminants, such as heavy metals, may be present (142). The potential harmful effects of the metabolic products, lactic acid, and hydrogen peroxide may be minimized by proper buffering, refrigeration, exclusion of oxygen, and possibly by the addition of catalase (142, 217). Paradoxically, glycerol and other substances which protect sperm during freezing also may be somewhat toxic (123, 150, 228).

7. Dilution

High dilution of sperm, particularly in electrolyte buffers, decreases motility and survival time (69, 142, 227, 255). Damage of the lipid components of the membrane is thought to be responsible. The addition of protein, amino acids, glycogen, catalase, and various other substances, particularly egg yolk, to the extender reduces this effect (83, 255). High extension rates which reduce bull sperm per milliliter to 5×10^6 motile cells in liquid semen (83) and to 20×10^6 motile sperm before freezing (183) do not reduce fertility. Therefore, while high extension rates may have a detrimental effect, separate from a reduction in sperm numbers inseminated, this has not been clearly demonstrated as a problem in the routine insemination of cattle. Semen from other species is extended at a much lower rate (Table V).

8. Gas Phase and External Environment

Anaerobic conditions generally favor sperm survival. Replacement of air by N_2 or other inert gas in sealed vials with glucose supplied as a substrate results in prolonged sperm viability (77, 249). VanDemark and co-workers (18, 217, 249) have shown that CO_2 results in (a) reversible inhibition of motility, (b) almost complete inhibition of glycolysis, and (c) maintenance of fertility for several days at room temperature. The effect is modified by several components of the liquid phase. When sperm are metabolically inhibited by freezing, the gaseous environment naturally assumes less importance (204).

Short (blue) wavelengths of visible light may be quite damaging to sperm cells (78, 170, 179), particularly if oxygen is present. Motility and the Feulgen-positive material (DNA) is reduced, probably by a photosensitive oxidative reaction. Therefore, sperm should receive minimal exposure to light.

B. LIQUID SEMEN PRESERVATION

Completely synthetic buffers and extenders which partially meet the requirements previously listed have been developed for laboratory studies. However, for use in artificial insemination semen extenders also contain either egg yolk or milk.

1. Ambient Temperature

This fluctuating temperature (a) poses minimal problems for protecting sperm against cold shock, (b) promotes extensive sperm metabolism, unless chemically inhibited, (c) requires excellent bacterial control, and (d) has the danger of sperm becoming overheated in hot climates. Sperm die within a few minutes if temperatures exceed 45°C. Incubation of rabbit sperm for 3 hours at 40°C resulted in 20% reduction in cleaved eggs (245).

Greatest use of this system is in countries having little refrigeration, or with minimal ambient temperature variation, and under the special cattle-breeding conditions in New Zealand. Several types of extenders have been tried (164). The most widely used one is IVT, a carbonated yolk-citrate-bicarbonate-KCL-glucose sulfanilamide extender (217, 249). A similar extender which contains glycine and citric acid, and to some extent is self-carbonating, is called CUE (81, 83, 84). Another modification, called Caprogen, used widely in New Zealand (162, 163), contains caproic acid and is gassed with nitrogen. Norman *et al.* and others (92, 169, 170, 171) have employed a coconut milk-egg yolk preparation. Most of these extenders contain catalase. Milk (157) or yolk citrate-glucose (154) have not been used extensively.

Boar semen commonly is stored at 15°C. IVT frequently is used for this purpose. Semen from other species may be used directly for insemination, but it is not usually stored at ambient temperature.

2. Storage at 5°C

Refrigeration of bull sperm at 5°C was the common method of storage until the method of freezing was developed. The same general types of extenders used at ambient temperatures may be used for storage at 5°C. The yolk-containing extenders are outgrowths of the early work with yolk-phosphate by Lardy and Phillips (127a) and yolk-citrate by Salisbury and co-workers (150, 217). Following extension and slow cooling to 5°C over a period of from 1 to 4 hours, semen may be used for several days. For example, semen used 0–1, 2, and 3–4 days after collection (84) averaged 78%, 75%, and 74% 60- to 90-day nonreturn rates, respectively. Other studies with yolk-citrate-glucose-glycine combinations (48, 83, 115, 150, 226) indicate that 60- to 90-day nonreturn rates generally range from 65–75%. The organic buffer Tris combines well with egg yolk (53) and gives good fertility (178).

Mihailov found that boiled milk, could be used for jack semen, and Almquist and co-workers (see reference 150) showed that heating milk to at least 92°C for 10 minutes inactivates the toxic substance, lactenin, probably by releasing the sulfhydryl groups in the milk during heating. Addition of sulfhydryl groups in the form of cysteine also detoxifies milk. Glycerol improves the fertility of bull sperm stored in milk for several days (5, 8). The 60- to 90-day nonreturn rates for semen used on days 1, 2, 3, and 4 were 72%, 64%, 57%, and 48%, and for similar milks containing 10% glycerol by volume corresponding values were 74%, 71%, 69%, and 67%. Milk-yolk combinations also are common (150). In Japan completely sterilized egg yolk-containing extenders called Neoseminan are available (164, 165). In Europe a yolk-citrate-phosphate-gelatin extender caller Spermasol and a powdered milk extender, Laiciphos, have been used (142, 164, 178).

Ram semen fertility declines with dilution and storage (200, 212, 221, 259). Lunca (135) observed only a small decline in fertility of semen used the day after collection, but fresh semen or semen used undiluted or diluted for 24 hours gave 63%, 39%, and 25% pregnancies, respectively (200). Lambing rates resulting from semen stored in yolk-citrate-glucose for 0, 1, 2, and 3 days were 60%, 50%, 30%, and 20% (212).

Fertility of boar semen in milk or buffered-yolk extenders ranges from 55–70% (164). Most semen is used within 1–2 days after collection. In a modified IVT extender fertility declined only 7% over a 4-day storage period (1). Often the sperm-rich fraction only is collected and extended, but any fertility advantages related to this method of collection are equivocal.

Variation in fertility in horses is large, partly due to the difficulty in anticipating ovulation. Both milk and buffered-yolk extenders have given fertility rates ranging from 30–70% (102, 166, 253) and were equal to rates obtained from natural service. Centrifugation and partial concentration of sperm before extension followed by use within a few hours is desirable.

Buffered yolk and milk extenders have been used to extend dog semen (103). Most inseminations are performed on bitches where natural service is not feasible (75, 106). Insemination of normal bitches on 2 successive days should produce about 70% conceptions (see Tables V and VI).

Oxytocin and other additives to extended semen, designated to stimulate spermatozoa or to influence contractions of the female reproductive tract, have been reported to influence fertility and the number of sperm required for insemination (15a, 150, 164, 224). Further study of the physiological responses following insemination of such semen is needed because conflicting and negative results have been obtained.

C. Frozen Semen Preservation

The general principles of freezing are described in Section V, 1. Numerous procedures, which appear to give similar results, have been published since the original work by Polge et al. (188). This suggests that (a) certain changes are allowable without detectable effects and (b) interactions between the different variables may require that a shift in one step of the processing be accompanied by other changes to produce an overall optimum freezing procedure (235). Reviews (1, 3, 103, 135, 150, 164, 217, 253) and references cited should be consulted for procedural details.

1. Cattle

Extenders for frozen semen include glycerolated yolk-citrate or milk, glycerolated yolk-lactose or yolk-raffinose (160), and a glycerolated dried yolk-citrate-multisugar combination called Minnesota GO (193). Glycerol is usually combined with part of the extender and added to the sperm-containing fraction after cooling to 5°C (240), although it may be added initially to Tris-buffered yolk (235). The amount of glycerol added ranges from 4–8% by volume for most egg yolk extenders and 10–13% for milk. Vegetable dyes may be included to facilitate semen identification (45).

Following cooling over a period of from 1–4 hours a variable period of a few hours is allowed for what has been called "glycerol equilibration" (5, 44, 144, 235, 251). However, it is likely that this period of time at 5°C allows the extended sperm to adapt to the cold environment. If glycerol equilibration is necessary, the time required is very short.

Cooling rates during early stages of freezing vary from 1–3°C per minute for ampuled semen (35) to more than 50°C per minute for pelleted semen (159). After passing through the most critical range from −10° to −35°C (35, 269), temperature is lowered rapidly to −196°C in liquid N_2 (19, 186). The simplest method for removing heat during freezing is to place the semen packaged at 5°C in nitrogen vapor (118, 192, 203).

In Europe a plastic "Cassou" straw (40) patterned after the early Danish system is increasing in popularity. Little storage space is required and good sperm survival and fertility are reported (41, 66, 118, 139).

A radically different method of freezing semen involves extending in concentrated form and freezing as pellets in small holes on a block of dry ice (159–161). Freezing is completed within a few minutes. The pellets are transferred to tubes and stored in liquid nitrogen. A major problem is individual identification.

Semen should be kept frozen until ready for use. Thawing rate, though not very critical, should be rapid (182). Semen has been successfully thawed in the cow (237). Harmful effects on fertility have been found when previously frozen semen was held at 5°C (29). However, if semen frozen concentrated in bulk is thawed and resuspended in optimal media for 5°C storage, satisfactory fertility has been reported (55, 175).

2. Other Species

Commercial use of frozen semen has been limited in other species. Conception rates of about 60% have been reported for goats (25). Fertility of frozen ram semen ranges from about 10–30% (70, 135), despite satisfactory post-freeze motility. A number of modifications in milk and yolk extenders (120), including the addition of low levels of dimethylsulfoxide (DMSO), along with glycerol (119), may improve survival.

Glycerol levels which provide some protection for boar sperm during freezing (125) are harmful to unfrozen boar sperm (1, 123). Boar sperm which survive freezing (1, 116), however, are essentially infertile.

Stallion sperm are reported to freeze best during the breeding season (202). The sperm-rich fraction or sperm concentrate suspended in glycerolized milk or yolk-glucose extenders low in electrolytes gives good sperm survival following freezing (36, 187, 202). Frozen epididymal sperm have been stored for 5 years (17). Limited fertility data (161) with pelleted semen suggests that not more than one-third of the mares inseminated conceived. However, current development work and field testing is promising.

Dog sperm survival is good following freezing in Tris-buffered yolk-glucose-glycerol extender (73), or in skim milk and buffers containing lecithin and other additives (145, 146). However, frozen dog sperm appear to be infertile, emphasizing the imperfect state of knowledge concerning preservation of sperm by the hostile environment of freezing.

D. Freeze-Drying of Semen

Many failures to revive sperm following drying have been reported. Sperm membrane damage by the procedure is pronounced (208), and any reported success is usually associated with incomplete drying (111, 152). No consistent revival of sperm following drying appears to be possible with present knowledge and techniques (152).

E. Processing Semen to Alter Sex Ratios

Alteration of the sex ratio has been one of man's cherished dreams. A variety of techniques for manipulating semen to separate the X-bearing from the Y-bearing sperm have been studied (50, 217). Recently, a procedure for sedimenting sperm proposed by Bhattacharya (21) has failed to alter the ratio, but variations in the sedimenting technique have been reported to result in some success (220). Further work is necessary to determine if the sex ratio can be effectively altered by this method. Normally, there is a slight preponderance of males among the births in cattle bred either artificially (4, 217), or under natural conditions.

VI. Insemination

The current techniques of insemination are well established, and detailed descriptions are available (50, 180, 217). The success of the insemination will depend chiefly upon (a) the inherent fertility of the sperm available, (b) proper handling of the semen prior to insemination, (c) insemination at the proper time during estrus, and (d) proper semen deposition. The latter requires knowledge of the anatomy and physiology of the female and skills acquired from experience.

A. Physiological and Anatomical Considerations

1. Detection of Estrus and Time of Insemination

Maximum fertility will be achieved by having highly fertile sperm present in the oviducts when ovulation occurs. Thus, insemination should precede ovulation. Time should be allowed for sperm capacitation if it is a factor. Fertility of sperm in the cow and ewe decreases in about 24 hours, in less than 24 hours in the sow, and perhaps not for several days in mares and bitches. Sperm transport appears to be rapid (177, 246), but inseminations a few hours after ovulation may result in ova dying before sperm are available. If old ova are fertilized, early embryonic death may follow.

Ovulation time is difficult to determine routinely, so insemination should be timed from the onset of estrus (Chapter 9). Checks for estrus must be done carefully and regularly. This is more difficult in range animals, but unless provisions are made for proper estrus detection, artificial insemination should not be undertaken. Because of the variability in length of estrus and time of ovulation, ranges for optimum insemination times are given in Table VI. Outside of these ranges chances for conception are reduced.

In the cow, estrus is indicated when the female stands to be mounted by another animal. Cows first seen in estrus in the morning should be inseminated the afternoon of the same day; those first observed in estrus in the afternoon should be inseminated the next morning. Reportedly, little or no capacitation of bull sperm is required in the female tract (141), although enzymic treatment possibly associated with capacitation may improve fertility. The stimulus of insemination may reduce the interval from the end of estrus to ovulation (162).

Vasectomized rams are used to detect ewes in estrus. Ram sperm require about 1.5 hours for capacitation (148), so insemination until the time of ovulation near the end of estrus is permissible. The simple management practice of teasing ewes with vasectomized rams for 6 hours after insemination increased lambing rates from 59% to 69% (197). This was interpreted as affecting sperm transport through release of oxytocin (246), but probable hastening of ovulation may have been a factor. Number of twins born has been reported to increase following two inseminations (61), and multiple inseminations may improve fertility. A single well-timed insemination is sufficient, and may be all that is practical.

Proper heat detection has been a problem in artificial insemination in swine. In the absence of the boar, estrus can be detected by applying heavy pressure on the back of the female. Estrus is indicated by a stationary "standing reflex" (23, 59). Gilts should be inseminated at the shorter interval shown in Table VI. Multiple inseminations have given variable responses (26).

Rectal palpation to determine the time of ovulation is especially valuable in mares because of the variable length of estrus (150, 166). Otherwise, insemination every 2–3 days starting on the second day of estrus is advised. With proper timing sperm doses may be reduced.

Acceptance of the male is the best indication of estrus in the bitch. Estrus length is variable. Insemination on the second and third day of standing estrus results in good fertility (75). Prolonged sperm survival (56) may assist in achieving good fertility.

2. Site of Semen Deposition

The major gateways through which sperm pass on their way to encounter ova are the cervix and the uterotubal junction. In species such as swine, horses, and dogs, where a temporary "locking" may take place at the time of normal copulation, the relatively large volume of serum ejaculated may be forced through the cervix into the uterus (177). In artificial insemination the sperm should be deposited into or through the cervix to minimize losses and make the most effective use of sperm. The

TABLE VI

INSEMINATION REQUIREMENTS AND FERTILITY IN DOMESTIC ANIMALS

Items	Females				
	Cow	Ewe	Sow	Mare	Bitch
Best time in estrus to inseminate	8 hours from onset to end	10 hours from onset to end	15–30 hours after onset of estrus	2 days from end[c]	Second and third day of estrus
Site of semen deposition	Uterus and cervix	Cervix	Cervix and uterus	Uterus	Cervix or uterus
Insemination dose					
Volume (ml)	1	0.05–0.2	50	20–40	2–5
Millions of motile sperm[a]	5–15	50	2000	1500	100
Maximum number of females that can be inseminated per male per week[b]	1500–4000	350	40	15	15
Conceptions to first insemination (%)	65	65	60	40–65	70

[a] Higher numbers are for frozen semen where some sperm are killed by freezing. Numbers represent minimum doses for maximum fertility.

[b] Lower number is for frozen semen. See Table IV for sperm output.

[c] Estrus is variable and requires insemination every 2–3 days starting on the second day unless ovulation is checked by rectal palpation. Ovulation occurs 1–2 days before the end of estrus.

essential equipment needed for artificial insemination is: a sterile inseminating catheter to place the semen, and an attached syringe, bulb, or plastic container to contain and/or to expel the semen. Care should be taken to pass the catheter dorsally while proceeding forward, to avoid cannulating the bladder. Details of equipment and insemination technique can be found in standard references on artificial insemination (*1, 3, 103, 135, 150, 180, 217*).

In the cow the best fertility can be obtained with the rectovaginal technique. Deposition of the semen barely through the cervix and in the anterior portion of the cervix is recommended for first services. No difference in fertility has been reported for either location with antibiotic-treated semen (*2*), but excess sperm were used in most tests. Repeat inseminations should be in the cervix, especially in cases of suspected pregnancy. Gentle massage of the cervix has been suggested as a means of hastening ovulation, but its effects have not been proven. Intracervical insemination through a speculum is simple, but it leads to inferior results (*217*).

The ewe is too small for the rectovaginal technique to be employed. A speculum with an anterior light to illuminate the cervix assists in placing the catheter into the cervical canal for semen deposition. Simple arrangements in large flocks for presenting many ewes in a restrained position convenient for rapid insemination have been devised, and syringes for delivering a series of accurately measured small volumes of semen are available. The importance of cervical placement was emphasized by Dun (*60*), who reported that 52%, 51%, and 60% of the ewes lambed when semen was deposited in the anterior vagina, on the cervical papillae, or in the cervical canal, respectively.

Gilts and sows usually are inseminated without restraint and without the aid of a speculum. The tapered vagina directs the pipette to the cervical canal. Of the many pipettes used most are large enough in diameter to wedge into the cervix or have an inflatable cuff to prevent slippage and loss of semen, should the sow move during insemination (*1, 150*). Semen is forced into the uterus.

Mares should be hobbled or otherwise prevented from kicking. The external genitalia should be cleaned and a well-scrubbed arm inserted into the vagina with the index finger through the cervix. A plastic catheter of the cattle type, with a large syringe attached, can be easily guided into the uterus for semen deposition.

In the bitch, a short plastic catheter (8–10 inches) is used to deposit sperm at the external os of the cervix or through the cervix. The former is done by gently inserting the catheter dorsally and forward until resistance is met in the anterior vault of the vagina. Cervical penetration in small dogs is possible by palpating and manipulating the cervix through the abdominal wall during insemination. Feathering the vagina following insemination (*75*) may aspirate sperm into the uterus.

3. Dose and Volume Inseminated

Recommendations for volumes used in insemination are summarized in Table VI. Increasing sperm numbers with old liquid semen or semen improperly frozen and stored cannot wholly compensate for the decline in fertility of aged and damaged cells.

The volume for insemination with cattle has become standardized at 0.5–1 ml. However, prepackaging of concentrated semen for freezing may reduce the volume while retaining similar sperm numbers. The actual number of sperm inseminated usually is less than the packaged numbers because of sperm residues in equipment (74). The fewest sperm (3.75 million per insemination) are used successfully in New Zealand (162, 163) to meet the heavy demand during the short breeding season. In the United States 5.0 million motile sperm with liquid semen (83) and 20 million motile sperm before freezing (183) show no decline in fertility. More sperm are used where the demand per sire is less (90, 164).

In ewes 50 million motile sperm in a small volume placed intracervically should be adequate (60, 209). Work by Dott (57) indicates that fertility of diluted sperm is not reduced, provided sperm are reconcentrated prior to insemination. Thus, the actual concentration of sperm as well as sperm numbers may influence the number penetrating the cervix.

In sows and in mares relatively large volumes of semen and numbers of motile sperm are required for maximum fertility (Table VI). The number of sperm accumulated at the uterotubal junction may have special significance in sows (198). When 100 million sperm were inseminated into sows egg cleavage rate was only 20% (101).

When dog semen is collected for the insemination of one bitch, all of it may be used, or it may be extended 1:4 and part stored at 5°C for a second insemination 1 day after the first. This provides more than the minimum dose shown in Table VI.

B. Conception Rate

The conception rates in Table VI refer to pregnancies maintained under good field conditions (1, 3, 59, 135, 151, 164). Actual nonreturn rates are higher (110, 217). Except in swine, fertility appears to be equal to natural service. Artificial insemination in swine may give equal results under experimental conditions (238), but natural-service conception rates in the field average about 15% higher (23). An average litter size of 11 pigs has been obtained by both methods.

C. Artificial Insemination in Estrous Cycle-Synchronized Animals

Estrous cycle synchronization has been tested experimentally in most animals and applied on a commercial basis to cattle, sheep, and swine. Objectives and techniques are described in Chapter 20. Artificial insemination must be an integral part of an estrous cycle synchronization program if the breeding power is to be supplied in a short time by the superior males. Synchronization at the second estrus following withdrawal of the hormones or other agents used is reasonably good and fertility often is higher. Multiple capsules to release sperm preserved at body temperatures for 1–2 days could eliminate the need for estrus checking altogether, if animals are highly synchronized. However, such capsules have not yet been perfected.

VII. Factors Affecting Fertility in Artificial Insemination

A. BULLS

The large-scale reporting of fertility information in artificially inseminated dairy cattle has provided extensive data on many factors affecting conception rates. The bull is one major component. Probably, there has been little selection practiced for high fertility on a genetic basis, and with the low heritability of fertility and lack of a marked relationship to other traits (108) this would be quite ineffective. However, bulls in heavy service can be accurately ranked on the basis of fertility, and many are culled because their fertility is low (20, 201). This raises the overall level of fertility and tends to make less obvious any relationship between advanced age of bulls and declining fertility.

B. SEMEN COLLECTION AND PROCESSING

Semen collection schedules and techniques, semen evaluation, the type of extender used, the inclusion of antibiotics, and proper cooling, freezing, and storage all play a role in the final fertility of each semen sample. Improved methods for identifying the inferior ejaculates and rejecting them could markedly improve fertility, particularly of frozen semen.

C. FIELD PRACTICES

Semen distribution to the field, geographical distribution and condition of the females to be inseminated, service policies of the organization, and many other factors affect the physiological condition of the sperm at the time it encounters the ovum, and the chance that it will encounter an ovum at all. In addition, the inseminating technician plays a key role. A large proportion of the observed differences among technicians represent true differences (225). Some of the important describable attributes include the ability (1) to properly care for the semen in his possession, (2) to skillfully manipulate the reproductive tract so as to place sperm at the proper site, and (3) to evoke an optimum physiological response by the female.

One of the most significant advances made to demonstrate and develop the recommended techniques of insemination has been the introduction of simple training devices (Fig. 4). Dye is used so that when the tract is examined, the exact site of deposition can be verified. The dye technique is repeated in live animals, and it has been found to be valuable in retraining technicians whose ability to inseminate cows artificially was substandard (42, 91, 140, 266).

Older liquid and frozen semen gives a lower initial nonreturn rate and more delayed returns (10, 213, 216, 217). The small decline in fertility of about 7% over an 8-year period of storage at −79°C (155) and the

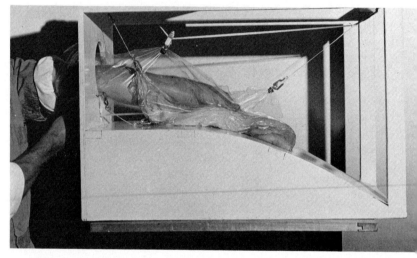

FIG. 4. A teaching aid to demonstrate and practice the coordinated efforts required for successful artificial insemination. Note the left hand grasping the cervix through a plastic-simulated rectal wall and the right hand manipulating the inseminating catheter.

greater protection given sperm at −196°C (186) indicates that the rate of aging is greatly reduced at low temperatures. Nevertheless, faulty handling may produce changes (181).

Disease is a constant potential hazard (Chapter 19). Artificial insemination is an effective means of controlling venereal diseases, but aseptic procedures of insemination and careful disinfection following each insemination are necessary to avoid spreading organisms among herds and flocks.

D. Reported Fertility: Return and Nonreturn Rates

Nonreturn rates are used to estimate fertility in artificial breeding. The nonreturn rate for first services indicates the percentage of females which do not return for a second insemination within a specified period of time. This has proven to be a fast and reasonable means of monitoring fertility following artificial insemination (*129, 217*). The shortest interval used is 28–35 days (4–5 weeks), which allows for one estrous cycle to pass. Longer intervals are tabulated on a monthly basis. Andersen (*10*) reported that 30- to 60-day and 60- to 90-day nonreturn rates and conception rates on more than 1 million cows were 75%, 68%, and 60%. In a population with higher fertility the 28- to 35-day, 60- to 90-day and 150- to 180-day nonreturn rates were found to be 82%, 73%, and 70% (*80*), the latter being about 2% higher than the conception rate (*85*). Fortunately, the final nonreturn values can be estimated accurately by using the 28- to 35-day nonreturns, [$r = 0.97$, reference (*80*)].

The return to service is the information actually reported from the field, and these are accumulated and subtracted from the number of services to tabulate nonreturns. The return to service has been reported to be a better indication of calving rate than the nonreturn (*15*).

Although many causes of variation in the nonreturn or return rates have been described, only a small portion of the variance has been clearly isolated (*62, 172, 225, 234*). Much of the variation is due to sampling. Part of this stems from the binomial nature of fertility measured in a cow as 0 (no conception) or 1 (conception) (*217*).

These studies show the need to carefully compare treatments on a large scale before one can be reasonably certain that small differences observed are real. The reader should bear this in mind as he delves into the scientific literature or contemplates experiments. Certainly, the opportunity for improvement of artificial insemination in the various classes of domestic animals is great; the more obscure pathways remain to be charted.

REFERENCES

1. Aamdal, J., *Proc. 5th Intern. Congr. Animal Reprod. Artificial Insemination, Trento* **4**, 147 (1964).
2. Adler, H. C., *Acta Vet. Scand.* **1**, 105 (1960).
3. Adler, H. C., *Proc. 5th Intern. Congr. Animal Reprod. Artificial Insemination, Trento* **4**, 40 (1964).
4. Adler, H. C., and Autrup, E. H., *Roy. Vet. Agr. Coll. Sterility Res. Inst. Ann. Rep. Copenhagen* p. 155 (1966).
4a. Almquist, J. O., *J. Dairy Sci.* **34**, 819 (1951).
5. Almquist, J. O., *J. Dairy Sci.* **45**, 911 (1962).
6. Almquist, J. O., and Cunningham, D. C., *J. Animal Sci.* **26**, 174 (1967).
7. Almquist, J. O., and Hale, E. B., *Proc. 3rd Intern. Congr. Animal Reprod., Cambridge, Engl., Plenary Papers* p. 50 (1956).
8. Almquist, J. O., and Wickersham, E. W., *J. Dairy Sci.* **45**, 782 (1962).
9. Amann, R. P., and Almquist, J. O., *J. Dairy Sci.* **45**, 774 (1962).
10. Anderson, H., *Roy. Vet. Agr. Coll. Sterility Res. Inst. Ann. Rept. Copenhagen* p. 101 (1965).
11. Asbury, A. C., and Hughes, J. P., *J. Am. Vet. Med. Assoc.* **144**, 879 (1964).
12. Ashdown, R. R., *J. Agr. Sci.* **58**, 65 (1962).
13. Ashdown, R. R., *J. Agr. Sci.* **58**, 71 (1962).

14. Austin, J. W., Hupp, E. W., and Murphree, R. L., *J. Dairy Sci.* **44**, 229 (1961).
15. Baker, F. N., and Salisbury, G. W., *J. Dairy Sci.* **47**, 1429 (1964).
15a. Baker, R. D., Dzuik, P. J., and Norton, H. W., *J. Animal Sci.* **27**, 8 (1968).
16. Bane, A., *Acta Agr. Scand.* **4**, 95 (1954).
17. Barker, C. A. V., *Can. Vet. J.* **3**, 221 (1962).
18. Bartlett, F. D., Jr., and VanDemark, N. L., *J. Dairy Sci.* **45**, 360 (1962)
19. Bean, B. H., Pickett, B. W., and Martig, R. C., *J. Dairy Sci.* **46**, 14 (1963).
20. Becker, R. B., *Proc. 13th Ann. Conv. Natl. Assoc. Artificial Breeder Louisville, Kentucky* p. 77 (1960).
21. Bhattacharya, B. C., Bangham, A. D., Cro, R. J., Keynes, R. D., and Row son, L. E. A., *Nature* **211**, 863 (1966).
22. Bielanski, W., *Proc. 5th Intern. Congr. Animal Reprod. Artificial Insemina tion, Trento* **4**, 645 (1964).
23. Boender, J., *World Rev. Animal Prod.* **2**, 29 (1966).
24. Bonadonna, T., *Proc. 3rd Intern. Congr. Animal Reprod., Cambridge, Engl Plenary Papers* p. 105 (1956).
25. Bonfert, A., *Proc. 5th Intern. Congr. Animal Reprod. Artificial Insemina tion Trento* **4**, 259 (1964).
26. Borton, A., Jaworski, A., and Nellor, J. E., *Michigan State Univ. Agr. Exp Sta. Res. Bull.* **8**, 80 pp. (1965).
27. Boucher, J. H., Foote, R. H., and Kirk, R. W., *Cornell Vet.* **48**, 67 (1958)
28. Boyd, L. J., and VanDemark, N. L., *J. Dairy Sci.* **40**, 689 (1957).
29. Bratton, R. W., Foote, R. H., and Cruthers, J. C., *J. Dairy Sci.* **38**, 4 (1955).
30. Bratton, R. W., Foote, R. H., and Henderson, C. R., *J. Dairy Sci.* **37** 1444 (1954).
31. Bratton, R. W., Foote, R. H., Henderson, C. R., Musgrave, S. D., Dunbar R. S., Jr., Dunn, H. O., and Beardsley, J. P., *J. Dairy Sci.* **39**, 1542 (1956)
32. Bratton, R. W., Musgrave, S. D., Dunn, H. O., and Foote, R. H., *Cornel Univ. Agr. Expt. Sta. Bull.* **940**, 45 pp. (1959).
33. Bratton, R. W., Musgrave, S. D., Dunn, H. O., and Foote, R. H., *Corne. Univ. Agr. Expt. Sta. Bull.* **964**, 24 pp. (1961).
34. Brooks, J. R., and Ross, C. V., *Univ. Missouri Agr. Expt. Sta. Res. Bul. 801*, 78 pp. (1962).
35. Bruemmer, J. H., Eddy, R. W., and Duryea, W. J., *J. Cellular Comp Physiol.* **62**, 113 (1963).
36. Buell, J. R., *Vet. Record* **75**, 900 (1963).
37. Buttle, N. R. L., Hancock, J. L., and Purser, A. F., *Animal Prod.* **7**, 5 (1965).
38. Campbell, E. A., and Lingam, S. A., *Australian Vet. J.* **41**, 147 (1965)
39. Carroll, E. J., Ball, L., and Scott, J. A., *J. Am. Vet. Med. Assoc.* **142** 1105 (1963).
40. Cassou, R., *Compt. Rend. Soc. Biol.* **144**, 486 (1950).
41. Cassou, R., *Élevage Insémination* **97**, 3 (1967).
42. Cembrowicz, H. J., *Proc. 5th Intern. Congr. Animal Reprod. and Artificia Insemination, Trento* **4**, 624 (1964).
43. Cheng, P. L., Wang, C. Y., Lin, P., and Tung, W., *Proc. 5th Intern. Congr Animal Reprod. Artificial Insemination, Trento* **3**, 504 (1964).

44. Choong, C. H., and Wales, R. G., *Res. Vet. Sci.* **5**, 228 (1964).
45. Clamohoy, L. L., and Foote, R. H., *J. Dairy Sci.* **46**, 61 (1963).
46. Clegg, E. D., Komarek, R. J., and Pickett, B. W., *J. Dairy Sci.* **48**, 1709 (1965).
47. Collins, W. J., Bratton, R. W., and Henderson, C. R., *J. Dairy Sci.* **34**, 224 (1951).
48. Courot, M., Ortavant, R., and Richeme, E., *Élevage Insémination* **77**, 13 (1963).
49. Cunningham, D. C., Almquist, J. O., Pearson, R. E. and Martig, R. C., *J. Animal Sci.* **26**, 182 (1967).
50. Cupps, P. T., Laben, R. C., Rahlmann, D. F., and Reddon, A. R., *J. Animal Sci.* **19**, 509 (1960).
51. Dalton, D. C., Pearson, M. E., and Sheard, M., *Animal Prod.* **9**, 1 (1967).
52. Davies, D. V., Mann, T., and Rowson, L. E. A., *Proc. Roy. Soc.* **B147**, 332 (1967).
53. Davis, I. S., Bratton, R. W., and Foote, R. H., *J. Dairy Sci.* **46**, 333 (1963).
54. DeAlba, J., and Riera, S., *Animal Prod.* **8**, 137 (1966).
55. Desjardins, C., and Hafs, H. D., *J. Dairy Sci.* **45**, 1242 (1962).
56. Doak, R. L., Hall, A., and Dale, H. E., *J. Reprod. Fertility* **13**, 51 (1967).
57. Dott, H. M., *J. Reprod. Fertility* **8**, 257 (1964).
58. Drevius, L. O., and Eriksson, H., *Exptl. Cell Res.* **42**, 136 (1966).
59. DuMesnil Du Buisson, F., and Signoret, J. P., *World Rev. Animal Prod.* **2**, 45 (1966).
60. Dun, R. B., *Zootec. Vet.* **7**, 244 (1962).
61. Dunlop, A. A., and Tallis, G. M., *Australian J. Agr. Res.* **15**, 282 (1964).
62. Dunn, H. O., *Proc. 4th Intern. Congr. Animal Reprod., The Hague* **4**, 756 (1961).
63. Dunn, H. O., and McEntee, K., *Intern. J. Fertility* **9**, 613 (1964).
64. Dutt, R. H., *J. Dairy Sci.* **43**, Suppl., 123 (1960).
65. Dutt, R. H., and Barnhart, C. E., *J. Animal Sci.* **18**, 3 (1959).
66. Dyrendahl, I., and Malnberg, G., *Svensk Husdjursskötsel* **11**, 437 (1966).
67. Dzuik, P. J., and Norton, H. W., *J. Reprod. Fertility* **4**, 47 (1962).
68. Elliott, F. I., *Proc. 20th Ann. Conv. Natl. Assoc. Artificial Breeders Hershey, Pennsylvania,* p. 109 (1967).
69. Emmens, C. W., and Blackshaw, A. W., *Physiol. Rev.* **36**, 277 (1956).
70. First, N. L., Sevinge, A., and Henneman, H. A., *J. Animal Sci.* **20**, 79 (1961).
71. Flipse, R. J., and Almquist, J. O., *J. Dairy Sci.* **44**, 905 (1961).
72. Flipse, R. J., and Almquist, J. O., *J. Dairy Sci.* **46**, 1416 (1963).
73. Foote, R. H., *Am. J. Vet. Res.* **25**, 37 (1964).
74. Foote, R. H., *Proc. 5th Intern. Congr. Animal Reprod. Artificial Insemination, Trento* **4**, 416 (1964).
75. Foote, R. H., *in* "Current Veterinary Therapy" (R. W. Kirk, ed.), p. 686. Saunders, Philadelphia, Pennsylvania, 1968.
76. Foote, R. H., *J. Dairy Sci.* **47**, 807 (1964).
77. Foote, R. H., *J. Dairy Sci.* **50**, 1338 (1967).
78. Foote, R. H., *J. Dairy Sci.* **50**, 1468 (1967).
79. Foote, R. H., and Boucher, J. H., *Am. J. Vet. Res.* **25**, 558 (1964).
80. Foote, R. H., and Bratton, R. W., *J. Dairy Sci.* **35**, 261 (1952).

81. Foote, R. H., and Bratton, R. W., *J. Dairy Sci.* **43**, 1322 (1960).

82. Foote, R. H., and Bredderman, P. B., *J. Dairy Sci.* **51**, 965 (1968).

83. Foote, R. H., and Dunn, H. O., *J. Dairy Sci.* **45**, 1237 (1962).

84. Foote, R. H., Gray, L. C., Young, D. C., and Dunn, H. O., *J. Dairy Sci.* **43**, 1330 (1960).

85. Foote, R. H., and Hall, A. C., *J. Dairy Sci.* **37**, 673 (1954).

86. Fowler, A. K., Pickett, B. W., Gosslee, D. G., and Cowan, W. A., *J. Dairy Sci.* **44**, 715 (1961).

87. Fowler, D. G., *Australian J. Exptl. Agr. Animal Husbandry* **5**, 247 (1965).

88. French, G. R., Norman, C., Dunbar, R. S., Jr., Porterfield, I. D., *West Va. Univ. Agr. Expt. Sta. Bull.* **471T** (1962).

89. Glover, F. A., and Phipps, L. W., *J. Reprod. Fertility* **4**, 189 (1962).

90. Goffaux, M., *Élevage Insémination* **90**, 11 (1965).

91. Graham, E. F., *Proc. 1st Tech. Conf. Artificial Insemination Bovine Reprod., Chicago, Illinois* p. 57 (1966).

92. Grove, D., *Deut. Tierärztl. Wochschr.* **72**, 350 (1965).

93. Haag, F. M., *J. Am. Vet. Med. Assoc.* **134**, 314 (1959).

94. Hafez, E. S. E., *Cornell Vet.* **50**, 384 (1960).

95. Hafez, E. S. E. (ed.), "The Behaviour of Domestic Animals." Williams & Wilkins, Baltimore, Maryland, 1962.

96. Hafs, H. D., Bratton, R. W., Henderson, C. R., and Foote, R. H., *J. Dairy Sci.* **41**, 96 (1958).

97. Hafs, H. D., Hoyt, R. S., and Bratton, R. W., *J. Dairy Sci.* **42**, 626 (1959).

98. Hafs, H. D., Knisely, R. C., and Desjardins, C., *J. Dairy Sci.* **45**, 788 (1962).

99. Hale, E. B., *J. Animal Sci.* **25**, Suppl. 36 (1966).

100. Hale, E. B., and Almquist, J. O., *J. Dairy Sci.* **43**, Suppl. 145 (1960).

101. Hancock, J. L., and Hovell, G. J. R., *Animal Prod.* **3**, 153 (1961).

102. Hansen, L. H., *Roy. Vet. Agr. Coll. Sterility Res. Inst. Ann. Rept. Copenhagen* p. 55 (1962).

103. Harrop, A. E., *Proc. 5th Intern. Congr. Animal Reprod. Artificial Insemination Trento* **4**, 33 (1964).

104. Hauser, E. R., Dickerson, G. E., and Mayer, D. T., *Missouri Univ. Agr. Expt. Sta. Res. Bull.* **503**, 56 pp. (1952).

105. Hay, M. F., Lindner, H. R., and Mann, T., *Proc. Roy. Soc.* **B154**, 433 (1961).

106. Hendrikse, J., *Tijdschr. Diergeneesk.* **87**, 1553 (1962).

107. Hendrikse, J., *Tijdschr. Diergeneesk.* **91**, 300 (1966).

108. Hickman, C. G., and Dunn, H. O., *Can. J. Genet. Cytol.* **3**, 391 (1961).

109. Hiroe, K., Masaki, J., Tomizuka, T., and Hanada, A., *Bull. Natl. Inst. Animal Ind.* **6**, 10 pp. (1964).

110. Hoffmann, H. H., and Hoffmann, H., *Tieraerztl. Wochschr.* **76**, 209 (1963).

111. Hoffman, W. F., *Dissertation Abstr.* **26**, 4926 (1966).

112. Hulet, C. V., *J. Animal Sci.* **25**, Suppl., 5 (1966).

113. Hulet, C. V., and Ercanbrack, S. K., *J. Animal Sci.* **21**, 489 (1964).

114. Hulet, C. V., Foote, W. C., and Blackwell, R. L., *J. Animal Sci.* **23**, 418 (1964).

115. Hutchinson, R. W., and Cooper, R. J., *Vet. Record* **73**, 857 (1961).

116. Iida, I., and Ikeda, K., *Japan. J. Zootech. Sci.* **37**, 417 (1966).

117. Iversen, S., *J. Agr. Sci.* **62**, 219 (1964).

118. Jondet, R., *Proc. 5th Intern. Congr. Animal Reprod. Artificial Insemination, Trento* 4, 463 (1964).
119. Jones, R. C., *Australian J. Biol. Sci.* 18, 877 (1965).
120. Jones, R. C., and Martin, I. C. A., *J. Reprod. Fertility* 10, 413 (1965).
121. Kennelly, J. J., and Foote, R. H., *J. Animal Sci.* 23, 160 (1964).
122. Kerruish, B. M., *Brit. J. Animal Behaviour* 3, 125 (1955).
123. King, G. J., and Macpherson, J. W., *A. I. Dig.* 14, (12) (1966).
124. King, G. J., and Macpherson, J. W., *Can. J. Comp. Med. Vet. Sci.* 30, 304 (1966).
125. King, G. J., and Macpherson, J. W., *Can. J. Comp. Med. Vet. Sci.* 30, 332 (1966).
126. Kirillov, V. S., and Morozov, V. A., *Problemy Zhivotnovodstva* 5, 90 (1933).
127. Lanz, R. N., Pickett, B. W., and Komarek, R. J., *J. Dairy Sci.* 48, 1692 (1965).
127a. Lardy, H. A., and Phillips, P. H., *Proc. Am. Soc. Animal Prod.* 32, 219 (1939).
128. Larson, L. L., and Kitchell, R. L., *Am. J. Vet. Res.* 19, 853 (1958).
129. Leidl, W., *Proc. 5th Intern. Congr. Animal Reprod. Artificial Insemination, Trento* 4, 62 (1964).
130. Lindahl, P. E., and Drevius, L. O., *Exptl. Cell Res.* 36, 632 (1964).
131. Lindner, H. R., *J. Endocrinol.* 25, 483 (1963).
132. Lindsay, D. R., *Animal Behaviour* 13, 75 (1965).
133. Lingam, S. A., and Campbell, E. A., *Australian Vet. J.* 41, 151 (1965).
134. Louw, D. F. J., and Joubert, D. M., *South African J. Agr. Sci.* 7, 509 (1964).
135. Lunca, N., *Proc. 5th Intern. Congr. Animal Reprod. Artificial Insemination, Trento* 4, 118 (1964).
136. McFee, A. F., and Eblen, J. R., *J. Animal Sci.* 26, 772 (1967).
137. Macmillan, K. L., and Fielden, E. D., *Proc. 5th Intern. Congr. Animal Reprod. Artificial Insemination, Trento* 4, 225 (1964).
138. Macmillan, K. L., Hafs, H. D., Desjardins, C., and Kirton, K. T., *J. Dairy Sci.* 49, 1132 (1966).
139. Macpherson, J. W., and King, G. J., *Can. J. Comp. Med. Vet. Sci.* 30, 109 (1966).
140. Macpherson, J. W., and King, G. J., *Can. Vet. J.* 6, 43 (1965).
141. Mahajan, S. C., and Menge, A. C., *J. Animal Sci.* 25, 1083 (1966).
142. Mann, T., "Biochemistry of Semen and of the Male Reproductive Tract." Methuen, London, 1964.
143. Maqsood, M., *Biol. Rev.* 27, 281 (1952).
144. Martin, I. C. A., *J. Agr. Sci.* 64, 425 (1965).
145. Martin, I. C. A., *J. Reprod. Fertility* 6, 441 (1963).
146. Martin, I. C. A., *Res. Vet. Sci.* 4, 304 (1963).
147. Martin, I. C. A., and Wallace, C. S., *J. Reprod. Fertility* 10, 425 (1965).
148. Mattner, P. E., *Nature* 199, 772 (1963).
149. Mattner, P. E., and Voglmayr, J. K., *Australian J. Exptl. Agr. Animal Husbandry* 2, 78 (1962).
150. Maule, J. P. (ed.), "The Semen of Animals and Artificial Insemination," Commonwealth Agr. Bur. Tech. Comm. 15. Farnham Royal, England, 1962.
151. Melrose, D. R., *World Rev. Animal Prod.* 2, 15 (1966).

152. Meryman, H. T., and Kafig, E., *J. Reprod. Fertility* **5**, 87 (1963).
153. Meschaks, P., *Ciba Foundation Symp. Mammalian Germ Cells* (G. E. W. Wolstenholme, ed.), p. 37. Little, Brown and Co., Boston, 1953.
154. Milovanov, V. K., and Sytina, M. V., *Tr. Vses. Nauch.-Issled. Inst. Zivotn.* **24**, 269 (1962); *Animal Breeding Abstr.* **32**, 326 (1964).
155. Mixner, J. P., and Wiggin, S. H., *Proc. 5th Intern. Congr. Animal Reprod. Artificial Insemination, Trento* **4**, 264 (1964).
156. Mizuho, A., Niwa, T., and Soejima, A., *Bull. Natl. Inst. Animal Ind.* (*Chiba*) **1**, 45 (1963).
157. Moyer, R. F., and Almquist, J. O., *J. Dairy Sci.* **45**, 383 (1962).
158. Mukherjee, D. P., *World Rev. Animal Prod.* **1**, 74 (1966).
159. Nagase, H., *Japan Agr. Res. Quart.* **1** (1966).
160. Nagase, H., and Graham, E. F., *Proc. 5th Intern. Congr. Animal Reprod. Artificial Insemination, Trento* **4**, 387 (1964).
161. Nagase, H., Soejima, S., Tomizuka, T., Oshida, H., Mikawa, T., Sagara, Y., Hoshi, S., and Niwa, T., *Japan. J. Animal Reprod.* **12**, 52 (1966).
162. *New Zealand Dairy Prod. Marketing Board* **40**, 102 pp. (1964).
163. *New Zealand Dairy Prod. Marketing Board* **41**, 92 pp. (1965).
164. Nishikawa, Y., *Proc. 5th Intern. Congr. Animal Reprod. Artificial Insemination, Trento* **7**, 162 (1964).
165. Nishikawa, Y., *Kyoto Univ. English Bull.* **2**, 43 pp. (1962).
166. Nishikawa, Y., "Studies on Reproduction in Horses." Japan Racing Assoc., Tokyo, 1959.
167. Niwa, T., *Natl. Inst. Agr. Sci.* (*Japan*) 13 pp. (1958).
168. Niwa, T., and Mizuho, A., *Bull. Natl. Inst. Agr. Sci.* (*Japan*) *Ser. G* **9**, 141 (1954).
169. Norman, C., *Proc. 5th Intern. Congr. Animal Reprod. Artificial Insemination, Trento* **4**, 269 (1964).
170. Norman, C., Goldberg, E., and Porterfield, I. D., *Exptl. Cell Res.* **28**, 69 (1962).
171. Norman, C., Johnson, C. E., Porterfield, I. D., Goldberg, E., Dunbar, R. S., Jr., and Min, H. S., *J. Agr. Sci.* **59**, 33 (1962).
172. Olds, D., Colvin, L. D., Cooper, T., and Deaton, D. W., *J. Dairy Sci.* **49**, 1004 (1966).
173. Ortavant, R., Mauleon, P., and Thibault, C., *Ann. N.Y. Acad. Sci.* **117**, 157 (1964).
174. Pakenas, P. I., *Proc. 5th Intern. Congr. Animal Reprod. Artificial Insemination, Trento* **6**, 20 (1964).
175. Parez, M., *Élevage Insémination* **88**, 3 (1965).
176. Park, R. W. A., Melrose, D. R., Stewart, D. L., and O'Hagan, C., *Brit. Vet. J.* **120**, 457 (1965).
177. Parkes, A. S. (ed.), "Marshall's Physiology of Reproduction," Vol. 1, Part 2, Longmans, Green, New York, 1960.
178. Paüfler, S. K., *Zuchthygiene* **2**, 67 (1967).
179. Paüfler, S. K., and Foote, R. H., *J. Dairy Sci.* **50**, 1475 (1967).
180. Perry, E. J., (ed.), "The Artificial Insemination of Farm Animals." Rutgers Univ. Press, New Brunswick, New Jersey, 1968.
181. Pickett, B. W., *Proc. 1st Tech. Conf. Artificial Insemination Bovine Reprod., Chicago, Illinois* p. 64 (1966).

182. Pickett, B. W., Hall, R. C., Jr., Lucas, J. J., and Gibson, E. W., *Fertility Sterility* **16**, 642 (1965).
183. Pickett, B. W., Hall, R. C., Jr., Lucas, J. J., and Gibson, E. W., *J. Dairy Sci.* **47**, 916 (1964).
184. Pickett, B. W., and Komarek, R. J., *J. Dairy Sci.* **47**, 905 (1964).
185. Pickett, B. W., MacDonald, W. A., Gosslee, D. G., and Cowan, W. A., *J. Dairy Sci.* **44** 1134 (1961).
186. Pickett, B. W., Martig, R. C., and Cowan, W. A., *J. Dairy Sci.* **44**, 2089 (1961).
187. Polge, C., and Minotakis, C., *Proc. 5th Intern. Congr. Animal Reprod. Artificial Insemination, Trento* **7**, 545 (1964).
188. Polge, C., Smith, A. U., and Parkes, A. S., *Nature* **164**, 666 (1949).
189. Prabhu, S. S., and Bhattacharya, P., *Indian J. Vet. Sci.* **24**, 35 (1954).
190. Probine, M. C., and McCabe, W. J., *J. Agr. Sci.* **50**, 260 (1958).
191. Quinn, P. J., and White, I. G., *J. Reprod. Fertility* **12**, 263 (1966).
192. Rajamannan, A. H. J., *A. I. Dig.* **14**, 8 (1966).
193. Rajamannan, A. H. J., Graham, E. F., and Smith, F., *Proc. 5th Intern. Congr. Animal Reprod. Artificial Insemination, Trento* **4**, 392 (1964).
194. Rapatz, G. L., *Proc. 1st Tech. Conf. Artificial Insemination Chicago, Illinois* p. 45 (1966).
195. Rathora, A. K., *Indian Vet. J.* **42**, 680 (1965).
196. Reid, J. T., *J. Dairy Sci.* **43**, Suppl., 103 (1960).
197. Restall, B. J., *Australian Vet. J.* **37**, 70 (1961).
198. Rigby, J. P., *J. Reprod. Fertility* **11**, 153 (1966).
199. Rikmenspoel, R., *Publ. Am. Assoc. Advan. Sci.* **72**, 31 (1962).
200. Roberts, E. M., and Houlahan, P. M., *Australian J. Exptl. Agr. Animal Husbandry* **1**, 156 (1961).
201. Roman, J., Wilcox, C. J., Becker, R. B., and Koger, M., *J. Animal Sci.* **26**, 136 (1967).
202. Rombe, S., Kotjagina, V., and Piler, N., *Konevod. Konnyi Sport* **35**, 34 (1965); *Animal Breeding Abstr.* **33**, 363 (1965).
203. Roussel, J. D., Kellgren, H. C., and Patrick, T. E., *J. Dairy Sci.* **47**, 1403 (1964).
204. Roussel, J. D., Patrick, T. E., and Kellgren, H. C., *J. Dairy Sci.* **45**, 527 (1962).
205. Roussel, J. D., Patrick, T. E., Kellgren, H. C., and Breidenstein, C. P., *J. Dairy Sci.* **46**, 1125 (1963).
206. Roussel, J. D., Patrick, T. E., Kellgren, H. C., and Guidry, A. J., *J. Dairy Sci.* **47**, 175 (1964).
207. Roussel, J. D., Patrick, T. E., Kellgren, H. C., and Shelwick, J. O., *J. Dairy Sci.* **46**, 1278 (1963).
208. Saacke, R. G., and Almquist, J. O., *Nature* **192**, 995 (1961).
209. Salamon, S., *Australian J. Agr. Res.* **13**, 1137 (1962).
210. Salamon, S., *Australian J. Agr. Res.* **15**, 645 (1964).
211. Salamon, S., and Morrant, A. J., *Australian J. Agr. Animal Husbandry* **3**, 72 (1963).
212. Salamon, S., and Robinson, T. J., *Australian J. Agr. Res.* **13**, 271 (1962).
213. Salisbury, G. W., *J. Dairy Sci.* **50**, 1683 (1967).
213a. Salisbury, G. W., *Publ. Am. Assoc. Advan. Sci.* **72**, 59 (1962).
214. Salisbury, G. W., and Baker, F. N., *J. Animal Sci.* **25**, 476 (1966).

352 R. H. FOOTE

215. Salisbury, G. W., Birge, W J., De La Torre, L., and Lodge, J. R., *J. Biophys. Biochem. Cytol.* **10**, 353 (1961).
216. Salisbury, G. W., and Flerchinger, F. H., *J. Dairy Sci.* **50**, 1675 (1967).
217. Salisbury, G. W., and VanDemark, N. L., "Physiology of Reproduction and Artificial Insemination of Cattle." Freeman, San Francisco, California, 1961.
218. Salisbury, G. W., and van Dongen, C. G., *J. Animal Sci.* **23**, 1098 (1964).
219. Sayed, A. A., Oloufa, M. M., and Badreldin, A. L., *Bull. Fac. Agr. Cairo Univ.* **213**, 16 pp. (1960).
220. Schilling, E., *J. Reprod. Fertility* **11**, 469 (1966).
221. Schindler, H., and Amir, D., *J. Agr. Sci.* **56**, 183 (1961).
222. Seidel, G. E., Jr., and Foote, R. H., *J. Dairy Sci.* **50**, 970 (1967).
223. Sengar, D. P. S., and Sharma, U. D., *Indian J. Dairy Sci.* **18**, 54 (1965).
224. Sergeev, N. I., *Proc. 5th Intern. Congr. Animal Reprod. Artificial Insemination, Trento* **6**, 177 (1964).
225. Shannon, P., *J. Dairy Sci.* **48**, 85 (1965).
226. Shannon, P., *New Zealand J. Agr. Res.* **7**, 357 (1964).
227. Sharma, U. D., and Mahajan, S. C., *J. Animal Physiol.* **8**, 107 (1961).
228. Sherman, J. K., *J. Cellular Comp. Physiol.* **61**, 67 (1963).
229. Shirley, R. L., Meacham, T. N., Warnick, A. C., Hentges, J. F., Jr., and Cunha, T. J., *J. Animal Sci.* **22**, 14 (1963).
230. Signoret, J. P., Du Mesnil Du Buisson, F., and Busnel, R. G., *Compt. Rend. Acad. Sci.* **250**, 1355 (1960).
231. Singh, S. G., and Prabhu, S. S., *Indian J. Vet. Sci. Animal Husbandry* **33**, 29 (1963).
232. Skatkin, P. N., *Tr. Vses. Nauch.-Issled. Inst. Konev. Moscow Seljhozgiz* p. 37 (1955); *Animal Breeding Abstr.* **24**, 335 (1956).
233. Snyder, J. W., and Ralston, N. P., *J. Dairy Sci.* **38**, 125 (1955).
234. Spears, J. R., Olds, D., and Cooper, T., *J. Dairy Sci.* **48**, 90 (1965).
235. Steinbach, J., and Foote, R. H., *J. Dairy Sci.* **50**, 205 (1967).
236. Stevermer, E. J., First, N. L., and Hoekstra, W. G., *J. Animal Sci.* **23**, 67 (1964).
237. Stoye, H., Mahler, R., and Dieckmann, W., *Zuchthygiene* **1**, 75 (1966).
238. Stratman, F. W., and Self, H. L., *J. Animal Sci.* **21**, 647 (1962).
239. Sullivan, J. J., Elliot, F. I., Bartlett, D. E., Murphy, D. M., and Kuzdas, C. D., *J. Dairy Sci.* **49**, 1569 (1966).
240. Sullivan, J. J., and Mixner, J. P., *J. Dairy Sci.* **46**, 463 (1963).
241. Swierstra, E. E., *Can. J. Animal Sci.* **46**, 107 (1966).
242. Swierstra, E. E., and Rahnefeld, G. W., *J. Animal Sci.* **26**, 149 (1967).
243. Thibault, C., Courot, M., Martinet, L., Mauleon, P., Du Mesnil Du Buisson, F., Ortavant, R., Pelletier, J., and Signoret, J. P., *J. Animal Sci.* **25**, Suppl. 119 (1966).
244. Turkheimer, A. R., Young, D. C., and Foote, R. H., *Cornell Vet.* **48**, 291 (1958).
245. Ulberg, L. C., and Burfening, P. J., *J. Animal Sci.* **26**, 571 (1967).
246. VanDemark, N. L., *Intern. J. Fertility* **3**, 220 (1958).
247. VanDemark, N. L., *Proc. 3rd Intern. Congr. Animal Reprod., Cambridge, Engl., Plenary Papers* p. 80 (1956).
248. VanDemark, N. L., Fritz, G. R., and Mauger, R. E., *J. Dairy Sci.* **47**, 898 (1964).

249. VanDemark, N. L., Koyama, K., and Lodge, J. R., *J. Dairy Sci.* **48**, 586 (1965).
250. VanDemark, N. L., and Mauger, R. E., *J. Dairy Sci.* **47**, 798 (1964).
251. VanDemark, N. L., Miller, W. J., Kinney, W. C., Jr., Rodriguez, C., and Friedman, M. E., *Univ. Illinois Agr. Expt. Sta. Bull.* **621**, 39 pp. (1957).
252. Van Duijn, C., Jr., *Netherlands J. Agr. Sci.* **13**, 378 (1965).
253. Vlachos, C., *Proc. 5th Intern. Congr. Animal Reprod. Artificial Insemination, Trento* **4**, 81 (1964).
254. Wales, R. G., and White, I. G., *J. Reprod. Fertility* **3**, 294 (1962).
255. Wales, R. G., and White, I. G., *J. Reprod. Fertility* **5**, 67 (1963).
256. Wierzbowski, S., *Proc. 5th Intern. Congr. Animal Reprod. Artificial Insemination, Trento* **3**, 351 (1964).
257. Wierzbowski, S., *Roczniki Nauk Rolniczych. Ser. B* **73**, 753 (1959); *Animal Breeding Abstr.* **28**, 111 (1960).
258. Wierzbowski, S., *World Rev. Animal Prod.* **2**, 66 (1966).
259. Wiggan, L. S., and Clark, J. B. K., *Brit. Vet. J.* **123**, 447 (1967).
260. Wiggins, E. L., and Terrill, C. E., *J. Animal Sci.* **12**, 524 (1953).
261. Wiggins, E. L., Warnick, A. C., Grummer, R. H., Casida, L. E., and Chapman, A. B., *J. Animal Sci.* **10**, 494 (1951).
262. Wilcox, C. J., Roman, J., and Becker, R. B., *J. Dairy Sci.* **50**, 884 (1967).
263. Willett, E. L., *J. Dairy Sci.* **40**, 1367 (1957).
264. Willett, E. L., and Ohms, J. I., *J. Dairy Sci.* **40**, 1559 (1957).
265. Wolf, F. R., Almquist, J. O., and Hale, E. B., *J. Animal Sci.* **24**, 761 (1965).
266. Wright, J. D. E., *Proc. 5th Intern. Congr. Animal Reprod. Artificial Insemination, Trento* **4**, 636 (1964).
267. Yassen, A. M., and Foote, R. H., *J. Animal Sci.* **26**, 1104 (1967).
268. Yassen, A. M., and Foote, R. H., *J. Dairy Sci.* **50**, 887 (1967).
269. Yassen, A. M., and Foote, R. H., *J. Dairy Sci.* **50**, 893 (1967).
270. Young, D. C., Foote, R. H., Turkheimer, A. R., and Hafs, H. D., *J. Animal Sci.* **19**, 20 (1960).

13 FERTILIZATION AND DEVELOPMENT OF THE EGG

C. R. AUSTIN

Most investigations on fertilization and associated phenomena in mammals have been made in the laboratory animals, and any reasonably comprehensive account of present-day knowledge must be based chiefly on what is known of them. In writing this account, however, particular attention has been given to setting down the available data for domestic mammals; where the text deals only with other species, it is because equivalent information for domestic animals is lacking or seems unreliable.

Fuller details of subjects discussed in this chapter, together with more extensive lists of references, are to be found in recent reviews (*1, 6, 7, 10, 20, 23, 45, 53, 54, 62, 63, 67, 76, 79, 100*).

I. Maturation, Ovulation, and Transport of Eggs

Before fertilization can take place, the egg must undergo maturation or ripening. Ovulation occurs before or during maturation, according to the species of mammal concerned. After ovulation, the egg is rapidly transferred to the fallopian tube where, in the great majority of animals, fertilization begins.

The primary oocyte (Fig. 1) consists of a body of cytoplasm, the vitellus, which is limited by a cell membrane (plasma membrane) and closely invested by the thick transparent zona pellucida. As the zona pellucida and

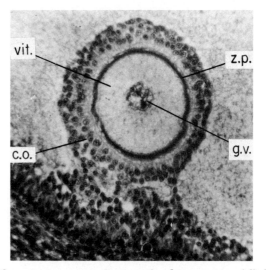

FIG. 1. The primary oocyte. Section of a large ovarian follicle in the cat, showing a primary oocyte: cumulus oophorus (c.o.); germinal vesicle (g.v.); vitellus (vit.); zona pellucida (z.p.). ×200. Section by courtesy of E. C. Amoroso.

the vitellus are in contact with each other, the space between them, the perivitelline space, is at this stage potential rather than real. Fine processes from certain of the immediately surrounding follicle cells traverse the zona pellucida and come into close relation with the surface of the vitellus— they are thought to represent the means whereby substances reach the egg for its growth and maintenance. Observations on the oocytes of kittens provided direct evidence for the transport of lipids (105). Somewhat eccentrically placed in the vitellus is the large spherical nucleus, the germinal vesicle, containing, usually, a single nucleolus. The eggs of the placental mammals do not differ much in size; in the majority of species, including the domestic animals and the rabbit, the overall diameter of the egg is around 120–180 μ (1 μ = 10^{-3} mm). Rodent eggs vary between 75–100 μ in diameter.

A. MATURATION AND ATRESIA OF OOCYTES

Maturation more overtly involves nuclear structures. The germinal vesicle moves toward the surface of the egg, the nuclear envelope and nucleoli disappear, and the chromosomes condense into compact and more easily demonstrable forms. The chromosomes then undergo two divisions: a reductional division, whereby the diploid number is reduced to the haploid—a condition that characterizes the mature germ cells of both sexes—and an equational division. At each division, chromosomes are rejected from the vitellus in polar bodies. After formation of the first polar body, the egg is known as a "secondary oocyte," and after the second polar body, as an "ootid."

Both meiotic divisions take place in broadly the same way, proceeding from prophase, through metaphase and anaphase, to telophase. In the later stages, a narrow granular zone, the intermediary body, forms in the middle of the spindle. The spindle then rotates about one pole through roughly 90°, and, as this happens, a cleft develops in the surfaces of the vitellus and passes inward in the wake of the intermediary body. The cleft eventually extends completely around the chromosome group at the pole of the spindle, thus cutting off a small mass of cytoplasm. Sometimes the chromosomes in the first polar body also undergo a second meiotic division and then the polar body itself may divide in two. In this way a total of three polar bodies may eventually be formed—a common occurrence in many invertebrate animals, but rare in mammals. Often the first polar body in the mammalian egg breaks up early, so that little or no sign of it may be seen after ovulation.

Coincident with extrusion of the first polar body, the vitellus undergoes a slight shrinkage; as a result, a true though small perivitelline space is formed. A second contraction, accompanied by a further enlargement of the perivitelline space, occurs at about the time of extrusion of the second polar body.

Atresia of oocytes may occur at any time in their growth and after they have reached full size, but is more common in later stages. It is the normal fate of the great majority of the oocytes present in the ovary at the birth of the animal. It is also the fate that overcomes oocytes in cystic follicles. Atresia is a cytoplasmic and nuclear regression of the oocyte and terminates in the death of the cell; it is distinguished by pyknosis and breakup of the nucleus and degenerative changes in the cytoplasm, with clumping of particulate components and extensive vacuolation. Oocytes destined for regression, however, sometimes first show stages of apparently normal maturation and cleavage. This kind of development is almost always terminated early, but may possibly be responsible for some cases of ovarian "pregnancy" in man.

B. Mechanism of Ovulation

Shortly before ovulation, follicular growth passes through a terminal phase in which the volume increases at an accelerated rate and a small elevation makes its appearance on the surface of the projecting follicle; soon the thin wall of the projection breaks down, leaving an aperture through which the follicular contents stream out. Emission of this material may be assisted to a small degree by contraction of the smooth muscle fibers of the theca externa, although generally the follicle undergoes little immediate diminution in size. It is possible that a similar muscular contraction, aided by rapid secretion of liquor folliculi, may raise intrafollicular pressure before ovulation and that, as a result, the act of ovulation may occur explosively. However, rupture under pressure is not the essential mechanism of follicular opening and, in most instances, ovulation is a gradual process, depending as much upon progressive changes in the structure of the follicle wall as upon the effect of internal pressure (26). Current views are that the changes in the follicle wall are attributable in part at least to the action of collagenases released by the follicle cells, under the direct or indirect action of messenger RNA (mRNA). The formation of the appropriate messenger seems likely to be induced by pituitary hormones.

When the egg leaves the follicle, it is still surrounded by the cumulus oophorus, which is probably important especially in providing a structure of sufficient size and suitable texture to permit its capture and transport by the fimbriae of the fallopian tube.

C. Time of Ovulation

In general, ovulation occurs near the end of estrus, but the precise time relation differs in different species. Estrus in the mare lasts 7 days on the average, though it may be as short as 3 days or as long as 30 days; irrespective of length of estrus, ovulation mostly occurs 1–2 days before its close. The time of ovulation in the cow is unusual—about 12–15 hours after the end of the 18-hour estrus. In other ruminants, the ewe and the goat, the eggs are ovulated a few hours before the end of estrus, which lasts an average of 24 and 40 hours, respectively. The sow's eggs are ovulated about 36 hours after the start of the 40- to 60-hour estrus. The bitch is another animal with a prolonged estrus, lasting about 9 days, and, uniquely, ovulation occurs on the first or second day after the beginning of sexual receptivity. In the cat (as in the ferret, rabbit, and a few other species) ovulation is induced by the act of coitus. Coitus in the cat, taking place at any time during the 3-day estrus, is followed by ovulation 24–30 hours later (*33*) or, sometimes, 40–54 hours later (*51*).

Most mammalian eggs are ovulated when the second maturation division has reached metaphase. In the dog and probably the horse, however, the egg is ovulated as a primary oocyte and passes through its maturation in the fallopian tube. Rather rarely, ovulation of primary oocytes may also occur in the pig (*44, 85*); in some eggs of this kind, sperm penetration into the vitellus was recorded, but there was no pronucleus formation (*73*).

D. PASSAGE OF EGGS TO THE SITE OF FERTILIZATION

The site of fertilization in the domestic animals is in the ampulla of the fallopian tube. The location is not susceptible to precise definition, since sperm penetration may well begin in the infundibulum, and during the process of fertilization, which occupies a period of 12 hours or more, the eggs may move down the ampulla as far as its junction with the isthmus. These relations seem to be true for most mammals, the only notable exceptions being the ferret, wherein fertilization is said to begin in the ovarian bursa, and the short-tailed shrew and the tenrecs of Madagascar, wherein spermatozoa can enter the follicles and penetrate the eggs before ovulation is completed.

At ovulation, the egg within its cumulus oophorus is liberated onto the surface of the ovary and very shortly passes into the infundibulum, the specialized ovarian end of the fallopian tube. The means whereby this transfer is effected are not yet clearly understood. Observations in the rabbit, in which the infundibulum is large and funnel shaped with well-developed fimbriae lined with ciliated mucosa, indicate that this structure becomes closely applied to the ovary at the time of ovulation, and it seems likely that the eggs could be taken up and moved along between opposing surfaces of the fimbriae, the cilia thus obtaining good purchase on the cumulus mass. Cinematographic records show that in the rat the eggs, suspended in the bursa fluid, drift from the ovary into the opening of the infundibulum, which in this species is not dilated and has much reduced fimbriae. Presumably the drift is attributable to currents set up by the action of cilia in the epithelium lining the internal surface of the fallopian tube and extending around the opening of the infundibulum. Though ciliary currents may assist the process in the domestic animals, the possession of funnel-shaped, fimbriated infundibula, particularly by the larger members of the group, suggests that the mechanism would more closely resemble that described for the rabbit. Once within the fallopian tube, contractions of the tubal wall may play a part, but ciliary currents could be of chief importance, for the mucosa of the whole tube contains an abundance of ciliated cells and the beat is uniformly directed toward the uterus.

Sometimes, an egg fails to pass into the fallopian tube on its own side and, by some obscure means, traverses the peritoneal cavity and enters the contralateral tube. This phenomenon is called "external migration" and has been reported in human subjects and the rabbit.

E. Fertile Life of Eggs

Precise data are difficult to obtain, but indications are that the eggs of domestic animals remain fully viable for 12–24 hours after ovulation and perhaps a little longer, except in the dog, in which the fertile life of the egg possibly exceeds 4 days and may even be as long as 8 days. Loss of viability is not sudden—aging eggs may be able to undergo apparently normal fertilization, but give rise to embryos that die before birth. With further deterioration, fertilization becomes abnormal or fails altogether.

F. Egg Transfer

Both rabbit and mouse oocytes have been stored *in vitro* and, in the case of the mouse eggs, even frozen for ½–3½ hours, and have then proved capable of undergoing fertilization and extensive development, on transfer to suitable host animals (*30, 82, 83*).

II. Transport of Spermatozoa

A. Deposition of Semen

At coitus, semen is passed into the female tract, but the volume of the ejaculate and the site of its deposition vary. In the horse, the ejaculate amounts to about 75–150 ml and the semen is projected into the cranial end of the vagina and through the relaxed cervical canal into the uterus. In the pig, the ejaculate is even more voluminous, amounting usually to 125–500 ml; it is slowly propelled through the vagina and cervix and into the uterus during the prolonged coitus. In the ox and sheep, the volumes of ejaculates are about 5 and 1 ml, respectively, and the semen is deposited in the cranial part of the vagina and on the cervix. In the dog and cat the ejaculates measure about 7.0 and 0.5 ml, respectively, and are deposited in the vagina.

B. Mechanism of Sperm Transport

To varying degrees in different animals, some transport of spermatozoa in the female tract occurs during coitus and while they are suspended in seminal plasma. Admixture with secretions of the female tract soon takes place, however, and as the spermatozoa approach the site of fertilization female secretions alone constitute the suspending medium.

In the horse, there is evidence that, as a result of the female orgasm, negative pressure may develop in the uterine lumen (58); this would no doubt facilitate the rapid passage of semen into the uterus. In both horse and pig, the ejaculate has been found to pass as far as the uterotubal junction (55). Radiopaque fluid, injected experimentally into the uterus of the estrous cow, has been observed to move rapidly to the uterotubal junction; when oxytocin was administered to simulate the effect of coitus, the fluid was found to enter the fallopian tubes within 2½ minutes of its injection (77). Movements of material within the uterine lumen are attributable to the contractions of the uterine wall. The contractions are powerful during estrus and are strongly augmented when orgasm is evoked (79); they have the effect of churning up the contents of the organ. Similar forces are brought to bear upon the spermatozoa when they reach the fallopian tube.

Thus, spermatozoa are transported, a little by their own motility (the main significance of which is probably that it keeps the cells in suspension), but very largely by the process of being passively mixed with the fluid contents of the tract. As a result, the distribution of spermatozoa in any one region tends to become progressively more uniform with time. Uniformity of distribution throughout the entire tract, however, is not even remotely achieved because of barriers presented by the cervix uteri, the uterotubal junction, and the isthmus of the fallopian tube. Consequently, where ejaculation is into the vagina, the concentration of spermatozoa remains higher in the vagina than in the uterus, and much higher than in the fallopian tube. The overall effect is that very small numbers of spermatozoa are rapidly brought to the site of fertilization.

C. RATE AND TIME OF SPERM TRANSPORT

Transport of spermatozoa to the ampulla of the fallopian tube is remarkably quick: times of 15 minutes or less have been reported for the cow, ewe, and bitch. In the cow (97) and ewe (57), dead spermatozoa were transported at a similar rate to living ones, which serves to emphasize the small contribution of the cells' own swimming movements toward their transport.

Under normal circumstances, and where full opportunity exists, coitus takes place early in the heat period, so that spermatozoa reach the site of fertilization several hours before the eggs. The termination of the period of sexual receptivity normally precludes the possibility of unduly delayed coitus and, consequently, the possibility that the eggs would have to wait long for the spermatozoa to arrive. In the cat, coitus-induced ovulation makes it even more certain that spermatozoa will be at the site of fertilization well before the eggs. With artificial insemination, however, unless due care is taken, there is a risk that the natural time relations will be disturbed and the level of fertility thus reduced.

D. Numbers of Spermatozoa

Average figures for the total number of spermatozoa in a single ejaculate may be given as follows: stallion, 6000×10^6; bull, 3000×16^6; ram, 800×10^6; boar, $20,000 \times 10^6$; dog, $35,000 \times 10^6$; cat, 800×10^6. These are enormous numbers and represent in each instance very many more spermatozoa than are necessary for normal fertility. If, for example, an average bull ejaculate is suitably diluted and used for the artificial insemination of about 500 cows, the great majority of them are likely to become pregnant.

The numbers of spermatozoa reaching the more ovarian regions of the tract progressively diminish; in the ewe, the average numbers in the uterus and fallopian tubes some hours after mating were found to be only 76,000 and 6500, respectively (101). The number in the ampulla of the fallopian tube, the site of fertilization, is evidently less than 100 in the rat and mouse, and less than 1000 in the rabbit and ewe (10).

E. Fertile Life of Spermatozoa

In general, spermatozoa, like eggs, are incapable of retaining full viability and fertility in the female tract for much longer than 24 hours. The longest period in most animals has been found to be 2–3 days, although in the mare it may be as long as 5 days. Motile spermatozoa have been found in the uterine lumen of the bitch 11 days after coitus (34a). A remarkable exception to the general rule is shown by some species of bats, in which coitus takes place in the autumn, and ovulation and fertilization do not occur until the following spring—an interval that may be as long as 5 months. Spermatozoa, like eggs, probably lose the ability to give rise to normal young before they cease to be capable of taking part in fertilization. In the course of artificial insemination studies on cattle, for example, it has been found that the percentage of nonreturns to service at 5 months of gestation decreased progressively if the semen was held *in vitro* for more than 3 days before insemination. Such an effect implies the occurrence of fetal mortality, and there is some evidence that the cause is to be found in deterioration or loss of sperm DNA (79).

III. Fertilization

Fertilization involves (a) the penetration of the spermatozoon into the egg, (b) the activation of the egg, (c) the formation and development of male and female pronuclei, and (d) the replacement of pronuclei by chromosome groups which come together in the prophase of the first cleavage of the zygote. The central feature of fertilization lies in the mingling of paternal and maternal chromosomes, whereby genetic information from two different sources comes to constitute the genome of the new individual. In addition, there are three other consequences of sperm entry: the diploid chromosome number is restored, sex is determined, and, through the medium of the sperm tail, paternal cytoplasmic elements are contributed to the embryo.

A. CAPACITATION AND THE ACROSOME REACTION

The arrival of spermatozoa at the site of fertilization before the eggs suggests that spermatozoa are not normally called upon to participate in fertilization immediately upon entering the female tract, but reside there for a period before exercising this function. Observations on rats and rabbits have consistently supported the idea that spermatozoa need to undergo some form of physiological preparation, referred to as "capacitation," to fit them for the task of penetrating the cumulus oophorus and zona pellucida of the eggs (8). Capacitation normally takes place in the female tract and appears to involve a change in the properties of the acrosome which leads to modification of its structure (acrosome reaction) and release of the lytic enzyme or enzymes that it carries. Capacitation takes about 2 hours in the rat and 4 hours in the rabbit, and about 1.5 hours in the sheep (56).

B. MEETING OF SPERMATOZOON AND EGG

The spermatozoids of certain plants (ferns, mosses, etc.) are known to be attracted to the egg cells by chemical substances secreted by them or by neighboring cells (76). Such chemotactic attraction of the male gamete by the female undoubtedly aids in assuring their union. Despite numerous investigations on animal gametes, mainly those of invertebrate animals, no unequivocal evidence has yet been produced that chemotaxis between eggs and spermatozoa operates in the animal kingdom, with the possible exception of some hydroid coelenterates.

In mammals, the meeting of spermatozoa and eggs appears to depend on chance, which is of about the same order in all species; although more spermatozoa reach the site of fertilization in sheep and rabbits than in rats and mice, the former animals have much larger ampullae and, consequently, much more space for the spermatozoa to occupy.

A special significance of the small number of spermatozoa at the site of fertilization deserves emphasis. The participation of more than one spermatozoon in fertilization (polyspermy) is a pathological occurrence in mammals and almost certainly leads to early death of the embryo (see Section III, I). As eggs themselves have imperfect direct protection against the penetration of more than one spermatozoon, it is important that the chances of fertilization should not surpass a certain upper limit. It is, of course, equally important that they should not fall below a lower limit, if fertility is to be maintained. An essential function of the female genital tract is, therefore, that of controlling the transport of spermatozoa in such a way that the number reaching the site of fertilization lies within these limits.

There is evidence that the meeting between spermatozoa and eggs is not entirely random in some circumstances, and that selective fertilization can occur, eggs of one type being more often involved than those of another (13). Under other circumstances, spermatozoa of certain genotypes are more successful than others at fertilizing eggs; in this instance, selection may in fact have operated by favoring the entry of some spermatozoa rather than others into the fallopian tube (24).

Sea urchin spermatozoa placed in sea water in which eggs have been standing become agglutinated, and this is attributed to an agent called "fertilizin" diffusing from the eggs and reacting with antifertilizin in the spermatozoon. The fertilizin-antifertilizin reaction is believed to have importance in making possible attachment of the spermatozoon to the egg, and in tending to prevent cross-fertilization by spermatozoa of other species through its species specificity (96).

Rabbit, mouse, bull, and human spermatozoa have been found to be agglutinated in the presence of eggs, more especially (with the first three species) when homologous eggs were used. It is suggested that, as in invertebrates, a fertilizin-antifertilizin reaction ensures attachment of the spermatozoon (19).

C. Sperm Penetration through Egg Investments

The eggs arrive in the fallopian tube surrounded by the cumulus oophorus, which consists of a large number of follicle cells embedded in a jellylike matrix composed of a hyaluronic acid-protein complex. Immediately about the egg, the cells are more densely packed and, particularly in dog, cat, and rabbit eggs, this region presents a distinctive appearance and is often termed the "corona radiata." At least some of the coronal cells evidently retain the direct attachment to the egg that they exhibited while in the follicle. In the mare, cow, and ewe, the cumulus breaks down early so that tubal eggs are generally recovered with few or no follicle cells attached.

The spermatozoon has been shown to carry, probably in the acrosome, an enzyme that is capable of depolymerizing the hyaluronic acid-protein matrix of the cumulus oophorus, and which is therefore named "hyaluronidase." The enzyme can easily be extracted from spermatozoa, and when such an extract is added *in vitro* to eggs, with their cumulus masses, the matrix dissolves and the follicle cells fall away. Eggs other than those of the dog, cat, and rabbit are thus stripped of adherent cumulus; in these three species, however, the corona radiata remains intact, although any matrix between the cells has presumably passed into solution.

Observations in the laboratory animals have shown that *in vivo* spermatozoa enter eggs before the cumulus has suffered noticeable disintegration.

It is believed that the spermatozoa, with the aid of hyaluronidase diffusing from reacted acrosomes, individually digest paths for themselves through the matrix of the cumulus and between the coronal cells. The cumulus is broken down later, during the course of fertilization. This appears to be brought about partly by hyaluronidase from spermatozoa at the site of fertilization, partly through an autolytic process, and partly through the action of bicarbonate ions in the secretion of the fallopian tube. Autolysis and bicarbonate ions may be jointly responsible for the early disappearance of the cumulus mass from about the eggs of the horse and the ruminants. In dog and cat eggs, however, the corona persists for much longer, even through early cleavage (see Fig. 3).

Less is known of the means by which the spermatozoon is able to penetrate the zona pellucida. A narrow curved slit that the spermatozoon leaves in the zona after it has passed through has been identified in eggs of the pig (34), sheep (36), rabbit and some rodents; this may mean that the spermatozoon carries an enzyme, provisionally called the "zona lysin," that acts upon the substance of the zona, permitting the spermatozoon to make its way through. Extraction of the lysin from the acrosome of the bull spermatozoon has been claimed (86).

An important function of sperm motility is that it helps to propel the cell through cumulus oophorus and zona pellucida.

D. Cytoplasmic Fusion of Spermatozoon and Egg

Passage through the zona pellucida is rapidly accomplished and the sperm head then projects into the perivitelline space and makes contact with the surface of the vitellus. Contact appears to be followed immediately by attachment and then, after a pause, the head, with tail still attached, is taken into the vitellus. The pause before actual entry into the vitellus was found to be about half an hour in some rodent eggs. For a while after sperm entry, the surface of the vitellus is elevated above the head in a manner that is reminiscent of the fertilization cone of some invertebrate eggs. In the great majority of animals, both vertebrate and invertebrate, the entire sperm tail passes into the vitellus with the head; exceptions among mammals include the field vole and Chinese hamster.

Cytoplasmic fusion between spermatozoon and egg has been extensively investigated in marine invertebrates by electron microscopy. Immediately following contact with the cytoplasmic body of the egg, fusion occurs between the plasma membranes limiting the two cells, so that the cells become effectively enclosed within a single continuum of plasma membrane. The sperm components—nucleus, centrioles, mitochondria, and tail fibers and sheath—pass into the egg cytoplasm, while the sperm plasma membrane is removed, partly by incorporation in the membrane limiting the vitellus and partly by breaking up into a large number of small vesicular structures which become dispersed in the egg cytoplasm. Observations in mammals, as yet limited to the rat, show that basically the same course of events ensues in these animals (71, 89, 92).

In most mammalian eggs the metaphase of the second maturation division is evident at ovulation, and meiosis does not normally continue until a spermatozoon head becomes attached to the surface of the vitellus. Entry of the spermatozoon is therefore accomplished during the early phase of the resumption of meiosis. Sperm penetration in the dog commonly occurs while the egg is still a primary oocyte; the sperm head then lies quiescent in the vitellus, showing little change until emission of the second polar body is completed (98).

E. CORTICAL REACTIONS OF THE EGG

Mention was made earlier of the fact that the significance of the very small numbers of spermatozoa at the site of fertilization was that the chances of polyspermic fertilization were thereby reduced. Complementary to this mechanism is the egg's own defense system, which is vested in two investments, namely, the zona pellucida and the cell membrane. In most mammals, it seems, both structures are capable of undergoing a change after the entry of the first spermatozoon. The alteration in the zona pellucida is termed the "zona reaction" (25) and that in the cell membrane the "block to polyspermy" (though both are, in effect, blocks to polyspermy). Evidence indicates that both are evoked by attachment of the sperm head to the vitelline surface. From the point of attachment of the spermatozoon, the block to polyspermy passes around the surface of the egg as a propagated change. In the sea urchin it takes only about 1 minute for the block to become complete over the whole egg surface—there is, as yet, no known way of determining the corresponding time for mammalian eggs. The zona reaction is thought to be induced by a substance released from the surface of the vitellus (possibly from the cortical granules as they break down—see later) and diffusing across the perivitelline space (9). The release of this agent seems to be propagated over the egg surface like the block to polyspermy, but the zona reaction itself may be comparatively slow, taking, in the rat, something between 10 minutes and 2 hours to reach completion.

Rabbit (and other lagomorph) eggs appear to be unique in that, though they can exhibit a block to polyspermy, they do not seem capable of developing a zona reaction: spermatozoa continue for several hours to pass through the zona and accumulate in the perivitelline space (see Fig. 2a). Spermatozoa that pass through the zona pellucida, but are excluded from the vitellus by the block to polyspermy, are known as "supplementary spermatozoa"; they are not known to have any role in fertilization or in the development of the embryo. Rabbit eggs may occasionally have as many as 200-odd supplementary spermatozoa. Rat and mouse eggs, however, give evidence of the capacity to develop both changes: they often have one or two supplementary spermatozoa, but seldom more. The eggs of several other animals, including the domestic animals, have not been observed with supplementary spermatozoa, although numerous spermatozoa commonly adhere to the outside of the zona pellucida; it is inferred that these eggs have a very rapid zona reaction and that this is mainly responsible for their protection against polyspermy.

A visible change that is contemporaneous with the block to polyspermy and the zona reaction, and which, therefore, may be causally related to one or both these reactions, is the breakdown of certain refractile granules that can be seen just below the surface of the egg. The granules are visible by phase-contrast microscopy in the hamster egg before sperm penetration, but disappear promptly following this event (3). Similar granules have been detected by electron microscopy in the eggs of the rat, mouse, guinea pig, golden hamster, rabbit, coypu (nutria), and pig (88), and stages in their breakdown in the rat egg have been described in detail (91). The material released from the granules may possibly be responsible for the zona reaction.

F. NATURE OF ACTIVATION

Attachment of the sperm head to the surface of the vitellus results in an awakening of the egg from a dormant state, a change that is known as "activation," and the details of its mechanism have been sought for many years. From work on invertebrates it has long been known that many agents of a chemical, physical, or mechanical nature can activate eggs, including heat and cold, acids and alkalis, hypertonic and hypotonic solutions, radiations, alkaloids, fat solvents, mechanical agitation, and electric currents. Activation may also occur apparently spontaneously, without the participation of any identifiable external factor. However, the particular property of the spermatozoon that is responsible for activation remains a mystery. Specific activation (by the spermatozoon) leads normally to pronucleus formation and development. Nonspecific activation (by some other means) is rarely followed by these processes in mammals—when it is, the phenomenon is regarded as the initiation of parthenogenesis (see Section IV, E).

Biochemical changes in activation have been studied intensively for many years in the eggs of marine invertebrates. Current views are that development in the unfertilized egg is blocked because either the ribosomes or the mRNA required for protein synthesis is in an inactive form; activation overcomes this inhibition in some way, possibly through the release of an enzyme (62). Activation also results in an increase in oxygen uptake, at least in the sea urchin egg.

G. PRONUCLEUS GROWTH AND FUNCTION

Soon after the sperm head enters the vitellus, it begins to swell and, by the production of nucleoli and a surrounding nuclear envelope, it is converted into a male pronucleus. Simultaneously, the second polar body is emitted and the group of chromosomes remaining within the vitellus becomes transformed into the female pronucleus. Ultrastructural studies on rat eggs have shown that the sperm head loses its nuclear envelope soon after entry into the egg (*92*). In the rabbit, it has been observed that the group of chromosomes left within the egg after the second meiotic division are at first naked but soon begin to acquire an outline made up of patches of double membrane arising apparently from the endoplasmic reticulum; as pronucleus formation is initiated, the patches extend and join up to constitute the nuclear envelope (*107*). The pronuclei increase progressively

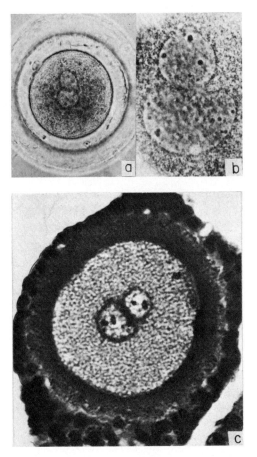

FIG. 2. Pronuclei. (a) and (b): Pronuclei in living rabbit eggs, as seen by phase-contrast microscopy. ×200 and 600, respectively. (c): Pronuclei in a section of a fixed dog egg. ×350. Pig egg pronuclei somewhat resemble rabbit pronuclei in appearance. Fig. 2c by courtesy of E. C. Amoroso.

in volume until they are about 20 times their original size, and move toward each other through the cytoplasm, so that when fully grown they are in close contact (Figs. 2a, b, c). Then, quite suddenly, they diminish in volume and finally fade out altogether, giving place to two chromosome groups. In their turn, these chromosome groups move together and form a single group which represents the prophase of the first cleavage division. The terminal stages, from contact between the pronuclei to union of the two chromosome groups, is known as "syngamy," at the conclusion of which fertilization is complete.

It has been demonstrated that pronuclear function at an early stage includes the synthesis of DNA, which would be required for the doubling of the chromosome complement. Incorporation of amino acid also takes place, both in the pronuclei and in the cytoplasm, which could reflect increased protein turnover, or even net synthesis (59, 90).

H. Time Relations of Fertilization

In the rabbit, spermatozoa reach the site of fertilization 6–7 hours before the eggs, and proceed to penetrate the eggs during 1 or 2 hours after ovulation. Pronuclei are formed about 1.5 hours later, and the first cleavage of the fertilized egg takes place 11–14 hours after ovulation, so that the pronuclear life-span is about 8–10 hours. Approximate data are available for some domestic animals. The more useful figures that have been published so far are as follows: (a) spermatozoon penetration takes place during the course of the second or third day after coitus in the cat (i.e., 1–2 days after ovulation); (b) sperm penetration begins about 3 hours after ovulation in the ewe; (c) pronuclei are formed between 11 and 39 hours after ovulation in the cow, 6 hours or longer after coitus in the pig, and about 3–9 hours after ovulation in the ewe; (d) the fertilized egg undergoes its first cleavage about 24 hours after ovulation in the pony mare, 30 hours after coitus in the goat, 19 to 24 hours after ovulation in the ewe, and between 20 and 50 hours after coitus in the sow (14, 35, 45).

I. Abnormalities of Fertilization

Experience with laboratory animals indicates that, under favorable circumstances, accidents rarely occur in fertilization, in spite of the complexity of the process. Abnormalities are likely to be induced, however, by anything that disturbs the normality of either gamete, such as defective genes, aging of the gametes, elevation of temperature, X-irradiation, and administration of certain toxic substances. The chief irregularities in fertilization that yet permit some degree of embryonic development involve polygyny, polyspermy, gynogenesis, or androgenesis (failure of either sperm nucleus or egg nucleus to develop), "immediate cleavage" (cleavage of the whole egg by the second polar spindle, which may be followed by fertilization of one or both halves), and disturbance of chromosome distribution between egg and second polar body through nondisjunction and chromosome scatter. Of these irregularities, polygyny and polyspermy have proved to be the most common.

Polygyny (also called "digyny"), incomplete maturation of the egg, nearly always takes the form of failure of emission of the second polar body—meiosis proceeds to anaphase or telophase, but both chromosome groups remain within the vitellus. As a result, the fertilized egg will have three sets of chromosomes and the embryo will be triploid.

Polyspermy ensues when two spermatozoa succeed in gaining entrance to an egg and participate in fertilization (70). Since neither the zona reaction nor the block to polyspermy can be instantaneous, such a risk inevitably exists even under normal circumstances. Both fertilizing spermatozoa form pronuclei which later undergo syngamy with the female pronucleus. Polyspermy, like polygyny, thus gives rise to a triploid embryo. Trinucleate, probably polyspermic, eggs have been recovered from cats at an incidence of about 3% (99).

Studies in rat and rabbit showed a high mortality of triploids at midterm (4, 21), and, except for some rather dubious claims for the rabbit and pig, there is as yet no record of the birth and survival to maturity of a pure polyploid mammal (15) (there are reports of the birth of children in whom many tissues were triploid; see, e.g., 22). Triploidy (attributable to polygyny, polyspermy, or both) has an incidence under normal conditions of only 1 or 2%, but can be greatly augmented when fertilization is delayed by late mating or artificial insemination, owing, presumably, to aging of the egg. Frequencies that have been reported for the pig are: 30% (43), 32% (94), and 15% (48), with different periods of delay.

J. Fertilization in Vitro

It has long been an ambition of biologists to find conditions that would permit the fertilization of the mammalian egg to proceed under direct observation in vitro, and numerous claims for success have been made. Few of these are convincing, however, for a variety of reasons, but mainly because of failure to establish satisfactorily the occurrence of spermatozoon penetration into the vitellus and to exclude the possibility of nonspecific activation of the egg (5). The best supported claims are those in which the rabbit and golden hamster have been the experimental animals (31, 106). Both sheep and pig eggs have also been fertilized in vitro, though only at a very low incidence (95). In all the successful experiments, except with hamster eggs, fertilization was obtainable only with uterine spermatozoa, which could be inferred to have undergone some measure of capacitation. Hamster eggs could also be fertilized with epididymal spermatozoa which, evidently, are able to undergo capacitation in vitro under appropriate conditions.

IV. Cleavage

The conclusion of fertilization marks the genesis of the embryo. Initially, the salient feature of embryonic development is a special form of cell division known as "cleavage," during which the protoplasmic mass is progressively divided until it composes a large number of cells and differentiation begins. Cleavage involves no gain and, indeed, some loss of total protoplasmic mass. Subsequently, cell division is associated with increase in total mass, that is to say, with the growth of the embryo.

A. CLEAVAGE MECHANISMS

Fertilization ends with the union of the paternal and maternal chromosome groups. The chromosomes become arranged on the first cleavage spindle and mitosis proceeds through metaphase and anaphase to telophase. The cytoplasm then divides into two, usually slightly unequal, cells called "blastomeres" (Fig. 3a). Cytoplasmic division begins with a dipping-in of the surface which is believed to be attributable, not to a ring of contracting cytoplasm, but to a stiffening and expansion of the general cell surface, possibly induced by the addition of extra material to it (61). Consistently, the egg becomes somewhat elongated before actual cleavage starts. As the cleavage furrow deepens, there is evidence of formation of new cell surface in the deeper regions. The plane of cleavage passes through the centers of the areas that were occupied by the male and female pronuclei at the beginning of syngamy. When cytoplasmic division is complete, the chromosomes resume the extended form, and vesicular nuclei make their appearance (Fig. 3b).

The second cleavage division usually occurs first in the larger blastomere, so that a 3-cell embryo is formed, and then the smaller of the first two blastomeres divides to give a 4-cell embryo. Completion of the third cleavage division in all these four blastomeres yields the 8-cell embryo (Fig. 3c); since divisions are seldom exactly synchronous, however, 5-, 6-, and 7-cell embryos may be seen earlier. After the fourth series of cleavage divisions, the embryo consists of 16 cells, and after the fifth, of 32 cells. Partly because of the restricted space within the zona pellucida and partly because the planes of the spindles of successive cleavage divisions tend to be orientated approximately at right angles to those of the previous divisions, the cells form a compact group known as a "morula" (Figs. 4a, b, and 5a). The constituent cells of the morula are not all equal in size and, in the embryos of the ewe, goat, sow, and cat, the smaller cells are gathered mostly toward one pole and the larger cells toward the other.

Several synthetic processes have been demonstrated to occur during the course of cleavage (59). The incorporation of tritiated thymidine into nuclear DNA has been observed in vitro in the early part of each interphase in the cleaving mouse egg, denoting a synthesis of DNA in chromosome

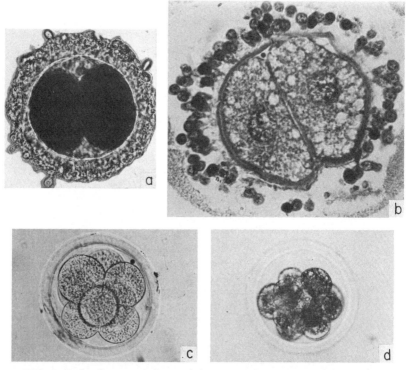

FIG. 3. Early cleavage embryos. (a): Living dog embryo at the 2-cell stage and (b) section of a 2-cell cat embryo, both showing adherent follicle cells. ×225 and 350, respectively. (c): Living 8-cell embryo of sheep and (d): living 8-cell embryo of pig. ×200 and 180, respectively. By courtesy of E. C. Amoroso.

replication. *In vivo*, it is possible that the precursor for nuclear DNA may be provided from stores of DNA which apparently exist in the cytoplasm. However, the cytoplasmic content of RNA appears to be constant up to about the 5-cell stage, despite indications of RNA turnover from the time of fertilization. From about the 5-cell stage, nucleolar synthesis of RNA is greatly augmented and is especially notable in morulae and blastocysts. The cytoplasmic content also rapidly increases. Protein appears to be manufactured before as well as after fertilization and becomes progressively more evident during cleavage. Indications are that protein synthesis up to the second cleavage is mediated by ribosomes of maternal origin, formed during the growth of the ovarian oocyte.

B. EARLY DIFFERENTIATION OF CELL TYPES

The next step is the formation, within the mass of cells, of a small fluid-filled cavity, which is the beginning of the blastocoele; the embryo is now termed a blastocyst (Figs. 5b and c, and 6). The cavity soon enlarges—in the rodents this happens with little or no change in the total volume of the embryo, but in the domestic animals the total volume increases considerably. In the latter group, the blastocyst becomes virtually a bag of fluid within 2 or 3 days. The ungulate blastocyst is a remarkably elongated structure; that of the pig may reach an average length of 112 cm or more, but in the uterus it is closely applied to the complex mucosal folds so that the actual length of uterus occupied is much less (69).

The structural changes involved in blastocyst growth are still incompletely understood and authorities differ in their interpretations. The processes may be said to be concerned with the separation of a group of "embryonic" or "formative" cells from which the fetus itself will develop,

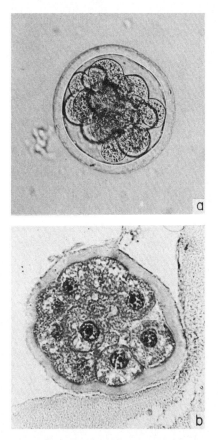

FIG. 4. Morulae. (a): Living sheep morula. ×200. (b): Section of a cat morula, showing the tendency for the smaller cells to gather near one pole and the larger near the other. ×330. By courtesy of E. C. Amoroso.

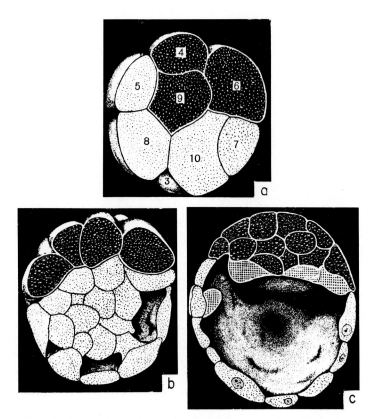

FIG. 5. Blastocyst formation in the goat. Diagrams of sections of goat embryos to illustrate early differentiation of cell types, according to Amoroso *et al.* (2). (a): Morula 98 hours after coitus. (b): Early blastocyst at 134 hours. (c): Blastocyst at 156 hours. Formative cells (white stipple on black); trophoblast cells (stipple); endoderm (crosshatch). (Numbers in (a) were used to identify specific blastomeres.) From Amoroso *et al.* (2).

and of a group of "extraembryonic" cells which later form the fetal membranes, including the fetal placenta.

Ultrastructural studies on blastocysts have been made in several nondomestic mammals (38). It has been found that the formation of a blastocoele coincides with, and may well depend upon, the development of junctional complexes (e.g., desmosomes) near the apical ends of the junctions between cells. Such junctional complexes are present only between trophoblast cells.

In rat embryos, the formative cells, constituting the inner cell mass, are surrounded early by the extraembryonic cells, constituting the trophoblast (32). Later, a layer of cells comes to line the inner surfaces of trophoblast and inner cell mass, and make up the endoderm; these cells are believed to have migrated from the trophoblast.

The changes in the sheep seem to follow similar lines, except that the endoderm is thought to arise by migration or delamination of cells from the inner cell mass (23). In addition, the inner cell mass later becomes intercalated in the trophoblast layer and then projects above this layer as a germinal disc, consisting of embryonic ectoderm.

In the goat, some distinctively large cells at one pole of the morula evidently go to form the embryonic ectoderm, while the trophoblast cells develop separately beneath this group (2). The endoderm is held to arise from trophoblast cells (see Fig. 5). Essentially the same process seems to occur in blastocyst development in the sow (47).

C. CELL LINEAGE

In some invertebrates it is possible to trace back certain of the organ-forming regions to early embryos, even to the undivided egg. Mammalian embryos, however, show evidence of differentiation relatively late, and the blastomeres of the early cleavage stages are each believed to be totipotent, i.e., capable of forming all parts of the body. It has been claimed that the blastomeres of the 2-cell rat embryo can be separated experimentally and that, on transfer to a suitable host, each can develop into an entire animal (66). Normal young rabbits have been born from 2-cell embryos in which one blastomere had been destroyed (80), and apparently normal blastocysts and implanted embryos have developed from 4-cell embryos in which three blastomeres had been destroyed (81). It has also been shown in the mouse that mosaic eggs can develop into single normal embryos—two to several embryos at stages ranging from 2 cell to morula, after removal of the zona pellucida, and on being brought together in vitro, will fuse and reorganize to form a single embryo (60, 93). Mosaic embryos made up from two original individuals have generally been found capable of developing to maturity. Nevertheless, there is evidence of some degree of determination in the early cleavage stages of mammalian embryos: by histochemical methods certain regions of the rat egg during fertilization and of the blastomeres of 2- and 4-cell embryos can be shown to contain material that will later characterize either the trophoblast or the inner cell mass (32). Early recognition of cell types is also reported in the goat (2) (see Fig. 5).

D. RATES OF CLEAVAGE AND VOLUME CHANGES

The rate at which cleavage occurs has been found to vary in a rather unpredictable way among different animals. Here again, the data for domestic animals (Fig. 7) lack precision because they are so often related to the time of coitus rather than to the time of ovulation. In general, the embryos of domestic animals and laboratory rodents cleave at a slower rate

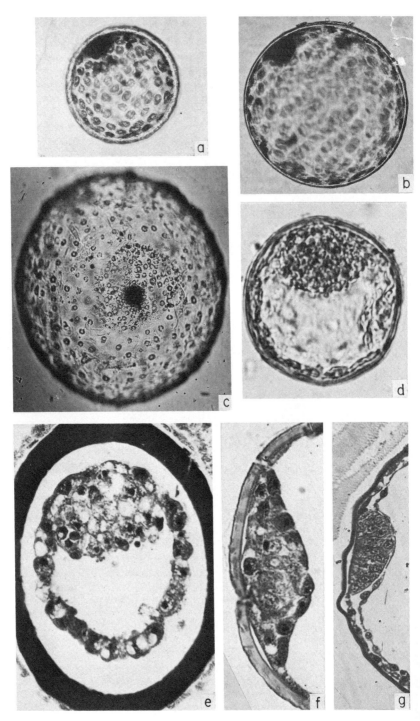

FIG. 6a–c

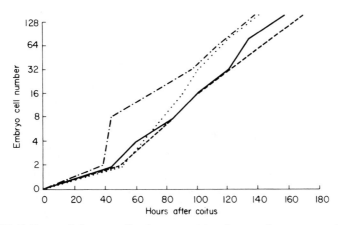

FIG. 7. Rates of cleavage. Graph summarizing data on cleavage rates in some domestic animals: goat (———); cow (- - -); sheep (- • - • -); pig (. . . . .). From Amoroso *et al.* (*2*).

than do those of the rabbit. The rabbit embryo reaches the 16-cell stage in just under 2 days from ovulation, while rat and mouse embryos take 3–4 days and embryos of the larger domestic animals take 3–5 days. The blastocyst stage in the rabbit is reached in 4 days, in the ewe, goat, and sow, in about 6 days, and in the cow, in about 8–9 days.

It has already been noted that the total mass of cytoplasm actually decreases during cleavage. Observations showed that the total volume of the cytoplasm in the 1-cell cow egg is about 900,000 μ^3 compared with a volume of the order of 700,000 μ^3 in the 8-cell embryo: this represents a diminution in cytoplasmic volume of about 20% (*42*). Corresponding figures for the sheep were about 1,000,000 and 600,000 μ^3: a loss of about 40%. In the ferret and mouse there were found to be losses of about 30 and 25%, respectively. The reduction in cytoplasmic volume presumably can partly be ascribed to the utilization of food stores (the yolk or deutoplasm), which initially would take up appreciable space within the cytoplasm.

E. PARTHENOGENESIS

In mammals, mechanisms by which either haploid or diploid parthenogenesis could take place are well recognized, and there are several reports of induced early parthenogenetic development in the eggs of laboratory animals (*15*). However, it is only in the rabbit that induced parthenogenesis

FIG. 6. Blastocysts. (a), (b), and (c): Living dog blastocysts at different stages of expansion (6–7 days after mating). In (a) and (b), the inner cell mass is seen in profile and, in (c), in plane view. ×110. (d): Living cow blastocyst (about 9 days). ×250. (e), (f), and (g): Sections of cat blastocysts (6–8 days), showing segregation of inner cell mass, differentiation of endoderm cells, and intercalation of embryonic ectoderm with trophoblast. ×450, 500, and 280, respectively. By courtesy of E. C. Amoroso.

has as yet been shown to lead to development as far as implantation. Though many investigators have described the apparently spontaneous parthenogenetic development of ovarian and tubal eggs in mammals, it is likely that all or the great majority of these eggs were, in fact, undergoing no more than a degenerative fragmentation. Nevertheless, the possibility does remain that very occasionally a parthenogenetic mammal arises spontaneously and survives to maturity. Such individuals would be difficult to detect, since successful development would probably have been contingent upon regulation to the diploid state.

F. TWINNING

The term "twin" identifies one of a pair of individuals developing in the same pregnancy, in animals that are normally monotocous. Twins may originate from a single fertilized egg, in which case they are termed "monozygotic" or "identical," or from two eggs, when they are known as "dizygotic" or "fraternal." Development from a single egg involves segregation of the cells composing the embryo into two distinct groups, forming two entire embryos. If this happens in the unimplanted blastocyst (as has been recorded in sheep and pigs), two sets of embryonic membranes are developed, but if it occurs at about the stage of gastrulation (as is more common in cattle), the embryonic membranes continue to be shared throughout gestation. Monozygotic twins necessarily have the same genetic constitution and are therefore of the same sex. Dizygotic twins may sometimes share some embryonic membranes, and associated blood supply, if implantation occurs in close spatial relation. Under these circumstances, dizygotic twins may exchange blood-forming elements and continue to have blood with the same antigenic and other properties after birth, but their genetic makeup is different, and they are just as likely to be of different as of the same sex. In cattle, owing to the tendency for fusion between chorion and allantois of dizygotic twins, the union between their blood systems is responsible for the development of freemartins when the embryos are of opposite sex.

V. Maintenance of the Preimplantation Embryo

After fertilization, the embryo passes along the fallopian tube and, in a few days, enters the uterus—this generally occurs when it is a morula or early blastocyst. The nutritive requirements of the embryo are met initially by the yolk material that it carries, by substances in the secretions of the fallopian tube, and later by the products of the uterine mucosa. After implantation, the embryo is maintained principally through the medium of the placenta.

A. Transport of the Embryo

It is likely that early embryos, suspended in tubal fluids, are transported by direct ciliary action and currents produced by cilia, and by contractions of the fallopian tube. The rate of passage varies widely. In the opossum and wallaby, transport is so rapid (less than 24 hours) that eggs still in the pronucleate state of fertilization arrive in the uterus. In most mammals, however, the journey takes 3–5 days, irrespective of the size of the animal and the length of the fallopian tube. Transport is relatively slow in the dog (6–8 days) and cat (5–7 days).

Implantation in the uterus does not take place immediately upon arrival of the embryo; for a period, the blastocyst lies free within the uterine lumen. The interval is normally about 3 days in rodents; for domestic animals, only approximate estimates can be given: mare, about 7 weeks; cow, 20–30 days; ewe, 11–14 days; sow, 4–7 days; bitch and cat, about a week.

While the blastocyst is free in the uterus, it is moved about, presumably by contractions of the uterine walls. This may result in the transference of an embryo to the opposing uterine horn, a shift that is known as "internal migration," and that has been reported to occur in all the domestic animals. In addition, in animals that bear several young in a given pregnancy, the embryos become arranged in such a way that their sites of attachment, whether mesometrial or antimesometrial, are always uniform, and more or less evenly distributed.

B. Transfer, Culture, and Analysis of Embryos

It is known that mammalian eggs and early embryos can tolerate short periods of exposure to experimental conditions outside the body. Transfer from one animal to another has been effected in several different species (including cows, ewes, goats, and sows) with the birth of normal young as the outcome (103). Two-cell sheep embryos have even been transferred to rabbits, have there developed normally to the blastocyst stage and then, on retransfer to a ewe, have continued development for several days (11, 12). Rabbit eggs during fertilization have been found to withstand freezing to −190°C and still to be able subsequently to pass through a few cleavage divisions in culture (84). Eggs have been transferred between cows by a nonsurgical technique involving manipulation through the cervix (78, 87).

Some success has been achieved in the in vitro culture of mammalian embryos (64). Rabbit embryos have developed from early cleavage to well-grown blastocysts in media containing serum and equilibrated with 95% oxygen and 5% carbon dioxide (40). Goat, sheep, and cow eggs have proved more difficult, passing through comparatively few divisions in culture (72, 104). Sheep eggs kept in serum for 48 hours at room temperature were found to be capable of developing for at least 25–30 days on being transferred to recipient ewes (46). Mouse embryos, hitherto considered rather refractory material, have now been cultured from the 2-cell stage to the blastocyst in media made up from crystalline serum albumin, glucose, lactate, and a buffer mixture (102), and similar results have also been achieved with chemically defined media (28). Studies have shown that 2-cell embryos require an energy source which can be lactate, pyruvate, oxalacetate, or phosphoenolpyruvate, but not glucose, fructose, acetate, malate, etc., and that serum albumin can be replaced by its component amino acids. The 8-cell embryo and later embryonic stages, however, can utilize glucose and other energy sources, and do not require an exogenous amino-nitrogen source (29).

Measurements have been made of the oxygen consumption of rat and rabbit embryos, and these suggest that a single embryo utilizes about 0.5–1.0 $m\mu$ liters O_2/hour (1 $m\mu$ liter $= 10^{-6}$ ml) (39, 65). There is evidence that the cytochrome oxidase system is present in these early tissues.

Biochemical studies have been made on the fluid contents of rabbit blastocysts just before and during implantation (days 6 and 7 from coitus), and also on the following day, when implantation is further advanced. The fluid was found to contain very little protein or glucose on day 6, more on day 7, and amounts approaching the serum concentration on day 8. Data showed that these substances had passed to the blastocyst from the maternal bloodstream. Concurrently, the phosphorus content doubled and the chlorides increased about threefold. The concentrations of potassium and especially bicarbonate, however, were distinctly higher on day 6 than on day 7, and fell to maternal serum levels as implantation proceeded. Water-soluble vitamins—thiamine, riboflavin, and, especially, nicotinic acid and vitamin B_{12}—were also present in assayable amounts in the blastocyst fluid (27, 49, 50, 52).

C. Tubal and Uterine Environments

The fallopian tubes are lined with nonciliated, as well as ciliated, columnar cells, the former having a secretory function. The rate of secretion in the tube is highest during estrus, when it amounts to about 0.79 ml in 24 hours in the rabbit, up to 2 ml in the ewe, and perhaps as much as 5 ml in the pig. Identified constituents of the secretion include mucoprotein, glycogen, phospholipid, lactate, and alkaline phosphatase; inorganic ions include mainly sodium, potassium, magnesium, calcium, phosphate, and bicarbonate. Glucose and fructose are not present in significant amounts. The oxygen partial pressure was found to be about 45 mm Hg in the estrous rabbit; this is approximately in equilibrium with the arteriolar supply and is sufficient to maintain an essentially aerobic environment (16–18, 37, 41, 68, 74, 75).

The uterine fluid in early pregnancy (histotroph) is of a distinctive character and is uniquely suited to the nutrition of the embryo. This feature has long been recognized; indeed, the fluid was first termed "uterine milk" nearly 300 years ago. The material is derived from the secretions of cells in the mucous membrane and uterine glands, and contains much cellular debris, leukocytes, and some red cells. It is especially copious in animals with epitheliochorial and syndesmochorial placentae, namely, the mare, cow, ewe, and sow. In these animals, histotroph probably contributes a large proportion of nutrients to the embryo throughout gestation. Its chemical composition varies a little between species, the protein content being higher in the mare (18%) than in the ruminants (10–11%), and the fat content much lower in the mare (0.006%) than in the ruminants (about 1%). It does not contain detectable amounts of glucose, fructose, or glycogen. The cellular debris derived from broken-down mucosal tissue is also of nutritive value; for this purpose, dissolution is unnecessary, as the trophoblast cells are known to be actively phagocytic (1).

REFERENCES

1. Amoroso, E. C., *in* "Marshall's Physiology of Reproduction" (A. S. Parkes, ed.), 3rd ed., Vol. 2, Chapter 15. Longmans, Green, New York, 1952.
2. Amoroso, E. C., Griffiths, W. F. B., and Hamilton, W. J., *J. Anat.* **76**, 377 (1942).
3. Austin, C. R., *Exptl. Cell Res.* **10**, 533 (1956).
4. Austin, C. R., *J. Cellular Comp. Physiol.* **56**, Suppl. 1, 1 (1960).
5. Austin, C. R., *Intern. Rev. Cytol.* **12**, 337 (1961).
6. Austin, C. R., "The Mammalian Egg." Blackwell, Oxford, 1961.
7. Austin, C. R., "Fertilization," Foundations of Developmental Biol. Ser. (C. L. Markert, ed.). Prentice-Hall, Englewood Cliffs, New Jersey, 1965.
8. Austin, C. R., *Intern. J. Fertility* **12**, 25 (1967).
9. Austin, C. R., and Braden, A. W. H., *J. Exptl. Biol.* **33**, 358 (1956).
10. Austin, C. R., and Walton, A., *in* "Marshall's Physiology of Reproduction" (A. S. Parkes, ed.), 3rd ed., Vol. 1, Part 2, Chapter 10. Longmans, Green, New York, 1960.
11. Averill, R. L. W., *Proc. 3rd Intern. Congr. Animal Reprod., Cambridge, Engl.*, Sect. III, 7 (1956).
12. Averill, R. L. W., Adams, C. E., and Rowson, L. E. A., *Nature* **176**, 167 (1955).
13. Bateman, N., *Genet. Res. (Cambridge)* **1**, 226 (1960).
14. Beatty, R. A., *in* "Handbook of Biological Data" (W. S. Spector, ed.), p. 124. Saunders, Philadelphia, Pennsylvania, 1956.
15. Beatty, R. A., "Parthenogenesis and Polyploidy in Mammalian Development." Cambridge Univ. Press, London and New York, 1957.
16. Bishop, D. W., *Am. J. Physiol.* **187**, 347 (1956).
17. Bishop, D. W., *Anat. Record* **125**, 631 (1956).
18. Bishop, D. W., *Proc. 3rd Intern. Congr. Animal Reprod., Cambridge Engl.*, Sect. I, 53 (1956).
19. Bishop, D. W., and Tyler, A., *J. Exptl. Zool.* **132**, 575 (1956).
20. Blandau, R. J., *in* "Sex and Internal Secretions" (W. C. Young, ed.), 3rd ed., Vol. 2, Chapter 14. Baillière, London, 1961.
21. Bomsel-Helmreich, O., *Ciba Found. Symp., Preimplantation Stages Pregnancy*, p. 246. Churchill, London, 1965.

22. Böök, J. A., and Santesson, B., *Lancet* **i**, 858 (1960).
23. Boyd, J. D., and Hamilton, W. J., *in* "Marshall's Physiology of Reproduction" (A. S. Parkes, ed.), 3rd ed., Vol. 2, Chapter 14. Longmans, Green, New York, 1952.
24. Braden, A. W. H., *J. Cellular Comp. Physiol.* **56**, Suppl. 1, 17 (1960).
25. Braden, A. W. H., Austin, C. R., and David, H. A., *Australian J. Biol. Sci.* **7**, 391 (1954).
26. Brambell, F. W. R., *in* "Marshall's Physiology of Reproduction" (A. S. Parkes, eds.), 3rd ed., Vol. 1, Part 1, Chapter 5. Longmans, Green, New York, 1956.
27. Brambell, F. W. R., and Hemmings, W. A., *J. Physiol. (London)* **108**, 177 (1949).
28. Brinster, R. L., *Exptl. Cell Res.* **32**, 205 (1963).
29. Brinster, R. L., *Ciba Found. Symp., Preimplantation Stages Pregnancy*, p. 60. Churchill, London, 1965.
30. Chang, M. C., *J. Exptl. Zool.* **121**, 351 (1952).
31. Chang, M. C., *Nature* **184**, 467 (1959).
32. Dalcq, A. M., *Proc. Soc. Study Fertility* **7**, 113 (1955).
33. Dawson, A. B., and Friedgood, H. B., *Anat. Record* **76**, 411 (1940).
34. Dickmann, Z., and Dziuk, P. J., *J. Exptl. Biol.* **41**, 603 (1964).
34a. Doak, R. H., Hall, E., and Dale, H. E., *J. Reprod. Fertility* **13**, 51 (1967).
35. Dziuk, P. J., *Anat. Record* **153**, 211 (1965).
36. Dziuk, P. J., and Dickmann, Z., *J. Exptl. Zool.* **158**, 237 (1965).
37. Edgerton, L. A., Martin, C. E., Troutt, H. F., and Foley, C. W., *J. Animal Sci.* **25**, 1265 (1966).
38. Enders, A. C., and Schlafke, S. J., *Ciba Found. Symp., Preimplantation Stages of Pregnancy*, p. 29. Churchill, London, 1965.
39. Fridhandler, L., Hafez, E. S. E., and Pincus, G., *Proc. 3rd Intern. Congr. Animal Reprod., Cambridge, Engl., Sect. I*, 48 (1956).
40. Glenister, T. W., *in* "Delayed Implantation" (A. C. Enders, ed.), Rice Univ. Semicentennial Publ., Univ. of Chicago Press, Chicago, Illinois, 1963.
41. Hadek, R., *Anat. Record* **121**, 187 (1955).
42. Hamilton, W. J., and Laing, J. A., *J. Anat.* **80**, 194 (1946).
43. Hancock, J. L., *Animal Prod.* **1**, 103 (1959).
44. Hancock, J. L., *J. Reprod. Fertility* **2**, 307 (1961).
45. Hancock, J. L., *Animal Breeding Abstr.* **30**, 285 (1962).
46. Hancock, J. L., *Animal Prod.* **5**, 237 (1963).
47. Heuser, C. H., and Streeter, G. L., *Carnegie Inst. Wash. Contribs. Embryol.* No. 109 **20**, 1 (1929).
48. Hunter, R. H. F., *J. Reprod. Fertility* **13**, 133 (1967).
49. Jacobson, W., and Lutwak-Mann, C., *J. Endocrinol.* **14**, xix (1956).
50. Kodicek, E., and Lutwak-Mann, C., *J. Endocrinol.* **15**, liii (1957).
51. Liche, H., *Nature* **143**, 900 (1939).
52. Lutwak-Mann, C., *J. Embryol. Exptl. Morphol.* **2**, 1 (1954).
53. McLaren, A., *in* "Reproduction in Farm Animals" (E. S. E. Hafez, ed.), Chapter 7. Bailliere, London, 1962.
54. Mann, T., "The Biochemistry of Semen." Wiley, New York, 1964.
55. Mann, T., Polge, C., and Rowson, L. E. A., *J. Endocrinol.* **13**, 133 (1956).
56. Mattner, P. E., *Nature* **199**, 772 (1963).

57. Mattner, P. E., and Braden, A. W. H., *Australian J. Biol. Sci.* **16**, 473 (1963).
58. Millar, R., *Australian Vet. J.* **28**, 127 (1952).
59. Mintz, B., *Ciba Found. Symp., Preimplantation Stages Pregnancy,* p. 145. Churchill, London, 1965.
60. Mintz, B., *Ciba Found. Symp., Preimplantation Stages Pregnancy,* p. 194. Churchill, London, 1965.
61. Mitchison, J. M., *Symp. Soc. Exptl. Biol.* **6**, 105 (1952).
62. Monroy, A., "Chemistry and Physiology of Fertilization," Biol. Studies Ser. Holt, New York, 1965.
63. Nalbandov, A. V., "Reproductive Physiology: Comparative Reproductive Physiology of Domestic Animals, Laboratory Animals and Man." Freeman, San Francisco, California, 1964.
64. New, D. A. T., "The Culture of Vertebrate Embryos." Logos Press, London (distributed by Academic Press, New York), 1966.
65. Nicholas, J. S., *Quart. Rev. Biol.* **22**, 179 (1947).
66. Nicholas, J. S., and Hall, B. V., *J. Exptl. Zool.* **90**, 441 (1942).
67. Parkes, A. S., *in* "Marshall's Physiology of Reproduction" (A. S. Parkes, ed.), 3rd ed., Vol. 1, Part 2, Chapter 9. Longmans, Green, New York, 1960.
68. Perkins, J. L., and Goode, L., *J. Animal Sci.* **25**, 465 (1966).
69. Perry, J. S., and Rowlands, I. W., *J. Reprod. Fertility* **4**, 175 (1962).
70. Pikó, L., *Ann. Biol. Animale Biochim. Biophys.* **1**, 323 (1961).
71. Pikó, L., and Tyler, A., *Proc. 5th Intern. Congr. Animal Reprod. Artificial Insemination, Trento* **2**, 372 (1964).
72. Pincus, G., *Proc. 1st Natl. Egg-Transfer Breeding Conf., Texas* p. 18 (1951).
73. Polge, C., and Dziuk, P., *J. Reprod. Fertility* **9**, 357 (1965).
74. Restall, B. J., *Australian J. Biol. Sci.* **19**, 181 and 187 (1966).
75. Restall, B. J., and Wales, R. G., *Australian J. Biol. Sci.* **19**, 687 (1966).
76. Rothschild (Lord), "Fertilization." Methuen, London, 1956.
77. Rowson, L. E. A., *Brit. Vet. J.* **3**, 334 (1955).
78. Rowson, L. E. A., and Moor, R. M., *J. Reprod. Fertility* **11**, 207 (1966).
79. Salisbury, G. W., and Vandemark, N. L., "Physiology of Reproduction and Artificial Insemination of Cattle." Freeman, San Francisco, California, 1961.
80. Seidel, F., *Naturwissenschaften* **39**, 355 (1952).
81. Seidel, F., *Naturwissenschaften* **43**, 306 (1956).
82. Sherman, J. K., and Lin, T. P., *Proc. Soc. Exptl. Biol. Med.* **98**, 902 (1958).
83. Sherman, J. K., and Lin, T. P., *Fertility Sterility* **10**, 384 (1959).
84. Smith, A. U., *Nature* **170**, 374 (1952).
85. Spalding, J. F., Berry, R. O., and Moffit, J. G., *J. Animal Sci.* **14**, 609 (1955).
86. Srivastava, P. N., Adams, C. E., and Hartree, E. F., *Nature* **205**, 498 (1965).
87. Sugie, T., *J. Reprod. Fertility* **10**, 197 (1965).
88. Szollosi, D., *J. Reprod. Fertility* **4**, 223 (1962).
89. Szollosi, D., *J. Exptl. Zool.* **159**, 367 (1965).
90. Szollosi, D., *Anat. Record* **154**, 209 (1966).
91. Szollosi, D., *Anat. Record* **159**, 431 (1967).
92. Szollosi, D., and Ris, H., *J. Biophys. Biochem. Cytol.* **10**, 275 (1961).
93. Tarkowski, A. K., *Ciba Found. Symp., Preimplantation Stages Pregnancy,* p. 183. Churchill, London, 1965.

94. Thibault, C., *Ann. Zootech.* **8**, Suppl., 165 (1959).
95. Thibault, C., and Dauzier, L., *Ann. Biol. Animale Biochim. Biophys.* **1**, 277 (1961).
96. Tyler, A., *Physiol. Rev.* **28**, 180 (1948).
97. Vandemark, N. L., and Moeller, A. N., *Am. J. Physiol.* **165**, 674 (1951).
98. Van der Stricht, O., *Arch. Biol.* (*Liege*) **33**, 229 (1923).
99. Van der Stricht, R., *Arch. Biol.* (*Liege*) **26**, 365 (1911).
100. Walton, A., *in* "Marshall's Physiology of Reproduction" (A. S. Parkes, ed.), 3rd ed., Vol. 1, Part 2, Chapter 8. Longmans, Green, New York, 1960.
101. Warbritton, V., McKenzie, F. F., Berliner, V., and Andrews, F. N., *Proc. Am. Soc. Animal Prod.* **30**, 142 (1937).
102. Whitten, W. K., *Nature* **179**, 1081 (1957).
103. Willett, E. L., *Iowa State Coll. J. Sci.* **28**, 83 (1953).
104. Wintenberger, S., Dauzier, L., and Thibault, C., *Compt. Rend. Soc. Biol.* **147**, 1971 (1953).
105. Wotton, R. M., and Village, P. A., *Anat. Record* **110**, 121 (1951).
106. Yanagimachi, R., and Chang, M. C., *Nature* **200**, 281 (1963).
107. Zamboni, L., and Mastroianni, Jr., L., *J. Ultrastruct. Res.* **14**, 95 and 118 (1966).

14 IMPLANTATION, DEVELOPMENT OF THE FETUS, AND FETAL MEMBRANES

W. A. KELLY AND P. ECKSTEIN

I. Introduction

The first object of the following account is to describe the processes of implantation, placentation, and early development in domestic mammals as concisely as is consistent with adequate coverage and accuracy, and the second, to center attention, wherever possible, on the "growing points" and more recent advances in these topics.

With these aims in mind, no attempt is made to review the intricacies, either morphological or functional, of the placenta, except where, as in the case of the ultrastructure of the fetomaternal barrier, this contributes to better understanding. For information on comparative anatomical, specific embryological, and more general physiological aspects of the subject reference is made to the many excellent and comprehensive accounts available in the literature, especially, the following: Amoroso (4), Boyd and Hamilton (19), Nalbandov (71), and Robinson (81).

The chapter is confined to the situation in the common domestic animals, that is, the sheep and cow (among ruminants), the mare and pig (nonruminant ungulates), and the bitch and cat (carnivores), but does not deal, or only marginally so, with other representatives of these orders.

II. Anatomy of the Uterus

The anatomical features of the female reproductive organs in domestic animals have been repeatedly described [e.g., Sisson (87), Eckstein and Zuckerman (35), Nalbandov (71)]. A diagrammatic comparison of the reproductive tract is shown in Fig. 1.

The uterus is bicornuate and communicates with the exterior through a single cervix and vagina. The two uterine horns show, however, some degree of external as well as internal fusion, which leads to the formation of a common uterine cavity of variable dimensions and shape. In ruminants and carnivores, in spite of considerable external fusion, this common cavity is minute, the two uteri remaining separated by a thin median septum which nearly reaches the cranial end (or internal os) of the cervical canal (see cow, bitch, in Fig. 1). In the sow this septum is shorter, with a con-

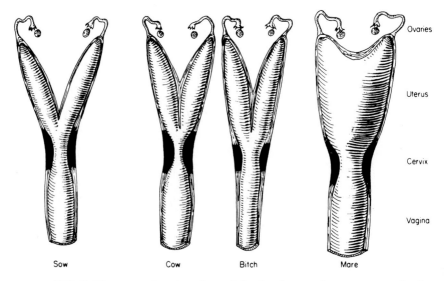

Sow   Cow   Bitch   Mare

Ovaries — Uterus — Cervix — Vagina

FIG. 1. Diagrammatic comparison of the female reproductive tract in the domestic animals. After Nalbandov (71).

sequent increase in the size of the common cavity, in spite of marked external separation of the horns. In the mare there is no trace of a midline septum, and the size of the internal cavity corresponds to the externally fused part of the uterus and forms a distinct single "body," except at its upper, paired extremities.

The cervix is a conspicuous segment in all the domestic animals, except carnivores. In ruminants it is provided with a series of hard, conical ridges or annular rings. These are less prominent in the sow and least developed or absent in the mare, bitch, and cat.

III. Implantation

A. TUBAL PASSAGE AND ATTACHMENT OF OVA

After fertilization (see Chapter 13), the cleaving ova pass through the fallopian tube into the uterus and, after a variable period of "free life" in its lumen, begin to adhere to the endometrium. This is followed by firm attachment, or implantation, and formation of a placental connection from the fusion of fetal and maternal tissues.

During this phase the developing conceptus is nourished, first by its own yolk substance and the tubal fluids, and then by the secretions of the uterine glands, the so-called uterine milk (see p. 404). Once formed, the placenta becomes chiefly responsible for maintenance and growth of the embryo.

In all the domestic animals the blastocyst remains within the uterine cavity and expands to fill its lumen; this is referred to as "central implantation." In other types of mammals implantation may be eccentric or interstitial (cf. 19).

1. Tubal Passage

Tubal passage of the ova in the domestic animals is relatively constant, as in other mammals, and generally lasts about 3–4 days (10, 19). The sow, however, appears to be an exception insofar as recent studies (78) show that in this animal the ova enter the uterus between 24 and 48 hours after ovulation, and not 72 hours, as was believed by earlier workers (26). The rapidity of tubal passage in the pig may be connected with the occurrence of multiple ovulation. It does not seem to be due to an excessive concentration of progesterone since its level in the blood at the time of ovulation is almost undetectable (39, 64). When superovulation is induced with gonadotropin, for instance, in the cow and ewe, ovum transport may be greatly accelerated and fertilization impaired (80).

2. Spacing and Attachment of Eggs

On arriving in the uterus, the eggs of domestic animals are distributed through the two horns. In the ewe and cow, in which usually only one egg is shed, it becomes attached in the distal part of the horn adjacent to the ovulating ovary, but in the mare it frequently moves to the opposite horn. When two eggs are released from a single ovary in the sheep, one generally migrates and attaches in the contralateral horn (19). In the polytocous sow, the eggs are evenly spaced between the two uterine horns (26). The mechanisms concerned in the spacing of blastocysts have been reviewed by Böving (18).

3. Timing of Ovum Implantation

Unlike nidation in higher mammals, attachment of the blastocyst in the farm animals is a relatively slow and gradual process, the precise timing of which in certain species (e.g., cow and ewe) is still in dispute; for detailed reviews the reader is referred to Boyd and Hamilton (19) and Robinson (81). Most of the reported discrepancies are due to differences of opinion, among observers, on what constitutes implantation, and some to lack of uniformity in relating implantation to either ovulation or estrus.

There are also marked species differences in the time of implantation, as exemplified by the pig and horse. In both, the placenta is of the non-cotyledonary, epitheliochorial variety (see Section V), but while attachment in the sow occurs on about the 11th day after ovulation (42), it does so in the mare toward the end of the seventh week and is probably not complete until the tenth week (4).

In the ewe the time of implantation is given variably as either day 11 or 17–20 days postcoitus, and in the cow as between the end of the second and fifth week of gestation (22, 31, 81). In the bitch and cat it is thought to occur between 2 and 3 weeks after mating (4).

In some close relatives of the domesticated animals nidation is constantly and markedly delayed. For instance, in roe deer among ruminants the "free vesicle" stage lasts for about 5 months (86) and in the badger, a carnivore, nearly a year (36).

B. Uterine Adaptations for Nidation

In view of the difficulty of determining the exact time of implantation in most domestic animals, it is impossible to distinguish preimplantation from postimplantation changes in the uterus. All the species considered here, except the cat, ovulate spontaneously and therefore develop functional corpora lutea during their unmated cycles. Hence, the changes in the uterus in the early stages of pregnancy are those of the luteal phase of the estrous cycle, namely, an increase in the vascularity of the endometrium and an increase in glandular growth and activity.

In the horse, pig, cow, and sheep the outer layer of the blastocyst, or trophoblast, is not very invasive and there is no pronounced decidual reaction in these species comparable to that found in rodents. In the carnivora in which the trophoblast penetrates the maternal tissue there is a decidual reaction.

The endometrial cups of the horse, which arise as modifications of the endometrium of the fertile horn, may be considered as a form of decidual reaction, since they contain enlarged stromal cells and form in response to the trophoblast.

The cups number about a dozen and are usually present from the sixth to the 40th week of pregnancy. They are distributed in roughly circular fashion around the attachment of the yolk sac (Fig. 2; also Fig. 6). The uterine glands opening into the depth of a cup pour their secretions into the space between it and the avillous chorion; the secretion is rich in the gonadotropic principle which characterizes the serum of the pregnant mare (PMS) between the second and fifth months of gestation (24, 25; see also Chapter 15). Interestingly, endometrial cups are formed both in the donkey and in the mare carrying a mule fetus, but the gonadotropin levels are very low, or undetectable by less sensitive tests, findings which suggest that the fetal allantochorion induces formation of the cups and PMS secretion (12, 85). Cups are also present in the zebra.

In ruminants growth of placental tissue only occurs in relation to specialized areas of the endometrium (cotyledons or caruncles; see p. 397, later). Uterine changes during pregnancy consist mainly of a pronounced increase in the vascularity of the cotyledons; in the intercotyledonary areas they are confined to the uterine glands. In the bitch and cat, too, there is a progressive development of the uterine glands and crypts and the endometrium becomes hyperemic.

C. Ovum Transfer and Luteolysin

Recent research, in both rodents and ruminants, has transformed previous views about the factors involved in the experimental transplantation of embryos and the rôle of the luteolytic principle in controlling activity of the corpus luteum.

It is now clear that successful ovum transfer in mammals depends on perfect correspondence between the age of the transplanted blastocyst and that of the recipient endometrium. This was first shown by Noyes et al. (72) in the rat, and has since been demonstrated also in the sheep by Rowson and Moor (83). For instance, when there was exact synchrony of donor and recipient, 75% of the recipient ewes became pregnant; when the donor and recipient differed by ±3 days, only 8% conceived.

The remarkable studies of Kirby in mice have established two further points: (1) the uterus is not necessarily an ideal environment for implantation and embryonic development, as shown by the successful "taking" and growth of mouse trophoblastic tissue in a variety of extrauterine sites (54), and (2) uterine factors are involved in this mechanism. For instance, if cleaving mouse eggs were obtained directly from the tube without having

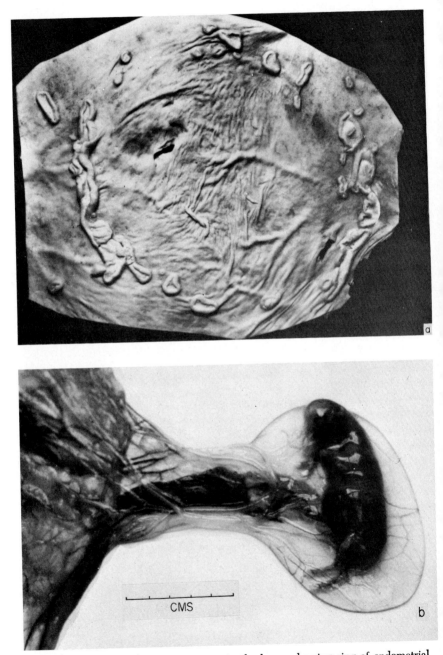

CMS

FIG. 2. (a) Fetal aspect of uterus in the horse, showing ring of endometrial cups around attachment of body stalk and yolk sac (see also Fig. 6). Mare about

passed through the uterus, they would only produce trophoblast and extra-embryonic membranes in extrauterine sites. If, however, uterine blastocysts were transplanted to such sites they would develop into embryos. This has not yet been shown in the case of ruminant blastocysts.

The existence of a luteolytic factor has, however, been convincingly demonstrated in several species of domestic animals such as the pig, sheep, and cow (9, 84). This factor is believed to be elaborated within the uterus and to be responsible for terminating the functional life of the corpus luteum of the cycle (16). Its preservation and conversion into the corpus luteum of pregnancy in sheep has recently been ascribed by Moor and Rowson (66, 67) to an active influence exerted by the early embryo. By means of ingenious experiments these authors established that removal of the sheep embryo before the 12th day of gestation leads to regression of the corpus luteum at the time usual for the cycle, the ewe remaining effectively unaware of having conceived. Alternatively, transfer of a 12- to 13-day-old embryo into a nonpregnant sheep causes the corpus luteum to be maintained and to be converted from the cyclic type to that of gestation. Moor and Rowson (67) believe that the embryo, in spite of being extremely young, and even before its attachment to the endometrium, exerts an active "antiluteolytic" effect and prevents regression of the corpus luteum normally brought about by the uterine lytic factor.

D. Nature and Origin of the Extraembryonic Membranes

The extraembryonic, or fetal, membranes are developed from the zygote, but form no part of the embryo itself. They protect and serve in nourishing the embryo, and are shed at birth. There are four: the amnion, chorion, yolk sac, and allantois, as in reptiles, birds, and mammals, generally; placentation has, therefore, not led to the evolution of any extraembryonic structures not already present in egg-laying vertebrates such as the hen. The process of formation of the extraembryonic membranes in the domestic animals is illustrated in Figs. 3–6.*

1. Amnion

The amnion of ungulates and carnivores is formed by folding, as in the chick. Circumferential folds of extraembryonic ectoderm and somatic mesoderm grow up around the embryo and then meet dorsally to enclose it completely in a fluid-filled amniotic sac, lined by ectoderm (Figs. 3–5). The

* The extraembryonic membranes are generally shown as single lines in these drawings, and, therefore, do not illustrate the basically bilaminar (i.e., ectodermal or endodermal plus mesodermal) nature of these structures.

8 weeks' pregnant; all fetal structures stripped off. Note variable size of cups. Photo provided by Dr. I. W. Rowlands. (b) Horse fetus within membranes at the same stage. Note prominent yolk sac. Photo provided by Dr. R. V. Short.

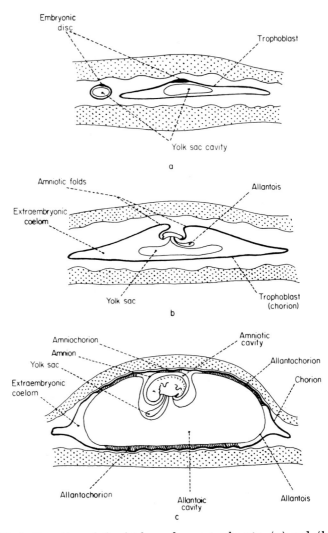

FIG. 3. Formation of the fetal membranes in the pig. (a) and (b): free-vesicle stage; (c): after attachment to the uterus. Based on Mossman (70) and Patten (77).

amnion provides the aqueous medium which supports the soft embryonic tissues.

2. Chorion

This constitutes the outermost of the extraembryonic folds. It is derived from the outer wall of the blastocyst, or trophoblast, and the term "chorion"

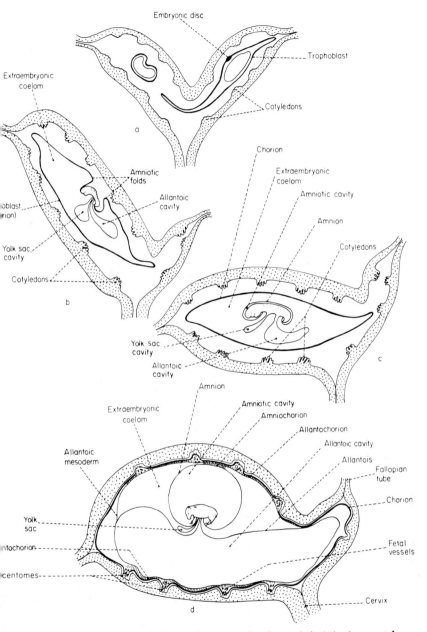

FIG. 4. Formation of the fetal membranes in the sheep. (a)–(c): free-vesicle stage; (d): after attachment to the uterus. Based on Mossman (70) and Boyd and Hamilton (19).

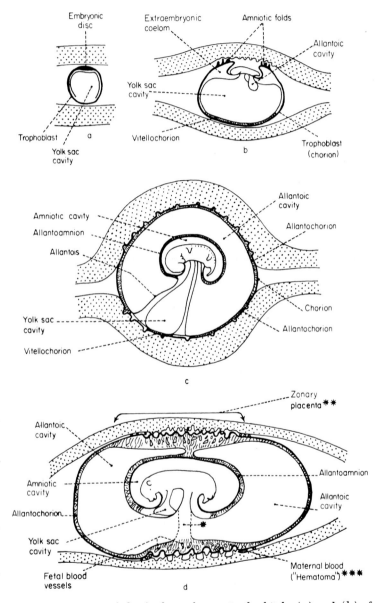

FIG. 5. Formation of the fetal membranes in the bitch. (a) and (b): free-vesicle stage; (c): after attachment to the uterus; (d): after formation of zonary placenta. (*) Course of allantoic vessels. (**) See Fig. 10a. (***) See text, Section VI, A. Based on Hamilton *et al.* (45).

is applied to it after the amnion has formed (see, e.g., Figs. 3 and 4). The ectoderm of the chorion is continuous with that of the embryo, and becomes lined with somatic ("somatopleuric") mesoderm.

Both the amnion and chorion originate from ectoderm and somato-pleuric mesoderm and are, therefore, nonvascular. The yolk sac and allantois, by contrast, develop from endoderm and splanchnopleuric (vascular) mesoderm, and are, thus, potentially capable of forming functional placentas after establishing contact with the uterus.

3. Yolk Sac

The yolk sac is formed from extraembryonic endoderm spreading over the inner surface of the trophoblast in the midgut region. The bilaminar structure becomes the trilaminar yolk sac by the insinuation of splanchnic mesoderm between the trophoblast and endoderm; when vascularized, it constitutes the vitellochorion (Fig. 5b,c).

4. Allantois

This forms as an outgrowth of the hindgut. It is covered by splanchnic mesoderm in which the allantoic vessels develop.

The allantois is particularly well developed in ungulates, but there is great variation in the relative size, degree of fusion, function, and persistence of all the extraembryonic membranes.

To establish an organ of interchange between mother and fetus, the outer chorion must be vascularized by an extraembryonic circulatory system. This may be provided by either the yolk sac vessels or the allantoic

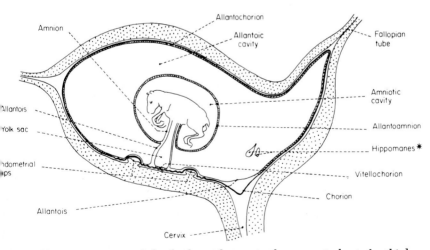

FIG. 6. Appearance of the fetal membranes in the mare at about the third month of gestation. Modified from Mossman (70) and Amoroso (4). (See also Fig. 2b.) (*) For the nature and mode of formation of hippomanes see Dickerson et al. (34).

ones. If it is vascularized by the vitelline vessels, a *vitellochorion* and, after contact with the endometrium, a yolk-sac type of placenta results. Alternatively, if vascularization is by the allantoic vessels, an *allantochorion* and, consequently, an allantochorial placenta is formed.

In eutherian mammals the allantochorial placenta is the chief form of placentation and the yolk sac placenta is usually only transitory. A true yolk-sac type of placenta only develops in the mare and carnivores (see Figs. 2b, 5c, and 6). In the pig and ruminants the yolk sac does not make close contact with the maternal tissues (see Figs. 3 and 4), but is believed to play a part in the nutrition of the early embryo by absorbing "uterine milk" (see Section VI, A).

The extraembryonic membranes develop with great rapidity during the first half of pregnancy. In the pig they grow faster than the fetus up to about day 65, but from then on their development falls behind that of the fetus (79). The allantoic fluid increases rapidly to a maximum from the third to the ninth week and then decreases as swiftly. According to Mc-Cance and Dickerson (62), the initial source of the fluid is the secretory activity of the allantois itself, and the fetal kidney only begins to contribute to it in later stages of pregnancy (1).

In the sheep it is believed that expansion of the allantois and the accumulation of fluid within it can be related to the activity of the fetal mesonephros as early as day 18 of gestation (30).

Fetal urine passes into the allantoic sac via the urachus until about the end of the third month. Subsequently, it drains increasingly into the amniotic sac, presumably because of occlusion of the urachus and greater patency of the urethra (2).

IV. Growth of the Conceptus and Formation of the Placenta

Among the domestic animals, early development of the conceptus is best known in the sheep and pig.

In the sheep, the blastocyst enters the uterus when it is in the 16- to 32-cell stage (41) toward the third day after fertilization. The zona pellucida is generally shed by the seventh to eighth day (41, 82), and attachment of the blastocyst is believed to be brought about by loose "surface-to-surface contact" (41). During this phase the conceptus elongates and grows with astonishing speed. Rowson and Moor (82) state that from the 12th day postestrus (or some 11 days after ovulation and fertilization) it changes within 24 hours from a blastocyst about 1 mm in diameter to an elongated chorionic sac with a mean length of 11.7 mm and has reached a length of over 100 mm on day 14 (Figs. 7, 8; see also Fig. 10b). The embryonic disc itself, however, grows only slightly during the same time. Between days 15 and 17 postcoitus the speed of growth of the conceptus increases even more (17, cf. 48).

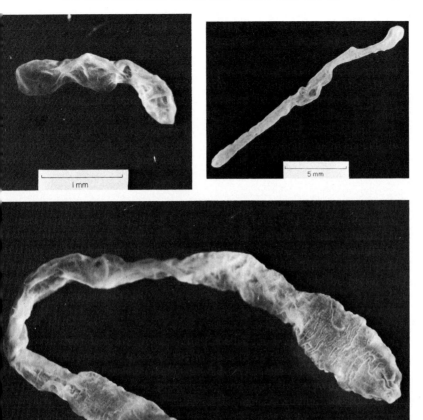

FIG. 7. Growth of the blastodermic vesicle of the sheep: (above) at the beginning of elongation, day 12 after estrus; (below) day 14 after estrus (total length 112 mm). Reproduced from Rowson and Moor (82).

Recent research has shown that the sheep conceptus, apart from its phenomenally fast rate of growth, begins to exert, as mentioned, a hormonal influence upon the corpus luteum and, after the 12th day postcoitus, to be responsible for its conversion into the corpus luteum of pregnancy (66, 67; see also p. 391).

Structure and Function of the Placentomes. The placenta in ruminants is cotyledonary or multiplex, that is, it is formed by the fusion of rounded projections of the uterine mucosa, the so-called caruncles or maternal cotyledons, with corresponding localized tufts of chorionic villi, the fetal

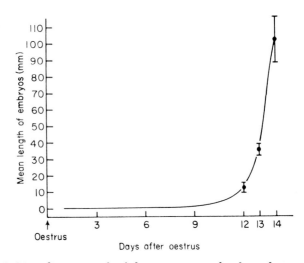

FIG. 8. Mean linear growth of the conceptus in the sheep during the first 14 days. Reproduced from Rowson and Moor (82).

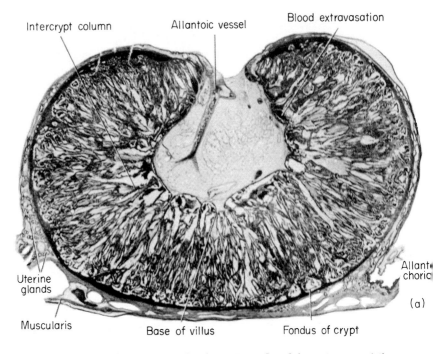

FIG. 9a. Placentome in the sheep. Reproduced from Amoroso (4).

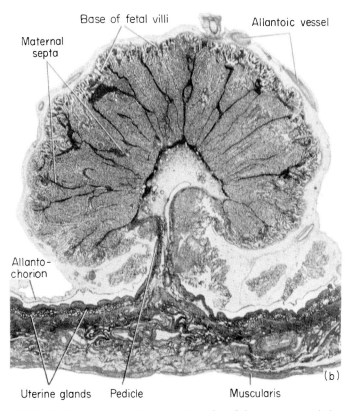

Base of fetal villi

Allantoic vessel

Maternal septa

Allanto-chorion

Uterine glands   Pedicle   Muscularis

(b)

FIG. 9b. Placentome in the cow. Reproduced from Amoroso (4).

caruncles, to form functional units known as "placentomes" (4, cf. 17). In the sheep the fetal caruncles appear on about the 22nd day, when fusion of the mesoderm surrounding the rapidly expanding allantois with that of the chorionic sac is complete (31). The wall of the chorionic vesicle begins to adhere to and eventually fuse with the maternal cotyledons, in this way forming placentomes. The maternal aspect of the placentome is concave in the ewe and convex in the cow (Fig. 9). The intercotyledonary or membranous portion of the chorion takes no part in the formation of placentomes.

During the process of formation of placentomes the uterine epithelium may disappear more or less completely, probably through cytolytic activity of the chorionic giant cells (31), and thus leave the chorionic epithelium in contact with the connective tissue of the uterus. Later, elongated slender chorionic villi, some 10 mm in length, develop and become attached to pits or "crypts" within the endometrial stroma. The placentomes of the sheep increase in size and number until there are 90–100 on about the 90th day, after which they begin to diminish in size and probably number. According to Hammond (46), development of the placentomes in the cow is not complete until the third or fourth month of pregnancy.

In the pig, early development and attachment of the ovum resemble those in the ewe and cow (26, 27, 42, 48). The relations between the fetal and maternal tissues remain very simple. No caruncles, and, hence, no placentomes, are present as in ruminants, and the pregnant uterine mucosa retains much the same structure as during the estrous cycle. The mouths of the endometrial glands are covered by minute circular collections, or domes, of trophoblastic cells, the so-called areolae, which are thought to be involved in absorption of uterine milk (see Fig. 10c). The chorion, with the allantois closely applied to its inner surface (see Fig. 3c), is in loose contact with the uterine epithelium. It can be easily detached throughout gestation by gentle traction, and at parturition the fetal membranes separate from the uterine tissues without lesion or hemorrhage, leaving behind an intact surface. Early, the uterine mucosa is smooth, but after about the second week, the epithelium becomes pitted. At the same time the chorion develops corresponding vascular folds or ridges [though not true villi (4)], which fit into the depressions of the mucosa and promote attachment and functional contact. The primitive yolk sac forms the first placental connection with the maternal tissues in the pig. It is quickly superseded by the vascular allantois, which expands rapidly after the third week and fuses with the chorion. Eventually, the extremities of the allantochorion become constricted into atrophic tips (Fig. 10c).

Throughout this early phase of development, the elongated and wrinkled chorionic vesicle grows with extreme rapidity. According to Corner (26), it measures 10–12 mm by 3 mm on the 12th day after ovulation, but 20–30 cm around the 14th day, and the contained embryo has 1–5 somites. By the 17th–18th day the uterine cavity is completely filled with embryonic vesicles measuring 30–40 cm.

There does not seem to be any pertinent information on growth of the conceptus in the mare and carnivores (cf. 4). Some data on fetal growth in the horse will be referred to later (p. 407).

It is generally recognized that the time around implantation represents one of the most critical stages of gestation. For instance, in the pig the bulk of prenatal mortality, estimated variously at between 30 and 40% (27, 79), is believed to have occurred by the end of the third week of pregnancy (79).

V. The Placenta and Ultrastructure of the Fetomaternal Junction

The basis and purpose of placentation is the transfer of nutritive material and oxygen from the mother to the fetus and, reciprocally, that of excretory products and carbon dioxide in the opposite direction.

All types of placenta comprise a maternal element, the uterus, and on the fetal side, the chorion. Hence, most simply defined, placentation means

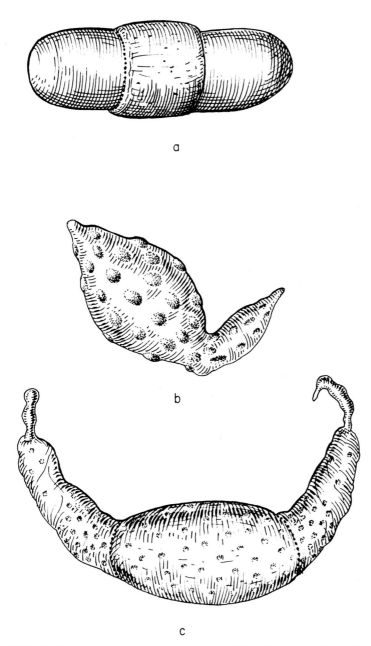

FIG. 10. Diagrammatic representation of the blastodermic vesicle. (a): carnivore (zonary placenta); (b): ruminant (cotyledonary placenta); (c): pig (diffuse placenta; note "areolae").

the more or less intimate fusion of the chorion with the endometrium to facilitate nutritive and gaseous exchange.

The definitive placenta of the domestic animals, like that of all higher mammals, is of the chorioallantoic type, that is, it is formed by the fusion of portions of the allantois with the adjacent parts of the chorion. Of the several ways of classifying the mammalian placenta, for instance, by its gross shape, structure or the distribution of chorionic villi (see Fig. 10), the one which has found the greatest measure of acceptance is that of Grosser (43, 44) which is based on the number of tissue layers separating the maternal and fetal circulations. Grosser recognized four principal types, the "epi-thelio-chorial," "syndesmo-chorial," "endothelio-chorial," and "haemo-chorial," and assigned the placenta of the mare and pig to the first, that of ruminants to the second, and that of the bitch and cat to the third (see Table I).

This relatively simple subdivision has been of great practical value and has enjoyed corresponding popularity. It is, however, now being increas-ingly recognized that Grosser's histological classification cannot be equated with physiological efficiency. Clearly, the nature and precise structure of the tissue intervening between the two circulations are critical in this context and call for investigation by electron microscopy. The results of recent ultrastructural studies of the fetomaternal junction zone (or barrier) in do-mestic animals are summarized here [see also the review by Amoroso (6)].

Mare and sow. Although there is direct apposition of maternal and fetal tissues and no invasion of the endometrium by the chorion, the position in the sow is not exactly as implied by Grosser's description. First, the space seen by light microscopy between the two epithelia in the interareolar re-gions is apparent rather than real and is, in fact, obliterated by interdigi-tating microvilli, so that uterine milk (see Section VI, A) cannot be ab-sorbed in these areas of the chorion. Second, in the sow the fetal epithelial cells at the tips of the chorionic ridges are displaced by fetal capillaries forming intraepithelial plexuses (33), and similar capillary plexuses exist also in the maternal epithelium. The two circulations are, therefore, sepa-rated only by thin sheets of epithelium and by the endothelia of the vessels.

In the mare, too, submicroscopic interdigitations of the plasma mem-brane of the maternal and fetal epithelium are found, except in the region of the endometrial cups.

Cow and sheep. In Grosser's classification, loss of the maternal epi-thelium in the region of the placentomes (see p. 397) is a characteristic feature of the syndesmochorial placenta of ruminants.

Recent electron microscopic studies have, however, revealed that in the cow (15), as in the sow (33), there is a microvillous junctional zone be-tween the epithelium lining the crypts and that covering the chorionic villi. In the cow the cryptal lining is cellular and believed to be of maternal origin, so constituting an epitheliochorial, rather than syndesmochorial type of placental membrane, as originally listed by Grosser.

TABLE I

TYPES OF MAMMALIAN PLACENTAS[a]

Type of placenta (Grosser's classification)	Tissues intervening between fetal and maternal blood						Fetomaternal junction		Gross shape of placenta	Representative species
	Maternal			Fetal			Maternal	Fetal		
	Endo-thelium	Connective tissue	Epi-thelium	Endo-thelium	Connective tissue	Epi-thelium				
Epitheliochorial	+	+	+	+	+	+			Diffuse	Pig, horse
Syndesmochorial	+	+	−	+	+	+			Cotyledonary or multiplex	Sheep, cow, goat
Endotheliochorial	+	−	−	+	+	+			Zonary	Cat, dog, ferret
Hemochorial	−	−	−	+	+	+			Discoid	Primates, bats, some rodents, insectivores

[a]Based on Amoroso (1942) and Flexner and Gellhorn (1937).

By contrast, in the sheep the cryptal lining is syncytial, and there is some diversity of opinion about its ultimate origin. Several workers (for instance, *15a, 59*) believe it to be maternal, but one group (*31*) thinks that the lining is derived from the trophoblastic giant cells and, hence, of fetal origin.

It may be concluded that electron microscopy, in spite of adding substantially to existing knowledge of structural detail, has so far not solved the old problem of the true nature of the fetomaternal junction in ruminants.

Bitch and cat. The endotheliochorial nature of the placenta has been substantiated by electron microscopy, both in the cat (*32*) and in the bitch (*8*). The enlarged endothelial cells of the maternal capillaries have a spongy cytoplasm and are separated from the trophoblast by an incomplete basement membrane, so that in some regions the plasma membrane of the endothelial cells may be in contact with the syncytial trophoblast.

VI. Fetal Nutrition and Growth

A. FETAL NUTRITION AND PLACENTAL FUNCTION

The two main sources of nutrition for the developing embryo are "histotrophe" and "hemotrophe," which together constitute the "embryotrophe" (cf. *4*).

Histotrophe is a milky fluid (more commonly referred to as "uterine milk") and consists of the secretions and debris of the endometrial glands plus extravasated maternal blood. Uterine milk is secreted into the uterine lumen and absorbed by the fetal membranes.

Hemotrophe consists of nutritive materials absorbed directly from the circulating maternal blood by the allantochorion or vitellochorion, where they are in contact with the uterine tissues.

The eggs of placental mammals contain very little yolk. The developing conceptus, therefore, depends on external sources of nutrients from the beginning of intrauterine life. In all types of mammal, histotrophe is essential before the establishment of the placenta, and in most domestic animals, especially the pig, horse, sheep, and goat, remains so throughout the greater part of pregnancy.

Until recently, both thoughts and most experimental work on the nutritive function of the definitive allantochorial placenta have been centered on the hemotrophe, largely ignoring the histotrophe, and dominated by Grosser's classification (see Section V) and its implications on placental permeability. It was generally assumed that the transfer of nutrients occurs by a process of diffusion and that there is a gradient from a high concentration in the maternal vessels to a lower one in the fetal vessels. Grosser's system of classifying placentas according. to the layers separating the two circulations fitted in naturally enough with this concept, the epitheliochorial and syndesmochorial types being considered more primitive and insufficient as organs of exchange than the other two. The fallacy of this interpretation was exposed by Barcroft (11) when he emphasized the high degree of maturity of the newborn foal and calf compared with the extreme immaturity of the human baby or rodent at birth, and concluded that there could be nothing physiologically inadequate about an appositional, epitheliochorial or syndesmochorial placenta.

Another argument frequently advanced in this context is the inverse relationship, demonstrated by Flexner and Gellhorn (37), between the number of layers in Grosser's four different types of placenta and their permeability to electrolytes and water (cf. 5, 29). The validity of the inferences drawn from their experiments has been questioned by Wislocki and Padykula (93), who pointed out that Flexner's results are based on transfer rates per unit *weight* of placenta, instead of transfer per *absorbing surface* of the placental membrane.

It is now generally recognized that, although the demonstrated rise in placental permeability during the course of gestation is accompanied by increasing vascularity and a thinning of the layers between the maternal and fetal vessels, the movement of substances across the placental membrane involves active transport systems as well as diffusion.

More recently, it has been shown that the distinction between histotrophe and hemotrophe is not always clear-cut. When studying the ultrastructure of the placental labyrinth in the ferret, Lawn and Chiquoine (58) established that secretions transmitted from the mother to the fetus were synthesized in the endothelium of the maternal blood vessels in much the same way as nutritive material is secreted by the uterine glands. Hence, what had been assumed to be hemotrophe was, by definition, histotrophe.

The zonary placenta of carnivores is also characterized by certain paraplacental structures, named "hematomas," which are concerned in the nutrition of the fetus. In these hematomas (see Fig. 5d), which constitute the so-called green or brown borders of the placenta in the bitch and cat, extravasated maternal blood accumulates between the chorion and the endometrium and is absorbed by the chorionic epithelium. The phagocytized red blood cells are an important source of iron for the fetus. Since the word "hematoma" has pathological implications, Creed and Biggers (28) have suggested that it should be replaced by the less ambiguous term "hemophagous organ."

B. RESPIRATION

Apart from the transfer of nondiffusible nutrients from mother to fetus and of excretory material in the opposite direction, the placenta also acts as an organ for gaseous exchange.

Diffusion of oxygen and carbon dioxide is generally believed to occur in the areas of the allantochorion in which the maternal and fetal circulations are in closest proximity, e.g., in ruminants gaseous exchange is in the cotyledons and not the intercotyledonary area.

With the progress of gestation growth of the placenta begins to lag behind that of the fetus and in the late stages the absolute weight of cotyledons decreases. There are divergent views about the relationship between the permeability of the sheep placenta to oxygen and the growing requirements for it of the fetus during the later stages of pregnancy. Barcroft (11) believes that from the 120th day onward the fetal lamb is exposed to an ever-increasing oxygen deficiency, from which it can only escape by birth, the alternative being death in utero. More recent workers (65), however, state that both the amount of oxygen taken up in the umbilical blood and the "diffusing capacity" of the placenta for oxygen actually rise as fetal weight increases. The metabolic requirements of the developing lamb and their relation to the respiratory area of the trophoblast and placental capillaries are, however, unknown and remain to be determined.

C. Fetal Growth

In spite of their frequent, and increasing, use in experimental work, the prenatal development of domestic animals has received comparatively little attention.

Systematic studies of fetal growth in acceptably homogeneous populations or single breeds, using sufficient numbers of accurately aged specimens, as well as adequate biological and statistical techniques, appear to have been carried out only in the sheep (51, 89) and, to a lesser extent, in the pig (79), but not in larger animals such as cows and horses. Again, in the past, most workers have confined themselves to recording growth purely in terms of weight or length or some other dimensional character, and have shown little interest in the development of individual organs or tissues and their maturation or of body composition as a whole.

The appearance, in 1946, of Barcroft's book "Researches on Pre-natal Life" (11), marked a significant change toward a new, more physiological approach; it cannot be recommended highly enough to students of the subject. It was soon followed by Wallace's important study (89) in the sheep, which showed clearly that insufficient food during the last trimester will not only reduce the weight of the ewe but also stunt the lamb. For more general surveys of the field reference is made to Brody (21), Pálsson (76), and Harvey (47; in the first edition of this book).

In the fetal sheep, length (forehead-rump, F-R) increases much more regularly than weight, and in the opinion of some authors like Barcroft (11), over the last two-thirds of pregnancy, F-R length grows in an almost linear relation to fetal age, with little difference between single and twin lambs. The view that fetal growth in length proceeds in linear fashion is not shared by other workers, who believe that it more nearly approximates an elongated S, or double-parabolic type of curve. Many, however, have found breaks in continuity of the curve, which may be ascribed to heterogeneity or scarcity of material at particular stages, but which may also reflect true alterations in the pattern of growth at these phases of intrauterine life [see Joubert (51) and Pálsson (76) for full discussions of these relationships].

There is, however, complete consensus that weight is far more variable and provides a less reliable index of fetal growth than length. For instance, in Joubert's series in sheep (51) the coefficient of variation of weight was almost twice as large (11.2%) as that of F-R length (6.23%). Variability is most pronounced throughout the last third of gestation, and during this phase the time-weight curve constructed from the means of the whole litter bears little relation to the growth of individual young. Why some fetuses appear to falter at this stage of prenatal growth while others do not is unknown and requires further study. Competition for food with others in the litter appears to be one of the most important factors, and it is well established that an increase in litter size is associated with a decrease in fetal and birth weight in pigs and sheep (47, 76). Fetal sex also has some influence, weight of the male usually slightly exceeding that of the female in cattle (23, 63).

Prenatal development of cattle is very similar to that in sheep (41, 76, 92). In both species, weight increases little during the first half of intrauterine life [for instance, the bovine fetus weighs less than 10 gm at 55 days and some 1400 gm at 135 days (76)], and the greatest gain in weight is made in both species during the last third of pregnancy.

It is of some interest that fetal growth of the horse plotted either as C-R length or as the cube root of weight, shows a linear relation to age (Fig. 11; from data gathered in observations of "hunter" or "vanner" mares, kindly provided by Dr. I. W. Rowlands).

The pronounced effect of prenatal influences on the size of the newborn foal was strikingly demonstrated by the reciprocal Shetland-Shire crosses carried out by Walton and Hammond (90). At birth the crossbred foal of the Shire dam was about three times as large as that of the Shetland mare.

VII. Chorioallantoic Anastomoses and Twinning

In multiple gestation in the cow there is usually fusion of the chorioallantoic blood vessels of adjacent fetuses; the fused vessels may have a diameter of 1 cm. When, in twin pregnancy, both fetuses occupy the same horn, fusion and vascular anastomoses occur in every case, and when one is in each horn, the incidence is 67% (91). The presence of common vascular channels between the fetuses is associated with the development of

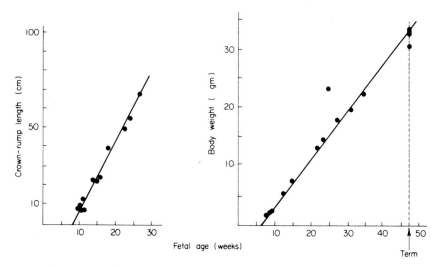

FIG. 11. Fetal growth in the horse. From data provided by Dr. I. W. Rowlands.

immunological tolerance of one twin for the other; an example of this is the freemartin.

*Freemartins.** If the twins are of unlike sex and have a common placental circulation, the male is normal and the female shows partial sex reversal into a sterile freemartin. This is characterized by atrophy or some degree of masculinization of the ovary ("ovotestis"), regression of the müllerian duct, and development of the wolffian duct and its derivatives; the external genitalia and mammary gland usually remain female. Over 90% of all females of heterosexual cattle twins are freemartins [see Biggers and McFeely (13)]. The genetic sex of the freemartin has been shown to be female (68).

Following the classic descriptions of Keller and Tandler (53) and Lillie (60, 61), it was widely believed that the freemartin state is brought about by "androgen," conveyed from the male twin through the vascular connections to the female fetus and affecting its reproductive tract during the indifferent stage of development. This theory presupposes that male reproductive function develops before that of the female and that androgens are produced by the testis at this very early stage of sex differentiation. There is no evidence in support of either assumption. Numerous experiments involving administration of androgens to pregnant cows have so far

---

* The term appears to have come first into use during the seventeenth century; it was well known during the eighteenth century. Its origin is obscure, but may be a corruption of "farrow" (signifying infertility) and "mart" (Gaelic for heifer or cow); see Koch (57). Freemartins have been recognized since antiquity, and were described by the Romans as "taurae."

failed to alter the gonads, although the external genitalia were masculinized [e.g., Jainudeen and Hafez (50)]. It has, therefore, become increasingly clear that the humoral theory alone is inadequate to explain the mode of origin of the cattle freemartin. Instead, there are grounds for assuming that a cellular mechanism may be involved. For instance, cattle twins, including heterosexual ones, frequently have identical blood groups and represent red cell "chimeras." This finding suggests that an interchange of blood-forming cells between fetuses occurs *in utero* (75). Additional support for this view has come from the work of Anderson *et al.* (7), who showed that identical (monozygous) twins in cattle could not be detected by reciprocal skin grafts, since even heterosexual twins sharing a common uterine blood supply were tolerant of each other's tissues in adult life. It can be inferred that transplantation antigens had been exchanged via the chorioallantoic anastomoses at a time when the fetus was immunologically tolerant, i.e., unable to distinguish between "self" and "non-self." More direct proof of a cellular explanation of the freemartin condition has also been obtained. Thus, Ohno and his associates (74) found female cells in metaphase in the testis of a male born twin to a freemartin. Since then, Ohno and Gropp (73) have established that functional anastomoses between the allantoic vessels are present in cattle twins as early as day 30 of gestation—that is, at a stage when germ cell migration normally occurs—and that primordial germ cells are present in the liver capillaries and could thus be exchanged with those of the co-twin (see also 40).

Freemartins, can, very rarely, also occur in other domestic animals. Isolated cases have been reported in pigs (49) and goats (52), but their true nature is doubtful. In sheep, however, the occurrence of freemartins seems definitely established (3, 69). It has also been shown that, as in the cow, the sheep freemartin is a genetic female as well as a bone-marrow chimera (38). The incidence of vascular anastomoses in sheep twin pregnancy is, however, only 5–10%, or far lower than in the cow, and that of red cell chimerism about 5% (88). This fact probably accounts for the extreme rarity of freemartins in sheep.

VIII. Immunological Problems of Pregnancy

A. THE FETUS AS A HOMOGRAFT

The fetus inherits transplantation antigens from both parents. Except, however, in inbred lines, the antigens inherited from the sire will be foreign to the dam and, to this extent, the fetus can be regarded as a homograft. One of the basic questions regarding pregnancy is why the mother nourishes this foreign tissue within her uterus and does not reject it as she would a skin graft with the same transplantation antigens.

To account for the biological "success" of the fetal homograft, several hypotheses have been advanced, namely, that (1) the fetus is antigenically immature, (2) the immunological reactivity of the mother is reduced during pregnancy, (3) a physical barrier exists between mother and fetus, (4) the uterus is an immunologically privileged site [cf. review by Billingham (14)].

The first two hypotheses have not withstood experimental test and are no longer tenable. The principal factor to account for the survival of the fetus appears to be the complete separation of the maternal and fetal circulations so that the mother is not sensitized to fetal transplantation antigens. Kirby and his co-workers (55) have studied the role of the trophoblast in the retention of the fetal homograft since it is the trophoblast, and not the fetus per se, which is in contact with maternal tissue. They suggest that in the mouse, which has an interstitial type of implantation (see previously, p. 387) a fibrinoid layer which surrounds the trophoblast may prevent the escape of fetal transplantation antigens. Recently, these workers (56) have shown, by transplanting blastocysts to the kidney and uterus of immunized mice, that in this species there is a dual protection against immunological attack during pregnancy, first, that provided by the decidual cells at the time of implantation and, later, by the development of a protective fibrinoid layer.

In a comparative study of the ultrastructure of the placental membrane, Wynn (94) found an acellular barrier comparable to that described by Kirby et al. (55) in those species in which the trophoblast is invasive. In the epitheliochorial placenta of the mare and cow, however, Wynn found no such barrier, and, therefore, suggests that in these species the reason why the fetal homograft is retained may be the absence of trophoblastic antigenicity.

B. PASSIVE IMMUNITY

Newborn mammals have limited powers of antibody production and during the postpartum period depend on passive immunity by antibodies of maternal origin. In the horse, pig, and ruminants the transmission of antibodies after birth occurs by means of the colostrum, and the intact antibodies are absorbed from the infant gut. In the dog there is some transmission of passive immunity before birth, but most takes place through the colostrum after birth.

The separation of the fetal and maternal circulation is not absolute, and there is occasionally an escape of fetal erythrocytes into the maternal circulation. The mother becomes sensitized to these foreign antigens on the red cells and produces antibodies, the consequence of which is hemolytic disease of the newborn. In horses, when this occurs naturally, the foal is born healthy, but develops the disease after feeding on colostrum. Hemolytic disease also occurs in mules, when it is due to antidonkey antibodies, and it has occurred in pigs when the mother has been immunized to fetal red cells by blood group antigens contained in a swine-fever vaccine. A review of passive immunity is given by Brambell (20).

REFERENCES

1. Adolph, E. F., *Quart. Rev. Biol.* **42**, 1 (1967).
2. Alexander, D. P., and Nixon, D. A., *Brit. Med. Bull.* **17**, 112 (1961).
3. Alexander, G., and Williams, D., *Nature* **201**, 1296 (1964).
4. Amoroso, E. C., *in* "Marshall's Physiology of Reproduction" (A. S. Parkes, ed.), 3rd ed., Vol. 2, p. 127. Longmans, Green, New York, 1952.
5. Amoroso, E. C., *Ann. N. Y. Acad. Sci.* **75**, 855 (1959).
6. Amoroso, E. C., *Brit. Med. Bull.* **17**, 81 (1961).
7. Anderson, D., Billingham, R. E., Lampkin, G. H., and Medawar, P., *Heredity* **5**, 379 (1951).
8. Anderson, J. W., *Anat. Record* **154**, 309 (1966).
9. Anderson, L. L., Bowerman, A. M., and Melampy, R. M., *in* "Advances in Neuroendocrinology" (A. V. Nalbandov, ed.), p. 345. Univ. of Illinois Press, Urbana, Illinois, 1963.
10. Austin, C. R., *in* "Reproduction in Domestic Animals" (H. H. Cole and P. T. Cupps, eds.), Vol. 1, p. 399. Academic Press, New York, 1959.
11. Barcroft, J., "Researches on Pre-natal Life," Vol. 1. Blackwell, Oxford, 1946.
12. Bielanski, W., Ewy, Z., and Pigoniowa, H., *Folia Biol.* **3**, 19 (1955).
13. Biggers, J. D., and McFeely, R. A., *Advan. Reproductive Physiol.* **1**, p. 29 (1966).
14. Billingham, R. G., *New Engl. J. Med.* **270**, 667, 720 (1964).
15. Björkman, N., and Bloom, G., *Z. Zellforsch.* **45**, 649 (1957).
15a. Björkman, N., *J. Anat.* **99**, 283 (1965).
16. Bland, K. P., and Donovan, B. T., *Advan. Reproductive Physiol.* **1**, p. 179 (1966).
17. Bonnet, R., *Arch. Anat. Physiol. (Leipzig) Anat. Abt.* **1** (1889), cited by Amoroso (4).
18. Böving, B. G., *in* "Mechanisms Concerned with Conception" (C. G. Hartman, ed.), p. 321. Pergamon, Oxford, 1963.
19. Boyd, J. D., and Hamilton, W. J., *in* "Marshall's Physiology of Reproduction" (A. S. Parkes, ed.), 3rd ed., Vol. 2, p. 1. Longmans, Green, New York, 1952.
20. Brambell, F. W. R., *Biol. Rev.* **33**, 488 (1958).
21. Brody, S., "Bioenergetics and Growth." Yale Univ. Press, New Haven, Connecticut, 1945.
22. Chang, M. C., *Anat. Record* **113**, 143 (1952).
23. Clegg, M. T., *in* "Reproduction in Domestic Animals" (H. H. Cole and P. T. Cupps, eds.), Vol. 1, p. 509. Academic Press, New York, 1959.
24. Clegg, M. T., Boda, J. M., and Cole, H. H., *Endocrinology* **54**, 448 (1954).
25. Cole, H. H., and Goss, H., *in* "Essays in Biology in Honor of Herbert M. Evans," p. 107. Univ. of Calif. Press, Berkeley, California, 1943.
26. Corner, G. W., *Carnegie Inst. Wash. Contrib. Embryol.* **13**, 117 (1921).
27. Corner, G. W., *Am. J. Anat.* **31**, 523 (1923).
28. Creed, R. F. S., and Biggers, J. D., *Am. J. Anat.* **113**, 417 (1963).
29. Dancis, J., *Am. J. Obstet. Gynecol.* **84**, 1749 (1962).
30. Davies, J., *Am. J. Anat.* **91**, 263 (1952).
31. Davies, J., and Wimsatt, W. A., *Acta Anat.* **65**, 182 (1966).
32. Dempsey, E. W., and Wislocki, G. B., *J. Biophys. Biochem. Cytol.* **2**, 743 (1956).

33. Dempsey, E. W., Wislocki, G. B., and Amoroso, E. C., *Am. J. Anat.* **96**, 65 (1955).
34. Dickerson, J. W. T., Southgate, D. A. T., and King, J. M., *J. Anat.* **101**, 285 (1967).
35. Eckstein, P., and Zuckerman, S., *in* "Marshall's Physiology of Reproduction" (A. S. Parkes, ed.), 3rd ed., Vol. 1, p. 43. Longmans, Green, New York, 1956.
36. Enders, A. C. ed., "Delayed Implantation." Univ. of Chicago Press, Chicago, Illinois, 1963.
37. Flexner, L. B., and Gellhorn, A., *Am. J. Obstet. Gynecol.* **43**, 965 (1942).
38. Gerneke, W. H., *J. South African Vet. Med. Assoc.* **36**, 99 (1965).
39. Gomes, W. R., Herschler, R. C., and Erb, R. E., *J. Animal Sci.* **24**, 722 (1965).
40. Goodfellow, S., Strong, S. J., and Stewart, J. S. S., *Lancet* **i**, 1040 (1965).
41. Green, W. W., and Winters, L. M., *Minn. Univ. Agr. Expt. Sta. Tech. Bull.* **169** (1945).
42. Green, W. W., and Winters, L. M., *J. Morphol.* **78**, 305 (1946).
43. Grosser, O., "Vergleichende Anatomie und Entwicklungsgeschichte der Eihäute und der Plazenta." Braumüller, Wien, Leipzig, 1909.
44. Grosser, O., "Frühentwicklung, Eihautbildung und Placentation des Menschen und der Säugetiere." Bergmann, München, 1927.
45. Hamilton, W. J., Boyd, J. D., and Mossman, H. W., "Human Embryology," 3rd ed. Heffer, Cambridge, 1962.
46. Hammond, J., "The Physiology of Reproduction in the Cow." Cambridge Univ. Press, London and New York, 1927.
47. Harvey, E. B., *in* "Reproduction in Domestic Animals" (H. H. Cole and P. T. Cupps, eds.), Vol. 1, p. 433. Academic Press, New York, 1959.
48. Heuser, C. H., *Carnegie Inst. Wash. Contrib. Embryol.* **19**, 229 (1927).
49. Hughes, W., *Anat. Record* **41**, 213 (1929).
50. Jainudeen, M. R., and Hafez, E. S. E., *J. Reprod. Fertility* **10**, 281 (1965).
51. Joubert, D. M., *J. Agr. Sci.* **47**, 382 (1956).
52. Keller, K., *Wien. Tierärztl. Monatsschr.* **7**, 146 (1920), cited by Koch (57).
53. Keller, K., and Tandler, J., *Wien. Tierärztl. Monatsschr.* **3**, 573 (1916).
54. Kirby, D. R. S., *in* "Preimplantation Stages of Pregnancy" (G. E. W. Wolstenholme and M. O'Conner, eds.), Ciba Found. Symp., p. 325. Churchill, London, 1965.
55. Kirby, D. R. S., Billington, W. D., Bradbury, S., and Goldstein, D. J., *Nature* **204**, 548 (1964).
56. Kirby, D. R. S., Billington, W. D., and James, D. A., *Transplantation* **4**, 713 (1966).
57. Koch, W., *in* "Intersexuality" (C. Overzier, ed.), p. 35. Academic Press, New York, 1963.
58. Lawn, A. M., and Chiquoine, A. D., *J. Anat.* **99**, 47 (1965).
59. Lawn, A. M., Chiquoine, A. D., and Amoroso, E. C., *J. Anat.* **97**, 306 (1963).
60. Lillie, F. R., *Science* **43**, 611 (1916).
61. Lillie, F. R., *J. Exptl. Zool.* **23**, 371 (1917).
62. McCance, R. A., and Dickerson, J. W. T., *J. Embryol. Exptl. Morphol.* **5**, 43 (1957).

63. McKeown, T., and MacMahon, B., *J. Endocrinol.* 13, 309 (1956).
64. Masuda, H., Anderson, L. L., Henricks, D. M., and Melampy, R. M., *Endocrinology* 80, 240 (1967).
65. Meschia, G., Cotter, J. R., Breathnach, C. S., and Barron, D. H., *Quart. J. Exptl. Physiol.* 50, 466 (1965).
66. Moor, R. M., and Rowson, L. E. A., *J. Endocrinol.* 34, 233 (1966).
67. Moor, R. M., and Rowson, L. E. A., *J. Endocrinol.* 34, 497 (1966).
68. Moore, K. L., Graham, M. A., and Barr, M. C., *J. Exptl. Zool.* 135, 101 (1957).
69. Moore, N. W., and Rowson, L. E. A., *Nature* 182, 1754 (1958).
70. Mossman, H. W., *Carnegie Inst. Wash. Contrib. Embryol.* 26, 129, (1937).
71. Nalbandov, A. V., "Reproductive Physiology," 2nd ed. Freeman, San Francisco, California, 1964.
72. Noyes, R. W., Dickmann, Z., Doyle, L. L., and Gates, A. H., *in* "Delayed Implantation" (A. C. Enders, ed.), p. 197. Univ. of Chicago Press, Chicago, Illinois, 1963.
73. Ohno, S., and Gropp, A., *Cytogenetics* 4, 251 (1965).
74. Ohno, S., Trujillo, J. M., Stenius, C., Christian, L. C., and Teplitz, R. L., *Cytogenetics* 1, 258 (1962).
75. Owen, R. D., *Science* 102, 400 (1945).
76. Pálsson, H., *in* "Progress in the Physiology of Farm Animals" (J. Hammond, ed.), Vol. 2, p. 430. Butterworths, London and Washington, D. C., 1955.
77. Patten, B. M., "Foundations of Embryology," 2nd ed. McGraw-Hill, New York, 1964.
78. Pomeroy, R. W., *J. Agr. Sci.* 45, 327 (1955).
79. Pomeroy, R. W., *J. Agr. Sci.* 54, 31, 57 (1960).
80. Robinson, T. J., *J. Agr. Sci.* 41, 6 (1951).
81. Robinson, T. J., *in* "Progress in the Physiology of Farm Animals" (J. Hammond, ed.), Vol. 3, p. 793. Butterworths, London and Washington, D. C., 1957.
82. Rowson, L. E. A., and Moor, R. M., *J. Anat.* 100, 777 (1966).
83. Rowson, L. E. A., and Moor, R. M., *J. Reprod. Fertility* 11, 207 (1966).
84. Short, R. V., *Recent Progr. Hormone Res.* 20, 303 (1964).
85. Short, R. V., Personal communication, 1967.
86. Short, R. V., and Hay, M. F., *Symp. Zool. Soc., London* 15, 173 (1966).
87. Sisson, S., "The Anatomy of the Domestic Animals," 4th ed. Saunders, Philadelphia, Pennsylvania, 1953.
88. Slee, J., *Nature* 200, 654 (1963).
89. Wallace, L. R., *J. Agr. Sci.* 38, 93, 243 (1948).
90. Walton, A., and Hammond, J., *Proc. Roy. Soc.* B125, 311 (1938).
91. Williams, G., Gordon, I., and Edwards, J., *Brit. Vet. J.* 119, 467 (1963).
92. Winters, L. M., Green, W. W., and Comstock, R. E., *Minn. Univ. Agr. Expt. Sta. Tech. Bull.* 151 (1942).
93. Wislocki, G. B., and Padykula, H. A., *in* "Sex and Internal Secretions" (W. C. Young, ed.), Vol. II, p. 883. Williams & Wilkins, Baltimore, Maryland, 1961.
94. Wynn, R. M., *Obstet. Gynecol.* 29, 644 (1967).

15   HORMONAL MECHANISMS DURING PREGNANCY AND PARTURITION

HUBERT R. CATCHPOLE

I. Introduction*

Pregnancy is defined as the time interval between the implantation of a fertilized ovum in the uterus and the expulsion of the fetus and its associated membranes. The event of implantation may be precise when a growing ovum erodes the endometrium, or indefinite when the junctions between maternal and fetal tissues remain tentative for longer or shorter periods. Parturition involves a preparative period (labor) of somewhat indefinite duration and merges into the postpartum epoch during which time the genital tract undergoes involution to approximately its prepregnancy state.

Pregnancy usually occupies a lengthy time span in the economy of the individual mammal, if we except the egg-laying order of Monotremata and the marsupials in which immature (12.5-day) embryos are born and trans-

* References to earlier work on pregnancy and parturition will be found in previous articles (14) and (15), respectively. None of the tabular material from reference (14) is duplicated here. Part of it is still reasonably contemporary, while a part is superseded by the present text.

TABLE I
LENGTH OF GESTATION, LITTER SIZE, AND RESULT
OF OOPHORECTOMY DURING PREGNANCY[a]

Species	Litter size	Length of gestation (days)	Aborts if oophorectomized before day of gestation
Cat	4	63	50
Cow	1–2	277–290	Term
Dog	Multiple; mean, 7.0	61	30
Guinea pig	2–4	68	38
Goat	1–3	145–151	Term
Horse	1	330–345	150–200
Monkey (*Macaca mulatta*)	1	168	25
Man	1	280 ± 9.2	30–60
Mouse	Multiple; mean 4.5–7.4	19–20	Term
Pig (domestic)	8–12	112–115	Term
Rabbit (domestic)	Multiple; mean 8.0	31	Term
Rat	6–9	22	Term
Sheep (domestic)	1–2	144–152	55

[a] Data compiled from several sources (*15, 82, 97*).

fer to a mammary pouch. The span of pregnancy may extend from about 3 weeks (mouse, rat, hamster) to 2 years (elephant). For convenience of reference, gestation times of some common laboratory and farm species are given in condensed form (Table I), and the reader is referred to Kenneth's extensive compilation (*50*). Asdell's "Patterns of Mammalian Reproduction" (*6*) continues to cover aspects of quantitative reproduction and Deanesly's chapter (*21*) is a modern treatment of pregnancy, fetal life, and parturition.

During gestation, the new organism or organisms achieve a total weight which is a significant fraction of the maternal body weight. The fetuses of the mouse at term may equal 33% of the total pregnant weight and 50% of the maternal body weight; a pig litter may reach 15% of the sow's weight at term and a thoroughbred foal 10% of the mare's weight. Development and normal functioning of the entire reproductive system depends on adequate nutrition (*53*) and inanition brings about severe disturbances in mother and offspring.

The uterus progressively adapts in size to the growing fetuses and their membranes and fluid-containing sacs, resulting in a profound increase in its total wet and dry weight. All cellular and extracellular elements of the endometrium and myometrium participate in this growth. Stretching may provide the proximate stimulus for uterine growth (*74*), but mediation of these effects are largely hormonal in nature. Similarly, endocrine and neuro-endocrine secretions feature largely in the preparation of the mammary gland during pregnancy and in the dynamics of parturition.

Any account of endocrine mechanisms in pregnancy must come to grips with the problems posed by the placenta, a bulky and characteristically "transient" tissue which has a well-demarcated life-span, and is shed shortly after the fetus. Whether or not the placenta "ages" seems to be largely a matter of definition. In all metabolic functions tested, placental activity decreases as gestation advances, although at different rates for different modalities. Thus, glycogen synthesis is the first function to decrease markedly (90). However, at term metabolic activities are still brisk and there is no sharp change to mark or explain the onset of labor. Morphologically, no unfavorable terminal changes which might indicate depressed physiological transfer are observed (94).

While it is natural to seek for general laws of endocrine behavior, it appears certain that different species solve their reproductive "problems" in different ways. Thus, the various luteotropic factors responsible for maintaining the corpus luteum of pregnancy appear to differ from species to species; a given hormone like relaxin is highly effective in the guinea pig, whereas sheep and pig symphyses pubes are quite insensitive to it.

Together with a description of hormonal relationships comes the additional task of defining the nature of hormonal action. At the present time, a strong current of opinion favors the idea that hormones are effective at some level of gene activation. It is too early to know if all types of hormone action must be included under this concept (49).

II. Hormonal Mechanisms in Pregnancy

A. MATERNAL ENDOCRINE FUNCTIONS

1. The Ovaries of Pregnancy

In the presence of fertilized and implanting ova, changes take place in the ovary which define its character for the remainder of gestation. Corpora lutea, which normally regress as a result of luteolytic actions, are stabilized as corpora lutea of pregnancy. These bodies are generally larger than the corpora of the estrous cycle, although individual cells are not greatly altered. The growth of follicles which would signal the onset of another cycle does not occur, and estrus is suppressed. These statements are subject to modification for the different species. Suppression of estrus may not be complete in early pregnancy, and cycles may continue. The life-span of the corpus luteum of pregnancy may cover the entire gestation period, or the gland may involute at some earlier stage of pregnancy (82, Table 103).

Events in the pregnant mare and other equidae are unique in this regard. The primary corpus luteum reaches maximal size by the 14th day and begins to regress by the end of the first month. A gonadotropin appears suddenly in the blood at the 40th to 50th day and provokes intense ovarian stimulation, ovulation, and the formation of multiple corpora lutea. These persist until the 150th to 200th day. In the cow the corpus luteum remains functional throughout pregnancy as indicated by assays for tissue progestogen. Progesterone and Δ^4-pregnene-20β-ol-3-one are present in a $3:2$ ratio. Levels of both hormones are high in early pregnancy, then fall after the third month and increase again in the third trimester (84). Values correlate well with ovarian venous blood assays (34).

Morphological and functional maintenance of the corpus luteum is effected through luteotropic factors, of pituitary or extrapituitary origin, released as a result of the presence of a conceptus.

a. *Role of Estrogen.* Estrogenic hormones are dominant at the time of fertilization, and they continue to be secreted by the ovary itself and by the placenta. In many species, estrogens, including the biologically active hormones and their active or inactive metabolites, tend to increase throughout gestation. Estrogenic effects on the genital tract proper include: cellular mitosis and growth (hyperplasia) of epithelial cells and glands; hypertrophy of muscle cells and synthesis of actomyosin, the contractile protein of smooth muscle; collagen synthesis; glycogen deposition in the circular and longitudinal muscle cells of the uterus and in the muscle cells of blood vessels; changes in epithelial alkaline phosphatase; disaggregation of connective tissue ground substance and increase in water-soluble mucoprotein, with water uptake by uterus, cervix, and vagina. The estrogen-stimulated uterus takes up vital dyes, a phenomenon interpreted as indicating either increased vascular permeability or connective tissue change. Endometrial ribonucleic acid (RNA), deoxyribonucleic acid (DNA), and succinoxidases are also increased. Some of these actions of estrogen clearly reflect a role in the increased demands placed on uterine metabolism by the increased synthesis of uterine components; others illustrate its action in facilitating the physical adaptation of the organ to the presence of the conceptus. A major action of estrogen is to promote cell multiplication (12).

b. *Role of Progesterone.* Progesterone adds a qualitative change to the development of a uterus already "prepared" by estrogen, a change perfectly appreciated in Marshall's classic "Physiology of Reproduction" of 1910 (58). The uterine mucosa undergoes an enormous complication in glandular structure, the "Swiss cheese" appearance of progestational proliferation, which forms the nidus in which ova will be entrapped and implanted. Progesterone produces less hyperemia than estrogen alone, and glands are dilated and inserted deeply into the submucosa. Cells of the mucosa become columnar in shape and mitoses are rare. The major action of progesterone is to produce a secretory endometrium (12).

Inhibition of estrus and ovulation in pregnancy remains an obscure process, and may involve local as well as systemic humoral factors. While the production of progesterone by the persisting corpus luteum is the dominant new hormonal event, a role of estrogen in acting to suppress pituitary function must also be considered. But is pituitary function actually suppressed during pregnancy, i.e., is there failure of synthesis, or failure of release, of pituitary gonadotropins? Newer evidence pointing to an increased hormone content of the pituitary during part, at least, of pregnancy, suggest the suppression of a releasing mechanism of neuroendocrine nature.

i. *Nidation.* The normal effective stimulus for the preparation of an implantation site is the ovum or blastocyst which, prior to implantation, lies free in the uterus for a variable period, from a few days in rodents and 2.5 weeks in sheep to some 40 days in the cow and mare. The continued integrity of the blastocyst depends on the presence of progesterone, which, through its action on the uterine mucosa, provides increased surface and glandular secretions related to nutrition of the embryo. Spacing of multiple embryos in the uterus appears to come about by local peristaltic waves arising from points of contact of embryo and uterus. Actual implantation may involve chemotactic secretions arising from epithelial cells or, possibly, the secretion of mucolytic enzymes which, by breaking down connective tissue barriers, would enable contact to be made with deeper layers of the mucosa.

ii. *Pseudopregnancy.* False pregnancy, or pseudopregnancy, is a normal phase of the cycle in the dog and marsupial cat, wherein the corpus luteum persists and becomes actively functional. In other species, mechanical stimulation of the genitalia, electroshock, drugs, or sterile mating can induce ovulation, corpus luteum formation, and pseudopregnancy. In the dog and rabbit, the proliferated uterine mucosa breaks down at the termination of pseudopregnancy and may bleed. When in natural or induced pseudopregnancy sterile threads are inserted in the uterine wall, an active proliferation and inflammatory reaction to the presence of a foreign body occurs, giving a deciduoma. Sterile beads or wax pellets introduced into the uterus produce a similar reaction.

c. *Endocrine Function of Relaxin.* Relaxin, a water-soluble polypeptide hormone, is isolated from ovarian extracts and appears in the blood of pregnant rabbits, pigs, and other animals. The hormone causes the fibrocartilaginous ligament of the symphysis pubis to relax, producing a widening of the gap which is maximal at parturition. The effect is most prominent in the guinea pig, mouse, and some other burrowing animals. In other species the symphysis is relaxed (man, macaque monkey), or the effect may be shown by other joints related to widening of the birth canal, e.g., the sacroiliac joints of the cow and sheep. Relaxin increases during pregnancy and extraovarian sources have been postulated.

Relaxin exerts its main effect on the connective tissue, and the softening of the symphysis pubis was ascribed to a molecular disaggregation of the glycoprotein colloids of the symphyseal ground substance with uptake of water and electrolyte. It normally acts on tissues already prepared by estrogen and progesterone, which also affect connective tissue elements (32). Relaxin also affects the uterine endometrium, myometrium, and cervix when given alone or in combination with steroids (43).

d. *Maintenance of Pregnancy.* Ovariectomy at almost any time terminates pregnancy, by abortion or resorption of fetuses, in rabbit, rat, mouse, guinea pig, dog, goat, and cow (see Table I). Pregnancy can be maintained by the injection of estrogen and progesterone in the proper amounts and proportions, varying with the species. Thus, in pregnant ewes ovariectomized at 3 weeks, a minimum dose of 0.15 mg/kg of progesterone maintained gestation until slaughter at 60 days (2). Dairy heifers could even be maintained through the critical stage of implantation, using progesterone and estrone in the ratio 4000:1 (40). Using the same proportion of hormones, gilts supported pregnancy with fair success (83), while dairy heifers oophorectomized at day 55 were maintained by an oral progestogen (98). Successful continuance of pregnancy in cows was obtained also by the injection of progesterone, with small daily doses reportedly more effective than large, less frequent ones (47).

The ovary is dispensable in man after the 40th to 70th day of pregnancy, in the mare after 200 days and 160 days in the two recorded cases (3) and in the ewe after the 55th day (see Table I). In man and ewe earlier castration leads to abortion and it is inferred that for the operation to be successful alternative sources of estrogen and progesterone must have developed. Supporting this is the finding that following successful oophorectomy in man, the postoperative blood and urinary estrogen values and the urinary pregnandiol level (pregnandiol is the major metabolite of progesterone in man) remain essentially normal (72).

Certain additional operative procedures permit pregnancy to persist in the absence of the ovaries. Reduction of fetuses to one in the rat, leaving placental sites intact allowed pregnancy to continue, possibly by a "pooling" of the placental hormone effect. Also, in the rat release of the fetuses to the intraperitoneal cavity circumvented fetal death, implying that one effect of castration is to cause a loss of uterine resilience. Certainly, estrogen and progesterone increase uterine plasticity (31) through their action on the uterine connective tissues, and relaxin may contribute to this effect, as already noted.

2. The Pituitary Gland of Pregnancy

It was noted years ago that the pituitary enlarges in pregnancy in man, mouse, cat, and macaque monkey. However, no correlation was found between fetal length and maternal pituitary weight in the cow or mare. Early cytological work was dominated by the concept of a specific "pregnancy cell," which at different times was thought to be a modified form of each of the "classical" cell types. The use of histochemical methods for a specific hormone or hormone complex was exemplified by the localization of a follicle stimulating hormone in basophils of the rat pituitary. A mild increase was seen in pregnancy, but the method has not to date been adequately applied to pregnant pituitary glands of diverse species (13). Staining of various types of "mucoid" granules of pituitary cells, using conventional fixatives, is unlikely to contribute to our knowledge of hormone localization, storage, or output (10). Use of the method of antigen-antibody localization, together with acceptable procedures of tissue and hormone preservation, was pioneered 15 years ago (59) and could give important information with the highly purified hormones now available.

a. *Biological Actions.* Systematic studies on the pituitaries of pregnant animals were hampered by the lack of adequate assay techniques, an area in which there is now intensive activity. Biological assays for total gonadotropin often showed a fall in activity, e.g., in man, cow, and mare, although the rabbit showed an increased activity until midpregnancy.

In the pregnant rat, use of modern assay techniques for luteinizing hormone (LH) showed an increase from day 1 to day 8, followed by a steady drop to term. Follicle stimulating hormone (FSH) showed increasing values from day 1 to day 12, a dramatic increase from day 12 to term, and rapid fall after delivery. All values were higher than those recorded for the estrous cycle (37). Results in the pig for FSH and LH activity, obtained in the cycle, during pregnancy and in lactation, also point to a reevaluation of the role of the pituitary in pregnancy. Both activities were increased by the 13th day of pregnancy to values in excess of those recorded for the estrous cycle (Table II) (61, 68). Total gland activity agreed with activity per milligram dry weight, and both showed rather complex variations having some parallels with the results cited for the rat. LH tended to be high in midpregnancy and fell in late pregnancy, while FSH showed a midpregnancy fall, high values in late pregnancy, and highest values in lactation. An extension of this valuable work to other species of domestic animals is urgently needed.

TABLE II

COMPARISON OF ANTERIOR PITUITARY FSH AND LH HORMONES
IN CYCLING, PREGNANT, AND LACTATING PIGS[a,b]

	Animals (number)	FSH[a] (μg/gland)	LH[a] (μg/gland)
Cycle (days)			
1 and 4	10	308, 396	31, 25
10–18	15	720–922	58–106
Pregnancy (day)			
13	8	1165	158
18	8	1530	216
40	8	1480	177
80	8	930	195
120	8	2852	157
Lactation (day)			
14	8	3170	112

[a] Expressed in terms of NIH standards, FSH-S1 and LH-S1.
[b] From Melampy et al. (61) and Parlow et al. (68).

Assays of the pituitary of pregnancy for prolactin (and luteotropic activity as measured in the rat) are scarce. The available evidence shows that prolactin increases at parturition in the rat, guinea pig, and rabbit, and during pregnancy and parturition in the goat and cow. Prolactin (pigeon crop) activity of the pregnant sow pituitary was significantly higher at the 85th day than at the 25th day (20).

No systematic assays are available for adrenocorticotropic, thyrotropic, and somatotropic hormones in pregnancy. It is probable that somatotropic hormone plays a role apart from its possible prolactin function, since successful hypophysectomy in rats and monkeys gave fetuses which were generally smaller than normal.

b. *Role in Maintenance of Ovary and of Pregnancy.* Hypophysectomy of the common laboratory animals before midpregnancy invariably causes fetal death and resorption. Thereafter, varying degrees of failure may be encountered, depending on the species. Rabbit and ferret are totally intolerant of the operation. The dog may be hypophysectomized in late pregnancy, but not at 5 and 7 weeks; guinea pigs at 40–41 days, but not at 34–36 days. In the rat, hypophysectomy not more than 4 days after coitus prevented implantation; at 7–10 days fetal death and resorption occurred, and after 11 days, fetal death, or persistence and possible prolongation of gestation with birth of living or dead fetuses. The monkey (*M. mulatta*) provides an exception, since it can be hypophysectomized between 27 and 156 days after conception and comes to term successfully at about the expected date. Hypophysectomy in goats at 38–120 days was followed by abortion in 3–9 days, and with stalk section at 44–129 days the animals did little better, aborting in 6–17 days. However, stalk section in sheep at 42–90 days, or hypophysectomy at 50–88 days allowed pregnancy to continue (18, 22). The rule is supported that pregnant animals tolerate hypophysectomy in inverse proportion to their dependence on the ovary as a source of estrogen and progesterone (see Table I) (14).

c. *Pituitary Luteotropins.* Pituitary extracts prolong the functional life of the corpus luteum in hypophysectomized laboratory animals. The luteotropic factor for mice and rats was clearly identified with prolactin, but for several other species prolactin failed to prolong luteal function, e.g., in the hypophysectomized rabbit (51, 73) and sheep (23). The active pituitary principle has often been identified with the lutenizing hormone (LH) itself, possibly acting very briefly at the time of ovulation (11). LH is also reported to be luteotropic in the cow (25); the mode of action may be through stimulation of interstitial tissue to produce estrogen, which, in turn, acts to preserve the corpora lutea.

3. Other Endocrine Glands in Pregnancy

Pregnancy involves homeostatic adjustments in all endocrine glands which help to monitor the various material shifts between mother and offspring. While the state of pregnancy may be consistent with removal of a given gland, certain aspects of pregnancy may be more or less seriously affected. Mammary development and lactation in particular are susceptible to endocrine removal when the gland concerned is involved in water and ionic balance. Cows thyroidectomized or parathyroidectomized showed 80% successful mating, but mammary development and lactation were impaired, and in the double operation hypocalcemia and abortion resulted (93). Goats thyroidectomized in pregnancy developed normal udders, but gave deficient milk and when thyroparathyroidectomized showed tetany and failure of udder development and lactation. Cows thyroparathyroidectomized in late pregnancy went to term, but with deficiencies in serum calcium and milk production.

The adrenal gland appears to increase its secretion in pregnancy, although no hypertrophy was seen in cat, dog, sow, cow, or ewe. For the adrenal or adrenal-like hormones the situation is extremely complex because maternal and fetal adrenals, placenta, and ovaries may all contribute steroid hormones to a common pool. An adverse effect of adrenalectomy on lactation may be partly explained by its role in salt and fluid balance. The effects of adrenalectomy in pregnancy may be partly mitigated by pregnancy hormones such as progesterone.

In man, the thyroid hypertrophies in pregnancy, while the sheep thyroid seemed to undergo only limited change as determined by the ^{131}I turnover rate (5). The parathyroid is enlarged in pregnancy and the serum shows parathyroid hormonelike activity.

Removal of the pituitary would be expected to react on glands such as the adrenal and thyroid which are normally supported by tropins, unless extrapituitary sources are available. In fact, the thyroid involutes in rat and monkey, pregnant or not, following hypophysectomy. Adrenals of mice lost weight, but adrenals of pregnant rats and monkeys were protected, presumably by extrapituitary ACTH deriving from placenta or fetal hypophysis. The action of the posterior pituitary will be examined in connection with parturition (p. 435).

4. Hormone Levels in Pregnancy

Hormones to be surveyed include: estrogens, androgens, progestins, adrenal cortical steroids, gonadotropins, prolactin, relaxin, and oxytocin. The readjustments which occur in pregnancy frequently give rise to enhanced amounts of hormones, which appear in the blood and other body fluids such as the bile, milk, saliva, and urine. Hormone levels may so differ from those in the nonpregnant animal as to be diagnostic of pregnancy. The literature of pregnancy diagnosis by hormonal means in man and the domestic animals was exhaustively documented to 1948 (17). Aside from additional literature based on more or less traditional tests but supplemented by elaborate techniques of separation, the main recent advance has been the detection of hormones by immunochemical means. This has greatly expanded the possibilities of assay of protein and polypeptide hormones.

a. *Steroid Hormones.* The steroid hormones were early shown to undergo conversion in the body, as well as *in vitro* and in surviving organs. Biosynthesis and interconversion of steroids has become a complex field of biochemistry (*26*). *In vivo*, the main tendency is for tissues to convert natural active hormones into substances which are either less active biologically, or completely inactive. While many tissues are able to effect these conversions, the major sites of steroid metabolism are the maternal and fetal livers and the placenta. Enzyme systems capable of catalyzing many such reactions have frequently been demonstrated in human placentas and in the late pregnancy placentas of cow, horse, sheep, sow, rabbit, and guinea pig (*1*).

i. *Estrogens.* The primary estrogen synthesized in the ovary and possibly the placenta of all mammals is estradiol 17-β. This occurs in reversible equilibrium with estrone and both are converted in man to the far less active estriol. The presence of estriol in animals other than man is dubious (*88*), although values are often reported for a compound similar to, but distinct from, estriol (*81*). In animals, the biologically least active metabolite corresponding to estriol seems to be estradiol 17-α which is present in urine of the pregnant mare, cow, goat, sheep, and rabbit, together with estrone. In pregnant mare urine, both estradiol 17-α and 17-β are found, and also a remarkable series of more unsaturated, biologically inactive metabolites related to equilin, which are highly specific for the equine. In the urine, phenolic steroids are largely conjugated with glucuronic or sulfuric acids, and the conjugates again are less biologically active than the parent compounds.

A major interest in pregnancy is the increased titer of estrogens found in many, and perhaps all, mammals. Where comparative studies have been done for total biologically active estrogen, the urine levels paralleled those for the blood serum. In man, urinary estrogens rise throughout gestation to a maximum of 20,000 μg/liter, and fall abruptly at parturition. In the mare, hormone appears at the 54th day, increases to maximum values of some 1500 μg/liter between 200 and 300 days, then decreases somewhat with a precipitous fall at parturition.

In the cow, observations of ancient vintage indicated that there was an increase in estrogens throughout pregnancy. More recent results show a rapid rise in the terminal stages of pregnancy with a peak just before parturition and a steady decline postpartum (*62, 63*). Estrogen occurs in the bile of pregnant cows, estrone and estradiol 17-β being the major components.

The sheep, on the basis of two animals studied, showed a pregnancy rise in estrogen, and for goats also the most that can presently be said is that estrogens and their metabolites have been identified in pregnancy urine in amounts greater than those recoverable from nonpregnant animals.

In the pig, a rather remarkable old report has now been confirmed in two laboratories. The hormone (estrone) is present from about the 23rd to the 31st day, then disappears until about the 80th day, when it reappears and increases to term (55, 75).

Plasma estrogen in the pregnant cow rose from undetectable amounts at 2–3 months to 1 μg/liter at 5–6 months and 7 μg/liter at 7–9 months (70), indicating that the ovary remains an important source of estrogen throughout pregnancy in bovines. A series of reports on levels of free plasma estrogens in the pregnant dog, deer, and guinea pig showed more types of estrogens being formed and metabolized than in the nonpregnant animal. Total free estrogens showed a peak at 3–4 weeks in the dog (64).

The conclusion to be drawn from these studies is that estrogen is an important hormone of pregnancy and is formed in increasing amounts until late pregnancy. The abrupt disappearance at parturition in some animals bespeaks a placental source.

ii. *Progesterone.* Attempts to recover progesterone from large volumes of urine of man and animals were equally unsuccessful. Metabolites of progesterone carry the label "pregnan" or "pregnen" (14), and the principal one in man, pregnanediol, is biologically inactive and appears in increasing amounts with the advance of gestation. Aside from the pregnant mare, pregnanediol appears not to be excreted in several domestic species studied; other metabolites like pregnanolone and allopregnanolone (sow, mare) and allopregnanediol (mare, cow) are most commonly found. Generally speaking, there are highly individual species differences in the metabolism of progesterone.

Progesterone is present in the blood serum of pregnant and nonpregnant animals, and determinations using a biological method appeared to show that titers increased during gestation in the ewe and rabbit. Application of a sensitive and specific chemical method to the blood of man and domestic animals has given some interesting results (79). In man the blood level rose steadily from the 11th to the 36th week of pregnancy, then more rapidly and persisted through the second stage of labor, and was present in cord blood after a normal delivery. The ewe showed no pregnancy rise beyond levels found in the luteal phase of the cycle. A closely related metabolite of progesterone was also present in a 1:1 ratio which did not change with time of gestation. There was no overall fall in blood level before parturition. Cattle blood progesterone also stayed constant throughout most of pregnancy, but fell some 10 days prepartum, indicating, it was believed, decreased production. The sow showed levels which were higher during most of pregnancy than just prior to parturition.

Blood progesterone behaves uniquely in the mare; it is high in the first 4 months when the corpora of pregnancy and the accessory corpora are active. After these regress hormone is no longer present in the blood, although pregnandiol is found in the urine in rising concentration. It is thought that after the placenta "takes over" the secretion of progesterone,

TABLE III

PLASMA PROGESTERONE LEVELS (MEANS ± S.E.) OF GUINEA PIGS
DURING PREGNANCY AS DATED BY VAGINAL PLUG[a]

State of animal	Day of pregnancy when killed	Analyses (number)	Plasma progesterone ($m\mu g/ml$)
Nonpregnant controls		5	32 ± 8
Pregnant, intact	11–17	6	64 ± 17
	20–25	6	190 ± 31
	30–35	4	266 ± 23
	40–45	6	264 ± 37
	50–55	6	221 ± 31
	60–65	4	140 ± 43
Pregnant, ovariectomized (day)			
28	34–35	5	75 ± 18
28–36	40–45	4	138 ± 18
33–40	50–55	4	154 ± 11
38	60–65	3	165 ± 92

[a] From Heap and Deanesly (*41*).

hormone is metabolized by maternal tissue before it reaches the maternal blood vessels, owing to the diffuse epitheliochorial nature of the equine placenta. Progesterone levels in cord blood of the foal were high at term. Plasma progesterone was measured chemically in a series of guinea pigs during pregnancy (Table III) (*41*). The hormone showed a rise in concentration in the first month corresponding to the growth of the corpus luteum, peak values at 30–45 days and a fall at 60–65 days. Animals were successfully ovariectomized from the 28th to the 38th day, and this reduced peak plasma progesterone by some 50%; however, 2 weeks before parturition the values were not significantly different from normal. Concentrations in placentas taken at 40–60 days did not differ for intact and ovariectomized animals. Placental production of progesterone was also shown by the very high values obtained for uterine venous plasma, which were some six times the systemic levels.

These studies reinforce the conclusion that the corpora lutea, or a substitute source, are active throughout pregnancy in maintaining or increasing the amounts of available progesterone. The point at which the placenta begins to add materially to the secretion, as well as its absolute contribution, is somewhat ill-defined. Since progesterone is an intermediate in the biosynthesis of the adrenal steroids, hormone from the adrenal gland would also be expected to contribute to the common metabolic pathway for progesterone.

iii. *Adrenal cortical steroids.* Steroids primarily elaborated by the adrenal cortex comprise two classes of hormones affecting carbohydrate and salt metabolism, respectively. The first group is represented by cortisol and corticosterone and the second by deoxycorticosterone or the naturally occurring aldosterone; in man both tend to increase in pregnancy. Aldosterone increases after the third month and remains elevated to term (89). Differing from man, a large proportion of aldosterone in the rat is excreted in the bile (56). The behavior and function of the adrenal hormones in the pregnant domestic animal is a decidedly neglected area, but plasma cortisol levels in pregnant ewes before and after parturition showed no readily interpretable pattern (78).

Androgens in the female are thought to be largely products of the adrenal cortex, and their metabolites, which carry the chemical label "androstan" or "androsten" are found in the urine of the pregnant mare, cow, and goat (14). These compounds are generally biologically inactive and it is not clear whether or not they increase in pregnancy.

b. *Gonadotropic Hormones.* An extensive review of gonadotropic titers in tissues and fluids of domestic animals has appeared (77). Chorionic gonadotropin (HCG, human cyonin, cf. 13) is found in the blood and urine of pregnant women, where it provides the basis of a biological or immunochemical pregnancy test (17, 95). Titers in the urine reach a peak of 1,000,000 IU/liter from the 6th to 10th week, then fall sharply to around 10,000 IU/liter, which is maintained until term, when values fall to 0. Blood values follow a parallel course with peak titers of 70,000 to 600,000 IU/liter between the 50th and 65th day. In monkeys, (*M. mulatta*) hormone is present in serum between the 18th and 35th day and is highest in the urine from the 22nd to the 32nd day. Maximum values were only a few score units per liter (85).

The hormone of pregnant mare serum (PMSG, equine cyonin, cf. 13) characteristically appears in the blood around the 42nd day of pregnancy, reaches peaks of 50,000–100,000 IU/liter between the 50th and 100th day and disappears by the 150th day. Adequate assays have been provided for mustangs, thoroughbreds, Welsh ponies, and Shetland ponies. In the latter, peak values of 400,000 IU/liter were found, but it does not appear to be generally true that the smallest breeds have the highest values. Pregnant donkeys and mares bearing mule fetuses showed low values (9, 16), and there was some tendency toward lower values in successive pregnancies. Pregnancy diagnosis in the mare is possible by immunoassay (92).

Gonadotropins have been recognized in the blood and urine or both of some other primates (macaque, chimpanzee, orangutan) and in the zebra, as well as the equidae just mentioned (17). Other animals, including cow, ewe, goat, rabbit, sow, and bitch, lack an explicitly gonadotropic hormone in their blood and urine; the rather few reports probably do not match the considerable efforts that have been expended to find such hormones in pregnant domestic animals.

c. *Prolactin, Growth Hormone, ACTH.* Prolactin was assayed in the serum of pregnant goats and showed little change until the fourth month, then a rise to within 10 days of parturition. There was a postpartum drop, then a further rise, which was maintained during 2 months of lactation (35). Prolactin was also detected in postpartum human urine and in the urine of newborns, in whom it elicits the secretion of "witches milk."

No systematic studies have been made of ACTH and growth hormone (STH) in pregnancy. But with increasing knowledge of the molecular make-up of all these hormones, the use of immunochemical assays may radically change this situation.

d. *Relaxin.* Increased secretion of relaxin is well documented in man, sow, cat, mare, rabbit, and guinea pig. Blood levels are low in early pregnancy, increase to plateaus in the last trimester, and fall after delivery.

5. *Uterine Growth and Involution*

Following implantation of the fetus or fetuses, uterine growth proceeds *pari passu* with the growth of the conceptus in a process which is exquisitely regulated to equilibrate volume and pressure changes. Uterine muscle cells probably do not increase in number, but they undergo profound hypertrophy, and there is active synthesis of the contractile protein, actomyosin (19). The uterine connective tissue hypertrophies, and collagen increases severalfold. The interfibrillar ground substance of the connective tissue, as shown by the staining of its glycoprotein elements, is strikingly increased and the vascular pattern of the uterus is progressively expanded. These changes can be reproduced in part by the administration of estrogen to a nonpregnant animal. In the sterile horn of a bicornuate uterus there are similar, if less drastic, changes. The local stimulus, as already stated, may be a mechanical or stretch factor. Also exceedingly important are hormonal or undefined biochemical stimuli provided by the blastocyst.

In uterine involution in the rat there is an exceedingly rapid loss of muscle cell cytoplasm (including actomyosin and nucleic acid), collagen, and ground substance. There appeared to be no preferential loss of water, and uterine dry weight decreased to one-sixth the immediately postpartum value in 5 days. Between 5 and 10 days, muscular elements reached nongravid proportions (36, 39, 57). In multiparous Angus cattle, uterine involution occupied 30 days, and the period was not significantly modified by a variety of procedures including: ovariectomy or removal of corpora lutea 2–4 days postpartum, removal of the calf at birth, addition of another suckling, and gonadotropin treatment leading to ovulation within a week of term (67).

The clinical and veterinary literature tends to describe uterine involution almost exclusively in pathological terms in which cell lysis, necrosis, hyaline change, and fatty degeneration figure prominently. While none of these features were seen in involuting rat uteri, it is possible that factors of birth trauma may be important in man and the larger domestic animals, and relatively less so in rodents. Certainly, investigation of this interesting process in the sow or sheep should be worthwhile.

6. The Mammary Glands in Pregnancy

The state of development of the mammary gland of an animal entering its first pregnancy depends on its prior hormonal history. The doe rabbit, which does not ovulate spontaneously, shows simple ductal growth and rudimentary alveoli characteristic of estrogen stimulation, while the bitch, which ovulates spontaneously and undergoes a prolonged and functional luteal phase, shows elaborate growth due to estrogen and progesterone action. Most domestic animals exhibit some variant of the latter situation. In pregnancy, the mammary gland undergoes further stimulation by estrogen and progesterone arising in the ovaries, placenta, and adrenal glands. Complete mammary development characteristically involves three stages: ductal growth conditioned by estrogen, lobular alveolar growth through the superimposition of progesterone, and initiation and maintenance of lactation by the action of prolactin. Qualitatively, these effects may overlap, and estrogens alone may produce extensive duct and alveolar development, with supervening lactation, in the guinea pig, goat, and cow. Progesterone alone may, similarly, produce extensive overall growth, but, in general, an optimal hormonal environment for mammary gland preparation involves progesterone to estrogen ratios varying for different species from 50:1 to 200:1, which, on the basis of an estimate for the cow (14), appears to hold true in pregnancy. In addition to hormonal factors directly bearing on the mammary gland, a favorable protein, fat, carbohydrate, water, and ionic metabolism must also be presupposed, since during milk production these components are sequestered from the blood and ultimately lost to the body.

B. PLACENTAL ENDOCRINE FUNCTIONS

Newton in 1938 (66) summarized the position of the placenta which he believed had an endocrine function in the control of gestation, but indicated that it was difficult to describe in precise terms, or to prove in detail. A somewhat similar view was expressed 25 years later (44). The placenta, "the liver of the fetus," is a metabolizing, storing, transmitting, and synthesizing organ, which seems to contain most things that have been sought in it. Placentas survive after removal of the fetus in rabbit, guinea pig, cat, mouse, rat, hamster, and monkey (60). In the monkey, fetuses may be removed from the 70th to 100th day of pregnancy and the placenta is delivered at about the expected time for normal birth. Its weight is then approximately the same as it would be if projected to the time of operation. Such persisting placentas are viable and continue to exert an endocrine role (86).

1. Steroid Hormones

Endocrine functions of the human placenta were reviewed (24). Lipid extracts of human, cow, sheep, and pig placentas which contained estrogen were obtained in the early 1930's, and estriol was isolated from the human placenta. The survey of Dorfman and Unger (26) lists no less than 21 steroids derived from placentas of different species, representing hormones or their metabolites, active or inactive biologically, which are identical with or related to naturally occurring steroid hormones. It appears well established that steroids are synthesized as well as transformed in the placenta, but the relative amounts of any given hormone formed *de novo* or transformed from maternal or fetal precursors are not known. At parturition, the urinary excretion of both estrogen and pregnanediol (in man) and of estrogen in the mare, cease abruptly, indicating a major contribution of the placenta or fetus, or both.

In the cow, where the ovary remains an important source of steroid hormones, fetal cotyledons contained estrone and estradiol 17-α and 17-β which were high in total amounts at calving and even higher postpartum (87).

Progesterone is found in human, monkey, and bovine placentas, but not in the placentas of ewe, sow, or bitch. However, pregnan or pregnen derivatives of progesterone are present in the placentas of man, horse, and sheep (14), and there seems every reason to suppose that the secretion of progesterone is a normal placental function in all species.

2. Polypeptide and Protein Hormones

The gonadotropic activity of human placenta was recognized from the earliest experiments of Zondek, and later work has identified the locus of synthesis with the Langhans cell.

In the pregnant mare placental attachment is tenuous before the 40th day although the uterine site is marked by an area of hyperemia (fertile endometrium) which, after the 40th day of pregnancy, was shown to contain large amounts of equine gonadotropin (PMSG), in contrast to other sites in the fertile and sterile horn, which were low in activity. At this time, highly specialized endometrial outgrowths, the "endometrial cups," begin to develop, closely invested by the allantochorion. Uterine glands in the cups enlarge and become filled with a mucoprotein-containing secretion which possesses very high gonadotropic potency, and stains intensely with iron hematoxylin and with the periodic acid-Schiff reagents. Cup secretion tends to parallel blood levels and there is circumstantial evidence that cells of the cup secrete the hormone, although the competent cell type has not yet been identified. Considerably less hormone is present in the endometrial cups of donkeys, and still less in mule pregnancies.

In spite of assiduous search, gonadotropic hormones have not been found in the placenta, endometrium, and amniotic fluid of the cow and sheep, nor in the placentas of sow, rabbit, or guinea pig.

3. Chemistry and Biology of Placental Gonadotropins

There has been intensive chemical, immunochemical, and biological study of the placental hormone of man (HCG) and the equine gonadotropin (PMSG) (33, 95). They are glycoproteins. The molecular weight of the HCG monomer is about 29,000 and that of PMSG in the region of 75,000, the latter figure explaining the virtual exclusion of the hormone from the urine of the pregnant mare. They differ from each other and from the accepted gonadotropins of the pituitary gland, LH and FSH, and also from the hormone of human menopause urine (HMG) in chemical and biological properties, while sharing a fair amount of immunochemical identity (27). Their function in man and the mare, and their absence in other species, has provided a continuing biological puzzle. In the mare, superovulation and luteinization of the ovarian follicles was correlated with peak titers of the hormone in the blood serum around the 60th day of pregnancy and indicates a gonadotropic function in the mare itself related to the provision and maintenance of a new crop of corpora lutea. There is presumptive evidence that the hormone is luteotropic in the mare and in some other species. In the human, new corpora are not formed, but the pregnancy hormone (HCG) is luteotropic in the rat, and this may be its function in man also. Alternatively, the hormones may be related to placental synthesis of progesterone.

4. Placental Luteotropins

The subject of luteotropins has been reviewed (76). Evidence for the existence of placental luteotropins is generally based on the rapid involution of the corpus luteum in unilaterally pregnant rabbits, cats, hamsters, and guinea pigs following removal of the gravid horn (4). Most of the cited work is over 30 years old. Possible luteotropic influences in the uterus other than the placenta, such as distention, presence of the fetus, and neurogenic stimuli mediated through the pituitary gland can be systematically eliminated, nor do deciduoma appear to be luteotropic (52).

In the ewe, a systematic study of synchronous embryo transfers to nonpregnant ewes showed that the presence of the blastocyst in the uterus by the 12th to 13th day of ovulation was essential to maintenance of the corpora lutea. The reciprocal experiment of removing embryos from mated ewes at selected times showed that if embryos were left until days 13–15, there was a marked extension of luteal function (65). Since sheep blastocysts lie free in the uterus until the 18th day, their luteotropic action does not seem to depend on actual attachment.

According to Astwood and Greep (7), rat placental luteotropin maintained corpus luteum function in hypophysectomized rats; it showed none of the usual gonadotropic actions in males or females and did not stimulate the pigeon crop. Ray et al. (71a) report, however, that rat placental extracts have luteotropic, mammotropic, lactogenic, and weak crop-sac-stimulating activities. Human pregnancy gonadotropin (HCG) was luteotropic in bovines (80). A substance has been obtained from human placenta, distinct from HCG and immunochemically related to human growth hormone (38, 45, 48), which is luteotropic in rats and lactogenic in pigeons and rabbits.

It now seems possible that a search for lactogens and luteotropins in placentas of different species could be profitable. Such substances, while not overtly gonadotropic, might show immunochemical affinities with existing hormones. Purification of the known hormones and production of specific antisera to them should provide one tool for this kind of study.

C. FETAL ENDOCRINE FUNCTIONS

The primordia of the endocrine glands are laid down in intrauterine life and differentiate so that by the time of delivery the glands usually possess a histological pattern of recognizably adult type, and may contain detectable amounts of their characteristic hormones. A systemic investigation of fetal endocrines would seek to determine: (1) when the gland becomes hormonally competent; (2) how the fetal endocrines react with each other; (3) how they respond at different times to maternal hormones in normal or abnormal amounts; (4) how the fetal secretions contribute to the placenta and to the maternal organism. Points 3 and 4 include questions of placental transmission. Relatively few of these objectives have been achieved in any instance. It is certain that steroid hormones which reach the fetus are transformed in various ways (96).

1. Fetal Gonads

Surgical or X-ray castration of fetuses late in intrauterine life produced partial or complete failure in development of the male (wolffian duct) accessories and persistence of female (müllerian duct) structures and the abnormality was prevented by administration of testosterone, suggesting that testicular androgen is formed before birth and determines the development of the fetal accessories. Moreover, extracts of fetal testes of the rat and bull are androgenic, if mildly so.

The gonads of both sexes, while genetically determined, normally develop in a maternal-fetal milieu, and attempts have been made to modify this by the addition of male or female sex hormones to the mother, or directly to the fetal circulation. More or less far-reaching modifications have been obtained in wolffian and müllerian ducts, the urogenital sinus, and the external genitalia in the rat, mouse, opossum, rabbit, and monkey. Thus, female pseudohermaphroditism was produced in the monkey M. mulatta by administration of testosterone propionate to the mothers beginning on the 41st to 69th day of a 168-day pregnancy (91).

Natural intersex production occurs in bovine twinning when through fusion of the chorioallantoic vessels a genetic female is masculinized. According to a time-honored hypothesis, male sex hormone proceeding from the male co-twin is responsible. Ovaries become testislike, male elements persist while female elements degenerate. Such freemartins are sterile. Sex reversal has not been produced experimentally in mammals, and some doubt has persisted as to the explanation of the phenomenon, particularly with regard to the nature of the fetal secretion responsible (See also Chapter 14).

Androgens injected into pregnant cows between the endometrium and the allantochorion at 37–80 days of gestation failed to transform the gonads, but did masculinize the external genitalia of female fetuses (46). In another study in which superfetation was produced hormonally with pregnant mare serum gonadotropin, it was observed that a single male fetus masculinized four female quintuplets to a lesser degree than in triplet or twin pregnancies. A hormonal gradient was postulated, based on concentration, surface area of anastomosis, and embryonic stage at the time the cross-circulation became effective (71).

The gonads of the horse fetus show a series of remarkable changes, related, presumably, to endocrine events in the mother. Beginning at a crown-rump length of 20 cm (100 days, approximately), the fetal gonads of both sexes undergo proliferation of interstitial cells, reaching a maximum size at 45–60 cm (6.5–8 months). In this process, the sex cells of the female are restricted to a narrow cortical zone and those of the male to scattered cords. The weight of the pair of gonads reaches 50–100 gm. Subsequently, involution of the interstitium sets in and at birth gonadal weight is reduced to 10–20 gm. Is PMSG responsible for the remarkable development of the fetal gonads? Although this gonadotropin disappears from the maternal blood before the fetal gonads reach their maximum size, reservoirs of the hormone in the allantochorionic pouches may account for the final stages of development (15a). Only traces of PMSG have been found, however, in fetal tissues. There is a close correlation of fetal gonad development with maternal estrogen which reaches the fetus and is detectable in fetal blood, gonads, liver, and kidneys. It may be the effective stimulus for interstitial proliferation (3, 77).

2. Fetal Thyroids

Accumulation of radioiodine is a sensitive indicator of thyroid function and has been successfully applied to a variety of animals. The thyroid acquires the capacity of accumulating iodine at a definite point in fetal life: near term in mouse and rat, at midpregnancy in the pig, at the beginning of the second trimester in sheep and man, and around the end of the first quarter in the bovine. In the macaque, uptake begins at the 75th day and steadily increases in parallel with an increase in follicular size and colloid content (69). The initial uptake of iodine may coincide with beginning follicle formation (mouse, rat, sheep) or be distinct from it (pig, cattle, macaque). The fetal sheep begins to accumulate iodine by the 50th day; by the 70th day, monoiodotyrosine, diiodotyrosine, and traces of thyroxine are demonstrable and after 115 days, triiodothyronine as well. Between the 70th and 130th day, a hundredfold increase in iodine-concentrating ability occurs (14).

3. Fetal Adrenals

In several species the fetal adrenal at birth is characterized by a thin outer cortical zone, which becomes the definitive cortex, and a thick inner zone, the androgenic zone, X-zone, or provisional zone. At birth the fetal adrenal of man is very large relative to the body weight, but soon the X-zone involutes and the gland becomes relatively and absolutely smaller in size. The endocrine basis of these relations continues to be obscure. However, the fetal adrenal is capable of forming steroids of androgenic and corticoid nature and is functional at birth, as shown by the excretion of 17-keto-steroids in the first 2 days of life and by the finding of glucocorticoids in the newborn.

Adrenalectomy of the mother (rat) produces hypertrophy of the fetal adrenal, presumably by an increase in maternal ACTH which crosses the placenta. The effect is abolished by hypophysectomy.

4. Fetal Hypophysis

The fetal hypophysis appears to control adrenal and thyroid size. Rabbit fetuses semidecapitated at 22 days (hypophyseopriva) grew comparably with litter mates, but thyroid and adrenal weights were significantly reduced by the 29th day (8).

III. Hormonal Mechanisms in Parturition

Observations on the domestic species have shown that the sex of the fetus and its genotype, the size of the litter, and the age and parity of the mother may all affect gestation length, although at what point in pregnancy the effects are exerted and how the change is mediated are not clear in any instance. The fetus could exert its influence through physical, metabolic, or hormonal means (15).

Experiments already quoted on the persistence of the placenta and its delivery at the normal expected time following fetal ablation should not be considered to negate the role of the fetus, but rather to emphasize that important elements of the parturition process are located at the uterine-placental locus. These influences are probably to a large extent hormonal in nature, and revolve around the intricate relationships between estrogens, progesterones, oxytocin, and relaxin.

A somewhat verbal approach to events in pregnancy and lactation is that the uterus proceeds from a state of estrogen dominance (at ovulation) to one of progesterone-dominance, which is maintained up to the time of parturition. A lifting of the progesterone "block" (which may be local at the site of placental attachment) initiates parturition. In pregnancy, besides the biochemical changes in the uterus already described, the major physiological change in the myometrium is an inhibition of spontaneous contractile activity and a decrease in sensitivity to the action of oxytocin. Both depend on estrogen and progesterone, but more particularly on the existence of a given ratio (19).

Important local differences exist within the uterus, and in the cow the differential sensitivity of corpus uteri and cervix to oxytocin favors retention of the fetus in midpregnancy and its expulsion later (15). Placental production of steroid hormones would permit local actions to determine uterine sensitivity (19).

A. ESTROGEN

Gradually rising amounts of estrogen characterize later pregnancy in man, mare, cow, sheep, and pig, and it seems likely that this is a general mammalian pattern. Estrogen is an anabolic hormone for the uterus, genital tract, and mammary gland and its presence throughout pregnancy may reflect this metabolic role. Estrogen increases the spontaneous activity of the myometrium, an action which is normally held in check by progesterone. In sufficient dosage, estrogens will terminate pregnancy in many species, including the rat, guinea pig, cow, and sheep, but not in the human (15). These facts point to a sensitizing action of estrogen on the myometrium of late pregnancy.

B. PROGESTERONE

In some species, such as the rabbit, rat, mouse, pig, and cow, there is evidence for one or more of the following criteria for progesterone involvement in parturition: (1) a periparturition fall in blood progesterone; (2) pregnancy is prolonged by progesterone injection; (3) ovariectomy terminates pregnancy unless progesterone is supplied. Such findings support the thesis that at parturition a progesterone block is removed. However, in the human, monkey, ewe, and mare, the ovaries are dispensable after a certain point without augmentation with progesterone and progesterone levels remain high in maternal or fetal blood until birth. The situation in these animals does not support a simple progesterone theory of parturition (79).

C. OXYTOCIN

It appears certain that oxytocin, an octapeptide hormone of the posterior pituitary gland, is involved in normal parturition and its main physiological actions generally become manifest late in pregnancy. The fact that hypophysectomy or posterior lobe removal do not appear to disturb the duration of gestation or parturition in rats, rabbits, or monkeys does not rule out participation of oxytocin released from the proximal end of the cut stalk.

Changing levels of estrogen and progesterone, and especially an increase in the estrogen:progesterone ratio, would be expected to sensitize the uterus to oxytocin whether the secretion of the latter is increased or not. The question of oxytocin release appears, in fact, to involve species differences. In the rat there is strong spontaneous uterine activity for several days before parturition, while the rabbit uterus is relatively quiescent, and parturition may involve the sudden release of a large amount of oxytocin in the latter (30). In the goat no oxytocin was detected in the jugular vein blood during a period from 80 days to 7.25 hours before the beginning of the second stage of labor. During this stage, hormone was found and rose to a maximum; following expulsion of the fetus, it fell abruptly. The interpretation of these results was that oxytocin is not essential for the induction of labor, but is released in response to distention stimuli to the vagina and vulva and assists parturition through its contractile effect on the uterus (29). Closely similar results were reported for the cow (28). In sheep, using radiosondes to record intrauterine pressure, no significant myometrial activity was observed until 12 hours before delivery. Here again, a sudden release of oxytocin at some stage of parturition appears probable (42).

D. Relaxin

Various roles of relaxin in the economy of the pregnant uterus have been suggested. In particular, the specific effect of relaxin on the ground substance of the connective tissue would tend to decrease the effect of muscular pull. It is difficult to visualize the pregnant uterus as undergoing a continuous process of "stretching." Rather, pressure-volume relations would seem at all times to be equilibrated by mutual adjustments of muscular and connective tissue elements of the myometrium.

The specific role of relaxin in loosening symphyseal and other joints at the time of parturition has already been noted (p. 419).

E. Fetus

While it is generally denied that the fetal endocrines play an important role in parturition, surgical lesions of the fetal lamb pituitary (or in both, in the case of twins) at 93 to 143 days caused prolongation of pregnancy beyond 160 days (54).

In the mare the fetal genotype determines the formation of the endometrial cups in the fertile uterine horn, and also their secretion and content of equine gonadotropin (PMSG). The nature of the fetal secretion responsible is entirely unknown. It may arise in certain exceedingly active-appearing cells of the allantochorion once thought to secrete the equine gonadotropin itself (13).

It is tempting to reproduce data on the gestation length of various horse and donkey crosses (Table 4) to illustrate further the effect of fetal genotype.

Additional clues to the relationship of fetus and time of birth may possibly be drawn from certain observations on delayed parturition. In macaque monkeys, the birth weights of fetuses carried naturally beyond the

TABLE IV
GESTATION LENGTH IN VARIOUS EQUINE CROSSES[a]

Reciprocal crosses	Gestation length (days)
Stallion × mare	340 (horse foal)
Stallion × jennet	350 (hinney foal)
Jack × mare	355 (mule foal)
Jack × jennet	365 (donkey foal)

[a] From Asdell (6) and Short (79).

mean gestation time of 167–168 days were well above the growth curve of infants born on the 167th day and maintained on a "best-known" dietary regime (86). This relative advantage lasted until the 180th day, showing that the uterine environment was entirely adequate up to this time. After the 180th day, birth weights invariably fell below the mean growth curve. It may be inferred that there is a critical point at which uteroplacental relations become unfavorable to the fetus. Is such a "negative" set of conditions able to trigger the birth process, and what is its nature? From the foregoing account, a unique mechanism for parturition has not been forthcoming and a newborn progeny, while it nicely explains itself, remains the enigma of pregnancy.

REFERENCES

1. Ainsworth, L., and Ryan, K. J., *Endocrinology* **79**, 875 (1966).
2. Alexander, G., and Williams, D., *J. Endocrinol.* **34**, 241 (1966).
3. Amoroso, E. D., in "5th Conference on Gestation," p. 15. Josiah Macy Jr. Found., New York, 1959.
4. Amoroso, E. C., in "The Placenta and Fetal Membranes" (C. A. Villee, ed.), p. 3. Williams & Wilkins, Baltimore, Maryland, 1960.
5. Annison, E. F., and Lewis, D., *J. Agr. Sci.* **52**, 79 (1959).
6. Asdell, S. A., "Patterns of Mammalian Reproduction." Cornell Univ. Press, Ithaca, New York, 1964.
7. Astwood, E. B., and Greep, R. O., *Science* **89**, 81 (1939).
8. Bearn, J. G., *J. Endocrinol.* **36**, 213 (1966).
9. Bell, E. T., Loraine, J. A., Jennings, S., and Weaver, A. D., *Quart. J. Exptl. Physiol.* **52**, 68 (1967).
10. Benoit, J., and DaLage, C., "Cytologie de l'Adenohypophyse." Masson, Paris, 1963.
11. Brinkley, H. J., Norton, H. W., and Nalbandov, A. V., *Endocrinology* **74**, 14 (1964).
12. Burrows, H., "Biological Action of the Sex Hormones." Cambridge Univ. Press, Cambridge, 1949.
13. Catchpole, H. R., in "Gonadotropins" (H. H. Cole, ed.), p. 40. Freeman, San Francisco, California, 1964.

14. Catchpole, H. R., *in* "Reproduction in Domestic Animals" (H. H. Cole and P. T. Cupps, eds.), Vol. 1, p. 469. Academic Press, New York, 1959.

15. Clegg, M. T., *in* "Reproduction in Domestic Animals" (H. H. Cole and P. T. Cupps, eds.), Vol. 1, p. 509. Academic Press, New York, 1959.

15a. Clegg, M. T., Boda, G. M., and Cole, H. H., *Endocrinology* **54**, 448 (1954).

16. Clegg, M. T., Cole, H. H., Howard, C. B., and Pigon, H., *J. Endocrinol.* **25**, 245 (1962).

17. Cowie, A. T., *Commonwealth Agr. Bur. (Gt. Brit.) Joint Publ.* **13** (1948).

18. Cowie, A. T., Daniel, P. M., Prichard, M. M. L., and Tindal, J. S., *J. Endocrinol.* **28**, 93 (1963).

19. Csapo, A., *Ciba Found. Study Group* **9**, 3 (1961).

20. Day, B. N., Anderson, L. L., Hazel, L. N., and Melampy, R. M., *J. Animal Sci.* **46**, 675 (1959).

21. Deanesly, R., *in* "Marshall's Physiology of Reproduction" (A. S. Parkes, ed.), Vol. 3, p. 91, Little, Brown, Boston, Massachusetts, 1966.

22. Denamur, R., and Martinet, J., *Ann. Endocrinol. (Paris)* **22**, 755 (1961).

23. Denamur, R., and Mauleon, P., *Compt. Rend. Acad. Sci.* **257**, 527 (1963).

24. Diczfalusy, E., *Federation Proc.* **23**, 791 (1964).

25. Donaldson, L. E., Hansel, W., and Van Vleck, L. D., *J. Dairy Sci.* **48**, 331, 1965.

26. Dorfman, R. I., and Ungar, F., "Metabolism of Steroid Hormones." Academic Press, New York, 1965.

27. Ely, C. A., and Chen, B. L., *Endocrinology* **79**, 362 (1966).

28. Fitzpatrick, R. J., and Walmsley, C. F., *J. Physiol. (London)* **163**, 13P-14P (1962).

29. Folley, S. J., and Knaggs, G. S., *J. Endocrinol.* **33**, 301 (1965).

30. Fuchs, A. R., *J. Reprod. Fertility* **12**, 418 (1966).

31. Gersh, I., *Harvey Lectures Ser.* **45**, 211 (1952).

32. Gersh, I., and Catchpole, H. R., *Perspectives Biol. Med.* **3**, 282 (1960).

33. Geschwind, I. I., *in* "Gonadotropins" (H. H. Cole, ed.), p. 1. Freeman, San Francisco, California, 1964.

34. Gomez, W. R., and Erb, R. E., *J. Dairy Sci.* **48**, 314 (1965).

35. Goto, T., and Notsuki, I., *Bull. Natl. Inst. Agr. Sci. Ser. G.* **20**, 199 (1961).

36. Grant, R. A., *J. Reprod. Fertility* **9**, 285 (1965).

37. Greenwald, G. S., *Endocrinology* **79**, 572 (1966).

38. Grumbach, M. M., and Kaplan, S. L., *Trans. N. Y. Acad. Sci.* [2] **27**, 167 (1964–1965).

39. Harkness, R. D., *Biol. Rev.* **36**, 399 (1961).

40. Hawk, H. W., Turner, G. D., Brinsfield, T. H., Whitmore, G. E., Norcross, M. A., and Sykes, J. F., *J. Animal Sci.* **19**, 1325 (1960).

41. Heap, R. B., and Deanesly, R., *J. Endocrinol.* **34**, 417 (1966).

42. Hindson, J. C., Schofield, B. M., Turner, C. B., and Wolff, H. S., *J. Physiol. (London)* **181**, 560 (1965).

43. Hisaw, F. L., Jr., and Hisaw, F. L., *Am. J. Obstet. Gynecol.* **89**, 141 (1964).

44. Hisaw, F. L., *in* "Gonadotropins" (H. H. Cole, ed.), p. 223. Freeman, San Francisco, California, 1964.

45. Ito, Y., and Higashi, K., *Endocrinol. Japon.* **8**, 279, 288 (1961).

46. Jaenudeen, M. R., and Hafez, E. S. E., *J. Reprod. Fertility* **10**, 281 (1965)

47. Johnson, K. R., and Erb, R. E., *J. Dairy Sci.* **45**, 633 (1962).

48. Josimovich, J. B., and Brande, B. L., *Trans. N. Y. Acad. Sci.* [2] **27**, 161 (1964–1965).
49. Karlson, P., and Sekeris, C. E., *Acta Endocrinol.* **53**, 505 (1966).
50. Kenneth, J. H., *Imp. Bur. Animal Breeding Genet.* (Edinburgh) *Tech. Commun.* **5** (1947).
51. Kilpatrick, R., Armstrong, D. T., and Greep, R. O., *Endocrinology* **74**, 453, (1964).
52. Kirby, D. R. S., *J. Reprod. Fertility* **10**, 403 (1965).
53. Leathem, J. H., *J. Animal Sci.* **25**, Suppl. 68 (1966).
54. Liggins, G. C., Holm, L. W., and Kennedy, P. C., *J. Reprod. Fertility* **12**, 419 (1966).
55. Lunaas, T., *J. Reprod. Fertility* **4**, 13, 1962.
56. McCaa, C. S., and Sulya, L. L., *Endocrinology* **79**, 815, 1966.
57. Maibenco, H. C., *Anat. Record* **136**, 59 (1960).
58. Marshall, F. H. A., "The Physiology of Reproduction." Longmans, Green, New York, 1910.
59. Marshall, J. M., *J. Exptl. Med.* **94**, 21 (1951).
60. Mayer, G., and Klein, M., "Les Hormones du Placenta." Masson, Paris, 1955.
61. Melampy, R. M., Henricks, D. M., Anderson, L. L., Chen, C. L., and Schultz, J. R., *Endocrinology* **78**, 801 (1966).
62. Mellin, T. N., and Erb, R. E., *J. Dairy Sci.* **48** (687), 1965.
63. Mellin, T. N., Erb, R. E., and Estergreen, V. L., Jr., *J. Animal Sci.* **25**, 955 (1966).
64. Metzler, F., Eleftheriou, B. E., and Fox, M., *Proc. Soc. Exptl. Biol. Med.* **121**, 374 (1966).
65. Moor, R. M., and Rowson, L. E. A., *J. Endocrinol.* **34**, 233, 497 (1966).
66. Newton, W. H., *Physiol. Rev.* **18**, 419 (1938).
67. Oxenreider, S. L., *J. Animal Sci.* **25**, 1264 (1966).
68. Parlow, A. F., Anderson, L. L., and Melampy, R. M., *Endocrinology* **75**, 365 (1964).
69. Pickering, D. E., and Kontaxis, N. E., *Endocrinology* **23**, 267 (1961).
70. Pope, G. S., Jones, H. E. H., and Waynforth, H. B., *J. Endocrinol.* **33**, 385 (1965).
71. Rajakoski, E., and Hafez, E. S. E., *J. Animal Sci.* **23**, 864 (1964).
71a. Ray, E. W., Averill, S. C., Lyons, W. R., and Johnson, R. E., *Endocrinology* **56**, 359 (1955).
72. Rebbe, H., and Alling Møller, K. J., *Acta Obstet. Gynecol. Scand.* **45**, 261 (1966).
73. Rennie, P., Davies, J., and Friedrich, E., *Endocrinology* **75**, 622 (1964).
74. Reynolds, S. R. M., "Physiology of the Uterus." Hafner, New York, 1965.
75. Rombauts, P., *Ann. Biol. Animale Biochim. Biophys.* **2**, 151 (1962).
76. Rothchild, I., *Vitamins Hormones* **23**, 209, 1965.
77. Rowlands, I. W., *in* "Gonadotropins" (H. H. Cole, ed.), p. 74. Freeman, San Francisco, California, 1964.
78. Saba, N., *J. Agr. Sci.* **64**, 11 (1965).
79. Short, R. V., *J. Reprod. Fertility* **1**, 61 (1960).
80. Simmons, K. R., and Hansel, W., *J. Animal Sci.* **23**, 136 (1964).
81. Skrzeczkowski, L., *Endokrynol. Polska* **16**, 243 (1965).
82. Spector, W. S., "Handbook of Biological Data." Saunders, Philadelphia, Pennsylvania, 1956.

83. Spies, H. G., Zimmerman, D. R., Self, H. L., and Casida, L. E., *J. Animal Sci.* **19**, 114 (1960).
84. Stormshak, F., and Erb, R. E., *J. Dairy Sci.* **44**, 310 (1961).
85. Tullner, W. W., and Hertz, R., *Endocrinology* **78**, 204, 1076 (1966).
86. Van Wagenen, G., and Catchpole, H. R., *Am. J. Phys. Anthropol.* **23**, 23 (1965).
87. Veenhuizen, E. L., Erb, R. E., and Gorski, J., *J. Dairy Sci.* **43**, 270 (1960).
88. Velle, W., *Advan. Vet. Sci.* **8**, 115 (1963).
89. Venning, E. H., Primrose, T., Caligaris, L. C. S., and Dyrenfurth, I., *Clin. Endocrinol. Metab.* **17**, 473 (1957).
90. Villee, C. A., *Ciba Found. Colloq. Aging* **2**, 129 (1956).
91. Wells, L. J., and van Wagenen, G., *Carnegie Inst. Wash. Contrib. Embryol.* **35**, 93 (1954).
92. Wide, L., and Wide, M., *Nature* **198**, 1017 (1963).
93. Williams, R. J., and Stott, G. H., *J. Dairy Sci.* **49**, 1262 (1966).
94. Wislocki, G. B., *Ciba Found. Colloq. Aging* **2**, 105 (1956).
95. Wolstenholme, G. E. W., and Knight, J., Eds., *Ciba Found. Study Group* **22** (1965).
96. Zander, J., *Ciba Found. Study Group* **9**, 32 (1961).
97. Zarrow, M. X., *in* "Sex and Internal Secretions" (W. T. Young, ed.), p. 958, Williams & Wilkins, Baltimore, Maryland, 1961.
98. Zimbelman, R. G., and Smith, L. W., *J. Animal Sci.* **22**, 868 (1963).

16 MAMMARY GROWTH AND LACTATION

R. L. BALDWIN

I. Introduction

The preparation of a general, concise treatment of mammary gland morphogenesis, growth, and the initiation and maintenance of lactation requires extensive reliance upon reference to previous treatments of the subject to provide guides to the historical development of knowledge in the area and to detailed treatments of specific topics. Emphasis in this chapter is placed upon summarization of information on the mammary gland and lactation and critical evaluation of literature in areas of current research emphasis.

II. Morphogenesis and Development of the Mammary Gland

Turner (111) considered both the gross and the microscopic anatomy of the mammary gland of cattle and other hoofed animals and of marine mammals. Other reviewers have considered the anatomy of the mammary glands of a number of other species, including lower mammals (70), rats (97), mice (34), guinea pigs (11), and humans (23). Raynaud (88), Turner (111), Jacobsohn (47), Munford (81), and others (19, 69, 102) have reviewed mammary gland morphogenesis and postnatal development in a number of species.

A. MORPHOGENESIS

The basic sequences of events during morphogenesis of the mammary glands are similar in most species (88, 111). Two milk lines become apparent on the abdomens of very early fetuses. Epidermal thickenings are soon formed at points along the milk lines which correspond in placement, to the points at which mammary glands will be formed in the particular species examined. In the case of the bovine fetus, for example, four epidermal thickenings are formed on the milk lines in the inguinal region between the hind limbs. The epidermal thickenings are called "mammary buds." The mammary buds themselves do not differentiate to form mammary structures, but rather serve as a focal point for the differentiation of dermis, ectodermis, and mesenchyme. Early in development, the mammary buds sink into the mesenchyme and a condensation of mesenchymal cells takes place around the bud causing the appearance of embryonic teat hillocks. Also at this stage, ectodermal cells overlying the bud proliferate to form a neck of epidermis connecting the mammary buds to the epidermis at the apex of the teat hillock. In subsequent stages, the epidermal neck increases in size and forms a funnel-shaped cone at the base of which an epithelial cord or primary sprout extending the length of the fetal teat develops. The primary sprout canalizes starting at the apex of the teat during the 19-cm stage such that when the fetus reaches 30 cm in length, structures corresponding to the streak canal and teat cistern are clearly defined. These are composed of a basement membrane and a double-layered lining of epithelial cells. At the base of the teat a clearly defined structure corresponding to the gland cistern, formed from the primary sprout during canalization and lined with a double layer of epithelial cells, is evident. Secondary and tertiary sprouts representing the beginnings of the duct system of the gland leave the cistern and penetrate the surrounding mesenchyme in various directions. During later stages of fetal development, the mesenchyme differentiates to form the connective tissue which will support the fully developed mammary gland, the connective glandular stroma which will ultimately surround the lobuloalveolar structures of the fully developed mammary gland, and adipose tissue which surrounds the glandular elements and comprises the bulk of the udder at birth.

The duct system is still rudimentary at birth and is confined to a very small area surrounding the gland cistern. The teats are well formed with the exception that the sphincter muscle surrounding the streak canal at the apex of the teat and the smooth muscle cells surrounding the teat cistern are not clearly evident. The connective stroma and the vascular and lymphatic systems are reasonably well developed.

Numerous data summarized by Raynaud (88) and Cowie and Folley (19) indicate that hormonal influences are not necessary for prenatal mammary development. Hardy (44), for example, reported that normal mammary growth and differentiation occurred when explants of the ventral body walls of embryos were cultured in vitro, in the absence of hormones. The primary hormonal effect during development occurs in the male as a result of the secretion of androgens by the developing testes. The androgens inhibit teat growth and stimulate the proliferation of mesenchymal cells surrounding the mammary bud at its junction with the epidermis, causing a constriction of the epithelial cord and, finally, detachment of the mammary bud from the external epidermis. This effect can be obviated in the male embryo through castration or irradiation of the testes or produced in female embryos by injection of testosterone. Although estrogens are not required, the developing mammary is sensitive to estrogens, large doses inhibit mammary bud growth and induce abnormal development (88).

B. PREPUBERTAL DEVELOPMENT

The development of the mammary glands from birth to puberty is largely characterized by generalized growth and maturation of elements not clearly defined at birth such as the teat sphincter and smooth muscle fibers. A number of techniques have been employed to investigate changes which occur during this period. Matthews et al. (69) and Swett et al. (102) used gross morphological criteria such as changes in the weights, dimensions, and capacities of udders of heifers to characterize growth and development. Cowie and Folley (17) and Silver (97), Flux (34), and Benson et al. (11) employed histological techniques for quantitative measurement of development and degree of branching of the mammary duct system.

Udder weight in calves was highly correlated with age (69). Udder size as assessed by palpation of calves between 3 and 5 months of age was somewhat related to subsequent lactation performance, an observation which led to the proposal that these measurements might be employed to cull calves of low production potential at an early age (102). However, the usefulness of size and weight criteria for predicting future lactational performance has been seriously questioned (81, 111) on the grounds that individual variance is very large and that these criteria do not distinguish between development of the mammary parenchyma and growth of associated adipose tissue. Criteria based upon measurement of increases in gland capacity or internal volume determined by injection of fluids appear to be useful; these have not been employed extensively to assess development, however, because of the difficult and unphysiological nature of the measurement. A steady increase in udder capacity or internal volume, presumably reflecting growth of the gland cistern and duct proliferation, has been reported for a number of species (69, 81, 91).

Measurements of mammary duct growth, degree of branching, and duct area in whole-gland mounts have been employed to characterize prepubertal mammary gland development in mice and rats (17, 34, 97). Mammary gland growth was isometric with respect to the rate of growth of the body as a whole for a period after birth, but became allometric (faster than the overall growth rate) several weeks prior to the onset of estrous cycles. In ovariectomized females and normal and castrate males, mammary gland growth rates were isometric throughout this period. The whole-gland mount technique is difficult to employ for the study of rats and mice after puberty because the glands start to develop in three dimensions at this time. The technique assumes a two-dimensional model. Nor, for this reason, can the technique be employed to study prepubertal development in species such as guinea pigs and goats, whose glands have a three-dimensional structure at birth. Techniques for the study of prepubertal and postpubertal growth in mammary glands having a three-dimensional structure have been developed (11, 80, 81). These techniques involve tedious measurements of percentage of gland parenchyma and of average cross-sectional areas of serial or sample sections of the gland. Results obtained with these techniques confirm the observation that mammary growth is isometric early in life and becomes allometric prior to puberty as a result of prepubertal ovarian activity (11).

C. Postpubertal Development

Although, as just indicated, allometric growth of the glandular epithelium commences prior to the onset of puberty, this period is generally considered to represent the time during which a rapid acceleration of the mammary development occurs. At the onset of puberty the gland cistern and the large ducts which lead from it are composed of a double layer of epithelial cells bordered by a slightly developed basement membrane surrounded by layers of connective tissue. The smaller ducts are composed of a single layer of epithelial cells surrounded by thin, delicate layers of connective tissue. Following puberty, the smaller ducts proliferate very quickly while estrogen levels are high and regress slowly during other phases of the estrous cycle. In each cycle, more ducts are formed during the period of proliferation than are lost during the period of regression with the net result that a highly branched matrix of ducts is slowly developed. This matrix represents the beginning of the development of true lobular structures. The proliferation of ducts and ductules is accompanied by or, in the human, preceded by development of the connective stroma, growth of adipose tissue, and further development of the myoepithelium and the vascular and lymphatic systems. It is at this stage that species differences arise due, in part, to differences in estrous cycles and, in part, to inherent species differences in the response of the glandular elements to the ovarian hormones. In the latter case, it has been noted that in cows, goats, and rodents (70, 111) considerable growth of adipose tissue occurs during this period and the development of the connective stroma lags behind duct growth, while in the human, adipose tissue growth is more limited and the connective stroma becomes highly developed (23). Mayer and Klein (70) noted that, in general, species which have short estrous cycles with a very short luteal phase exhibit, primarily, duct growth, while in species such as the dog where the cyclic corpus luteum is very long-lived, duct growth is accompanied by considerable lobuloalveolar development. Hence, estrogen is considered to be largely responsible, either directly or indirectly, for duct growth and lobuloalveolar development to be dependent upon progesterone.

D. DEVELOPMENT DURING PREGNANCY AND EARLY LACTATION

The mammary gland attains its maximum development during pregnancy or immediately thereafter. The development which occurs during this period is dependent upon estrogen, progesterone, and pituitary hormones. The role of pituitary secretions in development will be discussed in detail in Sections II, B and II, C.

The basic structure of the fully developed mammary gland is the lobule, which has a volume of 0.7–0.8 mm^3 (116) and is made up of alveoli and intralobular ducts and is surrounded by connective tissue. The intralobular ducts connect with interlobular ducts, these in turn join larger ducts, which provide the route for removal of milk formed in the alveolar cells to the gland cistern. The alveoli are small vesicles or sacs made up of secretory epithelial cells which face inward toward the lumen of the sac or alveolus. The alveoli are surrounded by a basement membrane, fine networks of capillaries and myoepithelial cells. Lymphatic capillaries are found in the interlobular connective tissue, but not in the intralobular areas. The mechanism of milk secretion by the alveolar epithelial cells has been reviewed by Turner (111) and Mayer and Klein (70). They concluded that although the secretory cells undergo considerable destruction as evidenced by the presence of enzymes (15, 32) and subcellular particles in milk (38), the mechanism of secretion is conservative or mesocrine in nature, except during milk removal, when it may be partially holocrine in type, resulting in cell decapitation.

Numerous studies summarized by Meites in the previous edition of this text (72) and elsewhere (73) have been undertaken with the goal of developing techniques for the artificial initiation of lactation. These studies were based on the premises that full mammary development occurs during pregnancy as a result of maintenance of an appropriate balance between the levels and ratios of progesterone and estrogen secretion; and, the initiation of lactation is caused by the abrupt changes in the levels of these hormones that occur at parturition. The most promising experimental techniques for initiating lactation are based upon the administration of estrogen or estrogen-progesterone combinations to induce udder growth, followed by administration of a "triggering" dose of estrogen to initiate lactation. The estrogen-progesterone combinations seem to be preferred because they usually induce the most satisfactory lobuloalveolar development as assessed by histological examination or measurement of the surface area of secretory epithelium. However, the results obtained with either estrogen-progesterone or estrogen alone are quite variable due to differences in hormone balances between animals and to side effects such as the development of cystic ovaries. Various methods of hormone administration ranging from daily subcutaneous injections to feeding have been attempted. The implantation of estrogen and progesterone containing pellets is one of the preferred techniques because it is more practical than daily injections or feeding. Meites (73) reported that pellets containing 100 mg diethylstilbestrol and 3 gm progesterone implanted in cows for 3 months followed by implantation of an additional pellet containing 1.5 gm diethylstilbestrol for 1 month caused good gland development and that lactation could be initiated by removal of both pellets followed by initiation of milking. Milk yields were usually below those observed in normal cattle after calving, but several animals produced at high levels and one cow produced up to 80 lb of milk per day. The discouraging aspect of the results is the large individual variations in milk production by cows and goats during induced lactations. The variations are presumably due, in part, to differences in the physiological backgrounds upon which the hormone treatments are imposed in individual animals (73).

Barnawell (8) induced lobuloalveolar development in intact rats, guinea pigs, hamsters, rabbits, and dogs by subcutaneous injection of various combinations of estradiol benzoate and progesterone in oil. Administration to rats of 0.5 μg estradiol benzoate and 2 mg progesterone daily for 15 days induced abundant lobuloalveolar development. In guinea pigs, small to moderate amounts of secretion were observed in addition to good lobuloalveolar development after 22 days of daily administration of 5 μg estradiol benzoate and 500 μg progesterone. Daily injections of 15 μg estradiol benzoate and 100 μg progesterone into rabbits induced abundant lobuloalveolar development.

E. Changes during Lactation and Involution

After the initiation of lactation very little additional development of glandular structures is evident histologically, although biochemical development continues in many species. The hormonal regulation of postpartum development and the hormonal requirements for the maintenance of lactation will be discussed in later sections. Some degeneration of glandular structures may occur during prolonged lactation, however, the major degenerative changes which occur are associated with cessation of milk removal or weaning and subsequent involution. The changes which occur during involution are characterized by a rapid decrease in metabolic activity, loss of secretory capacity, regression of lobuloalveolar structures within a few days, and, finally, return of the gland to an approximation of the virgin state. Several data indicate that the cessation of milk synthesis during the initial stages of weaning is due to feedback inhibition of key enzymes of milk synthesis by accumulated products (57, 68) and that normal rates of milk secretion can be restored by milk removal (111). Within a short period (days) after cessation of milk removal sufficient regression of the tissues has occurred such that lactation cannot be restored. This latter effect is presumably due to the release of lysomal enzymes (98) and to cessation of secretion of hormones required for gland maintenance (32).

III. Hormonal Requirements for Mammary Gland Development and Lactation

A. METHODS OF EVALUATION

1. Criteria of Development

Several of the morphological and histological techniques that have been employed to characterize and quantitate mammary gland development were discussed in previous sections on development during morphogenesis, puberty, and early pregnancy. Many of these techniques have also been employed in studies of hormonal effects upon mammary tissue and in the study of changes occurring in mammary glands during late pregnancy and lactation. However, their usefulness during these periods is impaired by a number of factors. The difficulty in assessing development in glands possessing a three-dimensional structure was referred to in Section I, D. Other factors which affect the interpretation and usefulness of histological methods include distention of glandular structures by colostral secretions during late pregnancy and accumulation of fluids in late pregnancy and early lactation. Differences in amounts of accumulated fluids and secretions must be corrected for when measurements of cross-sectional areas and percentages of parenchyma in selected or sequential gland sections are used to assess growth and development. Several histological techniques which avoid these difficulties have yielded considerable information concerning gland development in late pregnancy and lactation. One of these uses numbers of cell divisions as a criterion of continuing growth and development. Numbers of cell divisions are usually determined by estimating frequencies of mitoses directly (48, 84), by estimating frequencies of mitotic events in glands after treatment with colchicine which inhibits cell division at metaphase (48, 39), or by estimating numbers of radioactive nuclei present after administration of tritiated thymidine (101, 107). This latter technique provides a basis of assessing the types of cells being formed (*107*). Another approach involves histometric investigation of the numbers of alveoli in selected gland sections and numbers of cells (nuclei) per alveolus. When these estimates are coupled with counts of total nuclei per gland (*58*), numbers of alveolar cells per gland can be calculated (*80*). Munford (*81*) reviewed these techniques in considerable detail.

A number of biochemical techniques have been employed to study changes in numbers and types of cells in the mammary glands during pregnancy, lactation, and involution. Perhaps the most prominent index employed to study changes in cell numbers has been DNA content. Use of this index of cellularity implies acceptance of the assumptions that DNA per nucleus remains constant throughout various stages and that no changes in average numbers of nuclei per cell occur. Tucker and Reece (*108*) showed that DNA per nucleus remains constant throughout pregnancy and lactation in rats. However, the assumption that average numbers of nuclei per cell is constant is not totally valid since several data, reviewed by Mayer and Kline (*70*), indicate that there is an increase in numbers of multinucleate cells during late pregnancy and early lactation. The increase in multinucleate cells must be considered in the interpretation of DNA data, but does not reduce the usefulness of this measurement. Other measurements of gland composition, including dermal spreading activity (*81*), protein, collagen, lipid, and lactose (*118*), have been employed as criteria of gland development. Estimates of metabolic activity including estimates of oxygen uptake and RQ of gland slices and homogenates (*19, 89*), estimates of enzyme activities and *in vitro* studies of rates of synthesis of milk components (*4, 7, 40, 81*) have been employed to study development and to assess hormonal effects. Metabolic data must always be interpreted with great care since these generally reflect metabolic capacity or potential and not, necessarily, *in vivo* activity.

2. *In Vivo Techniques*

Studies of the hormonal requirements for gland development and the initiation of lactation in intact animals such as those discussed briefly in Section II, D have contributed significantly to the development of knowledge of hormonal relationships in mammary growth and lactation. However, interpretation of *in vivo* studies with intact animals within the context of defining specific hormone requirements becomes very difficult when one considers that the hormone treatments are usually imposed upon ill-defined or individually variable bases and that hormones can affect mammary development indirectly as well as directly. Consider, for example, estrogens which can alter ovarian function (Chapter 9) and prolactin secretion (Chapter 7), in addition to its direct influences in stimulating duct growth and increasing the responsiveness of the mammary gland to prolactin (*76*). In order to avoid secondary endocrine effects that can arise as a result of administration of hormones, various workers (*19, 21, 32, 66, 82*) preferred to use hypophysectomized, ovariectomized and/or adrenalectomized animals to study the hormone requirements for mammary gland development and the initiation and maintenance of lactation. Jacobsohn (*47*) emphasized that great care must be taken to determine the effects of these various endocrinectomies upon the general physiological status of animals and, in cases where replacement therapies are employed, to distinguish between "permissive" hormonal effects arising from improvement of physiological status and direct hormonal effects on the tissue.

3. In Vitro Techniques

In recent years, tremendous progress has been made in assessing the specific hormonal requirements for mammary gland growth and differentiation through the use of *in vitro* gland and cell culture techniques (*46, 55, 82, 87, 100, 101*). The clear advantages of these techniques are rigorous control and characterization of experimental conditions and specific manipulation of the environment. The primary difficulties or limitations encountered appear to arise from the small amounts of tissue available for study from gland cultures and from the loss of secretory activities in cell culture (*27*). These difficulties force the investigator to employ histological or very limited biochemical criteria for the assessment of hormonal effects in gland culture (*46, 101*) and make results obtained in established cell cultures difficult to interpret. In some instances the specific circumstances associated with the loss of certain activities can prove to be meaningful (*27*).

B. DEVELOPMENT DURING PREGNANCY

Several aspects of mammary gland development during puberty and pregnancy were discussed in Sections II, C and II, D, where it was implied that estrogen and progesterone are the primary hormones required for development in intact animals during this period, that estrogen stimulated duct growth, and that progesterone regulated lobuloalveolar development. In general, these implications are correct, but species differences, the role(s) of hormones from the anterior pituitary, and interactions between ovarian and pituitary hormones must also be considered.

Cowie and Folley (*19*) and others (*47, 73, 111*) considered species differences in response to ovarian hormones as representing three broad categories. Species in the first category include rats, mice, rabbits, and cats and are described as exhibiting only duct growth when physiological doses of estrogen are administered. In these species lobuloalveolar growth occurs only when progesterone is administered. The second category includes guinea pigs (*11*), goats (*32*), and cows (*78*), species which require both estrogen and progesterone for normal duct development. Some lobuloalveolar development occurs in these species when estrogens alone are administered. The bitch has been placed in a third category in which little or no mammary development occurs when estrogen alone is administered. These species differences may be due to differences in the actions of estrogens on glandular tissues (8), differences in the effects of estrogens on other tissues including the ovaries and the anterior pituitary (19, 26), differences in endogenous secretion of progesterone (19), differences in synergistic relationships between steroid hormones and prolactin and growth hormone (76, 82), or, as is most likely, a combination of these.

The literature concerning the role of the anterior pituitary in mammary development during pregnancy is quite extensive and will not be reviewed in detail. Early experiments with hypophysectomized animals indicated that little or no mammary development occurred unless anterior pituitary extracts were supplied. The anterior pituitary extracts employed prevented the atrophy of the gonads that accompanies hypophysectomy. Hence, it was suggested that the anterior pituitary hormones might act indirectly by restoring estrogen and progesterone secretion. A number of experiments, however, indicated that ovarian steroids administered alone were ineffective in stimulating mammary growth (1, 19, 47, 81) in hypophysectomized animals and these were interpreted as indicating that hormone(s) of the anterior pituitary acted directly in the regulation of normal mammary development. Ahren and Etienne (2) examined this conclusion from the point of view that the anterior pituitary hormones might act indirectly by affecting general metabolism and found that lobuloalveolar growth could be induced in hypophysectomized rats by injections of estrogen, progesterone, and long-acting insulin. These authors suggested that the effects of hypophysectomy on mammary growth might be due to atrophy of the gonads with resulting insufficiencies in estrogen and progesterone and to metabolic upsets corrected by insulin. Because anterior pituitary hormones affect general metabolism, the results of experiments indicating that these hormones are required for normal mammary development in hypophysectomized animals must be interpreted with great care (47). Also, consideration of the criteria employed to evaluate mammary development are of critical importance. As will be indicated later, prolactin and/or growth hormone are active in the final stages of mammary development associated with the onset of milk secretion but observations based on secretory activity may not be pertinent to the present discussion concerning the hormone requirements for mammary growth and lobuloalveolar development during pregnancy. Although the studies of Ahren and Etienne (2) indicate that great care must be taken to evaluate the general metabolic status of experimental animals, their results cannot be interpreted as excluding the possibility that hypophysial hormones have a direct effect on mammary growth during pregnancy (47). A number of observations indicate that anterior pituitary hormones promote mammary growth in nonlactating animals and are required for normal gland development during pregnancy. Lyons (65, 66), and later Mizuno and Naito (79), reported that intraduct injections of prolactin into rabbits caused, in addition to secretory activity, considerable localized growth of the alveolar epithelium as assessed histologically and by DNA measurements, respectively (Fig. 1). Dao and Gawlak (24) and Meites and colleagues (74, 103) reported that subcutaneous pituitary homographs supported localized lobuloalveolar growth in hypophysectomized rats, while contralateral control glands did not develop. Roth and Rosenblatt (95) prevented pregnant rats from licking their nipples and found that this retarded mammary development 50%; an effect attributed to a lack of stimulation of the neuroendocrine system involved in the regulation of secretion of anterior pituitary hormones (see Chapter 6). Lyons et al. (66) reported that treatment of triply operated (hypophysectomized, adrenalectomized, ovarectomized) rats with estrogen, growth hormone (STH), and adrenal corticoids for 10 days was required to induce normal duct development. When this treatment was followed by treatment with estrone, progesterone, STH, prolactin, and a corticoid for 10–20 days, normal lobuloalveolar growth was accomplished. A further treatment period with prolactin and cortisol was required for initiation of lactation. Nandi (82) reported that similar hormone treatments were required for normal duct and lobuloalveolar growth in triply operated mice. Frequent injections of large amounts of prolactin and STH were recently reported to induce lobuloalveolar growth in ovarectomized, adrenalectomized, and triply operated rats (75, 104). Ichinose and Nandi (46) examined the hormone requirements for induction of lobuloalveolar development in vitro in mammary explants from intact mice previously treated with estradiol plus progesterone for 9 days or estradiol plus progesterone plus prolactin plus STH for 6 days to promote duct development. Estrogen, progesterone, aldosterone, prolactin, STH, and insulin were required for induction of lobuloalveolar differentiation in the explants. These selected observations indicate that the anterior pituitary hormones ACTH, STH, and prolactin are required for normal duct and lobuloalveolar growth during pregnancy. ACTH acts indirectly through its effect on the adrenals, as indicated by replacement with corticoids. Prolactin and STH are capable of acting alone to produce lobuloalveolar development when given in large doses. Hence, estrogen and progesterone are believed to exert their effects in hypophysectomized animals and in vitro by synergizing with prolactin and STH and/or by sensitizing the mammary tissue to these hormones and, possibly, to the adrenal corticoids (75, 76). The ovarian hormones exert their effects in intact animals, such as during artificial initiation of lactation (see Section II, D) by stimulating secretion of prolactin and, possibly, STH and ACTH by the anterior pituitary and by synergizing with or sensitizing the gland to these hormones (76). Most data indicate that the effects of insulin upon development of mammary glands in vitro are not due solely to its effect on glucose transport (55, 87). The role of insulin is discussed in the next section.

The roles of prolactin, STH, and corticoids in the regulation of alveolar cell proliferation, as opposed to cell development, must be examined further; however, the data presently available strongly indicate that these hormones are required for mammary development during pregnancy.

FIG. 1. Two sectors of a mammary gland from a 5 months' old oophorectomized rabbit pretreated with 20 μg estrone plus 1 mg progesterone 5 days

C. Initiation of Lactation

The initiation of lactation is a complex phenomenon involving the inter-actions of a number of hormones, varying amounts of alveolar cell prolifer-ation, dramatic changes in metabolic activity and metabolic patterns, a rapid increase in the activities of a number of enzymes and in the levels of coenzymes and an increase in blood flow through the gland. *In vivo* experi-ments with hypophysectomized, ovariectomized and/or adrenalectomized mice (82), rats (18), and goats (20) and *in vitro* studies with a number of species (8, 27, 29, 46, 92) indicate that the primary hormones involved in the initiation of lactation are prolactin and cortisol or corticosterone (Figs. 2–5). STH can replace prolactin in mice (82), but not in certain other species (8). Oxytocin must be supplied to hypophysectomized ani-mals in order to facilitate milk removal (see Section V) by the young and prevent artifacts due to milk accumulation. Recently, attention has been focused on the study of cellular and biochemical changes that occur during the initiation of lactation. Unfortunately, current knowledge regarding these aspects of the initiation of lactation is incomplete, as was emphasized in a very excellent review by Munford (81). However, some progress in the clarification of the relationships between cell proliferation, biochemical de-velopment, and physiological factors such as blood supply in the initiation of lactation has been made. These relationships appear to be important to future developments in our understanding of the mechanism(s) of action of cortisol and prolactin in the regulation of the initiation of lactation and will be discussed with this potential development in mind.

Considerable controversy exists in the literature over the relationship between cell proliferation and the onset of lactation. Mayer and Klein (70), Folley (32), and Munford (81) reviewed much of the literature relevant to this controversy, which, apparently, continues to exist (106, 107). Many histological studies appeared to indicate that cell proliferation in the mam-mary glands of rats and mice is essentially complete by midpregnancy, but data based upon measurements of DNA levels (25, 39, 83, 109) and nuclei counts (7, 58) indicate that a three- to fivefold increase in cell numbers occurs during late pregnancy and lactation. Although, equating DNA levels and nuclei numbers to cell numbers may not be strictly correct, since in-creases in numbers of multinucleate cells are reported to occur in early lactation (70), the dramatic nature of the increase in DNA levels makes it difficult to accept the conclusion that cell proliferation is complete by mid-pregnancy. In support of the chemical (DNA) data which suggest that considerable cell proliferation occurs in the mammary glands immediately

---

weekly for 4 weeks; and then after a 3-day interval with 0.1 mg (3 IU) of ovine prolactin in 1 ml of 2% butanol into the right sector, and only 1 ml of butanol into the left. Milk in the right sector could be seen through the skin, and could be expressed by 48 hours. No other sector of any gland secreted milk. × 6. By per-mission of W. R. Lyons and Butterworths and Co., London.

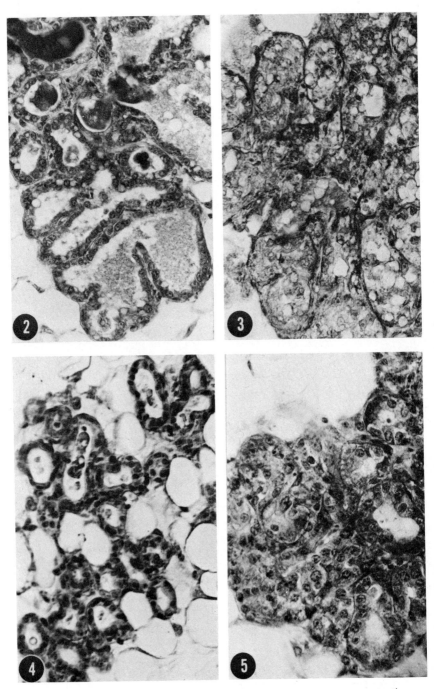

FIGS. 2–5. Photomicrographs of 10–14 day pregnant mouse mammary tissues after 5 days in organ culture in synthetic medium "199" containing hormone

prepartum and postpartum, an early report by Jeffers (*48*) and recent reports by Greenbaum and Slater (*39*), Munford (*80*), and Traurig (*107*) indicate that in rats cell proliferation resulting in increases in cells per alveolus occurs during early lactation. These latter reports are based on the use of colchicine, which inhibits cell division at metaphase, to determine, respectively, numbers of cell divisions, very careful counts of cells per alveolus, and incorporation of tritiated thymidine into DNA of alveolar cells. Perhaps the most convincing evidence indicating that cell proliferation is required for the initiation of milk secretion is the *in vitro* data reported by Topper and his co-workers (*62, 100, 101, 110*). These workers observed that under conditions necessary for induction of casein synthesis in mouse mammary explants (incubation of explants in medium containing insulin, prolactin, and cortisone) considerable cell proliferation occurred, and further, that inhibition of cell proliferation with colchicine or testosterone prevented induction of casein synthesis. It appears that the initiation of lactation in rats, mice, and guinea pigs (*39, 58, 83*) is accompanied by a two- to threefold increase in mammary cell numbers and that the newly formed cells are essential to the secretory process (*100, 110*).

Early studies of the enzymic and metabolic changes which occur during lactation were reviewed by Hansen and Carlson (*40*), Folley (*32*), and Munford (*81*). These studies were usually confined to comparisons of enzyme activities in nonlactating and lactating mammary glands and were undertaken to determine whether a given enzyme or pathway was functional in milk synthesis. Comparisons of the differences in enzyme activities in nonlactating and lactating glands indicated that the activities of some enzymes increased five- to tenfold, while others increased up to 100 times. The largest increases appeared to occur in the activities of enzymes whose functions were closely related to the synthesis of milk components.

Munford (*81*) and Baldwin and Milligan (*7*) considered the enzymatic

---

supplementation as indicated. Modified Masson's stain. Kindly supplied by Dr. Joel J. Elias, Dept. of Anatomy, University of California Medical School, San Francisco.

FIG. 2. Cortisol + insulin + prolactin, $5 + 5 + 5$ μg/ml, respectively. All three hormones must be present in the medium to obtain this active secretory response. Note abundant accumulation of proteinaceous material in lumina of alveoli, and fat secretion as indicated by lipid vacuoles in many cells and in the lumina. × 300.

FIG. 3. Cortisol + prolactin, $5 + 5$ μg/ml, respectively. In all media lacking insulin the tissue degenerates rapidly. × 400.

FIG. 4. Cortisol + insulin, $5 + 5$ μg/ml, respectively. When these two hormones are present together the tissue remains viable and shows some nonstainable clear secretion in the alveoli. Compare to Fig. 2, in which the addition of prolactin induces the active protein and fat secretion response. × 300.

FIG. 5. Insulin + prolactin, $5 + 5$ μg/ml, respectively. This response is also produced by insulin alone. There is survival of many individual cells, but considerable loss of alveolar organization. Compare to Fig. 2, in which the addition of cortisol produces the active protein and fat secretion response. × 400.

changes which occur during early lactation with reference to the period of rapid cell proliferation in rats. It was noted that the increases in enzyme activities occurred 18–24 hours after the period of rapid cell proliferation. This observation was interpreted as indicating that the initiation of lactation in rats was accomplished through the stimulation of cell proliferation followed by either inherent or hormonally directed development of pre-existing and newly formed secretory cells. The data obtained by Baldwin and Milligan (7) permitted examination of the nature of the enzymatic changes which occurred during the period of cellular development. These workers reported that the increases in enzyme activities were not restricted to enzymes closely associated with the synthesis of milk components as was previously believed, but rather the increases occurred in a uniform manner such that the ratios of the activities of a large number of enzymes representing a number of metabolic pathways remained relatively constant in secretory tissue throughout lactation. It was suggested that the apparent differential increase, during lactation, in the activities of enzymes closely associated with milk synthesis was because their activities were very low in nonsecretory glandular tissues and that a significant proportion of the enzymes extracted from mammary glands during pregnancy and early lactation arose from nonsecretory tissues. Under these conditions enzyme activities present in high levels in nonsecretory tissue would not increase dramatically during lactation, while the activities of enzymes associated with milk synthesis and not present in nonsecretory tissue would increase dramatically. These observations were later extended to guinea pigs (4), and the conclusions confirmed by examination of the rates of synthesis and turnover of several enzymes (31). These latter experiments indicated that slight, two- to threefold, preferential increase in the activities of some enzymes occurred in later stages of lactation.

Recently, Lockwood et al. (62) reported that they were able to separate hormonal effects associated with cell proliferation from those associated with secretory cell development in their in vitro system. By taking advantage of the observation that cell proliferation in gland cultures ceases after about 48 hours and that cell development can occur thereafter, these workers found that insulin was required for the initiation of DNA synthesis and was also required during the postmitotic phase; that cortisol was required during the mitotic phase; and that prolactin exerted its effect postmitotically. Although some of the effects of insulin might be attributed to effects upon energy metabolism, several recent data (71, 87) indicate that insulin exerts a specific effect upon nucleic acid metabolism and in either a permissive or synergistic fashion acts to enhance the effects of prolactin and cortisol. It is difficult, at present, to assess the significance of the apparent requirement for insulin and the lack of a requirement for prolactin for the regulation of cell proliferation in vitro (62) in terms of the regulation of glandular development and the initiation of lactation. Several in vivo experiments including those in which intraductule injections of prolactin stimulated cell proliferation as well as cell development (66, 79) and a recent report (6) that prolactin was required for the maintenance of normal rates of DNA synthesis in rats hypophysectomized in early lactation, appear to conflict with the report that prolactin was not required, *in vitro*, for the proliferation of secretory cells (62). The role(s) of cortisol during the mitotic and postmitotic phases have not been defined. The requirement for prolactin for the postmitotic development and maintenance of secretory cells appears to be clearly established (6, 62) although, again, its specific functions have not been elucidated.

The previous discussion has been devoted almost entirely to consideration of two aspects of glandular development associated with the initiation of lactation, namely, cell proliferation and cell development. It must be pointed out that rapid increases in DNA and enzyme activities occurring at the onset of lactation do not necessarily indicate a cause-and-effect relationship between the development of metabolic capacity and the onset of lactation. A recent study (4) of the enzymic changes in mammary glands of dairy cows during late pregnancy and lactation indicated that only minor changes in enzyme activities occurred. This observation suggests that the capacity for milk synthesis is present and unexpressed in cows prior to parturition and that, therefore, other factors such as blood flow through the tissue, uptake of metabolites from the blood, or inhibitory effects of prepartum secretions limit or prevent milk synthesis during pregnancy. These same factors might also limit the expression of enzyme activities in rats and guinea pigs, independent of increases in metabolic potential.

D. MAINTENANCE OF LACTATION

The hormonal requirements for the maintenance of lactation were recently reviewed in detail by Cowie and Folley (19) and appear to be well established. The minimal hormonal requirements for the maintenance of secretory activity in hypophysectomized animals are cortisol and prolactin (20, 66) and in secretory tissue cultured *in vitro* (46, 82) are insulin, cortisol, and prolactin. STH appears to enhance the effects of cortisol and prolactin and can partially or totally replace prolactin in some species (19, 32). The maintenance of lactation may not be dependent upon prolactin in all species (8, 32). It has not been possible to maintain optimal milk secretion in hypophysectomized animals administered STH, prolactin, and cortisol, and some enhancement of production is obtained with other hormones such as long-acting insulin and triiodothyronine (19, 32, 66). Treatment with these hormones does not completely restore milk yields, and it is not clear whether they exert their effects directly upon secretory tissue or indirectly by affecting general metabolism. After complete hypophysectomy, oxytocin (see Section V) must be administered to facilitate milk ejection. Otherwise, milk secretion ceases and the mammary glands degenerate due to accumulation of milk in the glands. Prolactin and cortisol retard but do not prevent gland degeneration due to lack of oxytocin administration and milk removal.

IV. Milk Synthesis

Considerable data are available regarding milk precursor:product relationships and metabolic pathways associated with energy metabolism and the synthesis of the major milk components. These aspects of lactation have been the subject of numerous investigations in recent years, and although a great deal of additional work is required, considerable progress has been made toward the goal of establishing quantitative relationships between blood precursors of the several milk components, mammary gland metabolism, and milk yield and composition. The data to be considered in subsequent sections were largely obtained in in vivo and in vitro experiments with isotope tracers, with arteriovenous and blood-flow measurements, and with enzymic techniques. The isotope tracer techniques have enabled investigators to determine the proportions and amounts of milk components formed from specific blood metabolites and to estimate the activities of specific metabolic pathways in mammary tissue. Studies based on blood-flow measurements and determinations of metabolite levels in arterial blood entering and venous blood leaving the mammary glands provide a basis for quantitative estimation of the amounts of blood metabolites absorbed by the mammary gland and, if coupled with isotope techniques, assessment of the amounts of milk components formed from each blood metabolite. One of the primary difficulties in the use of this approach to the study of precursor:product relationships appears to be accurate assessment of blood flow; estimates of the ratio of blood flow to milk yield ranging from 350 (90) to 650 (59) have been reported. Recently, Linzell (61) reported that results obtained using the thermal dilution technique were very reproducible and that 493 ± 15 ml of blood must flow through the mammary gland in order to provide the nutrients required for the secretion of 1 ml of milk. He also reported that a linear relationship exists between blood flow and milk yield (59). Enzymatic techniques have been employed primarily to characterize the enzymes and pathways of energy metabolism and of biosynthesis of milk components. A number of reviews pertaining to various aspects of milk synthesis are available. Barry (9, 10), Linzell (61), and Verbeke and Peeters (113) considered the quantitative balance between substrates and metabolic products of the mammary gland. Hansen and Carlson (40) reviewed some aspects of energy metabolism in mammary tissue. Garton (35), Van Soest (112), and Folley and McNaught (33) reviewed milk fat composition and biosynthesis. Leloir and Cardini (56) considered lactose biosynthesis, and Barry (9) and Larson (53) considered the synthesis of milk protein. Emphasis in the present discussion of milk synthesis is placed upon summarization of data relating to the quantitative precursor:product relationships, metabolic pathways, energetic efficiencies, and some factors affecting milk yield and composition.

A. Lactose Synthesis

The primary blood precursor of lactose is glucose (*10, 13, 56*), which is converted according to the reaction sequence (1)–(5):

$$\text{Glucose} + \text{ATP} \rightarrow \text{glucose 6-phosphate} + \text{ADP} \qquad (1)$$
$$\text{Glucose 6-phosphate} \rightarrow \text{glucose 1-phosphate} \qquad (2)$$
$$\text{Glucose 1-phosphate} + \text{UTP} \rightarrow \text{UDPglucose} + \text{PP}_i \qquad (3)$$
$$\text{UDPglucose} \rightarrow \text{UDPgalactose} \qquad (4)$$
$$\text{UDPgalactose} + \text{glucose} \rightarrow \text{lactose} + \text{UDP} \qquad (5)$$

$$2 \text{ Glucose} + \text{ATP} + \text{UTP} \rightarrow \text{lactose} + \text{ADP} + \text{UDP} + \text{PP}_i \qquad (6)$$

Reactions (1) through (5) are catalyzed by hexokinase, phosphoglucomutase, UDPGpyrophosphorylase and UDPgalactose-4-epimerase, respectively. These are well-known enzymes and their properties have been discussed elsewhere (*56*). Previous reviews (*56, 32*) indicated that the terminal reaction in lactose synthesis involved the condensation of UDPgalactose and glucose 1-phosphate yielding lactose phosphate, which was hydrolyzed to form lactose and inorganic phosphate [reactions (7) and (8)]. Watkins

$$\text{UDPgalactose} + \text{glucose 1-phosphate} \rightarrow \text{lactose 1-phosphate} + \text{UDP} \qquad (7)$$
$$\text{Lactose 1-phosphate} + \text{H}_2\text{O} \rightarrow \text{lactose} + \text{P}_i \qquad (8)$$

and Hassid (*115*), however, recently identified a new enzyme, lactose synthetase, which catalyzes reaction (5). This reaction (5) is presently preferred because it satisfies isotope data (*117*) and because the activity of lactose synthetase is quite high in mammary extracts and in milk (*15, 115*). Unfortunately, the kinetic characteristics of lactose synthetase have not been examined in detail, and present estimates of its activity in crude homogenates barely accommodate *in vivo* rates of lactose synthetase. This difficulty is presumably due to the fact that lactose synthetase is composed of two subunits [A and B (*15*)], which are differentially bound to microsomes. Homogenation could easily disrupt associations between the subunits and lead to misleadingly small estimates of potential activity. It is interesting to note that the B subunit of lactose synthetase is the well-characterized milk protein α-lactalbumin (*28*). This observation raises a question as to the possible functional nature of other components of milk protein and emphasizes the extent to which at least some cellular proteins are lost in the secretory process.

At present, there appear to be two potential sites at which the rate of lactose synthesis might be regulated. One of these sites is at the level of glucose uptake and activation by hexokinase; the other site is lactose synthetase. The former suggestion is consistent with reports that increases in lactose concentrations in milk can be related to increases in blood glucose levels (30, 41, 93); that depressed milk production is caused by depression of blood glucose (60); and that the levels of ATP in mammary tissue are low (40). Consideration of the possibility that the activity of lactose synthetase might be limiting must await the accumulation of further data on its kinetic characteristics, as indicated previously.

Lactose secretion is involved in the regulation of water secretion in milk. Rook et al. (94) and Schmidt (96) presented evidence which indicated that lactose secretion produces an osmotic pressure which, apparently, draws water and sodium from blood to milk.

The theoretical energetic efficiency of lactose synthesis in the mammary gland is readily calculated on the basis of reactions (1)–(5), and the common assumptions that glucose provides 38 ATP upon total oxidation via glycolysis and the citric acid cycle and that, hence, the net caloric loss associated with the formation and hydrolysis of one terminal pyrophosphate bond of ATP is 18 kcal/mole.* In the course of lactose synthesis, two ATP equivalents are expended, leading to an estimate of input of 2 moles of glucose (2 × 686 kcal/mole) plus 2 ATP (2 × 18 kcal/mole) or 1390 kcal. The heat of combustion of lactose is 1350 kcal/mole. Efficiency calculated on the basis of output/input, then, is 96%. Consideration of the net theoretical efficiency of lactose synthesis on a whole-animal basis, where energy costs associated with the digestion, absorption, storage, transport, and metabolism of precursors are considered in the input, reduces the estimate of efficiency of lactose synthesis in ruminants to 78% (5). This observation emphasizes the fact that although the mammary gland is very active metabolically, a considerable proportion of the intermediary metabolism and energy expenditure associated with milk synthesis occurs in other tissues.

B. PROTEIN SYNTHESIS

Casein and β-lactoglobulin make up about 90% of the protein nitrogen of milk and are not found in blood; therefore, most of the milk protein must be synthesized in the mammary gland from amino acids. Protein synthesis in mammary glands has not been investigated intensively, but the data (14, 53) indicate that the mechanisms involved are similar to those described in other systems as follows:

* Calculated on the basis of glucose, which has a heat of combustion of 686 kcal/mole and yields 38 moles ATP/mole when totally oxidized according to accepted pathways. When ATP formed from glucose is utilized in processes in which the initial and final states of the system acted on are identical (no net work)

$$\frac{686 \text{ kcal/mole glucose}}{38 \text{ moles ATP/mole glucose}}$$

or 18 kcal/mole ATP are lost as heat.

$$\text{Amino acids} + \text{ATP} + \text{tRNA} \rightarrow \text{aminoacyl-tRNA} + \text{PP}_i + \text{AMP} \quad (9)$$
$$\text{Aminoacyl-tRNA} + \text{GTP} \rightarrow \text{protein} + \text{``inactive'' tRNA} \quad (10)$$
$$\text{``Inactive'' tRNA} + \text{ATP} \rightarrow \text{tRNA} + \text{PP}_i \quad (11)$$

Reaction (9) is catalyzed by the amino acid-activating enzymes, which are present in high levels in rat (16) and guinea pig (4) mammary glands during lactation. Reaction (10) occurs on polyribosomes aggregated on messenger-RNA (mRNA). The levels of RNA in lactating mammary tissues of many species (4, 25, 39, 109) is very high, and the bulk of this RNA is ribosomal (6). The levels of transfer-RNA (tRNA) appeared to be limiting in guinea pig mammary glands. There are also a few data which suggest that the availability of ATP might limit the rate of amino acid activation (40, 53). Until detailed studies of polyribosome patterns and hormonal influences in the regulation of the rates of synthesis and turnover of various types of RNA and in the regulation of translation (10) have been conducted, however, the regulation of rates of synthesis of cellular and milk proteins in mammary glands cannot be considered.

Amino acid uptake and milk content of protein are, the data suggest, affected by the nutritional status of animals and blood amino acid levels. Rook and Line (93), for example, found that heavy grain feeding to cows increased plasma glucose and amino acid levels and milk concentrations of casein and albumin. It is not clear, however, whether the increase in milk protein should be attributed to a greater availability of energy in the form of glucose or the greater availability of amino acids.

Verbeke and Peeters (113) surveyed the literature regarding amino acid uptake by the mammary gland and, recently, Mepham and Linzell (77) reported a very complete study of the quantitative contributions of individual plasma amino acids to the synthesis of milk proteins in goat mammary glands. These studies, based on the anteriovenous technique, demonstrated that the uptake of amino acid nitrogen from the blood is sufficient to provide for the synthesis of milk proteins in the goat udder. They found that the uptakes of the essential amino acids and of most nonessential amino acids were equivalent to output in the milk. Uptakes of ornithine, which is not incorporated into milk protein, and arginine were in excess of output and, presumably, provided sources of nitrogen for the synthesis of nonessential amino acids, such as serine, which were present in milk in amounts in excess of uptake. This latter observation is in agreement with isotope studies (12), which indicated that significant quantities of glucose carbon were incorporated into several nonessential amino acids, including serine.

Because some rearrangements of amino acids occur in the mammary gland, it is difficult to develop a highly accurate, simple calculation of the theoretical efficiency of milk protein synthesis. Based on reactions (9)–(11) the efficiency of synthesis of 100 gm of protein, which represents approximately 1 mole of amino acids, can be estimated at 87% (570 kcal per

100 gm protein/567 kcal per mole amino acid incorporated + 5 ATP equivalents × 18 kcal per mole ATP).

C. MILK FAT SYNTHESIS

A great many problems have been encountered in the investigation of milk fat biosynthesis due, largely, to the complexity of and variation in composition of the milk triglycerides, the large number of potential and real precursors of milk fat found in blood, and the multiplicity of pathways for the synthesis and alteration of fatty acids in the mammary gland. The literature pertaining to these problems is much too extensive for specific consideration within the present context, and the reader desiring details is urged to consult reviews prepared by Garton (35), Folley and McNaught (33), Van Soest (112), and Barry (10), and recent papers by Hibbit (45), Smith and Dils (99), Lachance and Morias (52), and Gerson et al. (36) concerning biosynthetic pathways and factors affecting fatty acid composition of milk fat.

The primary blood precursors of the fatty acids in milk fat triglycerides in ruminants appear to be acetate (42, 50), β-hydroxybutyrate (51, 63), and triglycerides of the low density blood chylomicra (37, 54). Glucose and free fatty acids in blood are not significant sources of carbon for milk fat synthesis (49, 54). Table I presents generalizations from numerous

TABLE I
PRECURSORS OF MILK FAT

Fatty acid	Average mole percent in milk fat	Grams/100 gm milk fatty acid from:	
		Acetate + BHBA	Blood triglyceride
C_4	6	2.6	—
C_6	4	2.2	—
C_8	4	2.7	—
C_{10}	11	9.0	—
C_{12}	5	3.3	1.4
C_{14}	11	3.6	8.3
C_{16}	25	5.9	24.0
C_{18}	6	—	8.0
$C_{18}:1$	22	—	30.0

data pertaining to the contributions of the primary precursors of the fatty acids in milk triglycerides (10, 35). Only the major fatty acid components of milk fat are represented. β-hydroxybutyrate (BHBA) is the major blood precursor of butyrate and contributes significant proportions of hexanoate and octanoate (51). It appears to be converted to butyrate by a particulate system in the mammary gland similar to that described by Kumar et al.

(51) and Wakil (114) and which resembles but is not identical with a reversal of beta oxidation according to reactions (12)–(14). BHBA is converted to longer chain fatty acids according to reactions, (15), (16), (13), and (14), respectively (64, 114). Acetate is apparently converted to short-

$$RCHOHCH_2CO_2H + ATP + CoASH \rightarrow$$
$$RCHOHCH_2C{=}OS\text{-}CoA + AMP + PP_i \quad (12)$$
$$RCHOHCH_2C{=}OS\text{-}CoA \rightarrow$$
$$R{-}CG{=}CH{-}C{=}OS\text{-}CoA + H_2O \quad (13)$$
$$RCH{=}CHC{=}OS\text{-}CoA + NADPH_2 \rightarrow$$
$$RCH_2CH_2C{=}OS\text{-}CoA + NADP \quad (14)$$
$$R'C{=}O\text{-}S\text{-}CoA + acetyl\text{-}CoA \rightarrow$$
$$R'C{=}OCH_2C{=}OS\text{-}CoA + CoASH \quad (15)$$
$$R'C{=}OCH_2C{=}OS\text{-}CoA + NADH_2 \rightarrow$$
$$R'CHOHCH_2C{=}OS\text{-}CoA + NAD \quad (16)$$

chain fatty acids (up to C_6 or C_8) by a similar mechanism [reactions (15), (16), (13), and (14), respectively] and to longer chain fatty acids (C_8–C_{16}) by the pathway of fatty acid synthesis involving malonyl-CoA, as indicated in reactions (17)–(19) (52, 99). The mechanism of absorption of blood triglycerides is not clearly established, although partial hydrolysis

$$Acetate + ATP + CoASH \rightarrow$$
$$acetyl\text{-}CoA + AMP + PP_i \quad (17)$$
$$Acetyl\text{-}CoA + ATP + CO_2 \rightarrow$$
$$malonyl\text{-}CoA + ADP + P_i \quad (18)$$
$$Acetyl\text{-}CoA + (n)malonyl\text{-}CoA + (2n)NADPH_2 \rightarrow$$
$$long\text{-}chain\ fatty\ acid + 2(n)NADP + (n+1)CoASH \quad (19)$$

must occur, since some of the fatty acids are altered in the mammary gland, presumably, by a chain elongation system similar to that described in reactions (15), (16), (13), and (14) (114). Also, fatty acids originating from blood triglycerides are found in the same milk triglyceride molecules as fatty acids synthesized in the gland (35). Arteriovenous difference measurements indicate that a significant proportion of the blood triglyceride glycerol is taken up in the mammary gland (10) and incorporated into milk fat. Another major proportion of the glycerol-P required for fatty acid esterification in the gland is formed from blood glucose (50).

Milk fat is the most variable component of milk, and because of this, and the fact that depressions in percent milk fat in the milk of cows fed high concentrate and other diets are a problem of considerable practical importance, factors affecting milk fat synthesis have been studied extensively. It appears that milk fat synthesis is affected by the general metabolic status of the animal and by intracellular regulatory mechanisms in the mammary gland. Several data indicate that a large proportion of the depression in milk fat percentage in the milks of cows fed high concentrate diets can be attributed to changes in general metabolism caused by increases in energy intake and in the proportion of propionate formed in the rumen (112). The increase in availability of propionate, which is rapidly converted to glucose by the liver, apparently alters the metabolism of adipose tissue in two ways (85, 86). First, greater amounts of acetate are converted to fatty acids at this site, producing a decrease in the availability of acetate for fatty acid synthesis in the mammary tissue. Second, the fatty acids formed in the adipose tissue are not released and converted to blood triglycerides, resulting in a depression in blood triglyceride levels and, hence, a depression in the availability of long-chain fatty acids for milk fat synthesis. Although the intracellular mechanisms for the regulation of fatty acid synthesis in the mammary gland have not been studied in detail, sufficient data are available to justify the assumption that the regulatory sites and mechanisms in mammary glands are similar to those described in other tissues (105). The activities of NADP-linked dehydrogenases are very high in secretory tissues (4, 7, 67) and dramatic increases in the activity of the hexose monophosphate pathway have been reported to occur during the onset of lactation in rats (67) and cows (13). Citrate levels affect the patterns of fatty acids synthesized in mammary tissue, due, presumably, to its effect upon acetyl-CoA carboxylase (52, 99), the rate-limiting enzyme in the malonyl-CoA pathway of fatty acid synthesis [reaction (18)]. In nonruminant mammary glands citrate formed in the mitochondria from acetyl-CoA and oxalacetic acid is transferred to the cytoplasm, where it is cleaved by the citrate cleavage enzyme [reaction (20)] to re-form oxalacetate and acetyl-CoA, thus providing a mechanism for the transfer of acetyl-CoA formed from glucose

$$\text{Citrate} + \text{ATP} + \text{CoASH} \rightarrow \text{oxalacetate} + \text{ADP} + \text{acetyl-CoA} \quad (20)$$

via pyruvate from the mitochondria to the cytoplasm, where fatty acid synthesis occurs (105). In ruminants acetate absorbed from blood is converted to acetyl-CoA in the cytoplasm by aceto-CoA kinase [reaction (17)] and, hence, the role of the citrate cleavage enzyme in fat synthesis in ruminants is considerably less prominent than in nonruminants (43).

The complexity of the precursors and pathways of synthesis of milk fat makes calculation of the theoretical efficiency of milk fat synthesis at the mammary gland level difficult. However, for ruminants, if one assumes that the bulk of the milk fatty acids of milk fat arise from acetate either directly, as a result of synthesis in the glands, or indirectly, through synthesis in extramammary tissue and transport to the mammary gland in triglycerides, calculation of theoretical efficiency on a whole-animal basis is not difficult. It is merely necessary to calculate the output:input ratio for reactions (17)–(19) for the synthesis of a fatty acid of average chain length. Based on such a calculation the theoretical efficiency of milk fat synthesis was calculated to be 72% (5).

TABLE II

ESTIMATION OF THE EFFICIENCY OF MILK SYNTHESIS IN
GOATS FROM MAMMARY UPTAKE DATA[a]

| Uptake | | Output | |
Blood component $\left(\dfrac{\text{kcal uptake}}{100 \text{ gm milk}}\right)$		Milk component (kcal/100 gm milk)	
Glucose	32.0	Fat	38
Acetate	10.2	Lactose	18
BHBA	8.1	Protein	19
Triglyceride	43.0	—	—
Amino acids	20.0	—	—
	113.3		76

[a] $\text{Efficiency} + \dfrac{\text{input}}{\text{output}} \times 100 = \dfrac{76.0 \times 100}{113.3} = 67\%.$

D. EFFICIENCY OF MILK SYNTHESIS

The data presented in Tables II and III, adapted from Barry (10) and Baldwin (5), respectively, represent an attempt to formulate estimates of the efficiency of milk synthesis based upon arteriovenous mammary uptake data (Table II) and upon consideration of the metabolic pathways involved in the synthesis of individual milk components (Table III). Both of the estimates, 67% and 77%, respectively, agree fairly well with estimates of efficiencies of milk synthesis determined in respiration studies in whole animals which range from 50% to 70%. This comparison of theoretical and observed efficiencies shows that the data presently available concerning mammary uptake and metabolic pathways account for approximately three-fourths of the energy expenditure associated with milk synthesis.

V. Milk Ejection

Milk secreted by the alveolar cells of the mammary gland cannot be removed until the myoepithelial cells surrounding the alveoli contract and force the milk from the alveoli and small ducts to the large ducts and the gland and teat cisterns. The neural-endocrine reflex activated by suckling or milking, which regulates myoepithelial cell contraction and milk ejection, has been the subject of extensive investigation. The historical development of knowledge concerning milk ejection was treated in a very interesting

TABLE III
Estimation of the Efficiency of Milk Synthesis in Goats from Metabolic Pathways[a]

Milk component (gm/100 gm milk)		Estimated efficiency of synthesis	Input (kcal/100 gm milk)	Output (kcal/100 gm milk)
Fat	4.1	0.72	53.0	38.0
Lactose	4.7	0.78	23.1	18.0
Protein	3.3	0.84	22.6	19.0
	—	0.77	98.7	76.0

[a] $\text{Efficiency} = \dfrac{\text{input}}{\text{output}} \times 100 = \dfrac{76 \times 100}{98.7} = 77\%.$

review by Cowie and Folley (*19*). Recent advances regarding the functional innervation of the mammary glands, the hypothalamo-neurohypophyseal system and the role of oxytocin in milk expulsion have been reviewed in detail (*3, 22, 26, 32, 119*).

A. Functional Innervation of the Mammary Glands

The innervation of the mammary glands resembles that of the skin, as might be expected in view of their common embryological origin, and is comprised of somatic sensory and sympathetic motor fibers arising from different segments of the spinal cord depending upon whether a given species has thoracic, abdominal, and/or inguinal mammary glands. There has been some controversy regarding the presence or absence of parasympathetic innervation in the udders of ruminants, but, at present, no convincing evidence of such innervation is available (*22, 26*). The sensory nerves are distributed, primarily, in the skin surrounding the mammary glands and are present in exceptionally large numbers in the teats. The supply of sensory nerves to the mammary parenchyma appears to be very limited (*3, 22*). The motor nerve endings found in the mammary glands supply, primarily, the blood vessels, the connective stroma, the large ducts and the muscles surrounding the teat and gland cisterns, and the teat sphincter (*22*). Stimulation of the peripheral extremities of the mammary nerves and administration of adrenalin cause vasoconstriction, rhythmic contractions in the teats, and relaxation of smooth muscles surrounding the teat and gland cisterns (*26*). These observations and others mentioned later support the contentions that the autonomic fibers supplying the mammary gland are sympathetic and adrenergic and that motor endings do not supply the myoepithelial cells surrounding the alveoli and small ducts. Hence, motor elements are apparently not responsible for milk ejection.

B. REGULATION OF OXYTOCIN RELEASE

The sensory stimuli associated with suckling or milking lead to the liberation of the neurohormone, oxytocin, and possibly vasopressin into the blood. Considerable attention has been focused on examination of the efficiency of various visual, conditioned, and physical stimuli in evoking oxytocin release and subsequent milk ejection in the course of formulation of recommendations concerning proper, practical, premilking practices for dairy cattle and goats. These studies have resulted in the realization that practices which cause vasoconstriction (as by adrenalin) in the udder prevent milk ejection, due to the prevention of oxytocin entry to the udder and that the most effective stimulus to milk ejection is manipulation of the teats during suckling or the act of milking. In this connection, it is surprising that the types of stimuli, e.g., tactile, thermal, which excite the sensory nerve endings in the teats have not been characterized in detail. However, there is general agreement that excitations resulting from the complex of stimuli associated with milking and suckling are transmitted to the neurohypophysis and cause oxytocin release. Transmission of excitations from the teats involves a complex of ascending spinal paths and, possibly, medullary paths which analyze, integrate, and modulate these afferent impulses [see Denamur (26)] to the supraoptic and paraventricular nuclei of the hypothalamus, which, in turn, transfer the signal to the neurohypophysis (22, 26). The supraoptic and paraventricular nuclei perform two functions related to the release of oxytocin from the neurohypophysis. Oxytocin and vasopressin (ADH) are synthesized in these hypothalamic nuclei and are transported to the neurohypophysis along the axons connecting the nuclei to the neurohypophysis. Oxytocin and vasopressin thus synthesized and transported are stored in the neurohypophysis and released in response to nervous stimulation of and from the supraoptic and paraventricular nuclei. It should be pointed out that stimulations of the teats are not the only cause of oxytocin release. Other common stimuli include those arising from the genitals, a basis for some very interesting historical milking practices described by Cowie and Folley (19), and from the injection of hypertonic saline. This latter observation emphasizes the fact that stimuli causing oxytocin and vasopressin release from the posterior pituitary have a common origin in the hypothalami of many species (26). The role of the hypothalamus in the regulation of the secretion of adenohypophyseal hormones involved in lactation is described in Chapter 7.

Many of the early investigations of the effect of mammary stimulation on oxytocin release involved the use of biological criteria such as increases in intramammary pressure and milk ejection for the assay of oxytocin in blood and pituitary extracts. The data obtained using these criteria were very instructive, but many investigators encountered difficulties in attempting to show quantitative increases in oxytocin in blood and decreases in oxytocin in the posterior pituitary resulting from mammary stimulation using these techniques. Recently, direct quantitative methods for the assay of oxytocin have become available and have been employed to unequivocally establish the fact that oxytocin is released by the posterior pituitary as a result of mammary stimulation (26).

C. Milk Ejection

Oxytocin released by the neurohypophysis is transported by the blood to the mammary glands, where it acts upon the myoepithelial cells surrounding the alveoli and ducts of the glands and causes them to contract and expel the milk. Oxytocin also causes relaxation of the smooth muscles surrounding the large ducts and gland and teat cisterns, thus providing for enlargement of these structures to accommodate the milk ejected from the alveoli. Intramammary pressure rises as a result of the forcible ejection of milk from the alveoli and small ducts, and the suckling young or the milker has only to overcome the resistance of the teat sphincter in order to accomplish the final stage of milk removal (19). In many animals the buildup of intramammary pressure is sufficiently great to overcome the resistance of the teat sphincter and forces milk to drip or spurt from the teats (3, 19, 22, 26, 119).

Oxytocin is necessary for the effective removal of milk and maintenance of lactation. Hypophysectomy or severance of the afferent nerve fibers leading from the mammary gland causes accumulation of milk in the mammary glands and rapid involution unless replacement therapy with oxytocin is provided. In the case of hypophysectomy, the administration of prolactin and other adenohypophyseal hormones can retard but cannot prevent involution unless oxytocin is administered. Oxytocin produces effects upon the mammary gland other than milk ejection, including resorption of lactose and stimulation of glucose oxidation. Its primary function, however, clearly is milk ejection (26).

REFERENCES

1. Ahren, K., and Jacobsohn, D., *Acta Physiol. Scand.* **37**, 190 (1956).
2. Ahren, K., and Etienne, M., *Acta Endocrinol.* **28**, 89 (1958).
3. Averill, R. L. W., *Brit. Med. Bull.* **22**, 261 (1966).
4. Baldwin, R. L., *J. Dairy Sci.* **49**, 1533 (1966).
5. Baldwin, R. L., *J. Dairy Sci.* **51**, 104 (1967).
6. Baldwin, R. L., and Martin, R. J., *J. Dairy Sci.* **50** (1967).
7. Baldwin, R. L., and Milligan, L. P., *J. Biol. Chem.* **241**, 2058 (1966).
8. Barnawell, E. B., *J. Exptl. Zool.* **160**, 189 (1965).
9. Barry, J. M., in "Milk: the Mammary Gland and Its Secretion" (S. K. Kon and A. T. Cowie, ed.), Vol. 1, p. 389. Academic Press, Inc., New York, 1961.
10. Barry, J. M., *Biol. Revs.* **39**, 194 (1964).
11. Benson, G. K., Cowie, A. T., Cox, C. P., and Goldzveig, S. A., *J. Endocrinol.* **15**, 126 (1957).

12. Black, A. L., Kleiber, M., and Baxter, C. F., *Biochim. Biophys. Acta* **17**, 346 (1955).
13. Black, A. L., Kleiber, M., Butterworth, E. M., Brubacher, G. B., and Kaneko, J. J., *J. Biol. Chem.* **227**, 537 (1957).
14. Brew, K., and Campbell, P. N., *Biochem. J.* **102**, 265 (1967).
15. Brodbeck, U., and Ebner, K. E., *J. Biol. Chem.* **241**, 5526 (1966).
16. Bucovaz, E. T., and Davis, J. W., *J. Biol. Chem.* **236**, 2015 (1961).
17. Cowie, A. T., and Folley, S. J., *Endocrinology* **40**, 274 (1947).
18. Cowie, A. T., and Lyons, W. R., *J. Endocrinol.* **19**, 29 (1959).
19. Cowie, A. T., and Folley, S. J., *in* "Allen's Sex and Internal Secretions" (W. C. Young, ed.), 3rd ed., p. 590. Williams & Wilkins, Baltimore, Maryland, 1961.
20. Cowie, A. T., and Tindal, J. S., *J. Endocrinol.* **23**, 79 (1961).
21. Cowie, A. T., and Tindal, J. S., *J. Endocrinol.* **22**, 403 (1961).
22. Cross, B. A., *in* "Milk: the Mammary Gland and Its Secretion" (S. K. Kon and A. T. Cowie, ed.), Vol. 1, p. 229. Academic Press, New York, 1961.
23. Dabelow, A., *in* "Handbuck der mikroskopischen Anatomie des Menschen" (W. von Moellendorff and W. Bargman, ed.), Vol. 3, p. 277. Springer, Berlin.
24. Dao, T. L., and Gawlak, D., *Endocrinology* **72**, 884 (1963).
25. Denamur, R., *Compt. Rend. Acad. Sci.* **256**, 4748 (1963).
26. Denamur, R., *Dairy Sci. Abstr.* **27**, 193, 263 (1965).
27. Ebner, K. E., Hageman, E. C., and Larson, B. L., *Exptl. Cell Res.* **25**, 555 (1961).
28. Ebner, K. E., Tanahashi, N., and Brodbeck, U., *Federation Proc.* **26**, 558 (1967).
29. Elias, J. J., *Exptl. Cell Res.* **27**, 601 (1962).
30. Emery, R. S., personal communication (1966).
31. Emery, R. S., and Baldwin, R. L., *Biochim. Biophys. Acta* **136**, 223 (1967).
32. Folley, S. J., *Dairy Sci. Abstr.* **23**, 511 (1961).
33. Folley, S. J., and McNaught, M. L., *in* "Milk: the Mammary Gland and Its Secretion" (S. K. Kon and A. T. Cowie, ed.), Vol. 1, p. 441. Academic Press, New York, 1961.
34. Flux, D. S., *J. Endocrinol.* **11**, 223 (1954).
35. Garton, G. A., *J. Lipid Res.* **4**, 237 (1963).
36. Gerson, T., Wilson, G. F., Singh, H., and Sharland, F. B., *J. Dairy Sci.* **49**, 680 (1966).
37. Glascock, R. F., Welch, V. A., Bishop, C., Davies, T., Wright, E. W., and Noble, R. L., *Biochem. J.* **98**, 149 (1966).
38. Greenbaum, A. L., and Slater, T. F., *Biochem. J.* **66**, 161 (1957).
39. Greenbaum, A. L., and Slater, T. F., *Biochem. J.* **66**, 155 (1957).
40. Hansen, R. G., and Carlson, D. M., *in* "Milk: the Mammary Gland and Its Secretion" (S. K. Kon and A. T. Cowie, ed.), Vol. 1, p. 371. Academic Press, New York, 1961.
41. Hardwick, D. C., Linzell, J. L., and Price, S. M., *Biochem. J.* **80**, 37 (1961).
42. Hardwick, D. C., Linzell, J. L., and Mepham, T. B., *Biochem. J.* **88**, 213 (1963).
43. Hardwick, D. C., *Biochem. J.* **99**, 228 (1966).
44. Hardy, M. H., *J. Anat. London* **84**, 388 (1950).

45. Hibbit, K. G., *Biochim. Biophys. Acta* **116**, 56 (1966).
46. Ichinose, R. R., and Nandi, S., *J. Endocrinol.* **35**, 331 (1966).
47. Jacobsohn, D., *in* "Milk: the Mammary Gland and Its Secretion" (S. K. Kon and A. T. Cowie, ed.), Vol. 1, p. 127. Academic Press, New York, 1961.
48. Jeffers, K. R., *Am. J. Anat.* **50**, 257 (1935).
49. Kleiber, M., Smith, A. H., Black, A. L., Brown, M. A., and Tolbert, B. M., *J. Biol. Chem.* **197**, 371 (1952).
50. Kleiber, M., Black, A. L., Brown, M. A., Baxter, C. F., Luick, J. R., and Stadtman, F. H., *Biochim. Biophys. Acta* **17**, 252 (1955).
51. Kumar, S., Singh, V. N., and Keren-Paz, R., *Biochim. Biophys. Acta* **98**, 221 (1965).
52. Lachance, J. P., and Morias, R., *Biochem. Biophys. Res. Commun.* **20**, 269 (1965).
53. Larson, B. L., *J. Dairy Sci.* **48**, 133 (1965).
54. Lascelles, A. K., Hardwick, D. C., Linzell, J. L., and Mepham, T. B., *Biochem. J.* **92**, 36 (1964).
55. Lasfargues, E. Y., *Exptl. Cell Res.* **28**, 531 (1962).
56. Leloir, L. F., and Cardini, C. E., *in* "Milk: the Mammary Gland and Its Secretion" (S. K. Kon and A. T. Cowie, ed.), Vol. 1, p. 421. Academic Press, New York, 1961.
57. Levy, H. R., *Biochim. Biophys. Acta* **84**, 229 (1964).
58. Lewin, I., *Proc. Roy. Soc. Med.* **50**, 563 (1957).
59. Linzell, J. L., *J. Physiol. (London)* **153**, 492 (1960).
60. Linzell, J., *J. Physiol. (London)* **179**, 91 (1965).
61. Linzell, J. L., *Circulation Res.* **58**, 745 (1966).
62. Lockwood, D. H., Stockdale, F. E., and Topper, Y. J., *Federation Proc.* **26**, 603 (1967).
63. Luick, J. L., and Kleiber, M., *Am. J. Physiol.* **200**, 1327 (1959).
64. Luick, J. R., and Kameoka, K. K., *J. Dairy Sci.* **49**, 98 (1966).
65. Lyons, W. R., *Proc. Soc. Exptl. Biol. Med.* **51**, 308 (1942).
66. Lyons, W. R., Li, C. H., and Johnson, R. E., *Recent Progr. Hormone Res.* **14**, 219 (1958).
67. McLean, P., *Biochim. Biophys. Acta* **30**, 316 (1958).
68. McLean, P., *Biochem. J.* **90**, 271 (1964).
69. Matthews, C. A., Swett, W. W., and Fohrman, M. H., *U.S. Dept. Agr. Tech. Bull.* **993** (1949).
70. Mayer, G., and Klein, M., *in* "Milk: the Mammary Gland and Its Secretion" (S. K. Kon and A. T. Cowie, ed.), Vol. 1, p. 47. Academic Press, New York, 1961.
71. Mayne, R., Barry, J. M., and Rivera, E. M., *Biochem. J.* **99**, 688 (1966).
72. Meites, J., *in* "Reproduction in Domestic Animals" (H. H. Cole and P. T. Cupps, eds.), Vol. 1, p. 539. Academic Press, New York, 1959.
73. Meites, J., *in* "Milk: the Mammary Gland and Its Secretion" (S. K. Kon and A. T. Cowie, ed.), Vol. 1, p. 321. Academic Press, New York, 1961.
74. Meites, J., and Kragt, C. L., *Endocrinology* **75**, 565 (1964).
75. Meites, J., *Endocrinology* **76**, 1220 (1965).
76. Meites, J., and Nicoll, C. S., *Ann. Rev. Physiol.* **28**, 57 (1966).
77. Mepham, T. B., and Linzell, J. L., *Biochem. J.* **101**, 76 (1966).
78. Mixner, J. P., and Turner, C. W., *Missouri Univ. Agr. Expt. Sta. Res. Bull.* **378** (1943).

79. Mizuno, H., and Naito, M., *Endocrinol. Japon* **3**, 227 (1956).
80. Munford, R. E., *J. Endocrinol.* **28**, 1 (1963).
81. Munford, R. E., *Dairy Sci. Abstr.* **26**, 293 (1964).
82. Nandi, S., *Univ. Calif. (Berkeley) Publ. Zool.* **65**, 1 (1959).
83. Nelson, W. L., Heytler, P. G., and Aiccio, E. I., *Proc. Soc. Exptl. Biol. Med.* **109**, 373 (1962).
84. Nicoll, C. S., and Tucker, H. A., *Life Sci.* **4**, 993 (1965).
85. Opstvedt, J., Baldwin, R. L., and Ronning, M., *J. Dairy Sci.* **50**, 108 (1966).
86. Opstvedt, J., and Ronning, M., *J. Dairy Sci.* **50**, 345 (1967).
87. Prop, F. J. A., and Hendrix, S. E. A. M., *Exptl. Cell Res.* **40**, 277 (1965).
88. Raynaud, A., *in* "Milk: the Mammary Gland and Its Secretion" (S. K. Kon and A. T. Cowie, ed.), Vol. 1, p. 3. Academic Press, New York, 1961.
89. Rees, E. D., and Eversole, A., *Am. J. Physiol.* **207**, 595 (1964).
90. Reynolds, M., *Am. J. Physiol.* **209**, 669 (1965).
91. Richardson, K. C., *J. Endocrinol.* **9**, 170 (1953).
92. Rivera, E. M., *J. Endocrinol.* **30**, 33 (1964).
93. Rook, J. A. F., and Line, C., *Brit. J. Nutr.* **51**, 109 (1961).
94. Rook, J. A. F., Starry, J. E., and Wheelock, J. V., *J. Dairy Sci.* **48**, 745 (1965).
95. Roth, L. L., and Rosenblatt, J. S., *Science* **151**, 1403 (1966).
96. Schmidt, G. H., *J. Dairy Sci.* **49**, 381 (1966).
97. Silver, M., *J. Endocrinol.* **10**, 35 (1953).
98. Slater, T. F., Greenbaum, A. L., and Wang, D. Y., *Ciba Found. Symp. Lysosomes*, p. 311 (1963).
99. Smith, S., and Dils, R., *Biochim. Biophys. Acta* **84**, 776 (1964).
100. Stockdale, F. E., Juergens, William G., and Topper, Yale J., *Develop. Biol.* **13**, 266 (1966).
101. Stockdale, F. E., and Topper, Y. J., *Proc. Natl. Acad. Sci. U.S.* **56**, 1283 (1966).
102. Swett, W. W., Book, J. H., Matthews, C. A., and Fohrman, M. H., *U.S. Dept. Agr. Tech. Bull.* **1111** (1955).
103. Talawalker, P. K., and Meites, J., *Proc. Soc. Exptl. Biol. Med.* **107**, 880 (1961).
104. Talawalker, P. K., Meites, J., and Mizuno, H., *Proc. Soc. Exptl. Biol. Med.* **116**, 531 (1964).
105. Tepperman, J., and Tepperman, H. M., *Ann. N.Y. Acad. Sci.* **131**, 404 (1965).
106. Thibodeau, Philip S., and Thayer, Sidney A., *Endocrinology* **80**, 505 (1967).
107. Traurig, H. H., *Anat. Record* **157**, 489 (1967).
108. Tucker, H. A., and Reece, R. P., *Proc. Soc. Exptl. Biol. Med.* **111**, 639 (1962).
109. Tucker, H. A., Reece, R. P., *Proc. Soc. Exptl. Biol. Med.* **112**, 1002 (1963).
110. Turkington, R. W., and Topper, Y. J., *Endocrinology* **80**, 329 (1967).
111. Turner, C. W., *in* "The Mammary Gland. I. The Anatomy of the Udder of Cattle and Domestic Animals." Lucas Brothers, Columbia, Missouri, 1952.
112. Van Soest, P. J., *J. Dairy Sci.* **46**, 204 (1963).
113. Verbeke, R., and Peeters, G., *Biochem. J.* **94**, 183 (1965).
114. Wakil, S., *J. Lipid Res.* **2**, 1 (1964).
115. Watkins, W. M., and Hassid, W. Z., *J. Biol. Chem.* **237**, 1433 (1962).

116. Weber, A. F., Kitchell, R. L., and Sautter, J. H., *Am. J. Vet. Res.* **16**, 255 (1955).

117. Wood, H. G., Jaffe, S., Gillespie, R., Hansen, R. G., and Hardenbrook, H., *J. Biol. Chem.* **233**, 1264 (1958).

118. Wren, T. R., Delauder, W. R., and Bitman, J., *J. Dairy Sci.* **48**, 802 (1965).

119. Zaks, M. G., "The Motor Apparatus of the Mammary Gland." Oliver & Boyd, Edinburgh and London, 1962.

17 ENVIRONMENTAL FACTORS AFFECTING REPRODUCTION

M. T. CLEGG AND W. F. GANONG

I. Introduction

It has been known since ancient times that environmental conditions modify the breeding processes of most animal species. One important condition, the adequacy of the diet, is discussed in Chapter 18. Other factors have perhaps received less attention, but are nonetheless of practical as well as theoretical importance. These factors are multiple, and their role varies from species to species. For purposes of discussion, they have been grouped here under four headings: (a) light, (b) temperature and humidity, (c) "social stimuli," and (d) other factors. The neural mechanisms by which these factors affect reproductive function are discussed in Chapter 7 and have been reviewed by Clegg and Doyle (20). A comprehensive review of the current concepts of brain-endocrine interrelations is now available (72).

Other recent reviews (31, 46, 56, 118, 120) have also dealt in detail with a variety of aspects concerning the influences of environmental factors on reproduction. In the present chapter a few general principles are reviewed, and attention is focused on the role of environmental conditions in the reproductive physiology of the individual domestic species.

The role of incident light in controlling the onset of estrus in seasonally breeding animals has been the subject of a number of reviews (21, 71, 131), and has been well covered for domestic birds and mammals by Yeates

473

(125). The available evidence indicates that changes in the daily amount of light to which the animals are exposed are responsible for initiating the breeding season in most of the species which have an anestrous period during the year. Many species come into heat as the days lengthen in the spring. Estrus can be initiated in the laboratory at any time of year by simulating this increase in illumination. Another group of animals, notably the sheep and the goat, are stimulated by decreasing day length, and come into heat in the fall. However, variations in the amount of incident light also affect estrous cycles in species that are normally continuously polyestrous. The laboratory rat, for instance, is polyestrous, but continuous illumination eventually leads to a state of constant estrus in this species (12, 49). Ovulation can be induced in such animals by electrical stimulation of the brain (14), so the continuous estrus is probably due to failure of LH release from the pituitary. Other polyestrous species have not been subjected to experiments of this type, but there is evidence that light is important in other polyestrous animals, including cattle (75, 76).

Marshall (71) and others (125) have pointed out that reproductive photoperiodism, the dependence of breeding activity on changes in incident illumination, is a characteristic of species native to the temperate zones of the globe. Generally, with certain exceptions, the dependence is absent in tropical animals. This difference between temperate and tropical natives may be present even in strains of the same species. Strains coming from the northern latitudes show sharply limited breeding seasons, while strains native to the tropics, where day length varies little, breed at any time of year.

The development of photoperiodism is probably explained by natural selection. Marshall (70) and Yeates (125) both point out that the breeding season in animals native to the temperate zones is almost invariably timed for the young to be born at a time of the year most favorable to their survival. Since animals lacking the mechanism responsible for this limitation of breeding would tend to lose their young and die out, natural selection, apparently, has operated to develop reproductive photoperiodism. In the tropics, however, where an inimical climate is no problem, breeding persists throughout the year.

It is also of interest in this regard that various domesticated mammals have tended to lose their photoperiodism, while their wild counterparts continue to show it. The domestic rabbit, for example, often breeds throughout the year, while the wild hare has a spring and summer breeding season (64). Some mares are also said to be capable of breeding at times other than the spring and summer, and the cat and dog have lost the clearly seasonal nature of the breeding periods seen in their wild counterparts (29). This loss of photoperiodicity with domestication is not surprising because the food and shelter supplied by man eliminates much of the natural selection and, in some situations, animals are also bred for longer mating seasons. It should be kept in mind, however, that in most of the domestic species involved, the loss of photoperiodism has been partial, and the old patterns persist in part.

One interesting proposal is that light stimuli by way of the optic nerves and sympathetic fibers influence melatonin production by the pineal gland and affect the estrous cycle in rats (122).

Incident light is involved, not only in the control of reproductive physiology, but in other body processes as well. These processes are not directly related to the present subject, but are of interest and importance because they involve the economic value of the animal. Thus, there is some evidence that light controls hair-shedding in mammals, as well as the plumage changes that occur seasonally in birds (125). Furthermore, there is presumptive evidence that some environmental factor in addition to temperature is involved in the regulation of thyroid activity, and possibly also in growth.

Finally, it has been suggested that light is involved in the phenomenon of "delayed implantation" seen in the mink and its relatives, and possibly also in the horse (39, 45, 84). In the former animals, mating occurs and fertilization is accomplished, but the blastocyst does not implant immediately and, coincidental with this delay, the corpus luteum does not become active. Some weeks later implantation occurs and, at this time, the corpus luteum takes on a secretory character. This activation of the corpus luteum is not due to FSH or LH, and is probably due to a delayed increase in prolactin secretion (43, 44). Hammond has suggested that increasing amounts of light are responsible for this change in the corpus luteum, and there is some evidence to support this point of view (47). Whether or not a similar chain of events occurs in the horse has not been settled, but there is clear-cut evidence (39, 47) that the length of pregnancy in the mare varies with the season, longer pregnancies being characteristic of early spring fertilization.

Temperature is another environmental factor modifying reproductive activity. Before Rowan showed conclusively that incident light and not temperature controlled testis development in the junco (96), most seasonal breeding was generally assumed to be regulated by changes in the environmental temperature (102). However, it has now become clear that the role of temperature is of secondary importance in birds and most mammals. However, both excessive heat and excessive cold curtail reproductive performance. In birds, the effects of temperature may reinforce and increase those of light (15, 32). A low environmental temperature in the absence of changes in illumination leads to prolonged estrous cycles in the rat (59); and a few animals, such as the thirteen-lined ground squirrel, depend on prolonged cool weather, rather than light, as the stimulus for gonadal development (117). Changes in temperature also appear to have some effect on the breeding cycles of various domestic animals, as discussed later.

The well-known effect of temperature on spermatogenesis in the male of most species of mammals should also be mentioned. Placing the testes in the abdomen at body temperature leads to degeneration of the tubular epithelium and sterility; for normal sperm development to occur, the testes must be kept cooler than the rest of the body. Keeping the testes in the scrotum permits maintenance of a reasonably constant, cool environment for the spermatic epithelium. The efficiency with which the scrotum functions to maintain proper temperatures has been studied in various species, including domestic animals (33), in which it has been found that spermatogenesis proceeds essentially normally in intrascrotal testes when the environmental temperature ranges from 50° to 104°F. Nonetheless, high environmental temperatures may affect the reproductive potential in the male in some domestic species, as discussed later.

Another group of stimuli affecting reproduction is made up of those provided by the immediate environment and, particularly, by the presence of other animals. They have been classified here under the general term "social stimuli." Such stimuli play a role in mammalian reproduction and are prominent in reproduction in birds. In pigeons, for example, the female will ovulate only when another pigeon is visible (73). Most birds lay a definite characteristic number of eggs, and when this number is reached, further ovulation is inhibited. Many birds also engage in various mating displays and dances. Marshall (71) discusses these performances and other factors in the immediate environment from the point of view of their function in reproductive physiology. He concludes that the sexual displays and the presence of other animals serve to increase afferent stimuli to the hypothalamus, and thence, to the pituitary in both sexes. This mutual stimulation thus serves to synchronize pituitary activity in the prospective mates. In mammals, these factors are less obvious, operate more subtly, and vary from species to species. However, they do play a role in reproductive physiology in such animals as the mink and even in the mouse, as indicated by van der Lee and Boot's observation that the incidence of "spontaneous" pseudopregnancy is higher in mice housed in groups than it is in individually caged animals (60).

Additional evidence for the importance of social stimuli in regulating reproductive functions is provided by the work of several investigators. Whitten has found that when groups of female mice are exposed to a male mouse, their sexual cycles tend to become synchronous, and about half of them come into estrus on the third day (119). This effect can also be produced by placing the female mice in a cage recently vacated by a male, and it does not occur in females deprived of their sense of smell. Bruce and her associates have shown that exposure of pregnant female mice to cages in which males of a different strain have been kept causes abortion or resorption of the fetuses (13, 83). This ability to block pregnancy can also be acquired by androgenized female mice receiving implants of testosterone after ovariectomy. Exposure of mated females to the urine of androgenized females was also effective in blocking pregnancy (24). The effect is mediated by olfactory stimuli, and provides additional evidence of the importance of the olfactory sense in reproduction.

II. The Role of Environmental Factors on Reproduction in Individual Species

A. Sheep

In sheep developed in England reproductive activity usually begins near September first in the northern hemisphere and continues, in the absence of pregnancy, well into late winter. In the southern hemisphere, the appearance of sexual activity corresponds to the same season of the year, or about March to August (70). There is a gradation in length of sexual seasons according to the latitude and altitude of the animals' place of origin. Thus, sheep indigenous to countries in high latitudes have a shorter and more marked sexual season than those native to the tropics (34). This explains why some breeds, such as the Suffolk and Hampshire, tend to exhibit estrus early in the fall and continue to undergo cycles until late in the winter or early spring (41). Others, the Corriedale and Dorset Horn, for example, may exhibit estrus during the spring and summer months (100), while still others, such as the Merino (57), may breed at almost any season of the year. Even in the latter, however, there appears to be a short anestrous period which occurs during the spring and summer months (55, 90, 91, 95). Sheep transported from one hemisphere to another reverse their breeding season (70). This type of evidence suggests, and direct experimentation has confirmed, that the major factor affecting reproductive periodicity in the sheep is the amount of incident light. Thus, Sykes and Cole (108) found that if the light was gradually decreased, beginning in the latter part of March and extending through April and early May until a total deficiency of 6 hours of daylight was created, most of the treated ewes bred at least once and possibly twice during May and early June. All those conceiving gave birth to lambs in the early part of November, or at a time 4–5 months earlier than normally expected.

These results have been confirmed by others, who have clearly demonstrated that reproductive activity in sheep is regulated by changes in the light environment (34, 48, 123). By artificially providing additional amounts of light during the winter and decreasing the amounts of light during the summer, Yeates (123) demonstrated that the sexual season can be completely reversed. In these experiments, the rams were also apparently stimulated by the reversed seasonal lighting. They produced the highest quality semen and exhibited the greatest libido in the summer months of May, June, July, and August, a time in which the mating desire is normally lowest.

In another experiment (48), Suffolk sheep were subjected to a constant light rhythm: either 4 hours of light and 2 hours of dark, then 4 hours of light and 14 hours of dark; or 4 hours of light, 8 hours of dark, then 4 hours of light and 8 hours of dark. Either treatment was successful in producing a regular series of estrous cycles in the treated animals. Although estrous activity was displayed in a short time after the beginning of treatment, pregnancy did not result, in spite of many breedings. Nevertheless, as pointed out by Yeates (125), this method of controlling light changes may be of considerable practical importance if the problem of low conception can be overcome. Artificial lighting conditions are not required, but merely a blackout pen into which the sheep can be run during the middle of the summer day.

It has been reported that some strains of Merino ewes kept under the same geographical and seasonal conditions may commence their breeding early in the summer before the days have started to shorten (115). Although this observation was not confirmed by other investigations (127), it does raise the question of whether the proper stimulus for reproductive activity involves decreasing light or a critical light-dark ratio.

Whether or not an inherent rhythmic mechanism, with alternating periods of sexual activity and quiescence, exists in the sheep, has been much debated. Terry and Meites (110) showed that sheep kept for 7 weeks in summer on 24 hours of light, on no light, or on daylight all continued to cycle. Earlier lambing in the group on 24 hours of light was the only obvious effect. Similarly, when ewes were maintained under a constant light ratio (6 hours of light to 18 hours of dark) for 3 years, cyclical estrous activity became aberrant. In some, the onset of seasonal estrus was delayed; in others, the intervals of estrus occurred at varying frequencies not necessarily associated with the time of the normal seasonal period (19). There is, thus, usually some cycling in sheep independent of changes in daylight. Rams are also influenced by the duration of illumination. Testicular weight and epididymal sperm reserves are greatest when the photoperiod is approximately 8 hours; primary spermatocytes are at their peak at 10 hours (82). The pituitary gonadotropic content is also altered by length of the photoperiod. Hypophyses from rams maintained on a short-day cycle (8 hours) contain much greater amounts of both FSH and LH than those maintained on a long-day cycle (16 hours) (85).

Although light must certainly play a dominant role in controlling the seasonal sexual periodicity in sheep, other factors play a part and must be considered. The effects of temperature changes are one example, but because of the considerable temperature variation from day to day or within the day, it is unlikely that this factor plays a major role. The observation that low temperatures are not always associated with the onset of estrus also supports this view (123). Furthermore, the time of onset of the breeding season or incidence of estrus was not affected when the ewes were exposed to high environmental temperatures for a 6-hour period each day (124), or when they were subjected to different temperatures (65). In more recent investigations, however, an influence of temperature appears to have been demonstrated. Onset of estrus was significantly advanced by more than 50 days in ewes maintained in an air-conditioned room at 45°–48°F during the months of June, July, and August. Since light intensity and nutrition were the same for both treated and control groups, influence by these factors was eliminated (26).

The ram may retain a certain degree of fertility throughout the whole year, but in many cases fertility is curtailed during the spring and summer months (6, 9, 66, 88). Although an influence of light duration upon semen characteristics has not been ruled out, some have suggested that the high temperatures encountered at this time of year cause an elevated body temperature which depresses spermatogenesis (66, 86). This concept receives some experimental support from the finding that the semen from rams maintained at 45°–48°F during the summer months has a significantly higher motility rating and fewer abnormal cells than that of animals subjected to uncontrolled environmental temperatures. In these experiments those rams kept under the cool conditions had significantly lower rectal temperatures (26, 27). Furthermore, shearing of sheep results in lower body temperature, presumably by increasing rate of heat loss. This practice may have some practical application through an improvement of conception rate (28). High air temperatures have also been shown to have an adverse effect upon pregnant ewes by causing a low birth weight of the lambs (128).

Another factor which may have a favorable influence on the induction of estrus is the presence of the male. A number of studies (93, 94, 97, 98, 106, 111, 113) have led to the conclusion that the presence of the ram during the transition from the nonbreeding to the breeding season furnishes an exteroceptive stimulus to reproductive activity. Since this stimulus is only operative during the transition period, some have hypothesized that the presence of the ram brings about ovulation and, as a result, the subsequent formation of a corpus luteum. This structure becomes the waning corpus luteum which, according to some theories, is necessary together with a developing follicle to produce the behavioral manifestations of heat (40, 42).

B. Goat

The goat, like the ewe, is a polyestrous animal undergoing periods of cyclical sexual activity when the days are short and remaining anestrus in other seasons. The height of the breeding period is usually about November, in the northern hemisphere, but it may extend from September to February or even longer. Among the first experimental investigations on the effect of light on the breeding cycles in this species were those of Bissonnette (8). His results indicated that heat periods could be induced following the gradual reduction of light exposure, and would terminate earlier than normal following an increase. A constant light length similar to the number of daylight hours found during the month of October will also induce the onset of estrus during the nonbreeding season (130). Goats, like sheep, may have an inherent reproductive rhythm that operates independently of other external environmental factors. This problem, however, remains unsettled.

Bissonnette (8) indicated that changes in ambient temperature were not a major factor in the control of the breeding cycle in goats, but no controlled experiments have been conducted to test a specific temperature effect. Social factors may, however, influence reproductive activity, as suggested by one observation (109) in which the presence of the male appeared to stimulate the onset of the breeding season.

C. CATTLE

Most cows breed at all times of the year, but there is a strong tendency for them to calve more frequently in the months of February to April than at other times. The consistency of this observation implies an environmental effect upon reproduction in this species. Presumptive evidence that seasonal variations in hours of daylight were associated with alterations in the fertility levels of cattle was first offered by Mercier and Salisbury (75). In their report, they reviewed the available literature and analyzed data obtained from a study of fertility records of three herds of cattle located at different latitudes. They found significant differences in fertility levels of these herds between seasons, and from this association suggested that variations in the seasonal length of daylight influenced the reproductive capacity of cattle. In a later and more extensive analysis of data covering about 125,000 cows, they (76) observed a significant correlation between length of daylight and fertility level. Age, however, appeared to influence the light response; younger cattle being influenced more easily than mature animals. Winter was the poorest breeding season for all age groups, and fall most consistently gave the highest percentage of fertile conceptions when all cows were included. A beneficial effect of increased illumination upon conception rate has been suggested in one report from Alaska. The average natural daylight in this region amounts to approximately 8 hours. When additional light was provided, conception rate was improved and number of services per conception was decreased (107). Although these studies are significant, the simple correlation with one environmental factor, length of daylight, does not necessarily indicate it to be the cause of the observed differences. Other factors, particularly the changes in temperature associated with the season, have not been ruled out. Definite conclusions about the effect of light upon reproduction in cows must, therefore, be postponed until experiments in which both light, temperature, and other variables are systematically controlled.

Bulls also show periodic changes in fertility associated with the season of the year. Most authors agree that male fertility reaches its peak in the spring and drops to a minimum level between June and September (30, 78, 86, 97, 101, 116). Although warm weather may be conducive to the production of good quality semen (2), very high temperatures are associated with a depression of spermatogenesis (1, 25, 50, 87, 101). Occasionally, there may be a lag of about 1 month before a reduction in semen quality is noted. In most cases, the depression will extend for as long as 2 months after the hottest time of the year (78, 116). Thus, although increasing length of day may favor fertility, high temperatures cause an opposite response (99). In this case, temperature changes are exerting an important influence upon reproduction. The adverse effect of high temperature upon semen quality has been investigated experimentally by the use of controlled temperature chambers in which both humidity and light were maintained constant (18, 79). Exposure of bulls to high ambient temperatures caused a decrease in the average initial motility, sperm concentration, and total sperm count; but when temperatures were lowered, a gradual recovery took place (18). High environmental temperatures caused other physiological disturbances, including an increase in body temperature, a factor known to cause reduction in semen quality and loss of libido. The effects of a high environmental temperature upon seasonal fertility, therefore, may well be brought about through their effects on body temperature.

Other photoperiodic effects in cattle are known to occur. Shedding of hair is induced following increased illumination (58), and the normal seasonal coat cycle is regulated by seasonal fluctuations in the duration of daylight (126). When cattle were treated by exposure to artificial illumination for approximately 13 hours daily during the spring and autumn, complete shedding occurred. If, however, they received this treatment in summer, a rapid growth of hair was brought about. After adaptation to these new environmental lighting conditions, all the groups grew similar coats, which were permanently maintained and characterized by an intermediate length and fuzzy appearance (129).

The proximity of the male has not been shown to have a direct effect upon the initiation or inducement of estrous behavior in cows. Van Demark and Hayes (114) have made the interesting observation, however, that genital stimulation in the cow sets off intense uterine contractions, presumably due to release of oxytocin from the posterior pituitary. They report that such contractions are also initiated by the bull nuzzling the cow, or even by the mere presence of the bull. The symptoms of heat may be intensified following exercise, and conception sometimes may not occur if postcoital excitation is marked or prolonged (38). Presumably, this is due to expulsion of the semen from the vagina by the straining and increased activity associated with the sexual excitation.

It has been reported that exercise may benefit fertility of bulls (4, 35, 121). These observations, however, are equivocal in view of other results indicating no significant effect of exercise on semen quality (61, 105).

D. SWINE

The domestic pig has a cycle of about 21 days which recurs throughout the year except when pregnancy or lactation intervenes. Although wild swine in captivity breed in almost any month except January and February, in the wild state they are believed to have only one annual sexual season (29).

Season of year has no effect upon fertility (11), but may influence embryonic mortality. Poor litters occur more frequently in the winter than the spring and early summer (52). It has been claimed that the quality of semen obtained in autumn may be superior to that found in summer, but time of year apparently does not affect spermatogenesis. The number of tubules containing sperm and the spermatic activity of the testis do not show differences associated with season (81).

No light effect on reproductive activity in the pig has been demonstrated, but apparently temperature may have some effect. It has been suggested that sexual maturity in pigs in western Transvaal occurs later than it does in Europe because of the higher average temperature and lower humidity in this region (16). Nutritional differences, however, would appear to be a more likely explanation.

Social factors have been shown to be important in the mating behavior of the pig. Some females, although in heat, will not allow certain boars to mount. A preliminary courtship appears to be necessary before the female will accept the male. If the boar is permitted to run with sows, he will locate one in proestrus and give her his undivided attention. After she becomes accustomed to his "teasing," she will allow him to mount when estrus occurs (16). Some Russian work suggests that if boars are placed with sows, a higher percentage will show estrus within a shorter period of time than those sows not exposed to the male (89).

Both olfactory and auditory stimuli may also affect the "immobilization reflex" shown by estrous sows in response to manual pressure on the back. A combination of both stimuli elicits this reflex in 90% of the animals. This may be contrasted to 50% showing a normal response and 81% showing the response to olfactory stimuli alone (77, 103).

Mauleon and Signoret (74) have also shown disturbances of the estrous cycle following ablation of the olfactory bulbs. Complete removal caused involution of the genital tract and an elevation of FSH content in the pituitaries. LH content remained unchanged.

Audiogenic stimuli produce profound effects upon reproductive processes and have been classified as a form of stress. Other manipulations, such as transporting sows from one location to another, may also alter estrous activity. In one study this so-called stress of movement caused an earlier appearance of estrous in prepubertal gilts and tended to synchronize their cycles (84).

E. Horse

The horse is usually stated to be a seasonally polyestrous animal, with estrous cycles beginning about March and continuing into August. In the tropics it has been reported that two well-defined breeding seasons occur (3). A considerable variation in the number of animals showing estrus in any one month exists, the highest percentage usually occurring during the spring (53, 92). Many observations indicate, however, that the mare will breed at any season of the year (5, 22, 53, 92). When well fed and stabled, mares tend to show estrus throughout the year, but, when maintained on grass, they frequently show an anestrous period during the winter (22). This suggests that seasonal breeding may be due, in part, to nutritional factors.

The influence of light upon reproductive activity in the mare has been studied by Burkhardt (17). In his experiments, mares which were in anestrus, as judged by the absence of ovarian follicles and the characteristic anestrous appearance of the vagina and cervix, were divided into four treatment groups. Group I was directly exposed to an additional period of light by artificial illumination beginning in January. Group II was exposed to ultraviolet light applied to the flank and belly, which was gradually increased during a period of 4 weeks; the mares in this group had their eyes hooded. Group III was maintained in confinement under normal light conditions. Group IV was allowed to run in the paddock. No differences in reproductive activity or coat-shedding were noted between groups II, III, and IV. In group I, however, ovarian stromal growth, increased vascularity of the cervix and vagina, and shedding of the coat were noted within a period of about 15–30 days following the start of treatment. Follicles appeared soon afterward and the first appearance of estrus occurred, on the average, about 30 days earlier than in the other groups. From these results, Burkhardt concluded that the stimulus of light exerts a control on reproductive activity in the mare. Since direct irradiation of the ovaries did not change the normal occurrence of estrus, he suggested that the receptor organ was probably the eye.

Since the mare is predominantly a spring breeder, it would be expected to respond to increasing rather than decreasing day length, like the ewe and goat. This has been shown experimentally by Nishikawa et al. (80). They exposed anestrous mares to increased light by artificial illumination, beginning in mid-November and continuing to the end of February, and found that the ovaries began to function about 65–80 days earlier than normal. If the treatment was begun in August, the transition period between the breeding and nonbreeding season, the ovaries continued to be functional through the normally anestrous period. When animals were maintained in darkened stables, however, the appearance of ovarian activity was delayed, but not inhibited. Reproductive activity, therefore, appears to be controlled not by light alone; in this species, as in the ewe and cow, an inherent rhythm also exists.

The stallion shows seasonal changes in the quantity and quality of the semen (54). Changes in incident light are at least partly responsible for these variations. After continuous exposure to a reduced-light environment, sexual activity is inhibited, and sperm concentration as well as motility is reduced (62). Conversely, if stallions are exposed in mid-November to increasing light, testicular activity is rapidly increased. The volume and quality of the semen approach that found during the normal breeding season (80).

Specific effects of temperature on reproductive activity in the mare have not been critically studied, but from Hammond's observations, a cold, dry spring appears to be associated with heat periods that are longer than usual (39).

F. RABBIT

There is general agreement that the wild rabbit displays a seasonal periodicity with regard to the reproductive state. The season of activity usually begins in the winter months and, depending upon the species, extends into late spring or early fall (10, 36, 51, 69, 112). Some evidence, however, indicates that the length of the breeding season can be altered by external environmental influences. For example, Hammond (36) found it to depend to some extent upon temperature. Under exceptionally warm conditions, some wild does littered in late autumn or even winter. In addition to a temperature influence, light may play a role in the control of seasonal breeding. When New England cottontail rabbits were subjected to artificial light beginning in December, sexual activity began in January, 23 days earlier than the normal time (7). Seasonal changes in reproductive activity in the wild male have also been observed. During the stage of inactivity, the testes are small and are positioned in the abdominal cavity. At the start of the breeding season, they descend into the scrotum, enlarge, and reach an optimal functional state in early spring.

With domestication, the rabbit has lost its pattern of seasonal breeding since, under suitable conditions, does breed at any time of the year. Nevertheless, mating and conception occur more frequently during certain months (March to July) than at other times, particularly the late summer and fall (37, 63, 67). Seasonal differences in length of daylight may not be responsible for these observed seasonal differences in fertility in domesticated rabbits. When does were subjected to continuous light, continuous dark, increasing light, and decreasing light for 1 month, no significant effects on number of ovulations were found (104). Although the exposure of male rabbits to either an increased duration or intensity of light was found to significantly increase total sperm count, motility, and volume of liquid semen, exposure of animals to 23 hours of darkness daily did not alter semen characteristics when compared to nonartificially illuminated controls (23). Since others could find no influence of either continuous light or darkness for short or long periods on weights of testes, male accessory organs, and fructose content of the seminal vesicles (68), it is doubtful that seasonal changes in light duration exert an important influence on reproduction in the domestic male rabbit.

The rabbit remains in a constant estrous state and ovulation is normally induced by coitus, but it can also be brought about by sexual arousal from the sight of a male or from being mounted by another female (3). Thus, social stimuli become an important consideration with regard to an influence upon its reproductive state.

REFERENCES

1. Anderson, J., *Commonwealth Bur. Animal Breeding Genet., Edinburgh, Tech. Comm.* 6, 151 pp. (1945).
2. Anderson, J., *J. Agr. Sci.* 35, 184 (1945).
3. Asdell, S. A., "Patterns of Mammalian Reproduction." Cornell Univ. Press (Comstock), Ithaca, New York, 1946.
4. Bartlett, J. W., and Perry, E. J., *Proc. Am. Soc. Animal Production, 32nd Ann. Meeting, Chicago,* p. 243 (1939).
5. Berliner, V. R., *J. Animal Sci.* 1, 62 (1942).
6. Berliner, V. R., and Warbritton, V., *Proc. Am. Soc. Animal Production, 30th Ann. Meeting, Chicago,* p. 137 (1937).
7. Bissonnette, T. H., and Csech, A. G., *Biol. Bull.* 77, 364 (1939).
8. Bissonnette, T. H., *Physiol. Zool.* 14, 379 (1941).
9. Bogart, R., and Meyer, D. T., *Am. J. Physiol.* 147, 320 (1946).
10. Brambell, F. W. R., *Proc. Zool. Soc. London* 114, 1 (1944–1945).
11. Braude, R., Clark, P. M., and Mitchell, K. G., *J. Agr. Sci.* 45, 19 (1954).
12. Browman, L. G., *J. Exptl. Zool.* 75, 375 (1937).
13. Bruce, H. M., and Farrell, H. V., *Science* 131, 526 (1960).
14. Bunn, J. P., and Everett, J. W., *Proc. Soc. Exptl. Biol. Med.* 96, 369 (1957).
15. Burger, J. F., *J. Exptl. Zool.* 109, 259 (1948).
16. Burger, J. F., *Onderstepoort J. Vet. Res.* 25, Suppl. 2 (1952).
17. Burkhardt, J., *J. Agr. Sci.* 37, 64 (1947).
18. Casaday, R. B., Myers, R. M., and Legates, J. E., *J. Dairy Sci.* 36, 14 (1953).
19. Clegg, M. T., Weir, W. C., and Cole, H. H., *U.S. Dept. Agr. Misc. Publ.* 1005 (1965).
20. Clegg, M. T., and Doyle, L. L., *in* "Neuroendocrinology" (L. Martini and W. F. Ganong, eds.), Vol. II, p. 1. Academic Press, New York, 1967.
21. Critchlow, V. B., *in* "Advances in Neuroendocrinology" (A. V. Nalbandov, ed.), p. 377. Univ. of Illinois Press, Urbana, Illinois, 1963.
22. Day, F. T., *Vet. Record* 51, 1113 (1939).
23. Doggett, V. C., *Anat. Record* 30, 293 (1958).
24. Dominic, C. J., *J. Reprod. Fertility* 10, 469 (1965).
25. Dordick, I. L., *Acta Trop.* 6, 221 (1941).
26. Dutt, R. H., and Bush, L. F., *J. Animal Sci.* 14, 885 (1955).
27. Dutt, R. H., and Simpson, E. C., *J. Animal Sci.* 16, 136 (1957).
28. Dutt, R. H., and Hamm, P. T., *J. Animal Sci.* 16, 328 (1957).
29. Eckstein, P., and Zuckerman, S., *in* "Marshall's Physiology of Reproduction" (A. S. Parkes, ed.), 3rd ed., Vol. I, Part 1. Longmans, Green, New York, 1956.

30. Erb, R. E., Andrews, F. N., and Hilton, J. H., *J. Dairy Sci.* **25**, 815 (1942).
31. Farner, D. S., *Am. Scientist* **52**, 137 (1964).
32. Farner, D. S., and Menwaldt, L. R., *Science* **118**, 351 (1953).
33. Findley, J. D., and Beakey, W. R., in "Progress in the Physiology of Farm Animals" (J. Hammond, ed.), Vol. I, p. 252. Butterworth, London and Washington, D.C., 1954.
34. Hafez, E. S. E., *J. Agr. Sci.* **42**, 13 (1952).
35. Hamilton, J. G., and Symington, E. L., *Can. J. Comp. Med.* **3**, 337 (1939).
36. Hammond, J., *J. Agr. Sci.* **11**, 337 (1921).
37. Hammond, J., and Marshall, F. H. A., "Reproduction in the Rabbit." Oliver & Boyd, Edinburgh and London, 1925.
38. Hammond, J., "The Physiology of Reproduction in the Cow." Cambridge Univ. Press, London and New York, 1927.
39. Hammond, J., "Farm Animals," 2nd ed. Arnold, London, 1952.
40. Hammond, J., Jr., Hammond, J., and Parkes, A. S., *J. Agr. Sci.* **32**, 308 (1942).
41. Hammond, J., Jr., *J. Agr. Sci.* **34**, 97 (1944).
42. Hammond, J., Jr., *J. Endocrinol.* **4**, 169 (1945).
43. Hammond, J., Jr., *J. Endocrinol.* **7**, 330 (1951).
44. Hammond, J., Jr., *J. Mammal.* **33**, 218 (1952).
45. Hammond, J., Jr., *Vitamins Hormones* **12**, 157 (1954).
46. Hansel, W., and Dutt, R. H., *J. Animal Sci.* **25**, Suppl. (1966).
47. Hansson, A., *Acta Zool. Stockholm* **28**, 1 (1947).
48. Hart, D. S., *J. Agr. Sci.* **40**, 143 (1950).
49. Hemmingsen, A. M., and Krarup, N. B., *Kgl. Danske Videnskab. Selskab Biol. Medd.* **13**, 1 (1937).
50. Hilder, R. A., Fohrman, M. H., and Graves, R. R., *J. Dairy Sci.* **27**, 819 (1944).
51. Hill, M., and White, W. E., *J. Physiol. (London)* **80**, 174 (1934).
52. Hofmann, F., *Z. Schweinez* **45**, 85 (1938); *Animal Breeding Abstr.* **9**, 33 (1941).
53. Howell, C. E., and Rollins, W. C., *J. Animal Sci.* **10**, 789 (1951).
54. Kashiwabara, T., Japan, *J. Vet. Sci.* **9**, 39 (1947); *Animal Breeding Abstr.* **19**, 162 (1951).
55. Kelley, R. B., and Shaw, H. E. B., *J. Council Sci. Ind. Res.* **12**, 18 (1939).
56. Kelly, D. E., *Am. Scientist* **50**, 597 (1962).
57. Kupfer, M., *Union S. Africa Dept. Agr. 13th, 14th Repts. Direct. Vet. Serv. Animal Ind. Onderstepoort* **2**, 1211 (1928).
58. Laing, J. A., quoted by Yeates (Ref. *125*).
59. Lee, M. O., *Am. J. Physiol.* **78**, 246 (1926).
60. Lee, S., van der, and Boot, L. M., *Acta Physiol. Pharmacol. Neerl.* **5**, 213 (1956).
61. Lepard, O. L., Shuart, C. E., and Foster, A., *J. Dairy Sci.* **24**, 509 (1941).
62. Lintvareva, N. I., *Tr. Vses. Nauch. Issled. Inst. Konev. Moscow: Seljhozgig*, pp. 44–65 (1955); *Animal Breeding Abstr.* **24**, 333 (1956).
63. Lush, J. L., *J. Agr. Res.* **30**, 893 (1925).
64. Lyman, C. P., *Bull. Museum Comp. Zool. Harvard* **93**, 393 (1943).
65. McKenzie, F. F., and Phillips, R. W., *Missouri Univ. Agr. Expt. Sta. Bull.* **328** (1933).

66. McKenzie, F. F., and Berliner, V. R., *Missouri Univ. Agr. Expt. Sta. Bull.* **265** (1937).
67. Manresa, M., *Philippine J. Sci.* **51**, 323 (1933).
68. Maqsood, M., and Parsons, U., *Experientia* **10**, 188 (1954).
69. Marshall, F. H. A., "The Physiology of Reproduction." Longmans, Green, London, 1922.
70. Marshall, F. H. A., *Proc. Roy. Soc.* **B122**, 413 (1937).
71. Marshall, F. H. A., *Biol. Revs. Cambridge Phil Soc.* **17**, 68 (1942).
72. Martini, L., and Ganong, W. F. (eds.), "Neuroendocrinology," Vols. 1 and 2. Academic Press, New York, 1966, 1967.
73. Matthews, L. H., *Proc. Roy. Soc.* **B126**, 557 (1939).
74. Mauleon, P., and Signoret, J. P., *Proc. 5th Intern. Congr. Reprod. Artificial Insemination, Trento* **2**, 432 (1964).
75. Mercier, E., and Salisbury, G. W., *J. Dairy Sci.* **30**, 747 (1947).
76. Mercier, E., and Salisbury, G. W., *J. Dairy Sci.* **30**, 817 (1947a).
77. Mesnil du Buisson, F. du., and Signoret, J. P., *Ann. Zootech.* **11**, 53 (1961).
78. Morgan, R. F., and Davis, H. P., *Nebraska Univ. Agr. Expt. Sta. Res. Bull.* **104** (1938).
79. Naelapaa, H., Johnston, J. E., and Vizinat, J. J., *J. Dairy Sci.* **37**, 667 (1954).
80. Nishikawa, Y., Svjie, T., and Haracla, N., *Bull. Natl. Inst. Agr. Sci. Ser. G* **3**, 35 (1952); *Animal Breed. Abstr.* **22**, 103 (1954).
81. Niwa, J., and Milzohu, A., *Bull. Natl. Inst. Agr. Sci. Ser. G* **8**, 31 (1954); *Animal Breeding Abstr.* **23**, 403 (1955).
82. Ortavant, R., *Proc. 4th Intern. Congr. Animal Reprod., The Hague* **2**, 236 (1961).
83. Parkes, A. S., and Bruce, H. M., *Science* **134**, 1049 (1961).
84. Pearson, O. P., and Enders, R. K., *J. Exptl. Zool.* **95**, 21 (1944).
85. Pelletier, J., and Ortavant, R., *Ann. Biol. Animale Biochim. Biophys.* **4**, 17 (1964).
86. Phillips, R. W., and McKenzie, F. F., *Missouri Univ. Agr. Expt. Sta. Bull.* **217** (1934).
87. Phillips, R. W., Knapp, B., Jr., Hemmstra, L. C., and Eaton, O. N., *Am. J. Vet. Res.* **4**, 115 (1943).
88. Phillips, R. W., Fraps, R. M., and Frank, A. H., *Am. J. Vet. Res.* **6**, 165 (1943).
89. Polikarpova, E. F., *Ref. Rab. Ucrezden. Otd. Biol. Nauk. Akad. Nauk SSSR 1941–43*, 214 (1945); *Animal Breeding Abstr.* **14**, 159 (1946).
90. Quinlan, J., and Mare, G., *Union S. Africa Dept. Agr. 17th Rept. Direct. Vet. Serv. Animal Ind. Onderstepoort* **6**, 63 (1931).
91. Quinlan, J., Steyn, H. P., and DeVos, D., *Onderstepoort J. Vet. Sci. Animal Ind.* **16**, 243 (1941).
92. Quinlan, J., van Rensburg, S. W., and Steyn, H. P., *Onderstepoort J. Vet. Res.* **25**, 105 (1951).
93. Radford, H. M., and Watson, R. H., *Australian J. Agr. Res.* **8**, 460 (1957).
94. Riches, J. H., and Watson, R. H., *Australian J. Agr. Res.* **5**, 141 (1954).
95. Roux, L. L., *Onderstepoort J. Vet. Sci. Animal Ind.* **6**, 465 (1936).
96. Rowan, W., *Nature* **115**, 494 (1925).
97. Schinckel, P. G., *Australian Vet. J.* **30**, 189 (1954).
98. Schinckel, P. G., *Australian J. Agr. Res.* **5**, 465 (1954).

99. Schindler, H., *Bull. Res. Council Israel* **4**, 184 (1954).

100. Schott, R. G., Phillips, R. W., and Spencer, D. A., *Proc. Am. Soc. Animal Production*, 32nd Ann. Meeting, Chicago, p. 347 (1939).

101. Schultze, A. B., Davis, H. H., Blum, C. T., and Oloufa, M. M., *Nebraska Univ. Agr. Expt. Sta. Res. Bull.* **154** (1948).

102. Semper, C., "Natural Conditions of Existence as They Affect Animal Life." C. K. Paul & Co., London, 1881.

103. Signoret, J. P., and Mesnil du Buisson, F. du, *Proc. 4th Intern. Congr. Animal Reprod., The Hague*, p. 171 (1961).

104. Smelser, G. K., Walton, A., and Wetham, E. O., *J. Exptl. Biol.* **11**, 352 (1934).

105. Snyder, J. W., and Ralston, N. P., *J. Dairy Sci.* **38**, 125 (1955).

106. Stanica, P., *Ann. Inst. Natl. Zootech. Roumanie* **7**, 90 (1939); *Animal Breeding Abstr.* **8**, 53 (1940).

107. Sweetman, W. J., *J. Dairy Sci.* **33**, 391 (1950).

108. Sykes, J. F., and Cole, C. L., *Mich. State Univ. Agr. Expt. Sta. Quart. Bull.* **26**, 250 (1944).

109. Tebbe, H., *Deut. Landwirtsch. Tierzucht* **39**, 62 (1935); *Animal Breeding Abstr.* **3**, 4 (1935).

110. Terry, W. A., and Meites, J., *J. Animal Sci.* **10**, 1081 (1951).

111. Thompson, D. S., and Schinckel, P. G., *Empire J. Exptl. Agr.* **20**, 77 (1952).

112. Trippensee, R. E., *Proc. North Am. Wildlife Conf.*, p. 344 (1936).

113. Underwood, E. J., Shier, F. L., and Davenport, N., *J. Dept. Agr. W. Australia* **21**, 135 (1944).

114. Van Demark, N. L., and Hays, R. L., *Am. J. Physiol.* **170**, 518 (1952).

115. Watson, R. H., and Radford, H. M., *Australian Vet. J.* **31**, 31 (1955).

116. Weeth, H. J., and Herman, H. A., *Missouri Univ. Agr. Expt. Sta. Res. Bull.* **447** (1949).

117. Wells, L. J., and Zahsky, M., *Am. J. Anat.* **66**, 429 (1940).

118. Whipple, H. E., *Ann. New York Acad. Sci.* **117**, 1–645 (1964).

119. Whitten, W. K., *J. Endocrinol.* **14**, 160 (1956).

120. Wolstenholme, G. E. W., ed., *Ciba Found. Study Group* **26** (1967).

121. Woodward, E. G., *Wash. State Coll. Agr. Expt. Sta. Bull.* **158** (1920).

122. Wurtman, R. J., Axelrod, J., and Chu, Elizabeth W., *Ann. N.Y. Acad. Sci.* **117**, 228 (1964).

123. Yeates, N. T. M., *J. Agr. Sci.* **39**, 1 (1949).

124. Yeates, N. T. M., *J. Agr. Sci.* **43**, 199 (1953).

125. Yeates, N. T. M., *in* "Recent Progress in the Physiology of Farm Animals" (J. Hammond, ed.), Vol. I, p. 363. Butterworth, London and Washington, D.C., 1954.

126. Yeates, N. T. M., *Australian J. Agr. Res.* **6**, 891 (1955).

127. Yeates, N. T. M., *Australian J. Agr. Res.* **7**, 435 (1956).

128. Yeates, N. T. M., *Australian J. Agr. Res.* **7**, 440 (1956).

129. Yeates, N. T. M., *Australian J. Agr. Res.* **8**, 733 (1957).

130. Yoshioka, Z., Awasawa, T., and Suzuki, S., *Bull. Natl. Inst. Agr. Sci. Ser. G* **1**, 105 (1951).

131. Zuckerman, S., *Ciba Found. Colloq. Endocrinol.* **4**, 23 (1952).

18 NUTRITIVE INFLUENCES UPON REPRODUCTION

JOHANNES MOUSTGAARD

I. The Influence of Nutrition on the Development and Function of the Reproductive Organs

A nutrient deficiency may affect the development and function of the reproductive organs, either directly or indirectly; in the former case, the deficiency causes a disturbed cellular metabolism in the organs concerned, in the latter, the function of the endocrine system related to reproduction will be changed. Whether the direct or the indirect influence is of major importance may be difficult to decide, but the significance of nutrition for the normal functioning of the endocrine or neuroendocrine system is obvious from numerous experiments (*103, 106, 107, 108, 161*).

A. THE FEMALE REPRODUCTIVE ORGANS

1. Underfeeding and Overfeeding

In farm animals, undernutrition delays the onset of puberty and leads to impaired fertility in mature animals. Heat symptoms have been found to occur at later stages in underfed heifers than in heifers fed adequate diets (*5, 183*), a fact which has been clearly illustrated by Reid *et al.* (*164*) in experiments with calves and heifers fed normal (Morrisons standards), supernormal (140% of normal), and subnormal rations (65% of normal). On an average, the animals experienced their first heat period when they were 11.3, 9.4, and 17.3 months' old, respectively. The underfed animals had a subnormal conception rate, underdeveloped udders, and, in many cases, the animals gave birth to dead calves. In mature cows, underfeeding was found to impair estrous symptoms and to reduce fertility (167, 192). Several investigators have demonstrated that insufficient nutrients also may impair fertility in sheep (11, 30, 45, 59, 192) and swine (26, 30, 115). In a large-scale experiment with two groups of weaners one of which was fed ad lib and the other on a very restricted schedule puberty was reached at an average age of about 188 days (body weight 194 pounds) and 234 days (body weight 118 pounds), respectively (26). In other experiments (168, 178), evaluated and discussed by Casida (30), a less severe underfeeding (two-thirds ad lib) did not delay the onset of puberty; the rate of ovulation, however, was subnormal.

Several authors have reported that fat heifers and cows presented rather weak heat symptoms and that the rate of conception was subnormal in these animals; it remains an open question, however, whether the infertility of these animals was attributable to their obesity or whether they were fat because of the sterility. So far, it remains obscure whether excessive feeding of well-balanced diets may result in ovarian dysfunction; findings obtained in some experiments seem to contradict this assumption (164). As already mentioned, puberty occurs at an earlier stage (26, 178, 204) and the rate of ovulation is higher (30, 168) in gilts fed ad lib than in gilts fed restricted diets; the rate of embryonic mortality is apparently higher, however, in the former than in the latter category (168).

In sheep, increased supplies of concentrated food for a certain period prior to breeding may increase the rate of ovulation (11, 30) and the number of twin births (34). This practice is termed "flushing" (145); it will be successful if the feed intake prior to flushing is lower than that which otherwise would give optimal lamb crops (30, 163). Flushing may increase lamb crops by 10–20% (46, 145).

Everything considered, experimental results as well as practical experience have shown that the development and function of the female reproductive organs will be inhibited by marked underfeeding, but conditions are generally seen to normalize as soon as adequate diets are supplied (7, 163). The effect, whether of underfeeding or overfeeding, is undoubtedly attributable to a changed production or release of pituitary gonadotropins (65, 103, 106, 114).

2. Protein

The importance of adequate protein intake for the development and function of the female reproductive organs is well known from experiments with laboratory animals (107, 161, 182) and farm animals (30, 39, 119). Protein deficiency in farm animals is generally admitted to give rise to reproductive disturbances; underdevelopment of the ovary and uterus are common findings in heifers fed diets inadequate in protein. The reproductive function will usually be restored within a few weeks if adequate supplies of protein are administered to such animals. In swine, protein deficiency has also been found to impair the development and function of the reproductive organs (39). So far, it remains to be defined how functional disturbances of the reproductive organs are provoked by protein deficiency (103), as experimental results hitherto obtained are rather conflicting; most findings seem to indicate, however, that the gonadal hypofunction during malnutrition may be due to a lowered level of circulating gonadotropin (103, 108). Species differences, even sex differences, may also be involved (108, 182).

3. Minerals

In farm animals, reproductive failure due to phosphorus deficiency has been noted mainly in range cattle and was first described by Tuff in Norway (191) and Theiler et al. in South Africa (186). The latter team showed that supplies of bone meal to cows kept on phosphorus-deficient grassland would increase the annual number of calves born per 100 cows, viz., from 51 to 80. This observation has been substantiated by other investigators. Phosphorus deficiency in heifers may cause ovarian dysfunction, thereby postponing puberty (82, 84); in mature animals the result may be depressed heat symptoms, even anestrus (83).

In cattle (84), as in rats (69), a high calcium-to-phosphorus ratio might bring about a reduction in the phosphate absorption, thus causing "conditioned" phosphorus deficiency, especially if the phosphorus content of rations were at borderline levels. This condition may presumably be counteracted by adequate supplies of vitamin D (83, cf. also 102). It should be stressed that depressed estrous symptoms may represent the first and only sign of a phosphorus deficiency, whether of an absolute or conditioned nature (60); considering the high energy turnover in the pituitary and ovary, this is hardly surprising. In sheep, phosphorus deficiency may result in the same reproductive disturbances as in cattle (163).

A number of trace elements such as iron, copper, zinc, manganese, and selenium are all of fundamental importance for animal health; according to our present knowledge, however, only manganese deficiency may result in an impaired development and function of the female reproductive organs in laboratory animals (179), swine (36, 159), and cattle (14, 82). In experiments with gilts fed diets low in manganese (0.5 ppm of dry matter), heat symptoms were depressed or estrus failed to occur (36, 68, 159). In gilts fed diets containing 40 ppm of manganese, estrous cycles were normal (159). In cattle, manganese deficiency might upset the ovarian function (84, cf. also 83); in one study, the manganese content in hair was found to be related to the rate of conception (198). It remains obscure whether the disturbed ovarian function caused by manganese deficiency were due to a biochemical dysfunction of the ovarian tissue or it might be attributable to a reduced production of gonadotropin; in recent studies, the [54]Mn turnover rate in ovarian tissue was found to be very high (47).

4. Vitamins

Cattle (29, 80) and sheep (155) may show normal heat, ovulate, and conceive even though they are depleted of vitamin A to the point of night blindness and have cystic degenerative changes in the pituitary. In a comprehensive study of vitamin A deficiency in gilts, Palludan (150) observed slightly irregular estrous cycles in the animals; heat symptoms were normal or even intensified and the animals conceived at a normal rate. These results support previous findings (74, 87).

5. Plant Estrogens

In the year 1940 and later, severe reproductive irregularities in sheep in western Australia were observed; in unmated ewes, cystic hyperplasia of the endometrium was a common finding, various stages of uterine and vaginal prolapse being the outstanding symptom. Mammary development in ewes as well as in whethers was another symptom. This apparently endocrine anomaly had a disastrous spread in areas in which a new variety of clover (*Trifolium subterraneum* var. *dwalganup*) predominated in pastures (13). According to later studies, a series of plants belonging in the Geguminosa and Graminacea families were found to contain some isoflavine derivatives possessing estrogenic activity (18, 97). The action of plant estrogens is contingent on several factors (97). Certain breeds of sheep seemed to be more susceptible than others; horses and cattle which were grazed on the same pasture showed no clinical symptoms; impaired liver function seems to intensify the effect of plant estrogens; finally, use of fertilizers rich in phosphorus depressed the content of estrogens in the clover; besides, storage in a dry condition, not as silage, reduces the estrogenic potency of the plants. The estrogenic potency of plants is hardly a problem of practical importance today; the catastrophe in sheep breeding in western Australia serves, however, as an instructive example of the hazards involved when the feed of animals only comprises one species of plant.

B. THE MALE REPRODUCTIVE ORGANS

1. Underfeeding

In experiments with swine, gross undernutrition for long periods of time has been found to reduce the size of the testes; in addition, spermatogenesis ceased and the interstitial cells atrophied. Upon refeeding, tubules developed rapidly and the spermatogenesis recurred (41). Examination of young bulls revealed that reduced intakes of energy impaired growth of the body as well as of the endocrine glands and the reproductive organs; upon refeeding, growth would almost normalize, but the development and function of the testes, measured on the basis of number of sperm in semen, failed to become fully normal (*197*, cf. also *131*). Undernutrition (70% of recommended allowances) of bull calves has also been found (*21, 57*) to delay onset of sexual maturity, and besides, the sperm concentration and sperm mobility became subnormal; in supernormally fed calves (140–160% of normal) puberty was seen to occur at earlier stages than in calves fed normal diets. Experiments with triplet bull calves revealed in principle the same features (*147*). Undernutrition may not merely result in morphological changes, however; functional changes of the male sex organs may also be involved. This feature has been clearly illustrated by Mann *et al.* (*112, 118, 119*). In rats, a low energy intake was found to result in a depression of the secretory function of the accessory sex glands of the same order of magnitude as that caused by castration. Administration of androgens and gonadotropin would restore the secretory function (*112, 119*). Also the influence of underfeeding on the chemical composition of semen in bulls was elucidated by Mann and Walton (*120*); notwithstanding that the spermatogenic function of the testes seemed to remain normal throughout an observation period of more than 20 weeks, citric acid and fructose levels in semen were seen to fall to 60 and 30% of initial values, respectively. Recently, other investigators have obtained similar results (*180*). In addition, Mann and his group studied the influence of underfeeding on the onset of spermatogenesis and the secretory function of sex glands; monozygous twin calves served as experimental animals (*118, 121*). Underfeeding was found to delay onset of secretion of citric acid and fructose, but the action on the spermatogenesis was not equally marked. The androgenic activity, and thus excretion of the compounds mentioned, might be restored by application of gonadotropin.

2. Protein

In farm animals, the occurrence of puberty was found to be delayed in heifers fed diets low in protein (*165*); in adult bulls, the feeding of similar diets had no adverse effect on the gonads. Excessive protein underfeeding of young bulls (*131*) and rams (*202*) was found to reduce feed intake of the animals and to impair production of semen. Branton *et al.* (*19*) determined the influence of protein supplies on the production of semen; bulls kept on three different levels of totally digestible nutrients serve as experimental animals; they received 100, 120, and 140%, respectively, of the recommended maintenance requirement of dairy cows. Irrespective of feeding levels and protein intakes, the fertility of the semen used in these experiments seemed to be identical, although the concentration of spermatozoa in semen was highest in bulls that had received the highest quantity of protein. This finding, as well as findings in other investigations (*20, 105*), indicate that supplies of energy in quantities about 20% higher than calculated maintenance requirements, and of protein in quantities about 60–70% higher than maintenance requirements, presumably are sufficient for the achievement of optimal sperm production in bulls.

3. Minerals

In laboratory animals manganese deficiency might result in extensive testicular degeneration (17, 148); such dramatic sequelae of manganese deficiency have never been observed in farm animals. In experiments with boars raised on diets extremely low in manganese (3.3 ppm), the spermatogenesis remained normal (159).

Concentration of copper in semen is known to be rather high; in the spermatozoa the copper is localized mainly in the tail and the middle piece (118); its biochemical importance remains to be defined. In moderate hypocuprosis, the function of testes seems to remain normal.

The role of zinc in the reproductive process in male animals has been recognized for years. By means of chemical and autoradiographic methods, the accessory glands and the spermatozoa were found to have high contents of this mineral (129); the zinc concentration in the accessory sex glands was found to be reduced after castration; it could, however, be normalized by administration of testosterone (71). Zinc deficiency is known to inhibit the spermatogenic and endocrine testicular functions, a feature that may find its explanation in the concomitant inanition (132, 133); experiments including restricted feeding schemes suggested, however, that the disturbed spermatogenesis might be due to a lack of zinc per se. So far, an explanation of the biochemical significance of the high zinc concentrations in the reproductive organs of male animals remains to be given. It deserves to be mentioned that zinc presumably is a functional component of some of the hypophyseal hormones (162, 196).

It has been suggested (162) that zinc deficiency might be a factor of etiological importance in a pathological syndrome encountered in boys in Iran and Egypt, in whom symptoms included: dwarfism (retarded growth), hepatosplenomegaly, hypogonadism, and partial adrenal hypofunction. Levels of zinc and iron in serum were significantly subnormal, levels of copper and transferrin being relatively high. Zinc kinetic studies revealed an intensified zinc turnover rate; occasionally, the zinc content in hair might be very low. The authors suggested that development of the syndrome might be due to a pituitary hypofunction conditioned by zinc deficiency. Whether or not other factors are involved remains to be defined (181).

In protein-deficient pigs, the level of zinc in blood seemed to be lowered (158); protein deficiency might thus induce a secondary zinc deficiency (166).

Hypothyrosis due to iodine deficiency reduces the reproductive capacity of laboratory animals as well as farm animals (96). Accordingly, the development of the reproductive organs will be inhibited by thyroidectomy (25).

4. Vitamins

Vitamin A deficiency is known to provoke testicular atrophy in rats (49, 123), guinea pigs (177, 207), and farm animals (48, 111, 189; cf. also

118, 136, 150). According to Mason (*126*), the deficiency might result in a gradual loss of germinal cells in the seminiferous tubules, the spermatogonia and the primary spermatocytes apparently being most susceptible. These lesions paralleled ophthalmological changes attributable to the deficiency (*206*). In experiments with laboratory animals, the testicular changes were generally found to be associated with impaired development of the accessory sex glands, although it need not be a direct effect of the deficiency; rather the hypoplasia is caused by a subnormal production of androgenic steroids in the testis. Supplies of testosterone or gonadotropin (*130*) will obviate the hypoplasia. In contrast to lesions caused by vitamin E deficiency, the testicular lesions following vitamin A deficiency are not irreversible; in all species studied, the defective spermatogenesis could be repaired, to major or minor degrees, within 1 or 2 months (*126, 127, 150*).

Pronounced vitamin A deficiency in bulls delays onset of sexual maturity and suppresses libido; in addition, testicular degeneration is responsible for a reduced production and inferior quality of sperm (*48, 70, 85, 94, 117, 189, 190*). In a comprehensive experiment with bull calves which since the age of 3 days had been fed diets low in vitamin A, Hodgson *et al.* (*85*) observed that the occurrence of sexual maturity was delayed; in addition, degenerative changes in the spermatogenic tissue were noted; the testicular changes might be repaired by administration of carotene. Cystic changes in the pituitary were observed at autopsy, apparently a common feature in vitamin A-deficient, growing cattle (*48, 85*), sheep (*111*), and rats (*206*), but not in swine (*150*). It should be stressed that vitamin A deficiency in bulls does not result in severe disturbances in the spermatogenesis until such deficiency has progressed to an advanced stage (*22*); in guinea pigs (*207*) and in swine (*150*), testicular lesions represent the early manifestations of a deficiency. In rams, vitamin A deficiency might retard development of testes and impair production of sperms (*43, 111*). Palludan (*150, 151*) seems to be the only investigator who has studied the importance of vitamin A for the reproductive organs in male swine. In boars which since weaning had been fed vitamin A-deficient diets, this author observed that the weight of testes, expressed per 100 kg of body weight, in vitamin A-deficient boars ranged at 196 ± 11 gm, as compared with weights of 442 ± 21 gm in the controls, body weights and ages of animals being identical at the time of sacrifice. On the basis of biopsies obtained from testes, the injury inflicted on the spermatogenic tissue was found to parallel the degree of the deficiency.

In experiments with rats (*136*), cattle (*85*), and sheep (*111*), A avitaminosis was generally found to cause reduced rate of growth and impaired development of the accessory sex glands. Growth of swine is not inhibited, and the development of their accessory sex glands is not impaired either (*150*); this species difference may be due to the fact that swine continue to eat their rations right up to the terminal stage of the deficiency.

Several authors (cf. *136, 150*) have postulated that vitamin A deficiency in male animals might be associated with endocrine disturbances which, in turn, are followed by degenerative changes in the reproductive organs. In some of these experiments, although not in all, supplies of hormones (gonadotropin and testosterone) apparently obviated the injuries inflicted upon the testes. Whether the harmful effect of A avitaminosis were exerted via the endocrine system, or were due to a direct effect on the testicular tissue has recently been elucidated in experiments with swine (150, 151). It was clearly demonstrated that intratesticular application of small quantities of vitamin A dissolved in oil could restore spermatogenesis in the immediately surrounding tissue.

As early as 1924, Mattill et al. (128) found an irreversible testicular degeneration in rats to be provoked by vitamin E deficiency; this finding has later been substantiated (124, 125). Testicular degeneration caused by a deficiency in vitamin E or essential fatty acids (27, 28) is apparently a lesion encountered only in rats and, possibly, also in hamsters.

II. Nutrition and Prenatal Development

Pregnancy represents a physiological condition in which the nutritional requirements of the mother become greatly intensified, particularly during late stages of gestation. This applies not merely to requirements concerning energy, protein, and macroelements such as calcium and phosphorus but also to requirements for trace elements. If supplies of nutrients are insufficient to cover requirements of the maternal organism and requirements for the development of the products of conception, fetuses will in general have a first priority since the distribution of nutrients to organs and tissues in animals is related to the metabolic rate of the organs concerned (32, 78, 116). Thus, in any state of nutrition in which the content of nutrients in blood is prone to fall, the maternal organism will have to mobilize nutrients from its own tissue with a view to meeting the intrauterine feed requirements; findings in several experiments have lended support to this contention (199, 200). According to Hammond (78, cf. also 169), however, the fetus is only "parasitic" on the mother organism to some degree; if the maternal reserves fall below a certain limit, thereby involving impairment of the normal canalization of fetal development, the occurrence of death, and of morphological as well as biochemical malformations, or a reduced viability of the offspring can be the result.

So far, the ways and means of transplacental transmission and its regulation have not been thoroughly studied, mainly because of the technical difficulties involved. Furthermore, on account of the different architectures of placental barriers, it may be difficult to draw parallels from one species to another. Flexner et al. (56, cf. 37) demonstrated beyond doubt, however, that the placental exchange from maternal to fetal blood and vice versa was contingent on the character of the barrier; according to these investigators, quantities of ^{24}Na to be exchanged per gram of placenta per hour were distinctly different in, for instance, rats (hemochorial placenta) and swine (epitheliochorial placenta), stages of gestation being identical; the hematotropic nutrition is known to predominate in rodents, the histotropic predominating in swine (169). Differences in placental structures are also reflected in qualitative and quantitative differences between maternal and fetal blood plasma; in fact, the weaker the placental barrier, the smaller the differences between fetal and maternal blood. Fluctuations in the chemical composition of the maternal blood will not be reflected in the

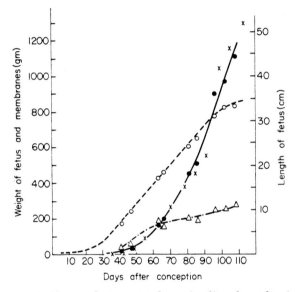

FIG. 1. Length (from end of snout to base of tail) and weight of membranes during pregnancy. Weight of fetus (———) and membranes (—•—•—); length of fetus (-----). De Villiers *et al.* (40) and Moustgaard (140).

fetal blood; the placenta serves as a fetal nutritional integrator, the compounds being taken up primarily into the trophoblasts to be transmitted later to the fetal blood according to requirements. By means of, inter alia, ^{59}Fe and ^{65}Zn, this feature was distinctly observed in laboratory animals (66, 185) and in swine (154).

No matter what the character of the placental exchange is, the latter is markedly intensified during the final half of gestation. As illustrated in Fig. 1, the fetal membranes have, in all essentials, completed their growth during the second third of pregnancy, while the fetal rate of growth is accelerated at this stage and during the last third (40, 140). When the rising fetal requirements still can be fulfilled, the reason is, in part at least, that the placental structure is altered (101).

In studies of the influence of nutrition on fetal development and on the viability of the offspring, no great attention has been attached to the fact that prenatal effects of malnutrition are not exclusively interrelated with the severity of the latter. The stage at which the deficiency becomes manifest is the decisive factor, whether in the embryonal or fetal phase of prenatal life (64, 150, 205); to this shall be added the significance of an interplay of hereditary factors (61, 98, 99). Whether malnutrition acts upon the gametogenesis or on the zygote, the outcome will be infertility (Fig. 2), possibly involving irregular sex cycles. If malnutrition happens to coincide with the first third of gestation, i.e., during the sensitive periods of the organogenesis, a development of malformations and even fetal death may

INJURIOUS ENVIRONMENTAL FACTORS

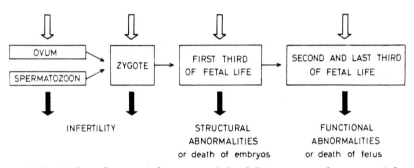

FIG. 2. The influence of the timing of the deficiency upon the nature of the disturbances in prenatal development. Palludan (153).

be the sequelae. In the fetal phase, i.e., during the second and last third of prenatal life, such deficiency may result in functional disturbances, manifest mainly in such organ systems as have several sensitive periods (150). In cases of extreme deficiency, death may ensue, or nonviable offspring may be born. In experiments on guinea pigs (51), swine (150), and sheep (8, 195) deficient in manganese, vitamin A, and copper, respectively, the stage at which the deficiency sets in was shown to be of decisive importance for the type of prenatal anomalies to develop.

1. Underfeeding

In pregnant animals, undernutrition in energy, protein, and other essential nutritional factors may impair the fetal development and the viability of the offspring (77, 86, 115). In experiments with laboratory animals (208), sheep (4, 77, 200), swine (79), and cattle (44, 165), the birth weight, the viability, and the milk production of the dam were repeatedly found to be reduced if supplies of food were markedly insufficient throughout the period of gestation or even during the last half of the period only.

This phenomenon was clearly demonstrated by Wallace (199, 200) in experiments with sheep and by others in experiments with cattle (165) and swine (173). Some ewes were kept on a low level of nutrition during the first part of pregnancy and on a high level during the last 2 months of pregnancy; other ewes were treated in the reverse order. Underfeeding from day 28 to day 91 during pregnancy had no appreciable influence on the development of the fetuses, while underfeeding during the last 2 months of pregnancy resulted in an emaciation of the ewes and besides, the birth weight of the offspring would be half that of normal. Some fetal tissues were more severely affected than others; the central nervous system and the heart competed more efficiently for the available nutrients than did, for instance, the liver tissue and the muscular tissue. In experiments on three groups of heifers, each group comprising 34 animals fed 62, 100, and 146% respectively, of normal requirements (Morrison's standards) during growth and pregnancy, the birth weight of calves from the individual groups were: 80, 85, and 91 pounds, respectively. During the first postnatal month, 8, 6, and 4 calves, respectively, were lost in the individual groups (165). This experiment confirmed findings obtained in previous studies of cattle (44, 95) and sheep (4, 77, 187), viz., that fetal growth was inhibited merely to a minor degree by moderate or short-term underfeeding; the maternal body reserves sufficed to cover requirements. Extreme underfeeding of sheep during the last third of gestation increases the tendency to toxemia of pregnancy (157, 187). In multiparous animals such as rats (171), swine (79, 92, 173), and mink (156), even relatively mild underfeeding during the last half of pregnancy might lead to reduced birth weights and impaired viability of the offspring. Experiments on laboratory animals (33) and farm animals (cf. 113) indicate that low nutritional levels during prenatal life, or even in the course of the suckling period, might reduce permanently the postnatal development, despite the fact that adequate nutrition was given after weaning. So far, the findings remain to be explained.

2. Protein

The significance of an adequate protein intake for the maintenance of normal pregnancy is generally recognized. In ruminants, inadequate protein supplies during pregnancy may result in a decreased fetal growth rate and impaired vitality of the offspring. Insufficient supplies of protein to sheep throughout pregnancy, or even during the last 2 months, were found to increase the rate of stillbirths, to reduce birth weights, and to step up the rate of postnatal mortality (4, 72, 188). After parturition, the ewes were weakened and their milk production was inadequate.

Insufficient protein supplies to pregnant gilts or sows may also result in reduced birth weights, increased rate of stillbirths, low viability of the offspring, and insufficient milk production (39, 79, 92). In the presence of a not too pronounced protein deficiency, the birth weights and the viability will not be seriously impaired; nevertheless, this condition causes debilitation of the mother and a lowered milk production.

3. Minerals

Calcium and phosphorus have undoubtedly attracted the most attention as minerals important for the function of the female reproductive system. In sows, as in rats, an insufficient Ca intake may seriously influence the viability of the offspring and the production of milk. In one experiment (50), pregnant gilts and sows were fed daily rations containing about 1 gm of Ca throughout several gestation-lactation periods; neither the litter size nor the birth weight were found to be markedly reduced, but the rate of stillbirths was high and most of the pigs born alive died within the first 24 hours, partly because they were born weak, partly because the sows did not produce any milk. During the experimental period, the Ca level in maternal blood fell to nearly half of normal values, and the sows presented characteristic symptoms of osteomalacia. They had great difficulties in farrowing. In principle, the same phenomenon was observed in later experiments (39). As to the influence of Ca intake on the reproductive organs in ruminants, the experimental results seem to be rather conflicting. In some experiments on sheep, daily supplies of 1 gm of Ca resulted in a pronounced fall in contents of Ca in the maternal plasma and delivery of stillborn, or greatly debilitated, lambs (62); in other experiments (42) in which the deficiency also resulted in hypocalcemia, the newborn lambs were apparently normal. These diverging results are probably attributable to differences in the Ca status prior to pregnancy and to different vitamin D supplies. Experiments in cattle indicate that insufficient Ca intake during pregnancy might result in stillbirth, delivery of nonviable offspring, and low milk production; but also in this species, the experimental findings are conflicting (55, 170).

As previously mentioned, severe ovarian dysfunction may occur in the presence of phosphorus deficiency; in pregnant animals, deficiency of P does not result in abortion or in a reduced viability of the offspring, whether in rats (69) or in ruminants (55).

Physiologically, iron is a unique mineral in that absorbed iron, for all practical purposes, is not excreted, and besides, the intestinal absorption of iron is to a certain degree determined by the requirement, thus safeguarding rather small variations in iron levels in plasma and the maintenance of almost constant levels of iron contents in tissues, including the placental tissues. This implies, however, that the intestinal iron absorption and/or the mobilization of iron from iron stores, increase during the last half of gestation, at which stage the intrauterine requirements for iron increase considerably. This process is facilitated, at least in human subjects (194) and in swine (154), by an increase in the content of plasma transferrin. Under natural conditions, the dam will be affected to a higher degree than the fetus by insufficient iron supplies; it has been found repeatedly that under such conditions the fetus is able to provoke an anemia in the mother, whereas the hemoglobin level in fetal blood remains normal. This, however, does not imply that iron deficiency in the dam is of no significance to the offspring; even though such mothers might bear offspring with normal hemoglobin level, they will be born with subnormal content of nonheme iron. The low iron status will predispose the offspring to anemia initially during its extrauterine life when milk poor in iron represents its only nutriment and its growth rate, and, consequently, its requirements for iron, are relatively high.

In all species, a fall in blood hemoglobin occurs during the first part of the extrauterine life, regardless of the iron supply to the dam and the newborn. This "physiological anemia" is undoubtedly attributable to the high hemoglobin values of fetal blood and the short half-life of fetal erythrocytes. If the animal is born with defective stores of iron, and does not receive iron during the first period of life, an iron deficiency anemia, will be added to the physiological anemia. This condition is well known in swine (3, 176). Considering the influence of the iron intake on the part of the mother on the congenital stores of iron of the offspring the following conclusion can be drawn: in the absence of a tendency to anemia in the mother during pregnancy, even an unphysiological high supply of iron will not increase the congenital iron reserves of the offspring (176).

The content of copper increases considerably in the liver (174) and the blood plasma during pregnancy in human individuals (146) as well as in swine (141); in particular the ceruloplasmin concentration will increase (1). This suggests that copper must be of essential importance for pregnancy; considering the biochemical importance of copper, this is not surprising. As in the case of iron, copper is stored in the fetal liver; the size of this store may, however, be influenced considerably through the maternal copper status (141, 194). In pronounced copper deficiency in ruminants the content of stored copper in the fetal liver may fall to a fraction of the normal values (122). Copper deficiency in ruminants may apparently be due either to a deficient copper intake or to an excessive content of molybdenum in the ration (194). No matter what the character of copper deficiency, it may lead to delivery of weak offspring; in calves a ricketlike disease and ataxia may be the consequences (2, 194); apparently, however, the latter symptom is not characteristic of hypocuprosis in calves. Pregnant ewes appear to be clinically normal in spite of marked depletion of copper; frequently but not always, however, the lambs of such ewes might develop incoordination of movement (neonatal ataxia or swayback). Histological examination of the central nervous system reveals a diffuse, symmetrical cerebral demyelination with secondary degeneration of the motor tracts of the spinal cord (8–10, 149); the condition is accompanied by a significantly reduced copper content and cytochrome oxidase activity in the brain and liver tissue (8). Numerous experiments have been carried out with a view to defining whether this congenital, biochemical malformation is attributable only to a copper deficiency (12, 194). It was found, inter alia, that the degree of ataxia and the copper status of the animal were not interrelated; low copper concentrations in maternal livers and plasma did not necessarily result in a delivery of ataxic lambs (194). The significance of a timing of the teratogenic action has been clearly defined in studies of the action of other environmental teratogenic factors (51, 150, 195). According to the findings, it is hardly to be expected that such demyelinating disease might originate in a copper deficiency except if the latter were excessive at the stage at which the myelin synthesis is at a maximum, i.e., during the final third of pregnancy (195). This might explain the discrepant findings, but the possibility cannot be excluded that a copper deficiency only provokes a susceptibility to the disease (9).

Orent and McCollum (148) were the first to demonstrate that prenatal manganese deficiency in rats might lead to a reduced viability or to locomotor disorders. Studies of this subject were later continued, e.g., by Hurley et al. (51, 88, 89, cf. also 58); they found "righting" reactions to be markedly impaired in the presence of manganese deficiency in the young, although any anomalies in the central nervous system were not observed and the cerebrospinal fluid pressure appeared to be normal. Later investigations revealed an abnormal development of the osseous labyrinth of the ear (51, 88); short-term supplementation with manganese pinpointed the teratogen-susceptible period to be manifest from the 14th to the 15th day of gestation. Supplies administered at later stages failed to counteract the delivery of malformed offspring (89). In guinea pigs, the deficiency reduces litter size and increases rate of stillbirths (51); in swine, experimentally produced manganese deficiency results in high embryonic mortality, or birth of weak offspring, which occasionally may be affected by ataxia (159).

The significance of zinc during fetal life has apparently never been investigated; it has been found in several investigations, however, that zinc intake during pregnancy influences the zinc concentration in colostrum (196).

Insufficient iodine supplies may provoke a compensatory hypertrophy of the thyroid gland, i.e., simple goiter, accompanied by a fall in the concentration of thyroid hormonal compounds in blood and tissues, i.e., hypothyroidism. This condition might also result in a fetal hypothyroidism. Delivery of hairless, weak, or even stillborn offspring is not uncommon in cattle and sheep raised in goitrous areas (52). Although not proved, large amounts of goitrogenous plants (Brassicacea) in food administered to pregnant animals may lead to abortion or birth of weak offspring (cf. 83); experimentally produced hypothyroidism in rats (53), swine (152), and sheep (25, 54) resulted in birth of malformed and weak offspring.

Selenium is an essential nutrient for animals (175, 194), but so far, the importance of this compound for fetal life remains obscure. In exceptional cases, administration of selenium to ewes was found to increase the number of lambs to be born and to curtail the incidence of muscular dystrophy in the latter (81).

4. Vitamins

Adequate supplies of vitamins during pregnancy are necessary if normal development and normal viability of the offspring are to be obtained. Hence, a sufficient supply of these accessory nutrients to the pregnant animal is not only of theoretical importance but also of practical concern.

In laboratory animals (64, 136, 201), in ruminants (29, 136), and in swine (75, 150, 152), deficiency of vitamin A during gestation leads to fetal deaths and delivery of malformed or poorly viable offspring. In experiments with swine, Palludan (150, 153) demonstrated beyond doubt that the severity of the deficiency and a timing of the stage of onset, were factors that determined the character of the organogenetic anomalies to develop. She confirmed previous findings by Hale (75) and others (12, 203), and demonstrated, furthermore, that defective organogenesis due to vitamin A deficiency might involve almost all organic systems; in addition, the character and scope of malformations were found to be, more or less, contingent on the developmental stage at which the deficiency became manifest in the embryo and fetus. In some animals, for instance in rabbits, malformations such as internal hydrocephalus may not become manifest until some weeks after birth (104). It deserves to be mentioned that A hypervitaminosis might provoke developmental anomalities resembling those described above (150).

In cattle, as in swine, a marked prenatal A avitaminosis might cause fetal death or the delivery of weak, mostly blind or otherwise malformed calves (136). A disorganized fetal development may be manifest even in the absence of distinct symptoms of such deficiency in the dam; the latter phenomenon applies mainly to swine (150).

In the presence of vitamin E deficiency in pregnant rats, fetuses will die during the latter half part of the pregnancy and be resorbed (171); upon administration of vitamin E at early stages during gestation, normal offspring will be born, but if administered in the period from the 8th to the 12th day of gestation, some of the offspring will be malformed (31, 93). It has not been possible to demonstrate such a dramatic effect of vitamin E deficiency in any other species. In ruminants and in rabbits (15, 16, 104), the reproductive capacity seems to remain normal even though their diets throughout long periods of time have been devoid of vitamin E. It cannot be precluded that vitamin E deficiency in pregnant sows may be the cause of low viability of the offspring and lowered vitamin E content of colostrum, but the feature remains to be finally defined.

Considering the vast significance of vitamin D for the exploitation of Ca and P, it might be reasonable to assume that vitamin D deficiency might be responsible for some disorganization as regards supplies of Ca and P to the fetuses, particularly during the last third of pregnancy.

Considering the importance of vitamin B complex for the intermediary metabolism, a pronounced deficiency in one or more of these vitamins will obviously, directly or indirectly, be responsible for a disorganized fetal development and impaired viability of the newborn (93, 99, 134). In experiments on gilts, moderate deficiency of pantothenic acid was found to be responsible for a reduced litter size and impaired viability of the offspring (38, 193). The relatively high pantothenic acid requirements for normal reproduction in swine (38) suggest that deficiency of this vitamin may occur under normal conditions. Deficiency of vitamin B_{12} in rats may impair the fetal development (67, 143), and the rate of mortality among the offspring will be high (110). In gilts and sows, the fetal rate of mortality was found to increase in the presence of experimentally produced deficiency of this vitamin (137, 139); besides, the viability as well as the growth rate among the offspring was reduced.

III. The Nutrient Requirement for Fetal Development in Cattle[*]

In evaluations of the feed requirement for fetal development, the quantity of nutrients deposited in the product of conception must be known. Gestation per se is known, however, to influence also the extrauterine metabolism in the mother; her hormonal status is changed and, at the same time, retention of labile protein and mineral reserves is intensified; besides, the energy metabolism as well as sizes of body fluid compartments are changed. Consequently, the nutrient requirements in total during pregnancy imply more than just the deposition of nutrients in the products of conception; a certain reserve is established in the maternal organism with a view to meeting the nutritional burden of lactation, which is even greater than that of pregnancy. The size of such extrauterine reserves may, however, vary considerably, being interrelated with feeding schemes and compositions of food; moreover, since the fetus has a first priority to the available nutrients, a moderate underfeeding need not influence its vital necessities. These factors combine to make it difficult to fix exactly the nutritive requirements of pregnant animals; nothing but approximate values are obtainable.

The order of magnitude of extrauterine deposits during pregnancy, the anabolism of pregnancy, has been studied mainly in laboratory animals (160, 172, 173) and swine (50, 173), either in balance experiments (50) or in studies of the extrauterine gain in weight and of the relative body composition in pregnant and nonpregnant animals (173). In experiments with swine, the level of extrauterine anabolism was found to be contingent on the composition of the food reaching its maximum at late stages of pregnancy (109, 144, 160).

[*] This discussion of the nutrient requirement for fetal development will be limited to the bovine.

Quantitative investigations of the nitrogen metabolism in cattle during pregnancy were first carried out by Crowther and Woodman (35), who determined the nitrogen retention in two dry cows, one of which was pregnant; apparently, retention of nitrogen did not intensify much until about 1 month before term. Problems involved in protein requirements have been studied in greater detail by chemical analyses of the products of conception, including analyses of fetus, fetal membranes, fetal fluids, and of the uterus per se. Initially, examinations of the intrauterine growth included only studies of weights and analyses of a few fetuses (73). In later experiments, carried out in our department, it has been endeavored to find a quantitative expression of the daily deposition of nutrients in the products of conception throughout the period of gestation; analyses for total nitrogen, organic dry matter, crude fat, crude ash, and for some minerals were made. According to the findings, the deposition can be expressed by an exponential function of time after conception (90, 139). The nitrogen deposition in total can be expressed by the function

$$W_N = 7.76e^{0.0182t}$$

in which W_N denotes deposition of N in grams and t denotes the number of days after conception; by differentiation of this function, the daily deposition is found to be

$$N/day = 0.141e^{0.0182t}$$

thus, the relative increase in nitrogen in the pregnant uterus is 1.82%/day. Similarly, the weight of the pregnant uterus can be expressed by the function

$$W = 1034e^{0.150t}$$

The estimated weight of the nonpregnant uterus, 1034 gm, is in accord with the directly determined weight of the nonpregnant uteri (91). It is apparent from the equations that the relative volume of daily depositions of nitrogen, 1.82%, is in excess of the relative increase in weight, 1.50%, in agreement with the increased content of nitrogen in fetus and fetal membranes during pregnancy (91, 138). As to the daily retention of nitrogen in the products of conception, the above findings are, in principle, in accordance with findings obtained in other, less comprehensive studies (cf. 135). The deposition of nitrogen in the mammary gland during pregnancy must also be taken into consideration since the development of the milk glands in heifers follows an exponential function of time (76). On the assumption that any appreciable magnitude of deposition is not achieved until after the 175th day of pregnancy, this feature can be expressed by the equation

$$W_N = 25.2e^{0.0236(t-175)}$$

On the basis of these equations, the daily nitrogen depositions in the reproductive organs during pregnancy can be calculated. If expressed by the sum of the differentiated forms of the deposition curves of nitrogen in the uterus and the mammary gland, and the value is multiplied by 6.25, the protein deposition at different times of pregnancy amounts to the values recorded in Table I. These values, which apparently conform with findings in studies of fetuses exclusively (135), represent merely the net requirement; genuine requirements can be calculated only if the degree of utilization of proteins during fetal growth is known. The main precursors of intrauterine synthesis of milk proteins are the free amino acids of plasma; it seems reasonable, therefore, to use the same factor in calculations of requirements for intrauterine protein synthesis as for production of milk proteins. If so, the values found should be multiplied by the factor $^{60}/_{34}$ because production of 34 gm of milk protein requires a supply of 60 gm of digestible protein (63, cf. 91, 139). Incidentally, the correctness of such calculation has been verified in balance experiments with pregnant and nonpregnant heifers (91). In calculations of the digestible protein requirements for fetus production in cattle, based on the above-mentioned balance experiments as well as on curves of protein deposition, the values recorded in Table I will be obtained; these values are in fair agreement. It should be mentioned that protein standards otherwise recommended as optimal if the protein requirements of pregnant cows are to be met, may vary considerably (138, 139).

In all species studied, depositions of the individual minerals have been found to increase markedly toward the end of pregnancy. Accordingly, this applies also to cattle in which the content of crude ash in fetuses was found to rise progressively from about 5 gm during the 15th week of pregnancy up to about 1050 gm at the end of pregnancy, a rise from about 20 gm up to 200 gm being manifest in fetal membranes and fluids. Depositions of calcium and phosphorus in total in the products of conception can be expressed by the functions

$$W_{Ca} = 0.28^{0.18t} \qquad W_P = 0.11e^{0.20t}$$

On this basis it was possible, as mentioned, to calculate the daily intrauterine depositions of Ca and P; the values obtained, together with values denoting the daily Ca and P requirements determined on the basis of an apparent digestibility quotient of 40, are recorded in Table I; excluded are values denoting the Ca and P requirements for development of mammary glands. The last third of pregnancy is of critical significance as regards the Ca and P requirements; in excess of the intrauterine deposition, the stores in the maternal skeletal system have to be built up in order to facilitate conditions for the animal in its requirements during lactation.

Intrauterine deposits on trace elements such as iron and manganese can be expressed by the functions

$$W_{Fe} = 1.7e^{0.0272t} \qquad W_{Mn} = 0.29e^{0.0174t}$$

in which W_{Fe} and W_{Mn} are milligrams of iron and manganese deposited

TABLE I

DAILY DEPOSITION OF PROTEIN, CALCIUM, PHOSPHORUS, AND IRON IN THE PRODUCTS OF CONCEPTION IN CATTLE, AND THE ESTIMATED DAILY REQUIREMENT

Months after conception	Protein Deposited (gm)	Protein Requirement (gm) 1[a]	Protein Requirement (gm) 2[b]	Calcium Deposited (gm)	Calcium Requirement (gm)	Phosphorus Deposited (gm)	Phosphorus Requirement (gm)	Iron Deposited (mg)
6	20	35	25	0.4	1	0.3	1	4
7	43	75	60	0.9	2	0.7	2	9
8	71	125	120	2.3	6	1.8	5	21
9	128	225	230	6.0	15	4.8	12	47
Last 2 weeks	164	290	310	8.0	20	7.4	18	92

[a] On basis of deposition curves.
[b] On basis of N balances.

and t denotes the number of days after conception. The daily deposits of iron, computed on the basis of this equation, are recorded in Table I.

A determination of the energy content of the pregnant uterus at different stages of pregnancy is a rather simple procedure, but it fails to provide information about the energy lost as heat of intrauterine or extrauterine origin. Besides, a determination of intrauterine energy deposition, an evaluation of the energy requirement of the pregnant animal also necessitates a determination of the increase in heat production during pregnancy, i.e., the heat increment of gestation (24). The influence of gestation on heat production has been studied in laboratory animals, including dogs (139); a distinct rise in BMR (basal metabolic rate) was seen to occur in dogs during pregnancy, the degree of such rise being interrelated with the number of fetuses (142). In studies, by now classic, carried out by Brody (24), the energy metabolism in pregnant farm animals was examined. On the basis of the oxygen consumption in heifers, these authors computed the ratio of heat production and "physiological weight" (cal/weight$^{0.73}$) before and during pregnancy. On the assumption that BMR varies with the 0.73 power of the body weight, a rise in this ratio will be indicative of a relative rise in metabolism. In the course of examinations of cattle as well as of other farm animals (horses, swine, goats, sheep), the percent rise in heat

TABLE II

ESTIMATION OF THE ORDER OF MAGNITUDE OF ENERGY
USED FOR FETAL DEVELOPMENT IN THE BOVINE[a]

Days after conception	Energy in product of conception[b]	Heat increment of pregnancy (BMR)[c]	Total energy used
100	40	575	615
150	100	960	1060
200	235	1670	1905
250	560	2635	3195
280	940	3550	4490

[a] Kilocalories/day.

[b] Calculated from energy deposition curves. Daily energy deposition: kcal = $7.24e^{0.0174t}$ (90).

[c] Calculated from Brody's result (24).

production was found to be much higher than that of the body weight; besides the heat increment was found to rise progressively throughout the period of gestation, a finding confirmed in recent experiments with sheep (23). According to Brody (24), the heat production due to pregnancy can be expressed by the formula $Q = 4400M^{1.2}$, in which Q denotes increase in heat production (kilocalories) and M denotes weight of the calf (kilograms) at birth. In the presence of birth weights of 40 kg, the heat increment during gestation may be estimated by the function

TABLE III

COMPUTED DAILY DEPOSITION AND MINIMUM REQUIREMENT FOR FETUS PRODUCTION IN PIGS, CORRECTED TO A NUMBER OF 10 FETUSES

Days after conception	Nitrogen			Calcium		Phosphorus		Iron	"Energy"		
	Deposited N		Requirement (gm digestible protein)	Deposited (gm)	Requirement (gm)	Deposited (gm)	Requirement (gm)	Deposited (gm)	Deposited (kcal)	Heat increment (kcal)	Requirement, metabolizable energy (kcal)
	Uterus	Milk gland (gm)									
40	1.0	—	10	0.1	0	0.1	0	3	50	350	400
60	1.9	—	20	0.4	1	0.4	1	5	90	750	840
80	3.6	0.8	50	1.2	2	0.9	2	9	170	1150	1320
100	6.6	1.8	95	4.0	8	2.2	6	18	320	1550	1870
110	9.1	2.7	135	7.2	14	3.7	9	25	440	1750	2190
115	10.6	4.7	175	9.8	20	4.7	12	30	510	1850	2360

$$\mathrm{kcal/day} = 216e^{0.01t}$$

Values thus obtained are recorded in Table II together with values denoting the daily intrauterine energy deposition, calculated on the basis of the energy deposition curve

$$W_{\mathrm{kcal}} = 416.2e^{0.0174t}$$

Consequently, the increase in energy requirements which occur during gestation will equal volumes of energy deposited in the uterus (and the mammary gland) together with the increased heat production. The degree to which the intra- or extrauterine metabolisms are responsible for the increased heat production is difficult to decide, but it can hardly be doubted that the increased metabolic rate in nonuterine tissue, caused by the changed hormonal status, for example, and increased thyroid function in the dam (*184*), is essentially responsible. This "metabolic rejuvenation" of maternal tissue during pregnancy arrives at a maximum at the final stages of pregnancy (*100*).

Values denoting the calculated total energy, Table II, equal the volume of metabolizable energy required in the daily intrauterine deposition and in the increased heat production. To this should be added the maintenance requirement for metabolizable energy, which in cows weighing 500 kg amounts to about 11,000 kcal (*6*).

In swine, as in cattle, retention of nutrients has been found to be progressively intensified during pregnancy (*140*). Calculated as described for cattle, the daily deposition in the reproductive organs during pregnancy and the minimum requirement for fetus production are recorded in Table III.

REFERENCES

1. Adelstein, S. J., Coombs, T. L., and Vallee, B. L., *New Engl. J. Med.* **255**, 105 (1956).
2. Adelstein, S. J., and Valle, B. L., *in* "Mineral Metabolism" (C. L. Comar and F. Bronner, eds.), Vol. 2, Part B, p. 371. Academic Press, New York, 1962.
3. Adsersen, V., *Vet. J.* **88**, 457 (1932).
4. Alexander, G., McCance, I., and Watson, R. H., *Proc. 3rd Intern. Congr. Animal Reprod., Cambridge,* **I**, 5 (1956).
5. Allen, G. S., *Vet. Rec.* **55**, 168 (1943).
6. Armsby, H. P., "The Principles of Animal Nutrition." Wiley, New York, 1908.
7. Asdell, S. A., *J. Dairy Sci.* **32**, 60 (1949).
8. Barlow, R. M., *J. Comp. Pathol. Therap.* **73**, 61 (1963).
9. Barlow, R. M., Purves, D., Butler, E. J., and Macintyre, I. J., *J. Comp. Pathol. Therap.* **70**, 396 (1960).
10. Barlow, R. M., Purves, D., Butler, E. J., and Macintyre, I. J., *J. Comp. Pathol. Therap.* **70**, 411 (1960).
11. Bellows, R. A., Pope, A. L., Meyer, R. K., Chapman, A. B., and Casida, L. E., *J. Animal Sci.* **22**, 93 (1963).
12. Bendixen, H. C., *Deut. Tieraerztl. Wochschr.* **57**, 150 (1950).

13. Bennetts, H. W., *Australian Vet. J.* **22**, 70 (1946).
14. Bentley, O. G., and Phillips, P. H., *J. Dairy Sci.* **34**, 396 (1951).
15. Blaxter, K. L., *Vitamins Hormones* **20**, 633 (1962).
16. Blaxter, K. L., and Brown, F., *Nutr. Abstr. Rev.* **22**, 1 (1952).
17. Boyer, P. D., Shaw, J. H., and Phillips, P. H., *J. Biol. Chem.* **143**, 417 (1942).
18. Bradbury, R. B., and White, D. E., *Vitamins Hormones* **12**, 207 (1954).
19. Branton, C., Bratton, R. W., and Salisbury, G. W., *J. Dairy Sci.* **30**, 1003 (1947).
20. Branton, C., Bratton, R. W., and Salisbury, G. W., *J. Dairy Sci.* **32**, 292 (1949).
21. Bratton, R. W., *Proc. Cornell Nutr. Conf.*, p. 5 (1953).
22. Bratton, R. W., Salisbury, G. W., Tanabe, T., Branton, C., Mercier, E., and Loosli, J. K., *J. Dairy Sci.* **31**, 779 (1948).
23. Brockway, J. M., MacDonald, J. D., and Pullar, J. D., *J. Physiol. (London)* **167**, 318 (1963).
24. Brody, S., "Bioenergetics and Growth." Reinhold, New York, 1945.
25. Brooks, J. R., Ross, C. V., and Turner, C. W., *J. Animal Sci.* **23**, 54 (1964).
26. Burger, J. F., *Onderstepoort J. Vet. Res. Suppl.* **2**, 1 (1952).
27. Burr, G. O., and Burr, M. M., *J. Biol. Chem.* **82**, 345 (1929).
28. Burr, G. O., and Burr, M. M., *J. Biol. Chem.* **86**, 587 (1930).
29. Byers, J. H., Jones, I. R., and Bone, J. F., *J. Dairy Sci.* **39**, 1556 (1956).
30. Casida, L. E., *Proc. 6th Intern. Congr. Nutr., Edinburgh, 1963* p. 366. Livingstone, Edinburgh and London (1964).
31. Cheng, D. W., Chang, L. F., and Bairnson, T. A., *Anat. Record* **129**, 167 (1957).
32. Child, C. M., *Biol. Bull.* **39**, 147 (1920).
33. Chow, B. F., *J. Nutr.* **83**, 289 (1964).
34. Clark, C. F., *J. Am. Vet. Med. Assoc.* **90**, 488 (1937).
35. Crowther, C., and Woodman, H. E., *J. Agr. Sci.* **12**, 40 (1922).
36. Cuthbertson, D. P., in "Progress in the Physiology of Farm Animals" (J. Hammond, ed.), Vol. 1, p. 144. Butterworth, London and Washington, D.C., 1954.
37. Dancis, J., in "The Placental and Fetal Membranes" (C. A. Villee, ed.), p. 85. Williams & Wilkins, Baltimore, Maryland, 1960.
38. Davey, R. J., and Stevenson, J. W., *J. Animal Sci.* **22**, 9 (1963).
39. Davidson, H. R., *J. Agr. Sci.* **20**, 233 (1930).
40. De Villiers, V., Havskov Sørensen, P., Jakobsen, P. E., and Moustgaard, J., *Aarsberetn., Inst. Sterilitetsforsk.*, p. 139 (1958).
41. Dickerson, J. W. T., Gresham, G. A., and McCance, R. A., *J. Endocrinol.* **29**, 111 (1964).
42. Duckworth, J., and Hill, R., *J. Physiol. (London)* **123**, 69P (1954).
43. Dutt, B., *Brit. Vet. J.* **115**, 236 (1959).
44. Eckles, C. H., *Missouri Univ. Agr. Expt. Sta. Res. Bull.* **35** (1919).
45. El-Sheikh, A. S., Hulet, C. V., Pope, A. L., and Casida, L. E., *J. Animal Sci.* **14**, 919 (1955).
46. Engdal, O. Th., *Tidsskr. Norske Landbruk* **46**, 317 (1939).
47. Englund, S. E., *Acta Obstet. Gynecol. Scand.* **39**, 575 (1960).
48. Erb, R. E., Andrews, F. N., Hauge, S. M., and King, W. A., *J. Dairy Sci.* **30**, 687 (1947).
49. Evans, H. M., *Am. J. Physiol.* **99**, 477 (1932).

50. Evans, R. E., *J. Agr. Sci.* **19**, 752 (1929).
51. Everson, G. J., Hurley, L. S., and Geiger, J. F., *J. Nutr.* **68**, 49 (1959).
52. Evvard, J. M., *Endocrinology* **12**, 539 (1928).
53. Faassen, F. van, "Hypothyreoidie en aangeboren misvormingen." Oosterbaan & Le Cointre N.V., Goes, Netherlands, 1957.
54. Falconer, I. R., *Nature* **205**, 703 (1965).
55. Fitch, C. P., Boyd, W. L., Eckles, C. H., Gullickson, T. W., Palmer, L. S., and Kennedy, C., *Cornell Vet.* **22**, 156 (1932).
56. Flexner, L. B., Cowie, D. B., Hellman, L. M., Wilde, W. S., and Vosburgh, G. J., *Am. J. Obstet. Gynecol.* **55**, 469 (1948).
57. Flipse, R. J., Snyder, J. W., Thacker, D. L., and Almquist, J. O., *Penn. State Coll. Agr. Expt. Sta. Progr. Rept.* **104** (1953).
58. Follis, R. H., "Deficiency Disease." Thomas, Springfield, Illinois, 1958.
59. Foote, W. C., Pope, A. L., Chapman, A. B., and Casida, L. E., *J. Animal Sci.* **18**, 453 (1959).
60. Ford, C. M., *Brit. Vet. J.* **112**, 177 (1956).
61. Fraser, F. C., in "Teratology, Principles and Techniques" (J. G. Wilson and J. Warkany, eds.), p. 21. Univ. of Chicago Press, Illinois, 1965.
62. Fraser, A. H. H., Godden, W., and Thomson, W., *Vet. J.* **89**, 408 (1933).
63. Frederiksen, L., *Beretn. Forsøgslab. Copenhagen* **136** (1931).
64. Giroud, A., *Excerpta Med. Intern. Congr. Ser.* **64** (1963).
65. Giroud, A., and Desclaux, P., *Ann. Endocrinol.* **6**, 107 (1945).
66. Glasser, S. R., Wright, C., Heyssel, R. M., and Davies, J., *Federation Proc.* **25** (2), 189 (1966).
67. Grainger, R. B., O'Dell, B. L., and Hogan, A. G., *J. Nutr.* **54**, 33 (1954).
68. Grummer, R. H., Bentley, O. G., Phillips, P. H., and Bohstedt, G., *J. Animal Sci.* **9**, 170 (1950).
69. Guilbert, H. R., and Hart, G. H., *Hilgardia* **5**, 101 (1930).
70. Guilbert, H. R., and Hart, G. H., *J. Nutr.* **10**, 409 (1935).
71. Gunn, S. A., and Gould, T. C., *Endocrinology* **58**, 443 (1956).
72. Guyer, P. Q., and Dyer, A. J., *J. Animal Sci.* **12**, 917P (1953).
73. Haigh, L. D., Moulton, C. R., and Trowbridge, P. F., *Missouri Agr. Expt. Sta. Res. Bull.* **38** (1920).
74. Hale, F., *J. Heredity* **24**, 105 (1933).
75. Hale, F., *Am. J. Ophthalmol.* **18**, 1087 (1935).
76. Hammond, J., "The Physiology of Reproduction in the Cow." Cambridge Univ. Press, London and New York, 1927.
77. Hammond, J., "Growth and Development of Mutton Qualities in the Sheep." Oliver & Boyd, Edinburgh and London, 1932.
78. Hammond, J., *Proc. Nutr. Soc.* **2**, 8 (1944).
79. Hanson, L. E., Ferrin, E. F., and Aunan, W. J., *J. Animal Sci.* **12**, 919P (1953).
80. Hart, G. H., *Nutr. Abstr. Rev.* **10**, 261 (1940–41).
81. Hartley, W. J., Grant, A. B., and Drake, C., *New Zealand J. Agr.* **101**, 343 (1960).
82. Hignett, S. L., *Vet. Record* **71**, 247 (1959).
83. Hignett, S. L., *Proc. Nutr. Soc.* **19**, 8 (1960).
84. Hignett, S. L., and Hignett, P. G., *Vet. Record* **64**, 203 (1952).
85. Hodgson, R. E., Hall, S. R., Sweetman, W. J., Wiseman, H. G., and Converse, H. T., *J. Dairy Sci.* **29**, 669 (1946).

86. Huggett, A. St. G., *Physiol. Rev.* **21**, 438 (1941).
87. Hughes, J. S., Aubel, C. E., and Lienhardt, H. F., *Kansas Agr. Expt. Sta. Tech. Bull.* **23** (1928).
88. Hurley, L. S., Wooten, E., and Everson, G. J., *J. Nutr.* **74**, 282 (1961).
89. Hurley, L. S., and Everson, G. J., *J. Nutr.* **79**, 23 (1963).
90. Jakobsen, P. E., *Proc. 7th Intern. Congr. Animal Husbandry, Madrid* **6**, 115 (1956).
91. Jakobsen, P. E., *Beretn. Forsøgslab. Copenhagen* **299** (1957).
92. Jespersen, J., and Olsen, H. M., *Beretn. Forsøgslab. Copenhagen* **192** (1940).
93. Johnson, E. M., *in* "Teratology, Principles and Techniques" (J. G. Wilson and J. Warkany, eds.), p. 113. Univ. of Chicago Press, Chicago, Illinois, 1965.
94. Jones, I. R., Schnautz, J. O., and Haag, J. R., *J. Dairy Sci.* **29**, 522 (1946).
95. Joubert, D. M., and Bonsma, F. N., *S. Africa Dept. Agr. Sci. Bull.* **371** (1957).
96. Jovanovic, M., Pantić, V., and Marković, B., *Acta Vet. (Yugoslavia)* **3**, 31 (1953).
97. Kallela, K., "The Incidence of Plant Oestrogens in Finnish Pasture and Fodder Plants with Special Reference to Their Possible Effects in Cases of Sterility in Ruminants." Tampereen Kirjapaino-Osakeythio, Finland, 1964.
98. Kalter, H., *in* "Teratology, Principles and Techniques" (J. G. Wilson and J. Warkany, eds.), p. 57. Univ. of Chicago Press, Chicago, Illinois, 1965.
99. Kalter, H., and Warkany, J., *Physiol. Rev.* **39**, 69 (1959).
100. Kleiber, M., "The Fire of Life, and Introduction to Animal Energenics." Wiley, New York, 1961.
101. Krölling, O., and Grau, H., "Lehrbuch der Histologie und vergleichenden mikroskopischen Anatomie der Haustiere." Parey, Berlin, 1960.
102. Laing, J. A., *in* "Progress in the Physiology of Farm Animals" (J. Hammond, ed.), Vol. 3, p. 760. Butterworth, London and Washington, D.C., 1957.
103. Lamming, G. E., *Nutr. Abstr. Rev.* **36**, 1 (1966).
104. Lamming, G. E., Salisbury, G. W., Hays, R. L., and Kendall, K. A., *J. Nutr.* **52**, 217 and 227 (1954).
105. Larsen, L. H., and Sørensen, E., *Beretn. Forsøgslab. Copenhagen* **209** (1944).
106. Leathem, J. H., *Recent Progr. Hormone Res.* **14**, 141 (1958).
107. Leathem, J. H., *in* "Sex and Internal Secretions" (W. C. Young, ed.), Vol. 1, p. 666. Williams & Wilkins, Baltimore, Maryland, 1961.
108. Leathem, J. H., *J. Animal Sci.* **25**, Suppl., 68 (1966).
109. Lenkeit, W. von, Gütte, J. O., Kirchhoff, W., Soehngen, F. K., and Fariés, E., *Z. Tierernaehr.* **11**, 337 (1956).
110. Lepkovsky, S., Borson, H. J., Bouthilet, R., Pencharz, R., Singman, D., Dimick, M. K., and Robbins, R., *Am. J. Physiol.* **165**, 79 (1951).
111. Lindley, C. E., Brugmann, H. H., Cunha, T. J., and Warwick, E. J., *J. Animal Sci.* **8**, 590 (1949).
112. Lutwak-Mann, C., and Mann, T., *Nature* **165**, 556 (1950).
113. McCance, R. A., *Proc. 6th Intern. Congr. Nutr. Edinburgh, 1963* p. 74. Livingstone, Edinburgh and London, 1964.
114. McClure, T. J., *J. Reprod. Fertility* **4**, 241 (1962).
115. McKenzie, F. F., *Missouri Univ. Agr. Expt. Sta. Bull.* **118** (1928).
116. McMeekan, C. P., *J. Agr. Sci.* **30**, 276, 387, 511 (1940).

117. Madsen, L. L., Eaton, O. N., Heemstra, L., Davis, R. E., Cabell, C. A., and Knapp, B., *J. Animal Sci.* **7**, 60 (1948).
118. Mann, T., "Biochemistry of Semen and of the Male Reproductive Tract." Methuen, London, 1964.
119. Mann, T., and Lutwak-Mann, C., *Physiol. Rev.* **31**, 27 (1951).
120. Mann, T., and Walton, A., *J. Agr. Sci.* **43**, 343 (1953).
121. Mann, T., and Rowson, L. E. A., *Proc. 3rd Intern. Congr. Animal Reprod., Cambridge* **I**, 21 (1956).
122. Marston, H. R., *Physiol. Rev.* **32**, 66 (1952).
123. Mason, K. E., *J. Exptl. Zool.* **55**, 101 (1930).
124. Mason, K. E., *Am. J. Physiol.* **131**, 268 (1940–41).
125. Mason, K. E., *Vitamins Hormones* **2**, 107 (1944).
126. Mason, K. E., *in* "Survey of Biological Progress" (G. S. Avery, Jr., ed.), Vol. 1, p. 89. Academic Press, New York, 1949.
127. Mason, K. E., and Wolfe, J. M., *J. Nutr.* **9**, 725 (1935).
128. Mattill, H. A., Carman, J. S., and Clayton, M. M., *J. Biol. Chem.* **61**, 729 (1924).
129. Mawson, C. A., and Fischer, M. I., *Biochem. J.* **55**, 696 (1953).
130. Mayer, J., and Goddard, J. W., *Proc. Soc. Exptl. Biol. Med.* **76**, 149 (1951).
131. Meacham, T. N., Cunha, T. J., Warnick, A. C., Hentges, J. F., and Hargrove, D. D., *J. Animal Sci.* **22**, 115 (1963).
132. Millar, M. J., Fischer, M. I., Elcoate, P. V., and Mawson, C. A., *Can. J. Biochem. Physiol.* **36**, 557 (1958).
133. Millar, M. J., Elcoate, P. V., Fischer, M. I., and Mawson, C. A., *Can. J. Biochem. Physiol.* **38**, 1457 (1960).
134. Millen, J. W., "The Nutritional Basis of Reproduction." Thomas, Springfield, Illinois, 1962.
135. Mitchell, H. H., "Comparative Nutrition of Man and Domestic Animals," Vol. 1. Academic Press, New York, 1963.
136. Moore, T., "Vitamin A." Elsevier, Amsterdam, 1957.
137. Moustgaard, J., *Proc. 6th Intern. Congr. Anim. Husbandry, Copenhagen* **3**, 71 (1952).
138. Moustgaard, J., *Proc. 3rd Intern. Congr. Anim. Reprod. Plenary Papers, Cambridge* p. 123 (1956).
139. Moustgaard, J., *in* "Reproduction in Domestic Animals" (H. H. Cole and P. T. Cupps, eds.), Vol. II, p. 169. Academic Press, New York, 1959.
140. Moustgaard, J., *in* "Nutrition of Pigs and Poultry" (J. T. Morgan and D. Lewis, eds.), p. 189. Butterworth, London and Washington, D.C., 1962.
141. Moustgaard, J., and Olsen, N. J. H., *Nord. Veterinaer med.* **3**, 763 (1951).
142. Murlin, J. R., *Am. J. Physiol.* **23**, Proc. xxxii (1908–1909).
143. Newberne, P. M., *Am. J. Vet. Res.* **24**, 1304 (1963).
144. Newton, W. H., *in* "Marshall's Physiology of Reproduction" (A. S. Parkes, ed.), Vol. 2, p. 442. Longmans, Green, New York, 1952.
145. Nichols, J. E., *J. Agr. Sci.* **16**, 365 (1926).
146. Nielsen, A. L., *Acta Med. Scand.* **118**, 92 (1944).
147. Olsen, H. H., Petersen, W. E., Gullickson, T. W., and Cummings, J. N., *J. Dairy Sci.* **33**, 390 (1950).
148. Orent, E. R., and McCollum, E. V., *J. Biol. Chem.* **92**, 651 (1931).

149. Owen, E. C., Proudfoot, R., Barlow, R. M., Butler, E. J., and Smith, B. S. W., *J. Comp. Pathol. Therap.* **75**, 241 (1965).
150. Palludan, B., "A-Avitaminosis in Swine. A Study on the Importance of Vitamin A for Reproduction." Munksgaard, Copenhagen, 1966.
151. Palludan, B., *Nature* **211**, 639 (1966).
152. Palludan, B., *in* "Swine in Biomedical Research" (L. K. Bustad and O. McClellan, eds.), p. 51. Frayn Printing Co., Seattle, Washington, 1966.
153. Palludan, B., *Proc. Symp. Vitamin A, E and K, Clin. Physiol. Problems, Berlin, 1967;* F. K. Schattaüer-Verlag, Stüttgart (in press), 1968.
154. Palludan, B., and Wegger, I., *Aarsberetn., Inst. Sterilitetsforsk. Copenhagen* **11**, 285 (1968).
155. Peirce, A. W., *Australian J. Agr. Res.* **5**, 470 (1954).
156. Petersen, F. H., *Norsk Pelsdyrblad* **24**, 234 (1950).
157. Phillipson, A. T., *in* "Toxaemias of Pregnancy" (J. Hammond, F. J. Browne, and G. E. W. Wolstenholme, eds.), p. 94. Churchill, London, 1950.
158. Platt, B. S., and Frankul, W., *Proc. Nutr. Soc.* **21**, vii (1962).
159. Plumlee, M. P., Thrasher, D. M., Beeson, W. M., Andrews, F. N., and Parker, H. E., *J. Animal Sci.* **15**, 352 (1956).
160. Poo, L. J., Lew, W., Lee, D. D., and Addis, T., *J. Nutr.* **19**, 505 (1940).
161. Pose, G., *Ernaehrungsforsch.* **8**, 241 (1963).
162. Prasad, A. S., Miale, A., Farid, Z., Sandstead, H. H., Schulert, A. R., and Darby, W. J., *Arch. Intern. Med.* **111**, 407 (1963).
163. Reid, J. T., *J. Am. Vet. med. Assoc.* **114**, 158, 242 (1949).
164. Reid, J. T., Trimberger, G. W., Asdell, S. A., Turk, L. K., and Smith, S. E., *J. Dairy Sci.* **34**, 510 (1951).
165. Reid, J. T., Loosli, J. K., Trimberger, G. W., Turk, K. L., Asdell, S. A., and Smith, S. E., *Cornell Univ. Agr. Expt. Sta. Bull.* **987** (1964).
166. Reinhold, J. G., *in* "Radioisotopes in Animal Nutrition and Physiology," p. 267. IAEA, Vienna, 1965.
167. Richter, J., "Die Sterilität des Rindes." R. Schoetz, Berlin, 1926.
168. Robertson, G. L., Casida, L. E., Grummer, R. H., and Chapman, A. B., *J. Animal Sci.* **10**, 841 (1951).
169. Robinson, T. J., *in* "Progress in the Physiology of Farm Animals" (H. Hammond, ed.), Vol. 3, p. 793. Butterworth, London and Washington, D.C., 1957.
170. Rushoff, L. L., *J. Animal Sci.* **9**, 666P (1950).
171. Russell, F. C., *Commonwealth Bur. Animal Nutr. Tech. Commun.* **16** (1948).
172. Salmon-Legagneur, E., Perissé, J., and Jacquot, R., *Compt. Rend. Acad. Sci.* **250**, 1921 (1960).
173. Salmon-Legagneur, E., and Rerat, A., *in* "Nutrition of Pigs and Poultry" (J. T. Morgan and D. Lewis, eds.), p. 207. Butterworth, London and Washington, D.C., 1962.
174. Schubert, G., Maurer, W., and Riezler, W., *Arch. Gynaekol.* **176**, 279 (1949).
175. Schwarz, K., *Z. Physiol. Chem.* **281**, 109 (1944).
176. Seamer, J., *Vet. Rev. Annotations* **2**, 79 (1956).
177. Sebrell, W. H., and Harris, R. S. (eds.), "The Vitamins," Vol. 1. Academic Press, New York, 1954.
178. Self, H. L., Grummer, R. H., and Casida, L. E., *J. Animal Sci.* **14**, 573 (1955).

179. Shils, M. E., and McCollum, E. V., *J. Nutr.* **26**, 1 (1943).
180. Shirley, R. L., Meacham, T. N., Warnick, A. C., Hentges, J. F., and Cunha, T. J., *J. Animal Sci.* **22**, 14 (1963).
181. Shoukry, A. S., Sandsted, H., Prasad, A., Gabr, M., Hifni, A., Mokhtar, N., Wyler, R., and Mohy-El-Din, O., *Proc. 6th Intern. Congr. Nutr. Edinburgh, 1963* p. 599. Livingstone, Edinburgh and London, 1964.
182. Srebnik, H. H., and Nelson, M. M., *Proc. 6th Intern. Congr. Nutr. Edinburgh, 1963* p. 375. Livingstone, Edinburgh and London, 1964.
183. Steensberg, V., *Brit. J. Nutr.* **1**, 139 (1947).
184. Sørensen, P. H., "Jodstofskifte og thyreoideafunktion hos kvæg og svin." Aug. Bang, Copenhagen, 1958.
185. Terry, C. W., Terry, B. E., and Davies, J., *Am. J. Physiol.* **198**, 303 (1960).
186. Theiler, A., Green, H. H., and Du Toit, P. J., *J. Agr. Sci.* **18**, 369 (1928); *Nutr. Abstr. Rev.* **1**, 359 (1929).
187. Thompson, D. S., *J. Dept. Agr. S. Australia* **53**, 352 (1950).
188. Thomson, A. M., and Thomson, W., *Brit. J. Nutr.* **2**, 290 (1948–1949).
189. Thorp, W. T. S., Keener, H. A., Bechdel, S. I., and Guerrant, N. B., *Am. J. Vet. Res.* **3**, 27 (1942).
190. Tribe, D. E., and Cumming, R. B., *Vet. Rev. Annotations* **1**, 69 (1955).
191. Tuff, P., *J. Comp. Pathol. Therap.* **36**, 143 (1923).
192. Tuff, P., *Norsk Vet. Tidsskr.* **56**, 1 (1944).
193. Ullrey, D. E., Becker, D. E., Terrill, S. W., and Notzold, R. A., *J. Nutr.* **57**, 401 (1955).
194. Underwood, E. J., "Trace Elements in Human and Animal Nutrition." Academic Press, New York, 1962.
195. Underwood, E. J., *Proc. 6th Intern. Congr. Nutr. Edinburgh, 1963* p. 289, Livingstone, Edinburgh and London, 1964.
196. Vallee, B. L., *Physiol. Rev.* **39**, 443 (1959).
197. VanDemark, N. L., Fritz, G. R., and Mauger, R. E., *J. Dairy Sci.* **47**, 898 (1964).
198. Van Koetsveld, E. E., *Tijdschr. Diergeneesk.* **83**, 229 (1958).
199. Wallace, L. R., *J. Physiol.* (*London*) **104**, 34P (1945).
200. Wallace, L. R., *J. Agr. Sci.* **38**, 93, 243, 367 (1948).
201. Warkany, J., *Harvey Lectures Ser.* **48**, 89 (1954).
202. Warnick, A. C., Meacham, T. N., Cunha, T. J., Loggins, P. E., Hentges, J. F., and Shirley, R. L., *Proc. 4th Intern. Congr. Animal Reprod. The Hague* **2**, 202 (1961).
203. Watt, J. A., and Barlow, R. M., *Vet. Record* **68**, 780 (1956).
204. Wiggins, E. L., Warnick, A. C., Grummer, R. H., Casida, L. E., and Chapman, A. B., *J. Animal Sci.* **10**, 494 (1951).
205. Wilson, J. G., *in* "Teratology, Principles and Techniques" (J. G. Wilson and J. Warkany, eds.), p. 251. Univ. of Chicago Press, Chicago, Illinois, 1965.
206. Wolbach, S. B., and Howe, P. R., *J. Exptl. Med.* **42**, 753 (1925).
207. Wolbach, S. B., and Howe, P. R., *Arch. Pathol.* **5**, 239 (1928).
208. Zuntz, L., *Arch. Gynaekol.* **110**, 244 (1919).

19 INFECTIOUS DISEASES INFLUENCING REPRODUCTION

JOHN W. OSEBOLD

I. Introduction

This chapter presents a brief account of the major infectious diseases which affect fertility, induce abortion, or cause abnormalities of progeny born at term. These infections are of interest for economic and public health reasons. They may create serious problems for the commercial livestock producer since several of the diseases are chronic and affect herd health over a period of many years. Some of the infections may strike unexpectedly to cause extensive losses in herd productivity, thus creating an added dimension of uncertainty in livestock production. Research workers in the field of reproduction in domestic animals also need to be aware of infections which may negate their data. When hazards to human health exist, as is the case with some of these infections, additional aspects of animal disease control are required.

II. Bacterial Infections

A. BRUCELLOSIS

1. Etiology

Brucellosis is a world-wide infectious disease affecting a variety of mammalian species, including man. Identification of the *Brucella* species is difficult since the organisms are similar in physical appearance, share common antigens, and have many physiological characteristics in common. Extensive studies have evolved a battery of differential characters for the separation of the three principle species, in addition to biotypes within each species (17). The most practical aspect of speciation within the genus relates to host specificity wherein the common reservoir hosts are as follows: *Brucella abortus*, cattle; *B. suis*, swine; *B. melitensis*, sheep and goats. All three organisms may produce brucellosis in man, although *B. abortus* is less virulent than the other two species.

2. The Disease

The organism may enter the body through a variety of routes, but ingestion is probably the most common mode of transmission under field conditions. Venereal transmission from bulls with lesions in the epididymis and testicle may also occur. This aspect of transmission has relevance to artificial insemination. Milk from infected cows commonly contains the organism, which may be viable in fresh milk, butter, and cheese. Much of the public health interest in brucellosis has focused upon this characteristic of the infection (6, p. 270).

Brucellosis in a susceptible herd of animals is associated with abortion following a primary attack by the agent. This may affect a very high percentage of the pregnant animals. A smaller percentage of abortions occur in subsequent years, but a new storm of abortions may follow additions to the herd of susceptible adult cattle or animals in their first pregnancy. Except for the act of abortion, which is often followed by retention of fetal membranes, the process of brucellosis in the adult may be described as "clinically silent." The organism commonly persists in the udder and mammary lymph nodes. In many cases, the infection continues over several lactation periods or even for the life of the animal. Persistent infection is associated with the sexually mature animal and the possible relationship of this to the endocrine system of the host is under investigation. During pregnancy, the organisms replicate in great numbers in the gravid uterus. Widespread necrosis and exudation occur in the uterine caruncles and the placenta. The chorioallantoic membrane is extensively involved with the organisms multiplying intracellularly. This peculiar predilection for bacterial replication at the site of fetal attachment to the dam has intrigued research workers. An explanation was recently presented with the demonstration that erythritol, a polyalcohol, stimulates the growth of brucellae and that this growth factor may be found in high yield in the placentas of species prone to experience abortion from *Brucella* infections (66).

Young animals are generally more resistant to infection than sexually mature adults. Thus, a calf born from an infected dam may have *Brucella* organisms in its tissues at the time of birth and may ingest many organisms when nursing, but these do not produce a clinical process in the young animal and within a month or two the agent is usually eliminated from the tissues.

3. Diagnosis and Control

Clinical signs are of limited value in diagnosing brucellosis because of the chronic and insidious nature of the disease. Isolation of the organism offers an undisputed basis for diagnosis and attempted isolation is an important aspect of the diagnosis in man and in certain naturally occurring infections in animals. However, it is a costly and time-consuming procedure which is not amenable with routine disease control.

The principal means of diagnosis is based upon immunological responses of the infected individual. Infected subjects display hypersensitivity of the delayed type and synthesis of humoral antibodies which may be detected by a variety of methods. Thus, there are procedures for detecting complement-fixing antibodies, agglutinating antibodies, and nonagglutinating or so-called incomplete antibodies. The latter test is proving useful in situations where the infection is suspected, but agglutinating serum antibodies are not demonstrable. Nonagglutinating antibodies are detected by adding the appropriate antiglobulin serum to the test system, which brings about agglutination of the bacteria after they have been sensitized by reacting with nonagglutinating antibodies (68).

The agglutination test is a good means for detecting antibody response from stimulation by *Brucella* antigens and it has the great advantage of being technically simple to perform. Most commonly used is the rapid plate agglutination test, wherein a concentrated suspension of stained *Brucella* organisms is mixed on a glass plate with differing volumes of serum or whey. Agglutination occurs within a few minutes when antibodies are present. The procedure is adjusted to correlate with the more classic tube test and, thus, it is customary to speak of titers of reacting antibodies as a function of the highest dilution of serum demonstrating the phenomenon of agglutination. For practical reasons, it has been necessary to define agglutination at a certain titer as indicative of infection, making the animal subject to removal from the herd. For cattle in the United States, this titer is 1:100 for nonvaccinated animals and 1:200 for those which have been vaccinated. Animals are classified as suspects when antibodies are detected at lower titers. It is prudent, however, to be concerned about animals in the suspect classification, since they may be newly infected individuals with a rising antibody response at the time of sampling, or they may represent chronically infected individuals demonstrating that the antibody response may wane and later rise again at varying stages in the infection.

An important adjunct to the control of bovine brucellosis has been the acceptance of the milk ring test (MRT) for herd diagnosis (19). In this procedure, an aliquot of whole milk, which may have been contributed from several animals, is mixed with a suspension of inactivated B. abortus organisms stained with hematoxylin. The procedure is again based on the phenomenon of agglutination, and agglutinated masses of bacteria tend to be carried up into the cream layer. The procedure has great value in control programs, since it obviates the necessity for collecting individual blood samples or even individual milk samples.

The control of brucellosis has depended upon the detection of infected individuals to prevent their introduction into susceptible herds, immunization to raise the general level of resistance of replacement animals on infected premises, and last, the test and slaughter of infected individuals when the level of infection has been reduced to a point that this becomes economically feasible. Brucellosis is a world-wide health problem, and the stages of the control programs vary in different regions. Control of bovine brucellosis in the United States is now at an advanced stage, with eradication of the disease from many states and a phasing out of immunization programs followed by extensive use of the test and slaughter procedure (6, p. 270). It may be anticipated that greater attention will be focused on brucellosis in swine in the United States in the near future.

Immunization has proved to be an indispensible facet of brucellosis control in heavily infected areas. A strain of B. abortus isolated by Buck in 1923 continues to be the most advantageous agent for immunizing against bovine brucellosis, in spite of many vaccine preparations which have been investigated since that time (8). The isolate described by Buck is known as strain 19, and it must be realized that this living agent does produce a mild form of brucellosis which can render it dangerous to man and animals unless used properly. It is highly agglutinogenic in adult animals. This characteristic has caused extensive problems in the control program with efforts to separate antibody response to the vaccine from that caused by natural infection. Calfhood vaccination has been the best approach to this problem since the agglutinin response of the young bovine is ordinarily a temporary one and diminishes sufficiently to avoid confusion with titers rom field infections. This must be balanced against the knowledge that immunization in older animals results in a higher level of increased resistance. Immunization of calves from 4 to 12 months of age is the common practice. Abortions can occur if pregnant animals are vaccinated.

The mechanisms of acquired resistance in brucellosis are undoubtedly complex. There is good evidence that the presence of antibodies alone cannot explain the immune state. Recent studies have focused on the importance of changes in the functional capacity of macrophages for dealing with the intracellular destruction of the *Brucella* organisms. The role of the macrophages is considered of great importance and is under investigation in studies on brucellosis and several other infections associated with intracellular parasitism (*16*).

The World Health Organization has been active in sponsoring research toward the development of vaccines to be used in goats and sheep for immunization against *B. melitensis*. Many strains of both living and inactivated organisms and their fragments have been investigated, but the most promising appears to be a streptomycin-independent strain of *B. melitensis* which is avirulent and inoculated as a viable organism. As is the case with *B. abortus* strain 19 in cattle, this vaccine will cause abortion if inoculated into pregnant goats. The preparation, known as Rev 1 vaccine, has been shown to protect pregnant goats in controlled experiments and against natural exposure in Malta, Iran, and Israel (*17*).

B. VIBRIOSIS

1. The Disease

Vibrio fetus produces disease in the genital organs of sheep, cattle, and occasionally man. There are important differences in the disease as it occurs in cattle from the condition in sheep. Different serological types of the organism are associated with infections in the two species.

Vibriosis has been considered by some investigators as the most important microorganism causing infertility in cattle. The bacterium is disseminated through the herd by venereal means, causing failure to conceive or early death of the embryo. Both events leave the impression of infertility since only a few of the aborted fetuses may be found. After 2–8 months, the infected females recover from the infection and demonstrate a resistance to reinfection. Bulls show no clinical signs even though the organism may be a permanent resident of the male genital organs. Recognized abortions are most common in midgestation, and lesions of the placenta are similar to those occurring in brucellosis. The vibrios may be widely disseminated within the fetus. The fetal stomach contains turbid fluid from which the organisms can be obtained in pure culture (*6*, p. 241).

Venereal transmission does not seem to be involved in vibriosis among sheep. It is assumed that the organism is picked up by the susceptible host from feed and water contaminated by the discharges of aborting animals.

Although the epizootiology of the condition is still uncertain, attention has been focused recently on the presence of persistent foci of infection in the gallbladders of ewes and the possible role that such carriers could have in maintaining the infection (38, p. 54). Vibriosis of sheep can be a dramatic event. It usually occurs about 4–6 weeks prior to the time of normal lambing, with abortions reaching 70% in some instances. A small percentage of ewes may die with lesions of necrosis in the maternal cotyledons. In contrast to the calf, the fetal lamb frequently develops marked lesions of focal hepatic necrosis. Ewes that have once aborted from vibriosis do not repeat the event on subsequent breedings. Infertility is not considered an important aspect of vibriosis in sheep.

2. Diagnosis and Control

When the herd history suggests vibriosis, the chief means of diagnosis are bacteriological recovery of the organism and immunological tests. Recovery of the organism is frequently difficult because V. fetus grows slowly and many of the tissues submitted for examination are grossly contaminated with bacteria that rapidly overgrow the culture. Fetal stomach fluid, semen from the male, and fluids from the female genital tract are most frequently cultured. An important advance in detection of infected bulls has been accomplished by using fluorescent antibodies to visualize V. fetus in preputial samples (39).

It is necessary to differentiate V. fetus from organisms of no pathogenic significance since there are many members of the genus Vibrio free in nature. Not infrequently, the bacteriologist encounters Vibrio bubulus from the genitalia of cattle, which is not considered to be pathogenic (45). Recent studies further indicate the importance of separating two types of the pathogen referred to as V. fetus venerealis and V. fetus intestinalis by Florent (20). The latter type may establish itself in the bovine genital tract, but is not thought to be a cause of infertility.

To be significant, agglutination tests should be performed on a herd basis. In most infectious diseases, serum is used as the source of antibodies for the measurement of antibody response. In the case of bovine vibriosis, much has been written to indicate that agglutination tests, employing serum, are unreliable. The infectious process appears to be localized within the genital tract and antibodies accumulate in that site. Tests for antibodies in vaginal mucus have become recognized as the best method for determining infection by the presence of antibodies (61). Greater sensitivity of the procedure is apparently obtained by adsorbing soluble antigens of the organism on latex particles which results in the agglutination of the latex rather than the more conventional agglutination of bacterial cells (37).

Infected bulls constitute the chief source of infection in cattle. The male can transmit the infection, either by natural service or in semen used for artificial insemination. Successful treatment of bulls by the use of topical antibiotics has been reported, but difficulties in isolating the organism from the male genital tract always leave a doubt regarding the success of the therapy. A valuable routine preventive is the addition of antibiotics to semen samples prior to their use for artificial insemination (30).

If infected cows are given several months of sexual rest, it may be assumed that the resistance mechanisms of the host will eliminate the vibrios. Some investigators report the use of antibiotic therapy on infected cows, but it is difficult to determine whether the therapy was truly successful or whether the individual recovered spontaneously. Vibriosis is particularly difficult to control in beef cattle under rangeland conditions. In situations where the infection of replacement cattle seems inevitable, Hoerlein (25) has suggested that 1-year-old heifer replacements be bred to infected bulls. The rationale is to obtain maximum exposure, with the observation that about 20% of these first calf heifers will produce viable calves. The remainder of the heifers will be resistant to vibriosis and have the advantage of extra growth and development when bred as 2-year olds.

In controlling ovine vibriosis, efforts should be made to isolate aborting ewes for 2–4 weeks. Aborted fetuses and placental tissues should be destroyed in an effort to keep the vibrios out of the feed and water supply.

Promising results have been obtained in efforts to immunize both sheep and cattle. Pregnancy rates in cattle were significantly higher following immunization with live or inactivated vaccines than in unvaccinated controls (26, 46). Long-term studies on the efficacy of killed *Vibrio* vaccines for the prevention of abortion in sheep are demonstrating that this procedure will have value (59).

C. Leptospirosis

1. The Disease

There are many species in the genus *Leptospira* which cause diseases. *Leptospira pomona* is the one of greatest importance as a factor in reproductive failure. In cattle, this infection produces an acute phase during which animals of varied ages and both sexes may demonstrate high fevers (103°–107°F) with accompanied depression and anorexia. This stage of the infection is associated with rapid lysis of erythrocytes resulting in the expected effects of icterus, hemoglobinuria, edema, and anoxia. Lactating cows have a sudden cessation of milk secretion. Mortalities occur at this stage of the disease with up to 33% losses in calves in some cases. Mortality among adult cattle is considerably less.

It is during the convalescent period that abortions occur. This important sequel to acute leptospirosis is seen 2–6 weeks after the early phase and occurs at a time when antibody response is high or near its peak. The incidence of abortion varies from a few premature births to 50%. Abortions occur most frequently in the last third of pregnancy (48). The act of expelling the fetus seems to have little ill effect on the dam, and the fetal membranes are usually expelled naturally. In contrast to diseases such as brucellosis, there is no massive infection of the placenta or caruncles in leptospirosis. The fetus dies *in utero*, but usually is not infected. It has been suggested that anoxia is the cause of fetal death following lysis of erythrocytes (*18*).

In the case of swine, the leptospirae can be found in weak, aborted pigs or in pigs farrowed by an infected sow. Clinical disease and the act of abortion are less frequently observed in swine than in cattle. It should be kept in mind from the standpoint of human health that urine from both species is a potential hazard.

2. Diagnosis and Control

Structurally, the leptospirae are delicate, spiral-shaped organisms, about 10–20 μ in length. They are sensitive to factors such as desiccation, heat, and cold, which cause them to perish rapidly after excretion from the infected host. A chronic carrier state becomes established in many animals wherein the organism usually resides in the kidneys. This permits exit of the parasite from the host in voided urine. Swine are thought to be the most important species in the epizootiological chain, although cattle also have been observed to shed the organism for as long as 3 months following an acute attack. Infected urine splashed on the nasal mucosa or conjunctiva is apparently the common mode of transmission.

Sanitation is an important means of control. Swine should not be permitted to mingle with cattle, and efforts should be made to avoid surface water, ponds, and slow-moving streams if there is reason to suspect that they could be contaminated with recently voided leptospirae from livestock or feral animals.

Serological tests in affected herds will demonstrate a percentage of animals reacting positively. There may be justification for some reservation about the diagnosis based on serological evidence if a clinical episode resembling the acute phase has not been a part of the disease pattern. There is value in taking a repeat reading a few weeks following the initial blood test to determine whether animals that were formerly negative are developing titers and whether the titers are rising in animals previously positive. Serodiagnosis is performed by several modifications of the agglutination phenomenon or by complement fixation. The test most commonly used is called the "agglutination-lysis test." Serum dilutions are mixed with living organisms and the phenomena of both agglutination and lysis are observed with the dark-field microscope.

Dark-field microscopy is also of value for obtaining prompt, presumptive diagnoses. It requires good timing to sample the animal when the organisms are in either the blood or the urine. Experience is required to differentiate the organism from artifacts.

The diagnostician is most satisfied if the organism can be recovered from the infected animal. This is an involved procedure in leptospirosis since it requires that samples be taken at the appropriate stage in the disease process and transferred promptly to media or indicator animals because the organisms die rapidly outside the host.

Immunization of cattle and swine with a vaccine prepared from inactivated *L. pomona* is now widely practiced. Unfortunately, the period of increased resistance is usually less than 1 year. The use of live avirulent vaccines shows promise for increasing the longevity of the resistant state (2). The reduction or elimination of the carrier state by antibiotic treatment may also be used (*14*, p. 323).

D. LISTERIOSIS

1. The Disease

Many species of mammals and birds have been found naturally infected with *Listeria monocytogenes* throughout the world. Similar disease syndromes from the agent may develop in man, cattle, and sheep. Since this organism frequently invades the brain and meninges, its effects on the central nervous system have received more attention than the genital disease aspects of the infection. More work is needed to critically determine the full dimension of this disease. Interest in the problem was increased considerably following several reports from Germany of cases in aborted human infants and newborn babies (*53*).

Among cattle, the recorded cases that abort are usually a small percentage of the animals in a herd. Many of the abortions occur between the fourth and seventh months of gestation, with evidence that the fetus had died *in utero* before the abortion. The fetuses may present multiple foci of necrosis in the liver and sometimes in other organs such as the spleen, kidney, and lung. The organism can be obtained from these organs and from the stomach contents. Pregnant ruminants have been experimentally infected by adding *L. monocytogenes* to the drinking water, showing that ingestion is probably an important mode of transmission. The interesting predilection for sites of placental attachment is observed here, as in certain other infections. The *Listeria* organism actively invades the fetal tissues, causing pathological responses in them. When infected calves are carried to term or nearly to term, they may be born weak and die in a few days (*43*). The uterus of the cow usually frees itself of the organism quite rapidly following expulsion of the fetus (*44*).

Listeria encephalitis and abortion are seen occasionally in the same animal. The more typical observation in an infected herd is a syndrome of either encephalitis or abortion. Following abortion, the cow usually recovers rapidly from the associated metritis.

Listeria abortions in sheep occur more commonly than incidence records would indicate. Abortion rates from 1 to 50% have been recorded from such diverse areas as Australia, England, and the United States (*53*).

2. Diagnosis and Control

Isolation of the organism is the only reliable means of diagnosis. *Listeria monocytogenes* is the single member of its genus which would suggest that identification should be relatively easy. However, the agent has been erroneously discarded from many specimens as a "diptheroid of no significance." This appellation is used in referring to many organisms that resemble *Corynebacterium diptheriae*, but have no recognized pathogenicity. The mistake is made when the laboratory is insufficiently aware of the *Listeria* agent and efforts are not made to separate it from members of the genus *Corynebacterium*. It has also been found that primary culturing of infected tissues frequently fails to disclose the organism. When the tissues are held in the refrigerator for a period of several weeks, the organism can often be recovered. This reculture phenomenon is related in part to an unusual ability to multiply at 4°C (*42*).

Serological methods, including agglutination and complement fixation tests, have been used with success experimentally. Their value for field diagnosis has been limited because nearly all normal adult ruminants have serum antibodies reactive with *Listeria* antigens. Recent studies have shown that these are IgM antibodies (19 S or high molecular weight antibodies). Following antigenic stimulation with *L. monocytogenes*, IgG antibodies (7 S antibodies) are also synthesized. Tests for this latter, more significant, population of antibodies can be performed by adding reducing substances to the serum, which depolymerize the IgM antibodies. This finding has promise for shedding new light on the diagnosis and epizootiology of listeriosis (*1*).

The tetracycline group of antibiotics is indicated for therapy when the dam is clinically affected from the abortion and in the diseased newborn.

Acquired resistance following vaccination has been shown experimentally, but reliable vaccines are not yet available for routine use. As in brucellosis, the mechanisms of immunity are complex, involving cellular immunity, which is obtained only by immunization with live organisms (*40*). A reliable attenuated strain is needed for vaccine preparation.

The public health aspects of this disease make it necessary to disinfect everything contaminated by infected animals. Human cases may follow the handling of aborting animals. The isolation of the organism from milk suggests a possible additional means whereby listeriosis may be transmitted to man.

E. Epididymitis in Rams

This disease is caused by a gram-negative bacterium of uncertain classification. Buddle referred to it as *Brucella ovis* in 1956 (*9*), but its classification in the genus *Brucella* has raised some objections because of dissimilarities to other members of that genus. In any case, there is agreement among investigators in Australia, New Zealand, and California that this organism produces a characteristic lesion in the male genital organs of the sheep. Lesions develop initially in the tail of the epididymis and in the interstitial tissue of the seminal vesicles and ampullae. This is followed by extravasation of sperm through the damaged epithelium. Investigators have been puzzled by the selective tissue pathogenicity shown by this organism since experiments demonstrate that the process is systemic at one stage, allowing wide tissue distribution of the organism (5). Sterility of the ram may result, although this is not necessarily complete since the process commonly involves only one testicle. Ewes will abort following intravenous injection of the organism and, although late abortions associated with natural infections have been reported, this is not a common process in the infection. Service from infected rams does not appear to affect the fertility of ewes.

Gross lesions can be detected by palpation of the scrotum. The high incidence of this disease was demonstrated in California wherein 27% of the examined rams were affected (31). Buddle introduced an unusual concept for immunization against the disease. This required the simultaneous inoculation of *Brucella abortus* strain 19 and inactivated *B. ovis* organisms suspended in a saline-in-oil adjuvant. The role of *B. abortus* in this procedure was uncertain, and in more recent studies, Buddle has reported that equal resistance could be induced with two doses of the inactivated *B. ovis* vaccine (10). Vaccination of yearlings rather than younger lambs resulted in better protection. Older rams showing clinical lesions should be culled and the remainder vaccinated any time up to 2 months prior to the breeding season.

III. Virus Infections

A. ENZOOTIC ABORTION OF EWES

The synonym for this disease is ovine virus abortion, although there is serious doubt about classifying the etiological agent as a virus. The organism belongs to the Bedsonia group, intracellular parasites having characteristics somewhere between viruses, rickettsias, and bacteria (64). They have been referred to in the past as the psittacosis-lymphograuloma-venereum group (PLV). Although this group of agents is quite large and the affected hosts diverse (mammals and birds), it contains a common heat-stable group antigen. Thus, the complement fixation test, as it is usually performed, is a test for antibodies to the group rather than an individual agent in the group.

Enzootic abortion of ewes (EAE) was first reported in 1950 by Stamp *et al.* in Scotland (57). Since that time, the disease has been reported from several countries in Europe and many parts of the United States (6, p. 748). Abortions and premature lambing occur during the last month of gestation. Retention of the placenta and vaginal discharge commonly follow the act

of abortion. Ewes may be visibly ill with some febrile response for a period of a few days. Those that do not expel the dead fetuses may die. In
a susceptible group of animals, the abortion rate may be as high as 30%, but
is more often 5% or less. Fertility of the ewes is not affected on subsequent
breedings, and rams exposed to the organism appear to remain uninfected.

Clinically, this disease resembles vibriosis, and it is necessary to eliminate *Vibrio fetus* as a factor in an epizootic. Smears prepared from infected
placentas can be used to demonstrate characteristic elementary bodies on
microscopic examination. In addition, infected placental tissue may be used
for isolation of the agent in embryonating chicken eggs. Complement fixation tests will give an indication of the morbidity rate within the population
of affected animals, but it must be remembered that the test is not specific
for the organism of enzootic abortion of ewes.

A vaccine prepared in England by formalin inactivation of the organism
cultivated in embryonating eggs has been used rather extensively in Europe
and the United States (22). This is reported to induce a resistant state
lasting more than 2 years, although there are some conflicting reports
concerning its efficacy.

B. Epizootic Bovine Abortion

In 1960, Storz *et al.* (58) reported the isolation of a Bedsonia agent
associated with a characteristic type of bovine abortion and lesion pattern
in the fetal calf. In several ways, the agent resembles that of enzootic abortion of ewes, and doubts exist as to whether or not these are the same
organism (33). Epizootic bovine abortion (EBA) is now receiving intensive
investigation in California, but it is likely that the problem occurs in many
parts of the world and may be identical to the disease reported by Schoop
and Kauker of Germany in 1956 (51).

In California, this disease has primarily affected beef cattle in the last
trimester of pregnancy, with abortions occurring in the fall and winter
months. In susceptible herds, females of all ages may abort, but in succeeding years, losses are limited to heifers in their first gestation. Abortion
rates of 60% have been encountered. The cows do not show systemic effects
from the disease and their fertility is unimpaired following the abortion.

Gross pathological changes are commonly apparent in the fetus. The
most characteristic change is seen in the liver which is enlarged, coarsely
granular, and friable. Histologically, these are seen to be lesions of granulomatous inflammation with massive infiltration of macrophages and extensive loss of glandular parenchyma. Diagnosis is based on criteria similar
to those described for enzootic abortion of ewes (EAE).

At the present time, there is no basis for the control of this disease. The
clinical observation that cows characteristically abort only once suggested
that successful immunization might be easily accomplished. Thus far, efforts
to prepare useful vaccines have been unsuccessful (34).

C. Virus-Induced Abortions in Horses

1. Etiology

Much progress has been made in the last few years toward understanding the role of viruses in equine abortions and the relationship of these viruses to respiratory diseases of the horse. In the recent past, a complex of respiratory diseases was thought to be equine influenza in different clinical forms. Progress was made on the viral etiology of abortion, but its relationship to the respiratory syndrome was not understood. Current knowledge indicates that the equine rhinopneumonitis virus causes respiratory disease in young horses and is also the agent of equine virus abortion. The equine arteritis virus causes a generalized disease process, including respiratory symptoms, and induces abortion in the pregnant mare. Equine influenza virus causes respiratory disease and does not appear to be a significant factor in abortion syndromes. In this discussion, attention will be directed toward the viruses of equine rhinopneumonitis and equine arteritis.

2. Abortion from Equine Rhinopneumonitis Virus Infection

In 1933, Dimock and Edwards described an epizootic form of abortion in mares in Kentucky and showed that the disease was caused by a virus. This work was later confirmed in many states and in several European countries. Eight years later, a report from Hungary called attention to the clinical relationship of what they regarded as "influenza" virus with equine abortion virus. They demonstrated that a mild respiratory illness followed instillation of virus-infected fetal tissue suspensions on the respiratory mucous membranes. Subsequent investigations have shown that the abortion virus of Dimock and Edwards is a common respiratory tract inhabitant of the horse and that abortions may be considered a secondary effect from an agent that usually produces respiratory disease (13). Thus, the agent is now renamed the "equine rhinopneumonitis virus."

In young horses, the equine rhinopneumonitis virus produces a respiratory disease. Nasal discharge, fever, depression, and cough are observed in the primary infection. Secondary bacterial infections may follow, causing the nasal discharge to become mucopurulent. Abscesses in the lymph nodes of the head may develop that can be confused with the disease of horses known as "strangles." Equine rhinopneumonitis virus seems to be spread by aerosols and primarily affects suckling or weanling foals. Immunity following the primary attack is transient. If the virus reinfects some months after the primary infection, the antibody response is accelerated and only mild form of the respiratory disease develops. Young horses may be subject to several repeated infections, which tend to enhance resistance by antigenic stimulation. In addition to the repeated effects of field exposure, unknown age factors contribute to the immunity of adults from clinical disease.

Pregnant mares may abort if they have not had a very recent exposure to the virus. The fetus dies *in utero* and is promptly expelled without evidences of autolysis. Most abortions occur from the eighth month to term. The mare shows no signs of illness, the fetal membranes are not retained, and the animal is able to breed normally following the abortion. Some foals are born alive, but they usually die within 36 hours. The virus infection may result in the abortion of only a few mares in a group, but abortions can be as numerous as 90%.

There are widely disseminated evidences of virus infection in the fetus. Characteristic intranuclear inclusion bodies may be found in the lung, liver spleen, lymph nodes, and the epithelium of the turbinate bones. Commonly observed gross lesions are multiple focal areas of necrosis in the liver and edema in the lungs.

Diagnosis is dependent upon the clinical history and the detection of characteristic lesions in aborted fetuses. Tissues should be examined histologically to demonstrate the intranuclear inclusion bodies. Virus isolation and virus typing can be done in special situations where this is indicated.

A control program has been described by Bryans (7) as a system of planned infection. The control procedure utilizes fully infectious virus. All horses on the premise are exposed to the virus twice yearly, in July and October. The vaccine is given by instilling 3 ml in one nostril. Mature horses show no reaction, but weanlings often have mild fever and nasal exudation following the first exposure. The dual purposes of the program are prevention of disastrous epizootics of abortion and immunization of young horses against the respiratory disease. Studies made on more than 9000 mares have indicated the value of this procedure to avoid infection at a time likely to result in abortion.

3. Abortion Associated with Viral Arteritis

In the past, viral arteritis was thought to be a form of equine influenza. In the German literature, it has been referred to as "influenza-erysipelatosa" or "rotlaufseuche," and in English writings, the terms "typhoid fever" or "epizootic cellulitis—pink-eye syndrome," have been used. In 1953, a newly recognized virus was isolated as the cause of this disease and named the "equine arteritis virus" (13). The horse is the only known susceptible animal and only one immunogenic type is known to exist. Outbreaks have occurred on horse-breeding farms in Ohio, Pennsylvania, Kentucky, and California.

The characteristic lesion of this disease is an inflammatory reaction in small arteries. These lesions can occur in widely distributed parts of the body and their secondary effects give rise to the characteristic "forms" of the disease. The pulmonary form is accompanied by pulmonary edema, emphysema, and large quantities of serofibrinous effusion in the pleural cavity. Such an animal would show pulmonary distress as well as edema of the limbs and swelling around the eyes. The abdominal or "typhoid fever" form results from infarction in mesenteric vessels and, secondarily, edema in the submucosa of the intestine. Mild or severe colic accompanied by a watery diarrhea may be seen in such cases. Adult horses suffering from this infection are depressed and show muscular weakness, but death from the process is apparently rare.

There are no residual effects following recovery. The associated abortions, which have occurred in about 50% of the mares in carefully studied outbreaks, may result in considerable economic loss. The tissues and the fluids of infected aborted fetuses contain large quantities of virus. Since the disease is spread by aerosols and contracted by inhalation, horses with signs of arteritis should be isolated for several weeks. It is anticipated that a modified live-virus vaccine will be useful for immunization against the equine arteritis virus (7).

D. INFECTIOUS PUSTULAR VULVOVAGINITIS

The virus causing this disease is responsible for several important disease syndromes in cattle. In 1958, Kendrick et al. (27) isolated the virus in tissue culture causing pustular vulvovaginitis or coital exanthema. Further investigations have proved this to be the same virus that Madin et al. isolated in 1956 (36) as the cause of infectious bovine rhinotracheitis, an important respiratory disease of cattle. Genital infection from this virus is seen as an inflammatory reaction of the vulva and vagina with circumscribed pustules appearing over the lymphatic follicles in the vulva. When the pustules coalesce, a purulent exudate accumulates as a sticky exudate on the outside of the vulva. This disease may spread rapidly through a herd and usually begins with febrile reactions. During its active stage of 10–14 days, the animals have considerable pain in the affected tissues and urinate frequently. Temporary infertility may occur at this time, although the process is not thought to result in permanent infertility or abortions. Lesions similar to those described in the female may occur on the penis or prepuce of the bull.

Immunization of cattle with a modified live-virus vaccine is now widely employed for the prevention of both infectious bovine rhinotracheitis and infectious pustular vulvovaginitis (52).

E. CATARRHAL VAGINITIS

In 1956, a form of vaginitis in cattle was described by Kendrick et al. (28) which was thought to be similar to a disease occurring in South Africa called "epivag." The later affliction is characterized by epididymitis in the bull and vaginitis with infertility in the cow (32). The relationship of these two infections still remains uncertain. The disease described in California was characterized by vaginal discharge without recognizable lesions in other parts of the genital tract and had a course lasting several days to 3 months. Fertility was lowered, but conception commonly occurred 2–3 months following onset of the inflammation. Some animals conceived while the vaginitis existed. No abnormalities were encountered in the testicle or epididymis of examined bulls. A virus was isolated which was shown to produce the disease by experimental infection. No specific control measures have been developed. It is assumed that natural transmission is by coitus and that artificial insemination can be used to avoid infection.

F. Viruses Affecting Fetal Development (Rubella in Man, Blue-Tongue in Sheep, and Hog Cholera)

The association of abnormalities in the newborn with infections sustained by the pregnant female was given world-wide attention in 1941 in a report by Gregg of Australia (23). An unusually severe rubella (German measles) outbreak had occurred there in 1940. Following the epidemic, 78 cases of cataract in the newborn were encountered after the mothers had contracted rubella during the first 3 months of gestation. In addition, a high percentage of the infants with cataracts had congenital heart defects. Further study of additional cases (60) showed that the syndromes arising from this virus infection included cataract, deaf mutism, heart disease, and microcephaly in infants.

Immunization against virus diseases is frequently accomplished by inoculating attenuated live viruses. Their use establishes a mild form of the virus infection at a time selected as appropriate for induction of the resistant state. In certain animal diseases, these immunization practices can result in diseases of the fetus similar to those following rubella infection in women.

Blue-tongue, a systemic virus disease of sheep, may be prevented by immunization with such a modified live-virus vaccine. If ewes are immunized around the fifth or sixth weeks of gestation, undesired consequences develop as described by Shultz and DeLay (54). They encountered lamb losses averaging 5% and reaching 50% in some groups. The lambs were carried to term, although some were stillborn with evidences of ascites. Others, termed "dummies," ignored their dams and made no effort to nurse. Affected lambs had a form of encephalopathy resulting in extensive cavitation and loss of cerebral and cerebellar tissue. In extreme cases, the cranial cavity was found to be essentially devoid of brain substance and filled with clear fluid. Experimental studies (67) indicate that the virus invades the fetus and affects the fetal vascular system. Neuraxial tissue is affected secondarily and cannot be repaired since differentiated central nervous tissues have little if any capacity for regeneration. This undesired effect from immunization can be eliminated by vaccinating ewes before the breeding season.

When pregnant sows are immunized against hog cholera with modified live-virus vaccine in the early months of gestation, congenital abnormalities may develop in the pigs. This is readily apparent in the form of ascites with extensive subcutaneous edema. In addition, structural abnormalities such as asymmetry of the head, lengthening and twisting of the snout, and malformation of the limbs may occur (14, p. 140).

IV. Protozoan Infections

A. TRICHOMONIASIS

1. The Disease

Trichomoniasis is a protozoan infection of the genital tract which is transmitted by the bull and in the female causes death of the fetus, abortion, pyometra, and sterility. *Trichomonas foetus* is a flagellate, 10–25 μ in length, with three anterior flagellae. It has an undulating membrane the length of the cell which is kept in constant motion as it moves through extracellular fluids (29, p. 84). The organism persists in the prepuce of bulls for years. The disease may become widespread in a herd when infected bulls breed the cows or are used for artificial insemination. Pregnancy following such a mating frequently terminates with death of the fetus in the first trimester. The fetus may then decompose in an accumulation of pus and fluid in the uterus. Maceration of the fetus in these fluids may continue for several months, or the uterus may expel an early embryo, permitting the cow to return to estrus. The discharge of exudates is a frequent observation in an infected herd. Physical examination will reveal the discharge on the floor of the vagina or exuding from the uterus.

2. Diagnosis and Control

The infection is diagnosed by demonstrating the organism in exudates from the female or preputial washings from the male. Care must be exercised to differentiate *T. foetus* from other flagellates that may be encountered. When samples are collected from the cow at a favorable time, the organisms can be seen in great numbers from fresh, unstained preparations. Demonstration of *T. foetus* in genital washings from the male is usually difficult. Negative results should not be considered proof of freedom from infection. A more reliable indicator of the infection status of the bull can be obtained by examination of vaginal samples from virgin heifers 12–20 days following natural service.

As soon as the disease is recognized in a herd, sexual rest is instituted because the organisms do not remain permanently in the genital tract of the female. After the uterus has voided its infectious contents, estrus becomes reestablished and the genital tract eliminates the trichomonads. The females may be bred by uninfected males 1–2 months after all discharge has ceased. Bartlett (3) has reported success in eliminating the organism from infected bulls with topical treatment. The procedure is complicated and time-consuming, and its application is limited to valuable sires. Systemic treatment of infected bulls by the oral administration of dimetridazole has been described (35). On limited trials, the procedure appeared to be successful, but further work is needed to establish its efficacy. Ordinarily, infected bulls should be eliminated from the herd. When applicable to the management of the herd, artificial insemination from a carefully supervised breeding service should be used.

B. TOXOPLASMOSIS

1. The Disease

Toxoplasmosis in man and animals is caused by a protozoan, *Toxoplasma gondii*. It received only scant attention until it was recognized as the cause of several diseases of man in 1939 (*50*). The parasite is a small, elongated organism (4–7 μ), tapered at both ends and frequently seen in compact masses or cystlike structures. Toxoplasmata multiply in macrophages, in cells of various viscera, and in the nervous system. In man, the toxoplasma organism is known to cause certain types of congenital encephalomyelitis, chorioretinitis, and a form of pneumonitis.

Among the common domestic mammals, the agent is responsible for disease in cattle, sheep, swine, dogs, and cats (*11*).

There are many symptoms of acute toxoplasmosis, such as fever, dyspnea, and central nervous disturbances. The important aspects relative to this discussion are the premature births, abortions, and stillbirths which have been observed in all of the species mentioned. There is evidence of intrauterine transmission of the organism resulting in high mortality in the newborn during the first few weeks of life. The highest incidence rates of genital infections have been reported from New Zealand with abortions in sheep 4–6 weeks before lambing time. Retention of fetal membranes is common (*24*). After aborting, the ewes usually lamb normally in the following year (*4*).

2. Diagnosis and Control

Diagnosis is based on isolation of the organism or serological tests. Isolation is an involved procedure requiring the inoculation of suspected tissue materials into *Toxoplasma*-free mice. A valuable serological procedure is the Sabin-Feldman dye test. Test serum is diluted out in the presence of viable *Toxoplasma* organisms, complement, and a methylene blue stain. In the presence of antibodies, the cytoplasm of the organism does not stain. At present these tests are performed in the laboratories of specialists working on the problem (*55*).

There is no specific treatment. However, sulfanomides have been shown to effect a clinical cure experimentally. Since the drugs affect only the proliferative forms and not the cysts, animals may persist as carriers. There are no reliable vaccines.

C. DOURINE

1. The Disease

This venereal disease occurs in members of the family Equidae and is caused by the hemoflagellate *Trypanosoma equiperdum*. The disease usually runs a chronic course of 6 months to 2 years and may terminate fatally in untreated cases. The disease was once common in western Europe and North America, but it has been successfully eradicated from those regions. It is still encountered in Asia, Russia, Africa, and eastern areas of Europe (29, p. 53).

In 2–12 weeks following infection by coitus, edema of the genitalia, and dependent parts of the body may be seen. A mucous discharge develops from the urethra and vagina. Some weeks later, the second stage of the disease occurs wherein circular, sharply circumscribed, urticarial-like plaques about 3 cm in diameter arise on the skin about the abdomen, croup, back, or shoulder. They arise and disappear within a few hours or a few days. Blood-tinged fluid containing trypanosomes may be found in the plaques. Muscular weakness followed by complete paralysis and death are observed in the final stages.

2. Diagnosis and Control

The best opportunities for demonstrating the trypanosome in an infected horse occur during the acute stage when edema fluid and discharges from the infected genitals contain the organism, or by examination of fluid from the urticarial-like plaques. Dogs or laboratory rodents may be used as indicator hosts by injecting them with blood or fluids from suspected horses. Animals in nonclinical or carrier stages of the disease may be diagnosed only by means of the complement fixation test. Application of this serological procedure began in the United States in 1913 and it was used extensively in an eradication program sponsored by the United States government. In 1949, the last infected area in this country was released from quarantine. Horses imported into the United States must be tested for dourine before being admitted. In areas of the world where dourine is enzootic, systemic drug treatment is used to prevent death loss (12).

V. Pathological Responses of the Genital Organs to Miscellaneous Infections

A. SALPINGITIS AND OVARITIS

Salpingitis or inflammation of the oviducts is usually caused by pyogenic bacteria as an extension from a process of metritis (49). The inflammation may extend throughout the length of the tube, causing it to become thickened. It may involve the fimbriated end and result in adhesions with permanent sterility on one or both sides. As pus formation proceeds, it may result in the formation of abscesses. This condition is termed "pyosalpinx" and usually results in permanent sterility on the affected side. Careful palpation of the genital tract through the rectum will frequently demonstrate the presence of these abnormalities.

Ovaritis is not common in domestic animals. Severe salpingitis involving the fimbria may result in adhesions with formation of a large abscess surrounding the ovary. Tuberculosis of the female genital tract may result in extreme pathological alterations involving the ovary.

B. Metritis, Pyometra, and Retained Placenta

Inflammation of the endometrium is associated with specific and nonspecific infections, trauma following dystocia, and retained placenta. The cotyledonary placenta of the cow is especially likely to be retained following any kind of inflammatory reaction in the maternal caruncles which render separation of the fetal villi more difficult. Several infections were mentioned in the preceding discussions which are associated with metritis and retained placenta. As long as the fetal membranes protrude through the cervix, closure of that orifice is retarded. For this reason, manual removal of the placenta is usually delayed for 24 hours, at which time the fetal cotyledons can be more readily peeled from their maternal attachments.

Trichomoniasis is the infection most commonly associated with pyometra, wherein the fetus disintegrates slowly and great accumulations of fluid and pus are retained in the uterus. This process may extend over a period of a year or more. Inadequate cervical dilation and uterine inertia are important factors in the persistence of this condition.

C. Cervicitis

In the cow, the annular rings of the cervix give it a rosette appearance. With manipulation or even exposure to air (following insertion of the vaginal speculum), the cervix quickly becomes congested. This congestion of the cervix is easily interpreted as an inflammatory reaction. However, except for lacerations which may occur from parturition, definite pathological alterations are seldom encountered. In general, when metritis, pyometra, or other uterine abnormalities are resolved, the cervix rarely needs special treatment.

D. Granular Vaginitis

"Granular vaginitis" or "granular venereal disease" are terms which are frequently used in the literature, but have not been associated with any specific infectious process. The name comes from the presence of small grayish nodules which may be seen on the mucous membrane of the vulva. These have been shown to be hyperplastic lymphatic nodules and probably represent a nonspecific reaction of the genitalia to inflammation. When the nodules are encountered in association with breeding problems in a herd, specific causes such as the virus of catarrhal vaginitis should be sought. In the absence of marked vaginal exudates and other signs of specific disease problems, the prevalence of the lymphatic nodules on the membranes is considered to be of little importance. Trautman (62) investigated the fertility rates of artificially inseminated cows with and without granular nodules in the vagina. The conception rates were high in both groups.

E. Sporadic Causes of Genital Infections

Space permits little more than mention of several organisms that are occasionally associated with reproductive deficiency. Some organisms which may be derived from the intestinal tract may be involved in abortions, such as *Escherichia coli*, streptococci, and staphylococci in several species of animals, and *Actinobacillus equuli* (*Shigella equuli*) in solipeds. *Salmonella abortusovis*, affecting sheep in Europe, and *Salmonella abortivoequina* in horses are two more organisms of the enteric group that occasionally cause abortions (6, p. 309; 47).

Other incriminated bacteria have been *Pseudomonas aeruginosa, Corynebacterium equi*, and *Corynebacterium pyogenes*. The latter organism is responsible for a wide variety of suppurative processes in various species of mammals. In the reproductive tract, it is commonly present in purulent metritis.

A newly described organism named *Actinobacillus seminis* has been described as causing epididymitis in rams (56). Mycoplasma organisms (pleuropneumonia-like organisms) have been isolated from aborted bovine fetuses and vaginal mucus. Their role in disease processes, however, is uncertain (41).

Some fungi, such as *Aspergillus fumigatus* and *Absidia ramosa*, invade the placental tissues and also produce lesions in the fetus (65).

Tick-borne fever, caused by a rickettsia-like organism, has been associated with infertility in the ram (63). There is increasing concern about the role of viruses as factors in embryo mortality and abortion. Dunne *et al.* (15) have described porcine reproductive failure associated with a newly identified group of picorna viruses. It has been reported that the infectious bovine rhinotracheitis (IBR) modified live-virus vaccine can cause abortions in cattle vaccinated late in pregnancy. Some additional viruses associated with reports of abortion or teratogenic effects are the Japanese-B encephalitis virus in swine, Wesselsbron virus in sheep, Rift Valley Fever virus in several species of ruminants, virus diarrhea in cattle, and the pseudo-rabies virus in swine (Aujeszky's disease) (21).

REFERENCES

1. Aalund, O., Osebold, J. W., Murphy, F. A., and Di Capua, R. A., *J. Immunol.* **97**, 150 (1966).
2. Abelseth, M. K., Johnston, T. V., Blegen, E., *Proc. Intern. Vet. Congr., 17th Congr. Hanover* **1**, 649 (1963).
3. Bartlett, D. E., *Am. J. Vet. Res.* **9**, 351 (1948).
4. Beverley, J. K. A., and Watson, W. A., *Vet. Record* **74**, 548 (1962).

5. Biberstein, E. L., McGowan, B., Olander, H., and Kennedy, P. C., *Cornell Vet.* **54**, 27 (1964).
6. Bruner, D. W., and Gillespie, J. H., "Hagan's Infectious Diseases of Domestic Animals," 5th ed. Cornell Univ. Press, Ithaca, New York, 1966.
7. Bryans, J. T., *Proc. Am. Vet. Med. Assoc.* p. 112 (1964).
8. Buck, J. M., *J. Agr. Res.* **41**, 661 (1930).
9. Buddle, M. B., *J. Hyg.* **54**, 351 (1956).
10. Buddle, M. B., *New Zealand Vet. J.* **10**, 111 (1962).
11. Cole, C. R., Sanger, V. L., Farrell, R. L., and Kornder, J. D., *North Am. Vet.* **35**, 265 (1954).
12. Davey, D. G., *Vet. Rev. Annotations* **3**, 15 (1957).
13. Doll, E. R., Bryans, J. T., McCollum, W. H., and Crowe, M. E. W., *Cornell Vet.* **47**, 3 (1957).
14. Dunne, H. W. (ed.), *in* "Diseases of Swine." Iowa State Univ. Press, Ames, Iowa, 1964.
15. Dunne, H. W., Gobble, J. L., Hokanson, J. F., Kradel, D. C., and Bubash, G. R., *Am. J. Vet. Res.* **26**, 1284 (1965).
16. Elberg, S. S., *Bacteriol. Rev.* **24**, 67 (1960).
17. Elberg, S. S., *in* "Bacterial and Mycotic Infections in Man" (R. J. Dubos and L. G. Hirsch, eds.), p. 698. Lippincott, Philadelphia, Pennsylvania, 1965.
18. Ferguson, L. C., Ramge, J. C., and Sanger, V. L., *Am. J. Vet. Res.* **18**, 43 (1957).
19. Fleischauer, G., *Berlin. Tieraerztl. Wochschr.* **53**, 527 (1937).
20. Florent, A., *Proc. Intern. Vet. Congr., 16th Congr., Madrid* **2**, 489 (1959).
21. Florent, A., *Rept. 5th Meeting Food Agr. Organ. U. N. Panel Livestock Infertility, Rome* p. 19 (1964).
22. Foggie, A., *Vet. Record* **71**, 741 (1959).
23. Gregg, N. M., *Trans. Ophthalmol. Soc. Australia* **3**, 35 (1941).
24. Hartley, W. J., Jebson, J. L., and McFarlane, D., *Australian Vet. J.* **30**, 216 (1954).
25. Hoerlein, A. B., *Calif. Vet.* **19**, 23 (1965).
26. Hoerlein, A. B., Carroll, E. J., Kramer, T., and Beckenhauer, W. H., *J. Am. Vet. Med. Assoc.* **146**, 828 (1965).
27. Kendrick, J. W., Gillespie, J. H., and McEntee, K., *Cornell Vet.* **48**, 458 (1958).
28. Kendrick, J. W., McKercher, D. G., and Saito, J., *J. Am. Vet. Med. Assoc.* **128**, 357 (1956).
29. Levine, N. D., "Protozoan Parasites of Domestic Animals and Man." Burgess, Minneapolis, Minnesota, 1961.
30. McEntee, K., Hughes, D. E., and Gilman, H. L., *Cornell Vet.* **44**, 395 (1954).
31. McGowan, B., and Shultz, G., *Cornell Vet.* **46**, 277 (1956).
32. McIntosh, B. M., Haig, D. A., Alexander, R. A., *Onderstepoort J. Vet. Res.* **26**, 479 (1954).
33. McKercher, D. G., *Rept. 3rd Intern. Meeting Diseases Cattle, Copenhagen* p. 3 (1964).
34. McKercher, D. G., Wada, E. M., Robinson, E. A., and Howarth, J. A., *Cornell Vet.* **56**, 433 (1966).
35. McLoughlin, D. K., *J. Parasitol.* **51**, 835 (1965).
36. Madin, S. H., York, C. J., and McKercher, D. G., *Science* **124**, 721 (1956).
37. Manclark, C. R., and Pickett, M. J., *J. Pathol. Bacteriol.* **90**, 627 (1965).

38. Marsh, H., "Newsom's Sheep Diseases," 3rd ed., p. 54. Williams & Wilkins, Baltimore, Maryland, 1965.
39. Mellick, P. W., Winter, A. J., and McEntee, K., *Cornell Vet.* **55**, 280 (1965).
40. Njoku-Obi, A. N., and Osebold, J. W., *J. Immunol.* **89**, 187 (1962).
41. O'Berry, P. A., Bryner, J. H., and Frank, A. H., *Am. J. Vet. Res.* **27**, 677 (1966).
42. Osebold, J. W., *63rd Ann. Proc.* p. 394 (1960).
43. Osebold, J. W., Kendrick, J. W., and Njoku-Obi, A., *J. Am. Vet. Med. Assoc.* **137**, 221 (1960).
44. Osebold, J. W., Kendrick, J. W., and Njoku-Obi, A., *J. Am. Vet. Med. Assoc.* **137**, 227 (1960).
45. Park, R. W. A., Munro, I. B., Melrose, D. R., and Stewart, D. L., *Brit. Vet. J.* **118**, 411 (1962).
46. Plastridge, W. N., Kersting, E. J., and Williams, L. F., *Am. J. Vet. Res.* **27**, 186 (1966).
47. Rasbech, N. O., *Nord. Veterinarmed.* **17**, 305 (1965).
48. Roberts, C. S., *in* "Diseases of Cattle" (W. J. Gibbons, ed.), p. 645. Am. Vet. Publ. Wheaton, Illinois, 1963.
49. Roberts, S. J., "Veterinary Obstetrics and Genital Diseases." Published by author, Ithaca, New York, 1956, distributed by Edwards, Ann Arbor, Michigan.
50. Sabin, A. B., *Am. J. Trop. Med. Hyg.* **2**, 360 (1953).
51. Schoop, G., and Kauker, E., *Deut. Tieraerztl. Wochschr.* **63**, 233 (1956).
52. Schwarz, A. J. F., York, C. J., Zirbel, L. W., and Estela, L. A., *Proc. Soc. Exptl. Biol. Med.* **96**, 453 (1957).
53. Seeliger, H. P. R., "Listeriosis." Hafner, New York, 1961.
54. Shultz, G., and DeLay, P. D., *J. Am. Vet. Med. Assoc.* **127**, 224 (1955).
55. Siim, J. C., Biering-Sorensen, U., and Moller, T., *Advan. Vet. Sci.* **8**, 335 (1963).
56. Simmons, G. C., Baynes, I. D., and Ludford, C. G., *Australian Vet. J.* **42**, 183 (1966).
57. Stamp, J. T., McEwen, A. D., Watt, J. A. A., and Nisbet, D. I., *Vet. Record* **62**, 251 (1950).
58. Storz, J., McKercher, D. G., Howarth, J. A., and Straub, O. C., *J. Am. Vet. Med. Assoc.* **137**, 509 (1960).
59. Storz, J., Miner, M. L., Marriot, M. E., and Olson, A. E., *Am. J. Vet. Res.* **27**, 116 (1966).
60. Swan, C., *J. Obstet. Gynaecol. Brit. Empire* **56**, 341 (1949).
61. Szabo, L., *Nord. Veterinarmed.* **3**, 597 (1951).
62. Trautman, E. C., *J. Am. Vet. Med. Assoc.* **124**, 184 (1954).
63. Watson, W. A., *Vet. Record* **76**, 1131 (1964).
64. Werner, G. H., *in* "Basic Medical Virology" (J. E. Prier, ed.), p. 502. Williams & Wilkins, Baltimore, Maryland, 1966.
65. White, D. S., *Irish Vet. J.* **18**, 168 (1964).
66. Williams, A. E., Keppie, J., and Smith, H., *Brit. J. Exptl. Pathol.* **43**, 530 (1962).
67. Young, S., and Cordy, D. R., *J. Neuropathol. Exptl. Neurology* **23**, 635 (1964).
68. Zinnemann, H. H., Glenchur, H., and Hall, W. H., *J. Immunol.* **83**, 206 (1959).

20 SEXUAL BEHAVIOR AND CONTROLLING MECHANISMS IN DOMESTIC BIRDS AND MAMMALS

L. L. ANDERSON

I. Introduction

A description of sexual behavior patterns in domestic birds and mammals is presented with emphasis on recent observations. This chapter is intended to include experiments which were designed primarily to elucidate some of the mechanisms controlling sexual behavior and reproductive processes. By necessity much information is either bypassed or mentioned only briefly. Only literature pertaining to domestic birds and mammals is included.

II. Domestic Birds

Several reviews on various aspects of reproductive physiology are available (18, 58–60, 70, 81, 82, 129, 130, 131, 141, 146, 207, 208, 227).

SEXUAL BEHAVIOR

Patterns of sexual behavior have been described extensively for the domestic chicken, less for the turkey and duck. Behavioral patterns in these species are usually specific, and in general are unlike those observed in wild birds. Seasonal breeding patterns are on an annual basis and are affected by environmental factors such as light and temperature. Any endogenous control of the seasonal breeding activity would include circadian rhythms, which are amply illustrated, but the physiologic mechanisms are less well known. Even in constant environmental conditions these endogenous activities are expressed. Seasonal breeding patterns have been modified, however, particularly in the domestic chicken, by selecting and breeding of genetic traits for increased productivity.

1. Behavioral Patterns in Chickens

Discussion of the patterns of sexual behavior in the chicken includes the descriptions of Guhl *et al.* (*83*), Guhl (*80–82*), Fisher and Hale (*64*), Williams and McGibbon (*220–222*), and Wood-Gush (*229–232*).

Courtship activity precedes coitus, and this synchronizes the sexual responses in both sexes. Thus coitus is attained when the sex drives of the male and female are synchronized. Courtship is initiated by the male, and this activity includes sexual approaches by a waltz, wing flutter and circling around the female, a rear approach to the female, placing one foot on the back of the hen and grasping her comb. Mating includes mounting, treading of the feet, outstretching wings, grasping her comb, everting the cloaca, ejaculation, dismounting, and sometimes waltzing again.

The responses of the female to courting and mating are usually more passive. She may be indifferent to approaches by the male, avoid him by stepping aside, escape by running, or may indicate sexual receptivity by making a sexual crouch with lowering of the head and spreading of the wings. At this point the male mounts and treads, she then moves her tail to one side, everts the cloaca, and receives semen from the male as the vents meet. After the male dismounts, she rises, ruffles her feathers, and circles the male.

Sex drive in the male is particularly important since the female plays a passive or receptive role. Sexual activity may be measured by the sexual approaches of the male and the degree of sexual receptivity by the female. The sequence of events during courtship and mating may require only a few seconds. Some suggestions and cautions for testing sexual effectiveness in the male chicken are presented by Justice *et al.* (*118*).

Behavioral patterns of the male may decline with successive daily introduction into the pen with the females. Guhl (*80*) found that all activities (courting, avoiding, crouching, and treading) are most frequent during the first 3 minutes after introduction of the male. During a period of 18 minutes there was a decline in courting activity. Crouching by the hen decreases with each successive male; the female becomes satiated, then she shows more avoidance behavior. By introducing a new male, however, the low receptivity by the female is compensated by the higher rate of courting activity. When males and females are penned together for a period of time, sex drive tends to decrease. Crouching by the hens increases with inactive males or in their absence.

Social Dominance and Sexual Behavior. Social dominance is evident in sexual behavior of the male hierarchy and is separate from the peck order of the females. The mating activity of an individual male in a group of males is regulated by his social rank (*83, 232*). The sexual crouch of the female facilitates courtship and mating behavior of the male. Social dominance among hens thus hinders heterosexual responses because of their decrease in submissive behavior toward the male. Sexual maturity of inbred chickens, as indicated by age at first semen production, was not associated with social dominance ability when social competition effects were minimized (*37*). Genetic differences were observed in the frequency of mating and in sexual behavior of the domestic male chicken, but no relation was found between mating rank of the male and quality of semen (*233*).

Flickinger (*65*) found a delay in testicular maturation accompanied by degenerative changes in subordinate chickens of small groups. Later investigation (*66*) of the effects of social interaction on the adaptive responses of the testes indicated that increases in group size resulted in an increase in social conflict within groups and reduction in the size of the testes. Testes weight was correlated with social rank; the most dominant males had the heaviest testes, while the subordinate ones had the lightest and occasionally atrophied testes. Social conflict may be an important factor in determining adaptive responses in the chicken.

In a study of potential ethological isolating mechanisms in different breeds and strains of domestic chickens, Lill and Wood-Gush (*132*) found females exhibit a preference for own-breed or own-strain males. Female solicitation behavior exerted a powerful effect on male mating behavior; males copulated only with hens that crouched to them. Female receptivity and passivity thus seemed to be necessary if copulation was accomplished. Males of different breeds and strains showed few quantitative differences in courtship display, and these differences were not correlated with the solicitation preferences shown by the females. The females discriminated between males on physical characteristics (plumage color, morphology, and vocalization) rather than quantitative differences in male courtship. Also males discriminated between females on visual indicators, particularly their plumage color.

2. Behavioral Patterns in Turkeys

Courtship display in the male turkey is characterized by slow and restricted movements with elaborate feather display (*97, 180*). The tail is elevated and fanned, feathers erected, wings lowered with the primary feathers spread, and the head is retracted to the body. The courting male paces slowly in front of the female, at intervals takes a series of 3 to 5 quick steps, and finally vocalizes a pulmonic puff. This sequence is repeated 1 to 10 times per minute. The sexually receptive female assumes a sexual crouch with the head held close to the body, the tail flexed ventrally, the legs flexed, and the wings drooped and fluttered. The male moves slowly toward the crouched female and mounts; this may be repeated several times. After a few seconds to minutes he moves to grip the wing base of the female with his feet in preparation for copulation. The female with raised head then responds by raising her tail and exposing the vent. The copulatory sequence then includes lowering of the tail by the male and everting the oviduct by the female. When cloacal contact is made by the male, ejaculation is completed. The male dismounts and the female stands, fluffs feathers, vocalizes, and may run in an arc. Sexual receptivity is terminated after everting the oviduct; she will not crouch again until after an interval of time characteristic of the individual. Thus tactile stimuli are of primary importance in the copulation sequence and visual stimuli prepare the female for the sexual crouch.

The onset of mating activity in the turkey follows ovarian development. Mating begins within 2 weeks from the beginning of a 14-hour day length and is maximal after 4–5 weeks. Mature males may copulate with 1 to 10 females in a period of 30 minutes, and those with high sexual activity early in the breeding season tend to remain more active than other males throughout the breeding season. The number of copulations achieved by the male is related to his social rank among males, though he continues to express mating activity despite repeated interference by dominant males.

3. Behavioral Patterns in Ducks

Sexual maturity in ducks is reached in the spring of the year following hatching. Spermatogenesis declines during the summer molt, and the resting condition persists until January of the following year. The seasonal cycle of breeding behavior is controlled by the activity of the gonads, which in turn are dependent upon the adenohypophysis and hypothalamus. The increasing photoperiod stimulates gonadal growth and onset of the breeding season.

Courtship activity of the mallard begins by grouping of the males, which ruffle their head feathers and shake themselves (33). Various displays of the males include mock preening to show bright colors of the extended wing, the grunt whistle with head bowed low to the water, the head-up-tail-up display with loud whistle, and down-up display when courting in a group of males. Precoital display consists of a mutual bobbing up and down of the head by the male and female. The female then flattens herself with outstretched neck and bill along the surface of the water, and the male mounts. After copulation the male dismounts and circles the mate in a nod-swimming fashion.

4. Effect of Early Experience on Sexual Behavior in Birds

The effect of early experience or imprinting on later sexual behavior has been investigated in the domestic chicken and turkey. When visual stimuli of members of its own species are deprived until maturity, the mating behavior of the male chicken remains similar to socially reared males (64, 228). The previously isolated male mates successfully and preferentially with hens, though persistent sexual fixations on humans can be induced by the early experience (84, 85). Later, Guiton (86) re-examined the effect of early experience [imprinting; for definitions and discussion see Fabricius, (57)] on the sexual behavior of the male chicken reared in isolation from hatching to 6 months of age. Birds reared in early isolation reacted sexually to a human stimulus object at 7 weeks of age, but there was a total loss of sexual responsiveness to the experimenter by the time the males were adult.

Early experience appears to play an important part in sexual behavior of the turkey (178, 179). Some turkeys reared in isolation for the first 2 weeks of life show a marked and stable sexual preference for the human, even after mating experience with turkey hens for several breeding seasons.

The domestic male and female chick exhibit precocious copulatory behavior when excited by a moving object (7). Early experience with the moving object does not affect the frequency of this behavior, whereas testosterone injection greatly increases this response. The juvenile copulation behavior in the chick may indicate a mechanism for sexual imprinting.

III. Domestic Mammals

Objective observation and development of experimental techniques are yielding more information in the important area of sexual behavior in domestic mammals. An initial compilation of research in this area appeared in 1962 (88). Various aspects of environmental factors affecting sexual behavior in farm animals have been reviewed by Walton (214, 215), Clegg and Ganong (29), and in a recent symposium (103). A review is presented of recent work in this area on pigs, cattle, sheep, goats, and horses.

SEXUAL BEHAVIOR

1. Pigs

Descriptive data relative to the estrous cycle and associated phenomena are found in Burger (25), Asdell (10), and Boda (23) (see also Cupps et al., Chapter 9). As an interesting aside, Sillar and Meyler (192) have recently published an anthology of the pig in literature and art.

During early stages of proestrus the female becomes nervous and restless, with particular interest in the boar at the later stages. Some females pursue the males on the day prior to estrus, show less of this activity during

the day of estrus, and again pursue the male the first day after estrus (92).
Proestrous and estrous females also actively mount and nuzzle diestrous
females. However, other females pursued, mounted, and nuzzled estrous
females, but showed little interest in proestrous females or in those in waning stages of estrus. The time of ovulation is associated with the duration
of estrus, the longer interval from onset of estrus to ovulation was observed
in those females exhibiting a long estrous period (25). During coitus the
female usually exhibits a rigid mating stance (2). A lordosis response is
effected by pressure exerted from the mounting male or by hand pressure
on the female's back. The female withstands jostling and is virtually immobilized during the mating stance. A successful mating occurs more frequently if the estrous female is mated in her accustomed environment as
compared with results obtained after moving her to a new location, such as
the pen of the boar.

Elucidation of different stimuli from the male that influence sexual receptivity in the female has been reported by Signoret et al. (189, 190).
To test sexual receptivity, pressure was applied to the back of the female
and the frequencies of observed mating stance were noted. Isolated animals
and females penned in groups showed the same response. Thirty-nine percent of the estrous females exhibited the mating stance by the tenth hour of
estrus, whereas 59% responded between the 24th and 36th hour. Similar
results were obtained by using the hand-pressure technique to determine a
positive response for artificial insemination of more than 10,000 pigs (47).
A farrowing rate of 58% was obtained after a single insemination of pigs
that showed the positive response to the hand-pressure test. All females
assumed the mating stance in the presence of the boar. The influence of the
male on olfactory, auditory, visual, and tactile receptor organs of the female
was determined by sexual responsiveness. Olfactory and auditory stimuli
from the males were important for the induction of the immobilization reflex in 90% of the females (Table I). Visual stimulation increased the response in these females an additional 7%, whereas tactile stimuli added 3%
more. These results indicated clearly that the male plays an important role
in the mating response of the sow, and that these stimuli can be measured
separately. Manipulation of the auditory stimulus by recording the *chant de
cour* of the boar and replaying it in the presence of estrous females was also
effective in increasing the immobilization response (189, 190). A replay of
the recorded boar song increased the number of positive responses from 51
to 58%, whereas when the recording speed was reduced by half only 9% of
the animals exhibited the immobilization reflex. The role of olfaction on the
reproductive behavior was further investigated by ablation of the olfactory
bulbs (191); estrous cycles became irregular or ceased completely, and the
corpora lutea regressed. There was an increase in the number of vesicular
follicles which were half the diameter of mature follicles. Olfactory ablation
inhibited luteotropic hormone secretion from the adenohypophysis, whereas
follicle stimulating activity continued. Later, Signoret (188) reported that
complete removal of the olfactory bulbs interfered with hypophysial dis-

TABLE I

MALE STIMULI ON SEXUAL RECEPTIVITY OF THE SOW

Females	Stimuli from males	Immobilization response[a] (%)
24–36 Hours after first signs of estrus	None	59
Chant de cour of boar	Auditory	71
Boar odor in pen	Olfactory	81
Song and odor	Auditory and olfactory	90
Boar in view	Auditory, olfactory, and visual	97
Boar in pen	Auditory, olfactory, visual, and tactile	100

[a] Based on 757 observations. Data from Signoret and du Mesnil du Buisson (190).

charge of FSH. Identification is lacking of a specific odor from the male which influences sexual behavior in the female, however, muscone substances have been isolated from the perineal glands of the male (51).

Postpartum estrus is exhibited in about half of the females within 48 hours after parturition (25). These animals will mate, but conception seldom occurs. The interval from weaning to estrus is usually 4–8 days, and the animals will conceive at this estrous period.

Puberty in the male is acquired before 220 days of age, though spermatozoa are present as early as 110–125 days (106). Coordinated behavior of responses to estrous females is usually deficient before 130 days. Between 4 and 6 days after transporting pigs to a new environment, about one-fourth of the animals exhibited behavioral estrus (46). The majority of these pigs were prepubertal. It was suggested that external stimuli provoked maturation of ovarian follicles and subsequent estrus.

Patterns of courtship behavior and mounting reactions by the male are described by Hafez et al. (92). Typical reactions include a mating song or chant de cour when pursuing an estrous female, frequent nuzzling, and attempts to mount before actual coitus. Experienced males may mount only once, whereas younger animals frequently mount the forequarters. Successful mounting also depends on the receptivity of the female and her ability to support the male. With vaginal intromission, the male seldom withdraws or dismounts until ejaculation is completed. Duration of copulation is 3–20 minutes with an average of about 9 minutes. Ejaculation frequency is variable and may range from about 4–8 times during a period of 3 hours (25, 163).

2. Cattle

For descriptive data relative to the bovine estrous cycle the reader is referred to Asdell (10) and Hansel (100), (see also Cupps et al., Chapter 9). Proestrous and estrous behavior are characterized by an increased amount of walking, mounting other estrous or diestrous cows, frequent urination, and restlessness. During copulation the animal usually stands quietly; a "urination posture" is shown for a short time after mating. The intensity of estrous behavior is affected by age, breed, and individual differences other than the abnormal condition of nymphomania.

The incidence of metestrous bleeding, cervical mucus, and mounting behavior in beef cattle was reported by Hafez *et al.* (*89*). Of these factors none was sufficiently correlated with estrus to provide reliable proof of estrus in the absence of behavioral indications. A low incidence of metestrous bleeding (32%) was observed as compared with 90–100% for dairy heifers (*101*). These beef heifers displayed some male and female mounting behavior in 43% of the cases. According to these authors, mounting of other females and of males was observed in 35% of the cases in the period from 3 days before to 3 days after their own estrus. In general, mounting was associated with estrus and usually did not occur at other stages of the cycle. During diestrus only 6% of these heifers mounted other females and 10% mounted males.

Social dominance in a herd of cows plays a role in the display of sexual behavior to the other animals (*213*). Cows in estrus appear interested in most animals that show an interest in their condition, but occasionally will drive away another cow. In several instances a top-ranking cow (pregnant or nonpregnant) was observed to exhibit great interest in an estrous cow, to follow her about, mount her, and attempt to keep other interested cows from approaching.

Exogenous estrogen induces estrous behavior in ovariectomized heifers (*11, 143*). A minimal level of 0.3 mg of estradiol benzoate in a single subcutaneous injection induced sexual receptivity in ovariectomized beef heifers (*166*). Furthermore, a single intramuscular injection of 2000 or 5000 IU of human chorionic gonadotropin (HCG) delayed the onset of estrus in these estrogen-treated ovariectomized animals. It was suggested that the HCG may have decreased the sensitivity of target organs to estrogen action or bound estrogen and therefore reduced its biological activity. In intact cows vaginal temperature fluctuates with the estrous cycle, being lowest just before estrus, high during estrous behavior, and low again at the time of ovulation (*209, 235*). Vaginal temperature was not correlated with induced estrous response in ovariectomized heifers (*144*), though it increased after injection of progesterone in ovariectomized animals (*236*). Johnson and Ulberg (*117*) observed variations in rectal temperatures in heifers with estrous cycles controlled by exogenous progesterone and estrogen. Even though the cycles were controlled, the exogenous hormones failed to influence rectal temperatures.

The interval from parturition to first silent or standing estrus and ovulation in dairy cows was 15 days and the second estrus occurred 17 days later (*145*). In these animals the third estrus was observed 21 days after the second. The occurrence of silent or unobserved estrus and ovulation decreased with each postpartum cycle. The frequencies of silent estrus at the first, second, and third periods were 79, 55, and 35%. Dairy animals having high milk production had a higher incidence of silent estrus than did low-producing cows, therefore estrous detection may become more difficult as production levels increase. The interval from parturition to first estrus is delayed by suckling (177). When calves were removed 24–36 hours after parturition and the cow was neither suckled nor milked, the postpartum estrous interval was 30 days (range 8–63). The interval in cows that suckled calves from birth was 45 days (range 24–79). Induction of ovulation or removal of the calf just at the time of parturition and allowing no suckling reduced the intervals for ovulation and onset of postpartum estrus (154).

A seasonal decline in fertility in cattle is observed during autumn and the beginning of winter, though lowered fertility in summer is attributed to high environmental temperature (153, 200).

In male sexual behavior the normal patterns culminating in successful copulation include courtship, erection and protrusion, mounting, intromission, ejaculatory thrust, and ejaculation and dismounting. These parameters are discussed by Hafez and Schein (90) and Walton (214, 215).

Sensory systems play an important role in sexual behavior patterns of the bull. Although vision is unimportant in the development of reproductive functions, visual stimuli do influence the immediate and direct control of sexual responses (95). The absence of vision, either permanent or temporary, reduces the probability that a bull will identify the sexual situation and initiate a sexual response. Visual stimuli facilitate initial responses, but are unessential after the first ejaculation. Sexual excitation of the bull did not result in more than a slight improvement in semen quality (187). Furthermore, absence of vision initially impairs orientation and reduces the ability of the animal to detect and respond to novel stimulation. Olfactory stimulation has not been demonstrated to play a role in the sexual behavior of bulls. According to De Vuyst et al. (43), auditory stimuli influenced mating behavior in bulls. Animals who refused to mount cows for a long time could be induced to mount again when acoustically stimulated by specific calls of cows emitted from a magnetophone.

Appropriate sexual stimuli, however, do not always elicit sexual responses. For example, responses of an active male to the same female decrease progressively and may cease. Providing a stimulus contrast from another female or by changing the location of the initial one evokes essentially complete renewal of sexual behavior (96). The nature of recovery from sexual satiation to a particular stimulus animal or environment varies greatly among individual bulls. Other exteroceptive factors which may influence sexual response in bulls include the degree of sexual preparation and presence of estrous versus anestrous females (94). For example, increased spermatozoa production was obtained by lengthening the period of sexual preparation and by increasing the number of false mounts (94, 186).

Furthermore, semen volume and spermatozoa production increased when estrous cows were used as exteroceptive stimuli for sexual preparation of the male. Macmillan and Fielden (140) reported an increase of 18% in spermatozoa production by using estrous versus nonestrous cows as teasers. The action of atropine in curtailing estrous behavior and delaying ovulation in dairy heifers is established (104); however, atropine did not influence sexual behavior in bulls, but their volume of semen and concentration of spermatozoa were reduced (185, 187). Sexual behavior was normal after injection of pilocarpine, but the number of spermatozoa and volume of semen increased (187); an increase in the time required to mount and the duration of ejaculation was observed by Baker et al. (12).

Sex drive in bulls, though unrelated to frequency of copulation, is genetically controlled as shown by differences between breeds and within families (13, 97). Sexual excitability, which is provoked by sex drive of the individual and exteroceptive stimuli, is much higher in the bull than in rams and stallions. The reaction to the teaser animal (i.e., estrous cow) is almost immediate; readiness for copulation averages about 7 seconds after exposure to the teaser (218). Sexual experience and physiological stress (i.e., disease, level of nutrition, and seasonal changes) also alter sex drive.

Sexual efficiency may be defined as the capacity to repeat copulation. Bulls possess much higher sexual efficiency than other farm animals. Almquist and Hale (1) collected 77 ejaculates from one bull in a period of 6 hours, and Wierzbowski (216) reported 83 copulations during a 24-hour period. Sexual efficiency remained at an average of 21 copulations per trial during irregular intervals from 1 to 20 days (217). An exhaustion test consisted of repeated copulations daily which depressed sexual efficiency by the fifth day. The regeneration of sexual efficiency after exhaustion trials of daily copulations is slow in the bull, requiring about 6 weeks. Repeated daily copulations reduced spermatozoa production to about 10% that of the first ejaculate.

Copulatory behavior was retained after castration of prepubertal bulls 4 months' old (67). The copulation tests were made when the animals were 7–16 months old. They exhibited pelvic thrusts, but mounting was slow and the forelegs were in a more anterior position than in intact animals.

3. Sheep and Goats

Robinson (174) and Asdell (10) (see also Cupps et al., Chapter 9), present descriptive data about the estrous cycle and associated phenomena in the sheep and goat.

The patterns of sexual behavior in these species have been described by Hafez (87), Hafez and Scott (91), Banks (14), and Pepelko and Clegg (156). Estrous behavior is associated with the ovarian cycle and confined to the breeding season. Environmental temperature and light are important factors influencing the onset and cessation of these cycles. Seasonal breeding is also affected by the breed of sheep; for example, the Dorset Horn and

Merino breeds have longer breeding seasons than Scottish Blackface and Border Leicester breeds (10, 87, 174). The goat is a seasonal breeder also, with behavioral estrous patterns occurring in the autumn. In general, goats have a less restricted breeding season than sheep.

Sexual behavior during estrus consists of the ewe or doe rubbing her neck and body against the male, seeking out and following the male, turning the head backward when the male approaches from the rear, elevating and quivering the tail in the presence of the male, and competing with other estrous females for the male's attention by intercepting the male as he attempts to approach or mount other females and standing still to receive him (88, 109, 142).

According to Banks (14), the sexual behavior in the ewe ranges through a spectrum of low to high and then low intensity responses during the 15–28 hours of estrus. Low intensity responses during the first 3–5 hours include standing, head lowered and pinnae of ears somewhat flattened, swinging the head back to watch the courting ram, and walking away and then standing and looking back at the ram. The ewe is aggressive from the 5th to the 15th hour of estrus. She approaches the ram, nuzzles and pushes her head into the flank and scrotal regions. The last phase of low intensity responses from the 15th hour to the end of estrus includes avoidance behavior. During anestrus, the ewe manifests either passive or active avoidance behavior depending upon the persistence of the ram.

Mattner et al. (142) described the mating behavior in flock-mated sheep. The estrous ewes tend to leave the main flock and gather about the ram, forming a definite group or harem, and the members compete for his attention. If the ram leaves the harem to search for estrous females in the main flock, he is followed by the harem. Some ewes remain close to the ram for most of estrus, but others stay part of the time with the harem and the remainder of the time with the main flock. Of the estrous ewes, 90% appear in the harem at least once during estrus. Lindsay (134) has observed that in large paddocks mobility of rams is voluntarily restricted, as the rams form small harems of estrous ewes and seldom seek ewes elsewhere. Most ewes mate with only one or two rams, even when more are available (136). If the ram is prevented from finding a ewe in estrus the ewe may actively seek the ram (114, 135, 137). Having made contact with a ram, the ewe usually does not continue to search for further rams, even if the first ram is unable to breed. Furthermore, the ewes were attracted and held not only by rams incapable of mating but also by rams that were not visible. Since neither mechanical nor visual contact is necessary, sound or smell appears to be the most probable means of establishing contact.

In the young animal behavioral signs of estrus, especially the first, are usually weak and incomplete with little attraction of females to males and reluctance to allow mating. Thereafter, the females are attracted to the male by sexual approaches from him. The ewe will mate 1–15 times during an estrous period with an average of 2 times for lambs and 4 times for adults of the Romney Marsh breed. The duration of behavioral estrus ranged from about 20 hours to 5 days and averaged 36 hours for adults and 23 hours for lambs of the Suffolk breed. Slee (193) reported fertile matings within 3 hours of the onset of estrus. Yearlings and adult ewes have a longer estrus than ewe lambs. According to Parsons and Hunter (155), the mating behavior of the rams or estrogen-treated (masculinized) ewes reduced the duration of estrus in the ewe, whereas mere sight, smell, and sound of the rams were inffective stimuli.

The onset of behavioral estrus may be related to the time of the day; a greater number of animals begin the period of estrus from 0600 hours to noon than from midnight to 0600 hours. In the Welsh Mountain breed, most mounting activity occurred between 2230 and 0630 hours, with a particular spurt of activity at dawn, between 0630 and 0730 hours (113). Proestrus and metestrus are not usually observed in all individuals because these behavioral stages are of short duration.

Estrous cycles in ewes range from 16 to 18 days. The duration of estrus in goats is about 40 hours and the estrous cycle is about 21 days (174). Sex drive in the female is influenced by the presence of the male and perhaps intermittent versus continuous association with the male (168). These ewes were changed at monthly intervals so that a new group of ewes were introduced to the males each month. A consistently higher percentage of ewes exhibited estrus throughout the year by intermittent association with males. These data indicated that presence of the ram influenced the incidence of estrus during the normally anestrous season. Introduction of the male to Merino ewes in the late spring and early summer in Australia leads to a synchronized estrus in a high proportion of ewes (201, 205) and goats (181). If a high proportion of the ewes exhibit a weak estrus (20 hours or less), the lambing percentage for the flock is usually reduced, though ovulation may be unimpaired (162). Lamond (125) found introduction of rams during the middle of the breeding season at a critical time near the end of a series of progesterone injections affected the normal return to estrus. This effect was not confined to hastening the onset of estrus since in some ewes it was possible that estrus was suppressed. The onset of estrus in a proportion of these Merino ewes was up to 2 days earlier than expected. Barrett et al. (16) reported an earlier onset of the breeding season in Merino ewes by introduction of rams near the end of the anestrous season.

In another series of experiments, Lamond (122) found Merino ewes kept continuously with rams during the period of January to September experienced a period of ovarian activity extending from approximately 1 month before to 1 month after the breeding season. Following comparable progesterone treatments, the number of ewes showing estrus after introduction of rams was greater at the beginning and end of the breeding season than in ewes associated with rams all the time. A psychic stimulus associated with rams influenced occurrence of estrus in these ewes given progesterone at certain times of the year. In Rambouillet ewes reared in Texas, a period of low estrous activity or a short anestrous period occurred in the spring. Introduction of the ram served as a stimulus to terminate the anestrus in those ewes not already cycling and resulted in a degree of synchronization (*182*). Estrous ewes, particularly those 2 years of age and older, take the initiative when necessary in seeking the ram for promoting copulation (*107*). Individual estrous ewes were mated from 0–18 times (mean 6.3) during one estrous period when a small group of ewes were confined with one ram.

The display of sexual behavior by the male is more elaborate than that of the female. Typical courtship reactions include attention to urination by the female, nosing the perineum, smelling the urine, followed by lip-curling (Flehmen) with head elevated, low grunting or gargling sounds, licking her flank, nudging by extension and flexion of one foreleg, tilting and lowering head, running the tongue in and out rapidly, pawing, rubbing along her side, turning or thrusting of the head under her flank, attempting to push and guide the female from the herd if other males are present, and making an attempt to mount (*14, 87, 91, 142, 156*). Sexual excitability and its intensity depends mainly upon the sexual drive of the individual and external sexual stimuli. Only 29 seconds or less are required for sexually exciting rams to readiness for copulation (*157, 219*).

During copulation the male mounts and makes frequent blind thrusting movements until the penis meets lack of resistance in the vagina and then makes a deep thrust. The characteristic service in successful copulation is that of a single thrust, and ejaculation invariably follows. After ejaculation the ram smells the vagina and then shows no further interest in the ewe, but remains standing quietly by her side with his head down slightly (*156*). Mounts with intromission but not ejaculation occur infrequently. In receptive females copulation may be accomplished within a few minutes after the initial encounter. The average number of mounts per ejaculation per ram was 1.6, and this decreased after the first ejaculation (*156*). Pursuit of the female and repeated attempts to copulate are made by the male if she is not completely receptive. The number of copulations per day or sexual efficiency varies; according to Wierzbowski (*219*), the mean number of copulations for rams was 7 with the highest number of 32 during a period of 24 hours. The mating performance of eight rams under a flock mating system was 8–35 services per day (*142*), whereas Pepelko and Clegg (*156*) observed an average of 5.5 ejaculations before sexual exhaustion (no mounts within a period of 20 minutes). Hulet (*107*) reported that the ram with the greatest libido mated 20 times per day, and Mattner *et al.* (*142*) observed 27 services on 2 consecutive days by one ram. For goats, the highest number of copulations during this period was 14 (*61*). Libido in rams that have already served a number of times (sexual exhaustion) is enhanced by introduction of unmated estrous ewes, but not introduction of a recently mated female (*156*). The number of services per hour was usually highest early in the morning and late in the afternoon (*142*).

Sexual drive in the male is influenced particularly by visual and perhaps olfactory stimuli from the female (198). Odor, as an exteroceptive stimulus, may play a role in sex drive in the male, but surgical removal of the olfactory bulbs of the ewe did not alter normal cyclic behavior (188). Banks et al. (15) found no significant change either in the courtship behavior of rams rendered temporarily anosmic by topical anesthesia or in the ability to select estrous ewes. Lindsay (133), however, concluded that the sense of smell of the ram plays a significant role in the selection of estrous from anestrous ewes. The olfactory bulbs were surgically eliminated in these rams. Anosmic rams mated successfully, but mating behavior was modified. There was very little foreplay preceding the actual mating attempt except an increased display of nudging. Olfactory stimuli from the estrous female appears to be more important for enhancing sexual drive in the male goat (139).

Patterns of social dominance are established when rams of different ages are placed with ewes in the breeding season (107, 110, 111). Dominance of one ram over another is associated with physical size or aggressiveness rather than with sexual vigor, and is clearly established within an hour after introduction of the rams into the flock (142). The subordinate ram then avoids conflict with the dominant ram by seldom approaching the ewes in a harem about the dominant ram. In flock-mating conditions however, the rate of service of the subordinate rams was not markedly depressed by the presence of a dominant ram. It was only when rams were in close proximity that performance of the subordinate ram was affected. Dominance order and the number of times the rams teased and mated were highly correlated. High ram densities had a depressing effect on the performance of individual rams (133).

Though earlier reports suggested a beneficial effect of flushing on advancing the onset of estrous behavior, more recent results indicate no differences in the rate at which ewes respond to the rams (35, 36). The influence of light on the breeding seasons of sheep has been reviewed by Hafez (87), Yeates (237), Clegg and Ganong (29), and Thibault et al. (200) and is considered in Chapter 17.

4. Horses

The horse is polyestrus for a part of the year, usually in the spring. The estrous cycle is about 22 days, pregnancy ranges from 329 to 345 days, age of puberty is about 20 months. For descriptive data about the reproductive cycle refer to Asdell (10) and Berliner (19) (see also Cupps et al., Chapter 9).

Patterns of sexual behavior in the horse have been described by Andrews and McKenzie (8), Berliner (19), Nishikawa (150), Bielanski (20), Hafez et al. (93), and Wierzbowski (216–218).

In the mare behavior during diestrus is defensive toward the stallion. This nonreceptivity to the male varies; some mares become aggressive, others are disinterested or mildly interested. Sexual receptivity is gradual, but during the transitional period from the anestrous to breeding season (onset of first estrus) some mares express an intense mating desire, whereas others show a low intensity of mating desire even during the estrous period. With onset of estrus the female allows the stallion to smell; she may bite and urinates frequently. Rhythmic contractions of the partly everted and swollen labia and thin mucous secretions from the vulva are present at this time. Mounting of other females seldom occurs. The full manifestation of estrus with readiness to copulate is shown by spreading of the hind legs, lowering the pelvis, lifting the tail to one side. During the estrous period the body temperature of the mare is higher than in diestrous or pregnant animals (27).

Most mares have an increasing mating desire with maturation of the ovarian follicle(s), however, some females fail to express sexual receptivity throughout this period. During the period of 4–8 days before ovulation there is usually a gradual increase in intensity of sexual behavior (150). Within 1 or 2 days after ovulation behavioral estrus declines rapidly, the mare showing either little interest in the stallion or defensive behavior.

Sexual behavior in the male is characterized by courtship, erection and protrusion of the penis, mounting, intromission, and ejaculation. Sexual excitability is provoked by seeing the mare and smelling her external genitalia and groin. The stallion displays the upcurled upper lip after smelling the mare and usually bites the female's croup (93). The readiness to copulate is much slower in stallions than in rams and bulls (218). The latency period for erection of the penis is reported to be about 140 seconds after viewing the mare, and 200 seconds later the stallion is ready to copulate again. In vigorous males the penis may reach full erection before seeing the mare. At each mounting of the mare the stallion performs several pelvic oscillations and then dismounts (216). Intromission occurs after several copulatory movements. This stimulates the engorgement of the penis with blood. After cessation of the pelvic oscillations the semen is ejaculated directly into the uterus (215); the first ejaculation is about 13 seconds after intromission. The penis about doubles in diameter after entering the vagina.

Ejaculation occurs after 1–4 mounts with an average of 1.4 mounts; at each mount the male performs several copulatory movements and then dismounts. In general, the number of mounts per ejaculate is a characteristic of the individual and also is influenced by tactile and exteroceptive stimuli. Most stallions show symptoms similar to orgasm, such as fast respiration, drooping of the head, and relaxation (219).

Sexual efficiency is low, about two successive copulations in a single period of sexual effort (218). Stallions can perform about 12 copulations in a period of 24 hours, with the highest known being 20. A period of 5–8 days is required for regeneration of sexual efficiency after sexual exhaustion trials. The number of spermatozoa in successive ejaculates is about 50% of that found in the first ejaculate (21).

Exteroceptive stimuli are important in erection by vascular engorgement of the penis and mounting behavior in the stallion (219). These include stimuli affecting the olfactory, visual, tactile, or auditory sense organs. Odors emanating from the flank region of the mare and from her urine, sight of the mare or certain sexual objects (i.e., presence of dummy), and pressure on surface of the penis during intromission are the most effective stimuli for enhancing sexual responses. Sexual experience accelerates the speed of the copulatory reflexes. For example, erection and mounting times are less in older stallions than in young males copulating for the first time. With sexual experience through copulation and sexual anticipation, specific stimuli can be eliminated for provoking sexual excitement, and this response persists after castration.

IV. Role of Gonadal Hormones in Controlling Sexual Behavior

The effect of exogenous progesterone on sexual behavior and luteal function has been investigated in several species and the results are quite variable. Exogenous progesterone will induce luteal regression after hysterectomy, suggesting that the steroid acts independently of the uterus (4, 197). In heifers, Ulberg et al. (202) found the interval between the end of progesterone treatment and the beginning of estrus was reduced as the level of hormone decreased. A partial suppression of luteal growth and function occurred when progesterone was injected at day 1 of the cycle, whereas treatment beginning at day 5 was without effect.

Exogenous estrogens may inhibit as well as facilitate ovarian function and sexual behavior. High dosages of estrogen in intact animals induce ovarian atrophy by suppressing gonadotropin secretion, whereas small amounts may induce the release of LH and ovulation in the cow and ewe. In the cow exogenous estrogens can suppress adenohypophysial activity and induce luteolysis and ovarian atrophy (78, 98, 223, 224). Daily injection of low levels of estrogen decrease the cycle length, delay ovulation, increase vaginal mucous secretion, and increase rectal temperature in the cow (164, 165). Exogenous estrogen maintains corpora lutea in the intact lamb (42) and the pig (45, 71). Absence of luteal maintenance by estrogen in hypophysectomized lambs and pigs may indicate an indirect action of this hormone on the life-span of the corpus luteum.

Estrogens and progestins act in a facilitory and inhibitory manner on the central nervous system to alter sexual behavior and affect the release of gonadotropins. Inhibitory actions of endogenous progestins in farm animals are evident by the absence of ovulation during different reproductive stages, such as the luteal phase of the cycle, during pregnancy, and after hysterectomy. Progesterone inhibition of the release of ovulatory hormone(s) from the adenohypophysis is terminated by the natural failure of the corpus luteum at the close of these reproductive stages. Stimulatory actions of progesterone were demonstrated by hastening ovulation in the cow (105). Progesterone given 4–5 hours before the onset of estrus also hastened ovulation, but ovulation time was not altered when the hormone was injected 5–6 hours after the beginning of estrus. In the ewe the onset of estrus and ovulation was hastened 4 hours by injecting progesterone near the beginning of estrus (48) and was induced during the anestrous season by progesterone (49).

Synergistic and antagonistic actions of combinations of estrogens and progesterone upon mating behavior have been observed in sheep, cattle, and pigs. Robinson (175) found that when progesterone treatment preceded the injection of estrogen, estrous behavior was exhibited in almost all treated ewes. Furthermore, with progesterone pretreatment the level of estrogen could be reduced markedly and the onset of estrus advanced by 12–24 hours. In the cow, progesterone may have either synergistic or antagonistic effects on estrous behavior in estrogen-conditioned ovariectomized animals (143). An antagonistic effect was exerted on induced estrus in ovariectomized pigs by giving combinations of estrogen and progesterone (40).

V. Pharmacological Synchronization of Estrus in Domestic Mammals

Development of methods for the pharmacological control of estrus and ovulation in domestic mammals has received considerable attention during the last decade. The advantages of controlling reproduction and improving reproductive efficiency in farm animals such as the pig, cow, and ewe have been stated frequently. Recent reviews of estrous cycle control in domestic animals include those by Anderson et al. (3, 5) and Lamond (119). Comprehensive reviews include those by Rothchild (176), Lloyd and Weisz (138), Bland and Donovan (22), and Short (184). A brief discussion is presented of recent research in this area.

A. ESTROUS SYNCHRONIZATION IN CATTLE

Following the initial experiments of Christian and Casida (28), several investigations have been reported on the suppression of estrous behavior and ovarian activity in cattle by daily subcutaneous or intramuscular injections of progesterone. The hormone was given at levels of 20–100 mg for periods of 7–24 days. In the majority of cases the interval from the end of treatment to estrus was 3–6 days. Though it is a reliable means of controlling cycles, the conception rate at the synchronized estrus is usually lowered. Nellor and Cole (149) found that a single subcutaneous injection of crystalline progesterone in starch suspension effectively inhibited estrus and ovulation in beef heifers regardless of the stage of the cycle when the hormone was given. According to Ulberg and Lindley (203), the injection of estrogen

soon after the end of a series of progesterone injections increased synchronization of estrus, but this treatment did little to increase conception rate
when compared with animals receiving progesterone alone. Wiltbank *et al.*
(*226*) found an increase in the synchronization of estrus in heifers by injection of estrogen concurrently with progesterone, but there was no
enhancement of fertility.

In investigations on the synchronization of estrus by injections of progesterone, hormone treatment usually was continued for the normal life-span
of the corpus luteum or continued beyond the expected estrus. By giving
progesterone for only 10 days beginning at estrus, Woody *et al.* (*234*) have
shown that the length of the cycle was reduced from 20.7 days in controls
to 16.7 days in treated cows. A seasonal variation in the effect of exogenous
progesterone on estrous cycles in beef heifers has been observed by Lamond
(*123*). During the late winter and spring months the ovarian cycles were
not suppressed by doses of progesterone that were satisfactory at other times
of the year. In addition, the interval from the last injection of progesterone
to the onset of estrus was shorter in the late winter–spring period.

Numerous experimental and field trials have demonstrated very effective
inhibition of estrus and subsequent synchronization of estrous cycles in beef
and dairy cattle by feeding various progestins for a period of 15–20 days.
In general a higher percentage of a group of cows will return to estrus
within a period of 2–5 days after the last feeding of 6-α-methyl-17-α-ace-
toxyprogesterone (MAP). A minimal effective daily dosage of 135 mg inhibits ovulation in dairy and beef heifers (*238*). Fertility in MAP-fed cattle
has been similar to that observed in control animals (*44, 99, 102*). Fertility
was not increased by injections of pregnant mare serum (PMS) and HCG
after the last feeding of MAP (*115*). The progestational compound, 6-
chloro-Δ^6-17-acetoxyprogesterone (CAP), is orally effective for inhibition
of estrus and ovulation at a daily dosage of about 10 mg. Estrus usually
occurs 4–8 days after treatment, and conception rates usually compared
favorably with untreated control animals (*3, 99, 102*). A daily oral dosage
of 0.2–2.0 mg melengestrol acetate (6α-methyl-6-dehydro-16-methylene-17-
acetoxyprogesterone:MGA) inhibits estrus and ovulation in heifers (*239*).
The interval from the last hormone treatment to estrus or ovulation ranged
from 2.7 days at 0.2 mg to 6.3 days at 2.0 mg, while conception rates were
42% at first service. Estrus was synchronized by feeding daily 500 mg of
acetophenide 16α,17-dihydroxyprogesterone to beef heifers for 20 days
(*225*). The heifers returned to estrus within 48 hours after the end of the
treatment period. Though the average length of the estrous period was 4.5
hours less in treated than in control animals, the interval from the beginning
of estrus to ovulation was about 33 hours for both groups. Fertilization rate
was reduced in the treated animals. When the steroid was fed for only 9
days in conjunction with an injection of estradiol valerate, the cycles were
synchronized and fertilization rate, ova transport, duration of estrus, or time
from the beginning of estrus to ovulation were similar to control animals.

Experimental control of cycles has been accomplished by progestin-impregnated intravaginal sponges in cattle (26, 183). The intravaginal sponges containing 17α-acetoxy-9α-fluoro-11β-hydroxyprogesterone effectively suppressed estrus and ovulation, and the animals usually returned to estrus within 3 days after withdrawal of the sponge. Some heifers, however, failed to retain the cylindrical sponges during the treatment period. After withdrawal of the sponge fertility was reduced. The experimental results indicate that this method of hormone administration is not superior to the feeding or the intramuscular injection of progestins.

A single injection of estrogen causes early regression of the corpus luteum in cycling, pregnant, and hysterectomized heifers (151, 223, 224). Daily injections of small amounts (20–640 μg) of estradiol 17β also induced luteal regression. By giving luteinizing hormone or HCG after a single injection of estrogen or concurrently with daily injections of the hormone, the corpus luteum persisted and estrous behavior was suppressed. Further experimentation is desirable to determine the effectiveness of synthetic derivatives of estrogen for possible synchronization of estrous cycles in this species.

Exogenous gonadotropins induce luteal development in the cow, but they show little promise as an effective means for the synchronization of estrous cycles (3). The daily injection of oxytocin will induce luteal regression during the early part of the cycle (9), but this treatment is ineffective for induction of luteolytic action when the corpus luteum is fully developed. Furthermore, the corpus luteum persists in hysterectomized heifers in spite of continued injections of oxytocin. An important role of the uterus in the control of ovarian function is substantiated by the local luteolytic effect of exogenous oxytocin in unilaterally hysterectomized heifers (74).

In general, effective methods are available for the synchronization of estrous cycles in the cow, but fertility has not been improved by these techniques. Further research is needed on the mechanisms controlling the development and regression of the corpus luteum, particularly an evaluation of the role of the central nervous system, pituitary gland, and uterus, as well as the influence of environmental factors on reproduction in this species.

B. ESTROUS SYNCHRONIZATION IN SHEEP

1. Induction of Estrus during the Anestrous Season

The induction of ovulation by injection of gonadotropin during the anestrous season was reported initially by Cole and Miller (31, 32). Pregnant mare serum or FSH induces ovulation in a high proportion of ewes, but very few of them show estrus (17, 30, 49, 171). By giving two PMS injections a cycle interval apart ovulation is induced and fertile matings result (30–32), but the incidence of estrous behavior at the second ovulation is low (75).

Exogenous estrogen induces estrous behavior in these animals, but ovulation usually is absent (206). An antagonistic effect on estrous behavior and ovulation usually results when either an estrogen or testosterone and a gonadotropin are given (30, 171, 173, 206).

Progesterone given daily induces both estrus and ovulation within a few days after the last treatment (49, 172). A minimum of 8–12 days of progesterone pretreatment at a daily dosage of 5 or 10 mg is satisfactory for preparing anestrous ewes for induced ovulation (172, 173). When progesterone pretreatment is followed by a single injection of gonadotropin, controlled estrus and ovulation occur in the majority of ewes (49, 75, 76, 172). The ova released after this treatment are capable of fertilization, but few animals conceive (76, 172). The injection of estrogen with PMS following the progesterone pretreatment period increases the proportion of ewes in estrus within a shorter time interval, but suppresses ovulation in some cases (172, 173). A procedure described by Gordon (77) for the induction of estrus followed by a high conception rate involves a 9-day progesterone pretreatment period followed by PMS; the progesterone-PMS treatment is repeated after 1 week.

Orally administered steroids in combination with injections of gonadotropins have been used for inducing estrus and ovulation. Daily doses of MAP or CAP administered at levels of about 50 and 1 mg, respectively, with a single injection of gonadotropin (i.e., PMS at 750–1000 IU) at the end of the hormone-feeding period to anestrous nonlactating or lactating ewes induces estrus in a high proportion of the animals within 1–4 days after the gonadotropin treatment (52, 55, 99, 112, 210). Two injections of the gonadotropin (PMS) at 14–16 day intervals, either or both preceded by progestin treatment, increase fertility in nonlactating and lactating anestrous ewes (77, 99, 112, 210). Favorable conception rates of 50–85% have been achieved by these methods. A combination of a single injection of CAP followed by oral administration of MAP and then injection of PMS did not increase the estrous response or fertility (169).

Seasonal differences have been observed in the suppressive action of progesterone in Merino ewes (121, 124–126). The period from the last injection of hormone to onset of estrus and the fertility of the ewes were influenced by dosage, interval between consecutive progesterone injections, the time of day they were given, and the introduction of the rams at a critical time near the end of the hormone therapy.

2. Induction of Estrus during the Breeding Season

The control of estrous cycles in sheep by injections of progesterone was first reported by Dutt and Casida (50). Daily levels of 5–20 mg of the hormone inhibited estrus and ovulation during a treatment period of 14 or more days, and heat usually occurred 1–4 days after the last injection (50, 68, 69, 126, 127, 152, 211). Fertility at the controlled estrus was variable, with half or less of the ewes conceiving. By giving progesterone only 6 days, the estrous interval is reduced from 16.5 to 12.7 days (234), indicating a reduction in corpus luteum size in the formative stages of its development. An injection of PMS after the last progesterone treatment has been used in an attempt to control the onset of estrus and ovulation (38, 39, 170). Control of ovulation was attained when PMS was given either on the final day of progesterone treatment or 24 hours later, followed by an injection of HCG 24 hours after PMS (24, 194). Following progesterone treatment, high levels of HCG given in combination with PMS caused increased follicular growth, luteinization of follicles, endometrial cysts, and inhibited or delayed estrus (120). Foote and Hulet (68) have found a low incidence (10%) of ovulation in progesterone-suppressed ewes treated with estradiol 17β alone (10 mg), and PMS alone (1200 IU), compared with a high incidence (80%) when these hormones were given together. The onset of estrus is similar (about 52 hours) after removal of the corpus luteum, ligation of its blood supply, or luteal enucleation (128). There is little evidence of lytic action from ovine uterine extracts (196).

The daily oral administration of MAP (minimum effective level of 50–60 mg) or CAP at an optimum level of 1.0 mg for 14–20 days effectively suppresses estrus and ovulation (34, 52, 56, 99, 108, 194, 210). The ewes return to estrus about 3 days (range 2–6) after the last feeding of the hormone. Conception rates for MAP-fed animals at first service are similar to control ewes, whereas those fed CAP experience reduced fertility. At the second post-treatment estrus in CAP-fed ewes, fertility is similar to that found in untreated controls. These orally effective steroids provide a suitable means for synchronization of cycles in the ewe.

C. Estrous Synchronization in Pigs

The suppression of estrus and ovulation in pigs was achieved initially by daily injections of progesterone (204). Orally administered MAP, CAP, norethynodrel with 1.5% 17-α-ethynyl-3,17-estradiol-3-methyl ether or 17α-acetoxy-6-methylpregna-4,6-dien-3,20-dione effectively inhibited estrus, and heat usually occurred 3–7 days after treatment (6, 52, 53, 62, 63, 116, 147, 148, 161, 167, 212). After withdrawal of either injected or orally administered steroids, reduced fertility and ovarian follicular cysts have been encountered frequently. In some cases abnormal cycle intervals resulted.

Exogenous estrogen increases the life-span of corpora lutea, and, thus, the diestrous phase (71).

In the pig, gonadotropins have been used for the induction of ovulation (40, 41, 54, 195, 199). These ovulations occur without estrous behavior when they are given during the luteal phase of the cycle. The use of exogenous gonadotropins for synchronization of estrus usually does not reduce fertility at the first mating after treatment. Estrus can be effectively induced in lactating sows with PMS after the 40th day of lactation (106a).

The daily oral administration of a nonsteroid compound, 1-α-methylallyl-thiocarbamoyl-2-methyl-thiocarbamoylhydrazine (ICI 33828), at a dosage of about 1 mg/kg body weight effectively suppresses estrus and ovulation in pigs (*72, 73, 79, 158, 159*). Following withdrawal of the treatment, almost all the animals return to estrus within 5–7 days, and fertility and embryonic survival are similar to control pigs. An effective control of estrus, ovulation, and subsequent fertility has been achieved by first suppressing ovarian function with ICI 33828 for 20 or more days and then inducing ovulation with PMS followed by an injection of HCG 96 hours later (*160*).

REFERENCES

1. Almquist, J. O., and Hale, E. B., *Proc. 3rd Intern. Congr. Animal Reprod., Cambridge* p. 50 (1956).
2. Altmann, M., *J. Comp. Psychol.* **31**, 481 (1941).
3. Anderson, L. L., Schultz, J. R., and Melampy, R. M., *in* "Gonadotropins" (H. H. Cole, ed.), p. 171. Freeman, San Francisco, California, 1964.
4. Anderson, L. L., Dyck, G. W., and Rathmacher, R. P., *Endocrinology* **78**, 897 (1966).
5. Anderson, L. L., and Melampy, R. M., *U.S. Dept. Agr. Misc. Publ.* **1005**, 64 (1964).
6. Anderson, L. L., and Melampy, R. M., *J. Animal Sci.* **18**, 1550 (1959).
7. Andrew, R. J., *Animal Behaviour* **14**, 485 (1966).
8. Andrews, F. N., and McKenzie, F. F., *Missouri Univ. Agr. Expt. Sta. Res. Bull.* **329** (1941).
9. Armstrong, D. T., and Hansel, W., *J. Dairy Sci.* **42**, 533 (1959).
10. Asdell, S. A., "Patterns of Mammalian Reproduction." Cornell Univ. Press, Ithaca, New York, 1964.
11. Asdell, S. A., de Alba, J., and Roberts, S. J., *J. Animal Sci.* **4**, 277 (1945).
12. Baker, R. D., VanDemark, N. L., Graves, C. N., and Norton, H. W., *J. Reprod. Fertility* **8**, 297 (1964).
13. Bane, A., *Acta Agr. Scand.* **4**, 95 (1954).
14. Banks, E. M., *Behaviour* **23**, 249 (1964).
15. Banks, E. M., Bishop, R., and Norton, H. W., *Proc. 16th Intern. Congr. Zool. Washington, D.C.*, **2**, 25 (1963).
16. Barrett, J. F., Reardon, T. F., and Lambourne, L. J., *Australian J. Exptl. Agr. Animal Husbandry* **2**, 69 (1962).
17. Bell, T. D., Casida, L. E., Bohstedt, G., and Darlow, A. E., *J. Agr. Res.* **62**, 619 (1941).
18. Benoit, J., *Gen. Comp. Endocrinol. Suppl.* **1**, 254 (1962).
19. Berliner, V. R., *in* "Reproduction in Domestic Animals" (H. H. Cole and P. T. Cupps, ed.), Vol. 1, p. 267. Academic Press, New York, 1959.
20. Bielanski, W., *Publ. Inst. Zootech. Krachow* **116** (1960).
21. Bielanski, W., and Wierzbowski, S., *Proc. 4th Intern. Congr. Animal Reprod., The Hague* **2**, 279 (1961).
22. Bland, K. P., and Donovan, B. T., *Advan. Reprod. Physiol.* **1**, 179 (1966).
23. Boda, J. M., *in* "Reproduction in Domestic Animals" (H. H. Cole and P. T. Cupps, ed.), Vol. 1, p. 335. Academic Press, New York, 1959.
24. Braden, A. W. H., Lamond, D. R., and Radford, H. M., *Australian J. Agr. Res.* **11**, 389 (1960).
25. Burger, J. F., *Onderstepoort J. Vet. Res. Suppl.* **2** (1952).
26. Carrick, M. J., and Shelton, J. N., *J. Reprod. Fertility* **14**, 21 (1967).

27. Chieffi, A., Gouveia, P. F., Kalil, E. B., Marques dos Reis, J., and Marchi, E., *Proc. 5th Intern. Congr. Animal Reprod. Artificial Insemination, Trento* 4, 211 (1964).
28. Christian, R. E., and Casida, L. E., *J. Animal Sci.* 7, 540 (1948).
29. Clegg, M. T., and Ganong, W. F., *in* "Reproduction in Domestic Animals" (H. H. Cole and P. T. Cupps, ed.), Vol. 2, p. 225. Academic Press, New York, 1959.
30. Cole, H. H., Hart, G. H., and Miller, R. F., *Endocrinology* 36, 370 (1945).
31. Cole, H. H., and Miller, R. F., *Am. J. Anat.* 57, 39 (1935).
32. Cole, H. H., and Miller, R. F., *Am. J. Physiol.* 104, 165 (1933).
33. Collias, N. E., *in* "The Behaviour of Domestic Animals" (E. S. E. Hafez, ed.), p. 565. Bailliere, London, 1962.
34. Combs, W., Botkin, M. P., and Nelms, G. E., *J. Animal Sci.* 20, 968 (1961).
35. Coop, I. E., *J. Agr. Sci.* 67, 305 (1966).
36. Coop, I. E., *World Rev. Animal Production* 4, p. 69 (1966).
37. Craig, J. V., and Baruth, R. A., *Animal Behaviour* 13, 109 (1965).
38. Davies, H. L., *Australian Vet. J.* 36, 20 (1960).
39. Davies, H. L., and Dun, R. B., *Australian Vet. J.* 33, 92 (1957).
40. Day, B. N., Anderson, L. L., Hazel, L. N., and Melampy, R. M., *J. Animal Sci.* 18, 909 (1959).
41. Day, B. N., Neill, J. D., Oxenreider, S. L., Waite, A. B., and Lasley, J. F., *J. Animal Sci.* 24, 1075 (1965).
42. Denamur, R., Mauléon, P., *Compt. Rend. Acad. Sci.* 257, 527 (1963).
43. De Vuyst, A., Thines, G., Henriet, L., and Soffie, M., *Experientia* 20, 648 (1964).
44. Dhindsa, D. S., Hoversland, A. S., and Smith, E. P., *J. Animal Sci.* 26, 167 (1967).
45. du Mesnil du Buisson, F., Thesis Doct. Sci. Paris, 135 pp. (1966).
46. du Mesnil du Buisson, F., and Signoret, J. P., *Ann. Zootech.* 11, 53 (1962).
47. du Mesnil du Buisson, F., and Signoret, J. P., *World Rev. Animal Production, Spec. Issue*, p. 45 (1966).
48. Dutt, R. H., *Iowa State J. Sci.* 28, 55 (1953).
49. Dutt, R. H., *J. Animal Sci.* 12, 515 (1953).
50. Dutt, R. H., and Casida, L. E., *Endocrinology* 43, 208 (1948).
51. Dutt, R. H., Simpson, E. C., Christian, J. C., and Barnhart, C. E., *J. Animal Sci.* 18, 1557 (1959).
52. Dziuk, P. J., *U.S. Dept. Agr. Misc. Publ.* 1005, 50 (1964).
53. Dziuk, P. J., and Baker, R. D., *J. Animal Sci.* 21, 697 (1962).
54. Dziuk, P. J., and Polge, C., *Vet. Record* 77, 236 (1965).
55. Evans, J. S., and Dutt, R. H., *J. Animal Sci.* 21, 1022 (1962).
56. Evans, J. S., Dutt, R. H., and Simpson, E. C., *J. Animal Sci.* 21, 804 (1962).
57. Fabricius, E., *Symp. Zool. Soc. London* 8, 139 (1962).
58. Farner, D. S., *Am. Sci.* 52, 137 (1964).
59. Farner, D. S., *in* "Circadian Clocks" (J. Aschoff, ed.) p. 357. North-Holland Publ., Amsterdam, 1965.
60. Farner, D. S., and Follett, B. K., *J. Animal Sci.* 25, Suppl., p. 90 (1966).
61. Fielden, E. D., and Berker, C. A. V., *Proc. 5th Intern. Congr. Animal Reprod. Artificial Insemination, Trento* 4, 488 (1964).
62. First, N. L., Hoefer, J. A., and Nellor, J. E., *J. Animal Sci.* 19, 1321 (1960).

63. First, N. L., Stratman, F. W., Rigor, E. M., and Casida, L. E., *J. Animal Sci.* **22**, 66 (1963).
64. Fisher, A. E., and Hale, E. B., *Behaviour* **10**, 309 (1957).
65. Flickinger, G. L., *Gen. Comp. Endocrinol.* **1**, 332 (1961).
66. Flickinger, G. L., *Gen. Comp. Endocrinol.* **6**, 89 (1966).
67. Folman, Y., and Volcani, R., *Animal Behaviour* **14**, 572 (1966).
68. Foote, W. C., and Hulet, C. V., *J. Reprod. Fertility* **11**, 51 (1966).
69. Foote, W. C., and Waite, A. B., *J. Animal Sci.* **24**, 151 (1965).
70. Fraps, R. M., *in* "Control of Ovulation" (C. A. Villee, ed.), p. 133. Pergamon, Oxford, 1962.
71. Gardner, M. L., First, N. L., and Casida, L. E., *J. Animal Sci.* **22**, 132 (1963).
72. Gerrits, R. J., and Johnson, L. A., *J. Animal Sci.* **24**, 917 (1965).
73. Gerrits, R. J., and Johnson, L. A., *Proc. 5th Intern. Congr. Animal Reprod. Artificial Insemination, Trento* **3**, 455 (1964).
74. Ginther, O. J., Woody, C. O., Mahajan, S., Janakiraman, K., and Casida, L. E., *J. Reprod. Fertility* **14**, 225 (1965).
75. Gordon, I., *J. Agr. Sci.* **50**, 152 (1958).
76. Gordon, I., *J. Agr. Sci.* **60**, 43 (1963).
77. Gordon, I., *J. Agr. Sci.* **60**, 67 (1963).
78. Greenstein, J. S., Murray, R. W., and Foley, R. C., *J. Dairy Sci.* **41**, 1834 (1958).
79. Groves, T. W., *Vet. Record* **80**, 470 (1967).
80. Guhl, A. M., *Kansas Agr. Expt. Sta. Tech. Bull.* **73** (1953).
81. Guhl, A. M., *in* "Sex and Internal Secretions" (W. C. Young, ed.), p. 1240. Williams & Wilkins, Baltimore, Maryland, 1961.
82. Guhl, A. M., *in* "The Behaviour of Domestic Animals" (E. S. E. Hafez, ed.), p. 491. Bailliere, London, 1962.
83. Guhl, A. M., Collias, N. E., and Allee, W. C., *Physiol. Zool.* **18**, 365 (1945).
84. Guiton, P., *Animal Behaviour* **9**, 167 (1961).
85. Guiton, P., *Symp. Zool. Soc. London* **8**, 227 (1962).
86. Guiton, P., *Animal Behaviour* **14**, 534 (1966).
87. Hafez, E. S. E., *J. Agr. Sci.* **42**, 255 (1952).
88. Hafez, E. S. E., (ed.), "The Behaviour of Domestic Animals." Bailliere, London, 1962.
89. Hafez, E. S. E., Jainudeen, M. R., and Lindsay, D. R., *Acta Endocrinol.* **50**, Suppl. 102 (1965).
90. Hafez, E. S. E., and Schein, M. W., *in* "The Behaviour of Domestic Animals" (E. S. E. Hafez, ed.), p. 247. Bailliere, London, 1962.
91. Hafez, E. S. E., and Scott, J. P., *in* "The Behaviour of Domestic Animals" (E. S. E. Hafez, ed.), p. 297. Bailliere, London, 1962.
92. Hafez, E. S. E., Sumption, L. J., and Jakway, J. S., *in* "The Behaviour of Domestic Animals" (E. S. E. Hafez, ed.), p. 334. Bailliere, London, 1962.
93. Hafez, E. S. E., Williams, M., and Wierzbowski, S., *in* "The Behaviour of Domestic Animals" (E. S. E. Hafez, ed.), p. 370. Bailliere, London, 1962.
94. Hafs, H. D., *J. Animal Sci.* **25**, Suppl., 44 (1966).
95. Hale, E. B., *J. Animal Sci.* **25**, Suppl., 36 (1966).
96. Hale, E. B., and Almquist, J. O., *J. Dairy Sci.* **43**, Suppl., 145 (1960).
97. Hale, E. B., and Schein, M. W., *in* "The Behaviour of Domestic Animals" (E. S. E. Hafez, ed.), p. 531. Bailliere, London, 1962.
98. Hammond, J., Jr., and Day, F. T., *J. Endocrinol.* **4**, 53 (1944).

99. Hansel, W., *U.S. Dept. Agr. Misc. Publ.* **1005,** 1 (1964).
100. Hansel, W., *in* "Reproduction in Domestic Animals" (H. H. Cole and P. T. Cupps, eds.), Vol. 1. Academic Press, New York, 1959.
101. Hansel, W., and Asdell, S. A., *J. Animal Sci.* **11,** 346 (1952).
102. Hansel, W., Donaldson, L. E., Wagner, W. C., and Brunner, M. A., *J. Animal Sci.* **25,** 497 (1966).
103. Hansel, W., and Dutt, R. H., *J. Animal Sci.* **25,** Suppl. (1966).
104. Hansel, W., and Trimberger, G. W., *J. Animal Sci.* **10,** 719 (1951).
105. Hansel, W., and Trimberger, G. W., *J. Dairy Sci.* **35,** 65 (1952).
106. Hauser, E. R., Dickerson, G. E., and Mayer, D. T., *Missouri Univ. Agr. Expt. Sta. Res. Bull.* **503** (1952).
106a. Heitman, H., Jr., and Cole, H. H., *J. Animal Sci.* **15,** 970 (1956).
107. Hulet, C. V., *J. Animal Sci.* **25,** Suppl., 5 (1966).
108. Hulet, C. V., *J. Reprod. Fertility* **11,** 283 (1966).
109. Hulet, C. V., Blackwell, R. L., Ercanbrack, S. K., Price, D. A., and Wilson, L. O., *J. Animal Sci.* **21,** 870 (1962).
110. Hulet, C. V., Ercanbrack, S. K., Blackwell, R. L., Price, D. A., and Wilson, L. O., *J. Animal Sci.* **21,** 865 (1962).
111. Hulet, C. V., Ercanbrack, S. K., Price, D. A., Blackwell, R. L., and Wilson, L. O., *J. Animal Sci.* **21,** 857 (1962).
112. Hulet, C. V., and Foote, W. C., *J. Animal Sci.* **26,** 545 (1967).
113. Hutchinson, J. S. M., O'Connor, P. J., and Robertson, H. A., *J. Agr. Sci.* **63,** 59 (1964).
114. Inkster, I. J., *New Zealand Sheep Farming* p. 163 (1957).
115. Jainudeen, M. R., and Hafez, E. S. E., *Intern. J. Fertility* **11,** 47 (1966).
116. Jöchle, W., and Schilling, E., *J. Reprod. Fertility* **10,** 287 (1965).
117. Johnson, A. D., and Ulberg, L. C., *J. Animal Sci.* **24,** 403 (1965).
118. Justice, W. P., McDaniel, G. R., and Craig, J. V., *Poultry Sci.* **41,** 732 (1962).
119. Lamond, D. R., *Animal Breeding Abstr.* **32,** 269 (1964).
120. Lamond, D. R., *Australian J. Agr. Res.* **13,** 707 (1962).
121. Lamond, D. R., *J. Reprod. Fertility* **4,** 111 (1962).
122. Lamond, D. R., *J. Reprod. Fertility* **8,** 101 (1964).
123. Lamond, D. R., *J. Reprod. Fertility* **9,** 41 (1965).
124. Lamond, D. R., *Nature* **186,** 971 (1960).
125. Lamond, D. R., *Nature* **193,** 85 (1962).
126. Lamond, D. R., and Bindon, B. M., *J. Reprod. Fertility* **4,** 57 (1962).
127. Lamond, D. R., and Lambourne, L. J., *Australian J. Agr. Res.* **12,** 154 (1961).
128. Lang, D. R., *J. Reprod. Fertility* **9,** 113 (1965).
129. Lehrman, D. S., *Ibis* **101,** 478 (1959).
130. Lehrman, D. S., *in* "Sex and Internal Secretions" (W. C. Young, ed.), Vol. 2, p. 1268. Williams & Wilkins, Baltimore, Maryland, 1961.
131. Lehrman, D. S., *in* "Social Behavior and Organization Among Vertebrates" (W. Etkins, ed.), p. 143, Univ. of Chicago Press, Chicago, Illinois, 1964.
132. Lill, A., and Wood-Gush, D. G. M., *Behaviour* **25,** 16 (1965).
133. Lindsay, D. R., *Animal Behaviour* **13,** 75 (1965).
134. Lindsay, D. R., *Animal Behaviour* **14,** 73 (1966).
135. Lindsay, D. R., *Animal Behaviour* **14,** 419 (1966).
136. Lindsay, D. R., and Robinson, T. J., *J. Agr. Sci.* **57,** 137 (1961).
137. Lindsay, D. R., and Robinson, T. J., *J. Agr. Sci.* **57,** 141 (1961).

138. Lloyd, C. W., and Weisz, J., *Ann. Rev. Physiol.* **28**, 267 (1966).
139. Lohle, K., *Z. Tierz. Zuecht. Biol.* **62**, 356 (1954).
140. Macmillan, K. L., and Fielden, E. D., *Proc. 5th Intern. Congr. Animal Reprod. Artificial Insemination, Trento* **4**, 225 (1964).
141. Marshall, A. J., *in* "Biology and Comparative Physiology of Birds" (A. J. Marshall, ed.) Vol. 2, p. 307, Academic Press, New York, 1961.
142. Mattner, P. E., Braden, A. W. H., and Turnbull, K. E., *Australian J. Exptl. Agr. Animal Husbandry* **7**, 103 (1967).
143. Melampy, R. M., Emmerson, M. A., Rakes, J. M., Hanka, L. J., and Eness, P. G., *J. Animal Sci.* **16**, 967 (1957).
144. Melampy, R. M., and Rakes, J. M., *Iowa State J. Sci.* **33**, 85 (1958).
145. Morrow, D. A., Roberts, S. J., McEntee, K., and Gray, H. G., *J. Am. Vet. Med. Assoc.* **149**, 1596 (1966).
146. Nalbandov, A. V., *in* "Control of Ovulation" (C. A. Villee, ed.), p. 122. Pergamon, Oxford, 1961.
147. Nellor, J. E., *J. Animal Sci.* **19**, 412 (1960).
148. Nellor, J. E., Ahrenhold, J. E., First, N. L., and Hoefer, J. A., *J. Animal Sci.* **20**, 22 (1961).
149. Nellor, J. E., and Cole, H. H., *J. Animal Sci.* **15**, 650 (1956).
150. Nishikawa, Y., "Studies on Reproduction in Horses." Japan Racing Assoc., Shiba Tamuracho Minatoku, Tokyo, 1959.
151. Niswender, G. D., Kaltenbach, C. C., Shumway, R. P., Wiltbank, J. N., and Zimmerman, D. R., *J. Animal Sci.* **24**, 986 (1965).
152. O'Mary, C. C., Pope, A. L., and Casida, L. E., *J. Animal Sci.* **9**, 499 (1950).
153. Ortavant, R., Mauléon, P., and Thibault, C., *Ann. N.Y. Acad. Sci.* **77**, 157 (1964).
154. Oxenreider, S. L., and Melampy, R. M., *J. Animal Sci.* **25**, 1264 (1966).
155. Parsons, S. D., and Hunter, G. L., *J. Reprod. Fertility* **14**, 61 (1967).
156. Pepelko, W. E., and Clegg, M. T., *Animal Behaviour* **13**, 249 (1965).
157. Pepelko, W. E., and Clegg, M. T., *J. Animal Sci.* **24**, 633 (1965).
158. Polge, C., *Outlook Agr.* **5**, 44 (1966).
159. Polge, C., *Proc. 5th Intern. Congr. Animal Reprod. Artificial Insemination, Trento* **2**, 388 (1964).
160. Polge, C., and Day, B. N., *J. Animal Sci.* **26**, 1495 (1967).
161. Pond, W. G., Hansel, W., Dunn, J. A., Bratton, R. W., and Foote, R. H., *J. Animal Sci.* **24**, 536 (1965).
162. Quinlan, J., Steyn, H. P., and DeVos, D., *Onderstepoort J. Vet. Sci.* **16**, 243 (1941).
163. Quinot, M. G., *Philippine Agr.* **41**, 319 (1957).
164. Rahlmann, D. F., and Cupps, P. T., *J. Dairy Sci.* **45**, 1003 (1962).
165. Rahlmann, D. F., and Cupps, P. T., *J. Dairy Sci.* **45**, 1011 (1962).
166. Ray, D. E., *J. Reprod. Fertility* **10**, 329 (1965).
167. Ray, D. E., and Seerley, R. W., *Nature* **211**, 1102 (1966).
168. Riches, J. H., and Watson, R. H., *Australian J. Agr. Res.* **5**, 141 (1954).
169. Roberts, E. M., and Bindon, B. M., *J. Reprod. Fertility* **12**, 155 (1966).
170. Robinson, T. J., *Australian J. Agr. Res.* **7**, 194 (1956).
171. Robinson, T. J., *J. Agr. Sci.* **40**, 275 (1950).
172. Robinson, T. J., *J. Agr. Sci.* **46**, 37 (1955).
173. Robinson, T. J., *J. Endocrinol.* **24**, 33 (1962).

174. Robinson, T. J., *in* "Reproduction in Domestic Animals" (H. H. Cole and P. T. Cupps, ed.), Vol. 1, p. 291. Academic Press, New York, 1959.
175. Robinson, T. J., *Nature* **173**, 878 (1954).
176. Rothchild, I., *Vitamins Hormones* **23**, 209 (1965).
177. Saiduddin, S., Riesen, J. W., Graves, W. E., Tyler, W. J., and Casida, L. E., *J. Animal Sci.* **26**, 950 (1967).
178. Schein, M. W., *Z. Tierpsychol.* **20**, 462 (1963).
179. Schein, M. W., and Hale, E. B., *Animal Behaviour* **7**, 189 (1959).
180. Schein, M. W., and Hale, E. B., *in* "Sex and Behavior" (F. A. Beach, ed.), p. 440. Wiley, New York, 1965.
181. Shelton, M., *J. Animal Sci.* **19**, 368 (1960).
182. Shelton, M., and Morrow, J. T., *J. Animal Sci.* **24**, 795 (1965).
183. Shimizu, H., Toyoda, Y., Takeuchi, S., Kawai, T., and Adachi, S., *J. Reprod. Fertility* **13**, 555 (1967).
184. Short, R. V., *Ann. Rev. Physiol.* **29**, 373 (1967).
185. Signoret, J. P., *Ann. Biol. Animale Biochim. Biophys.* **2**, 163 (1962).
186. Signoret, J. P., *Proc. 4th Intern. Congr. Animal Reprod., The Hague* **2**, 166 (1961).
187. Signoret, J. P., *Proc. 5th Intern. Congr. Animal Reprod. Artificial Insemination, Trento* **3**, 532 (1964).
188. Signoret, J. P., *Proc. 2nd Intern. Congr. Endocrinol., London* p. 198 (1965).
189. Signoret, J. P., and du Mesnil du Buisson, F., *Proc. 4th Intern. Congr. Animal Reprod., The Hague* **2**, 171 (1961).
190. Signoret, J. P., du Mesnil du Buisson, F., and Busnel, R. G., *Compt. Rend. Acad. Sci.* **250**, 1355 (1960).
191. Signoret, J. P., and Mauléon, P., *Ann. Biol. Animale Biochim. Biophys.* **2**, 167 (1962).
192. Sillar, F. C., and Meyler, R. M., "The Symbolic Pig." Oliver & Boyd, Edinburgh and London, 1961.
193. Slee, J., *J. Agr. Sci.* **63**, 403 (1964).
194. Southcott, W. H., Braden, A. W. H., and Moule, G. R., *Australian J. Agr. Res.* **13**, 901 (1962).
195. Spalding, J. F., Berry, R. O., and Moffit, J. G., *J. Animal Sci.* **14**, 609 (1955).
196. Spies, H. G., *U.S. Dept. Agr. Misc. Publ.* **1005**, 83 (1964).
197. Spies, H. G., Zimmerman, D. R., Self, H. L., and Casida, L. E., *J. Animal Sci.* **19**, 101 (1960).
198. Symington, R. B., *J. Agr. Sci.* **56**, 165 (1961).
199. Tanabe, T. Y., Warnick, A. C., Casida, L. E., and Grummer, R. H., *J. Animal Sci.* **8**, 550 (1949).
200. Thibault, C., Courot, M., Martinet, L., Mauléon, P., du Mesnil du Buisson, F., Ortavant, R., Pelletier, J., and Signoret, J. P., *J. Animal Sci.* **25**, *Suppl.* p. 119 (1966).
201. Thompson, D. S., and Schinckel, P. G., *Empire J. Exptl. Agr.* **20**, 77 (1952).
202. Ulberg, L. C., Christian, R. E., and Casida, L. E., *J. Animal Sci.* **10**, 752 (1951).
203. Ulberg, L. C., and Lindley, C. E., *J. Animal Sci.* **19**, 1132 (1960).
204. Ulberg, L. C., Grummer, R. H., and Casida, L. E., *J. Animal Sci.* **10**, 665 (1951).

205. Underwood, E. J., Shier, F. L., and Davenport, N., *J. Dept. Agr. W. Australia* **21**, 135 (1944).

206. Vander Noot, G. W., Reece, R. P., and Skelley, W. C., *J. Animal Sci.* **8**, 583 (1949).

207. van Tienhoven, A., *in* "Reproduction in Domestic Animals" (H. H. Cole and P. T. Cupps, ed.), Vol. 2, p. 305. Academic Press, New York, 1959.

208. van Tienhoven, A., *in* "Sex and Internal Secretions" (W. C. Young, ed.), Vol. 2, p. 1088. Williams & Wilkins, Baltimore, Maryland, 1961.

209. Vollmann, R., and Vollmann, U., *Schweiz. Arch. Tierheilk.* **84**, 403 (1942).

210. Wagner, J. F., *U.S. Dept. Agr. Misc. Publ.* **1005**, 28 (1964).

211. Wagner, J. F., Reineke, E. P., Nellor, J. E., and Heneman, H. A., *J. Animal Sci.* **19**, 607 (1960).

212. Wagner, J. F., and Seerley, R. W., *J. Animal Sci.* **20**, 980 (1961).

213. Wagnon, K. A., Loy, R. G., Rollins, W. C., and Carroll, F. D., *Animal Behaviour* **14**, 474 (1966).

214. Walton, A., *in* "Progress in the Physiology of Farm Animals" (J. Hammond, ed.), Vol. 2, p. 603. Butterworth, London and Washington, D.C., 1955.

215. Walton, A., *in* "Marshall's Physiology of Reproduction" (A. S. Parkes, ed.), Vol. 1, Part 2, p. 130. Longmans, Green, New York, 1960.

216. Wierzbowski, S., *Publ. Inst. Zootech. Krachow* **154** (1962).

217. Wierzbowski, S., *Proc. 5th Intern. Congr. Animal Reprod. Artificial Insemination, Trento* **3**, 351 (1964).

218. Wierzbowski, S., *World Rev. Animal Production* **2**, 66 (1966).

219. Wierzbowski, S., and Hafez, E. S. E., *Proc. 4th Intern. Congr. Animal Reprod., The Hague* **2**, 176 (1961).

220. Williams, C., and McGibbon, W. H., *Poultry Sci.* **34**, 1172 (1955).

221. Williams, C., and McGibbon, W. H., *Poultry Sci.* **35**, 969 (1956).

222. Williams, C., and McGibbon, W. H., *Poultry Sci.* **36**, 30 (1957).

223. Wiltbank, J. N., *J. Reprod. Fertility, Suppl.* **1**, 1 (1966).

224. Wiltbank, J. N., Ingalls, J. E., and Rowden, W. W., *J. Animal Sci.* **20**, 341 (1961).

225. Wiltbank, J. N., Shumway, R. P., Parker, W. R., and Zimmerman, D. R., *J. Animal Sci.* **26**, 764 (1967).

226. Wiltbank, J. N., Zimmerman, D. R., Ingalls, J. E., and Rowden, W. W., *J. Animal Sci.* **24**, 990 (1965).

227. Wolfson, A., *Cold Spring Harbor Symp. Quant. Biol.* **25**, 507 (1960).

228. Wood-Gush, D. G. M., *Animal Behaviour* **6**, 68 (1958).

229. Wood-Gush, D. G. M., *Brit. J. Animal Behaviour* **2**, 95 (1954).

230. Wood-Gush, D. G. M., *Brit. J. Animal Behaviour* **3**, 81 (1955).

231. Wood-Gush, D. G. M., *Brit. J. Animal Behaviour* **4**, 133 (1956).

232. Wood-Gush, D. G. M., *Brit. J. Animal Behaviour* **5**, 1 (1957).

233. Wood-Gush, D. G. M., *Brit. J. Animal Behaviour* **4**, 102 (1956).

234. Woody, C. O., First, N. L., and Pope, A. L., *J. Animal Sci.* **26**, 139 (1967).

235. Wrenn, T. R., Bitman, J., and Sykes, J. F., *Endocrinology* **65**, 317 (1959).

236. Wrenn, T. R., Bitman, J., and Sykes, J. F., *J. Dairy Sci.* **41**, 1071 (1958).

237. Yeates, N. T. M., *in* "Recent Progress in the Physiology of Farm Animals" (J. Hammond, ed.), Vol. 1, p. 363. Butterworth, London and Washington, D.C., 1954.

238. Zimbelman, R. G., *U.S. Dept. Agr. Misc. Publ.* **1005**, 17 (1964).

239. Zimbelman, R. G., and Smith, L. W., *J. Reprod. Fertility* **11**, 185 (1966).

21

REPRODUCTION IN DOMESTIC FOWL

F. W. LORENZ

I. Introduction

The reproductve physiology of fowl differs strikingly in some characteristics from those considered elsewhere in this book primarily because of the oviparous pattern of avian reproduction. Even among oviparous vertebrates, however, birds possess some almost unique characteristics because the sequential pattern of egg production requires special adaptations for sperm movement in the oviduct. In spite of these features—and sometimes because of them—the fowl is a valuable experimental tool for the study of reproductive physiology and has been much used for this purpose. In addition, the fowl is an important domestic animal whose economic value has been greatly enhanced by extraordinary improvements in reproduction resulting from applications of genetic, nutritional, and physiological findings. Thus, detailed considerations of reproductive physiology in fowl are justified in their own right.

The first edition of this volume attempted exhaustive coverage of the literature through 1959 on such topics as gonadal development and endocrine control of the gonads, spermatology, artificial insemination, and fertility, but today this approach would far exceed space limitations. Fortunately, however, these topics have been covered by numerous excellent reviews; the author leans heavily on them for summary information and for citations. Original papers are cited directly only when necessary to the argument, and no attempt is made to be exhaustive. Thus, many excellent contributions are necessarily omitted. The reviews, themselves, are cited where they are drawn upon. The reader's attention is especially called to an extensive review on reproductive physiology of birds by van Tienhoven (203), and to recent reviews on the male and fertility by the present author (115) and by Lake (100, 102, 103), and on egg formation by Gilbert (66).

II. Sex Development

A. EMBRYONIC GONADAL DIFFERENTIATION

In birds the female is the heterogametic sex; thus, the sex of the offspring is determined by the genetic constitution of the ovum. During development of the zygote, primordial germ cells develop in the extraembryonic splanchnopleure and migrate to the genital ridge (22, 219), more to the left than to the right ridge, causing a larger development of the left gonad.

Starting normally during the seventh day of incubation, the medulla of the male gonad starts to develop, eventually forming seminiferous tubules, while the cortex gradually regresses. In the female, both medulla and cortex develop. The cortex forms follicles around primordial germ cells, but normally develops only in the left gonad, and eventually the medullary right gonad regresses. At hatching, the female chick has a single, grossly visible left ovary and a microscopically small rudimentary right ovary.

The embryonic gonads are apparently not affected by pituitary gonadotropins (60, 195); they are unaltered by hypophysectomy, injection of pituitary hormones, or transplantation of pituitary glands into the embryos. In contrast, they are sensitive to direct action of the gonadal hormones, as described in Chapter 5. Numerous attempts have been made for economic purposes to alter the sex ratios of hatched chicks by injection of estrogens into eggs (12, 22, 44, 225), but such attempts have not been successful. Not only do the effects—some of which can be quite striking at hatching—tend to regress to the condition of the genetic sex during posthatching development (37, 202), but the altered embryonic endocrine environment produces structural abnormalities, such as nonpatent gonaducts or cystic right oviducts, which in turn result in serious reproductive disorders in birds of both sexes (202).

The effects of estrogen administration on embryos appear to be somewhat more persistent in turkeys than in chickens; Poole (161) observed a fairly high incidence of adult birds from treated eggs (presumably genetic males) with a left ovotestis and sometimes no visible right gonad. Some birds were observed to be completely agonadal.

B. POSTHATCHING DEVELOPMENT

After hatching, the hormonal sensitivity of testicular tissue and of the left ovary changes strikingly. Sensitivity to gonadal hormones is reduced or abolished, and these tissues become normally responsive to a stimulation by anterior pituitary hormones. The sensitivity pattern of the rudimentary right female gonad remains embryonic, however. Minute amounts of estrogens—such as produced by the immature or resting ovary—completely suppress the development of medullary tissue, and the cortical tissue which could respond to estrogen is usually missing, so that macroscopic development rarely occurs during the life of the bird (93, 190). If the left ovary is destroyed by disease or removed surgically, the right gonad develops as a testis or ovotestis or—less commonly—an ovary (43, 44, 93, 190). Such birds remain sterile, however; the vas deferens is lacking, and the patent left oviduct is unavailable to a regenerated right ovary.

The behavior of the right gonadal rudiment would thus appear to be paradoxical. It is completely inhibited by the left ovary, but, once this inhibition is removed, it grows and maintains itself while often producing approximately as much estrogen as was produced by the very organ that inhibited it. Once it starts to develop, its hormonal sensitivity apparently shifts (as the left ovary did earlier) from the embryonic to the adult pattern. This explanation does not account for all circumstances, however, and Gardner, Wood, and Taber (63) adduced tentative evidence for a nonsteroidal ovarian hormone of unknown constitution which may exert additional inhibition on rudimentary cortical tissue.

Normal development of the gonads follows the mammalian pattern closely, with interstitial tissue primarily responsive to LH, and germinal tissue responsive to FSH. Interstitial tissue is the source of androgen, and LH thus controls production of this hormone in the testes, and, to a lesser but significant extent, also in the ovary. FSH stimulates germinal tissue, thus initiating spermatogenesis in the testes and follicular growth in the ovary. FSH alone or with LH controls production of the estrogen in the female. More detailed accounts follow of the development and functions of the male and female gonads and accessories.

III. The Female Reproductive System

A. THE OVARY

The functions of the ovary of the fowl have been reviewed extensively by Fraps (53), Nalbandov (137, 138), van Tienhoven (203), and, most recently, Gilbert (66). The following discussion depends in large measure on these reviews, to which the reader is referred for further details.

1. Gametogenesis

The immature ovary is a small, flattened, pear-shaped organ attached by a short mesovarium to the dorsal body wall and covering the left adrenal gland, which is partially imbedded in it. It contains microscopic or semi-microscopic follicles, but the majority of its bulk is medullary tissue. Yolk deposition starts before hatching, but is slow and limited principally to protein and water (129, 173). A second phase, initiated in individual follicles after the onset of puberty, lasts about 60 days, during which time the follicles grow to about 6 mm in diameter through deposition of white yolk. The

FIG. 1. Ovary of a mature chicken, showing a typical hierarchy of developing follicles. At the top of the picture is an empty follicle, 1 hour postovulation, and immediately to the right is the follicle that ovulated on the previous day.

third phase of yolk deposition is very rapid; the ova expand from 6 to some 30 mm in diameter in 9–11 days (206) (Fig. 1), and this phase typically ends in ovulation. Yolk deposited during this phase is much richer in fat and carries the typical yellow yolk pigment.

It is established that growth of the ovum is an essentially passive process, the function of the follicle being to transport yolk constituents from the blood to the ovum. Changes in the composition of the yolk material deposited, as well as in the rate of deposition, in the different stages must be due to successive changes in the permeability of the follicle (97). Pinocytosis apparently plays a role, at least in the rapid growth stage (see 66).

Such massive yolk deposition leaves the original nucleus and cytoplasm as a minute spot under the vitelline membrane. About 24 hours before ovulation, the germinal vesicle starts to break down, but there are no nuclear changes until 4 or 5 hours before ovulation. Then, meiosis occurs, with extrusion of the first polar body (153, 154); the second polar body is not extruded until after penetration by spermatozoa.

The follicle consists of a theca externa and a theca interna, and is lined with granulosa cells, but contains no follicular fluid. The vitelline membrane of the contained yolk is in direct contact with the granulosa cells. Branches of the ovarian artery run up each follicular stalk and form spiral arteries in the follicular walls, which constrict when the follicle ruptures (140). These arteries supply an extensive capillary and venous system, which returns blood through the ovarian veins to the vena cava. The venous system makes a clearly visible network on the entire surface of the follicle except for a narrow region opposite the stalk, known as the stigma, where the vessels are so small as to be invisible to the naked eye. Follicular rupture at the time of ovulation occurs within the stigma. Ruptured follicles degenerate rapidly without forming anything resembling luteal tissue. The follicle is extensively innervated, and the nervous system includes a variety of structures resembling sensory end organs (65), whose functions are unknown.

2. Endocrine Functions

The avian ovary secretes estrogen, androgen, and progestogen. Three estrogens—estradiol, estrone, and estriol—have been identified in the active ovary of the chicken (111), though only the first two have been found in the plasma of the laying hen (152). They are thought to be produced by the thecal cells, but Chieffi and Botte (29) found an enzyme important in steroidogenesis only in the granulosa. A major function of estrogen is to stimulate growth of the müllerian duct to form an oviduct, although synergistic action of other ovarian hormones, androgen and/or progestogen, are necessary to bring it to full functional capacity. With synergistic action of the thyroid, estrogen causes the female shape and pigment distribution in feathers. Estrogen also elicits female behavior patterns and sexual responses to the male.

Estrogen stimulates absorption and mobilization of substances necessary for egg formation, and synthesis in the liver of certain yolk components (113), notably, lipids and proteins. Thus, the blood of laying hens or estrogen-treated birds contains complex protein material that is completely undetectable in the blood of untreated males or immature chicks. First recognized by Laskowski (109) and Roepke and Hughes (172; see also 132, 171), this material was called serum vitellin because of similarities to, and presumed fate as, egg yolk vitellin. Extensive subsequent work by a number of investigators (32, 82–84, 124 182, 194) has demonstrated in the blood of estrogenized (or normal-laying) birds at least two new proteins: the phosphoprotein phosvitin, which is also the principal protein of egg yolk, and a lipoprotein, livetin. Each can bind calcium; in fact, both remain in solution in the blood as soluble calcium complexes. Phosvitin, at least, has been shown to carry its calcium complement with it into the yolk (194), but, once absorbed, it appears as an insoluble complex with livetin (182)— a complex that used to be called "ovovitellin."

Estrogen results in increased levels also of substances, such as vitamins, which cannot be synthesized in the body but are normal yolk constituents (113). The mechanism for this regulation is unknown, but it suggests that an elevated blood level may be important for transfer through the follicular membrane.

Under estrogen, the liver produces a variety of neutral fats, phospholipids, and cholesterol compounds faster than they can be deposited in yolk or fat depots, and a pronounced lipemia is thus a normal concomitant of the laying condition. Excess lipids are deposited in depots, and laying hens tend to become obese. Exogenous estrogens have been used to increase fat deposition in young fowl being reared for the table (113).

The increased levels of most yolk constituents in plasma are usually some 2–10 times as great during the laying condition as in nonlaying birds. Treatment with large (and unphysiological) estrogen doses, however, may result in extraordinarily high plasma levels (113). Blood plasma has been observed containing as much as 15% lipids (compared with 0.4% in males and nonlaying birds). The viscosity of the blood in such conditions is so increased that circulation may be impaired, but birds with lipid levels like those cited have been observed in apparently reasonably good health. Thyroid hormone inhibits these increased blood levels.

Estrogen also stimulates an elevated level of bound calcium, all or nearly all of which is held by the two proteins phosvitin and livetin, as described previously; its increased level is thus probably secondary to synthesis of these proteins. The laying hen has a heavy requirement for calcium for eggshell formation, and it was once thought that the increased bound calcium was necessary for this purpose. It is ionic calcium, however, that is the immediate precursor of eggshell; Urist et al. (194) presented telling arguments that bound calcium contributes only to the yolk, although there is evidence that it apparently forms an immediate reservoir for ionic calcium through dissociation (223). Blood passing through a uterus in the process of shell calcification exhibits an arteriovenous drop in the bound calcium fraction only (224). Hypercalcification of the skeleton normally accompanies activation of the ovary, but the mechanisms also provide for withdrawing calcium reserves from the skeleton if needed for eggshell formation. A heavily laying bird on a suboptimal calcium diet may suffer considerable skeletal decalcification before egg production is halted. The entire question of calcium movements in the body, which involves absorption by the gut, bone calcification and decalcification, vitamin D and the parathyroid glands, and the synergistic action of estrogen and androgen, is too complex for further discussion here; it has recently been discussed in some detail by Gilbert (66).

Androgen is thought to be produced in the ovarian stroma (11) in cells resembling the Leydig cells of the testes. Its secretion is manifested by growth of the hen's comb whenever the ovary becomes active. It synergizes with estrogen in growth of the oviduct, stimulating especially the muscular tissue (120). Androgen or progestogen are also necessary synergists with estrogen to bring the oviduct into full secretory activity (18, 85).

Many uncertainties remain concerning the normal functions of progestogens in birds. Exogenous progesterone may stimulate the development of ovarian follicles or may cause atresia, with stoppage of egg production and molting, and has inhibited broodiness in turkeys (see 203 for review). Progesterone injections can also precipitate premature ovulation (57); thus, progestogens are believed to act as the normal regulator of the ovulation cycle through stimulating release of ovulation-inducing hormone (doubtless LH, see below) via a neural mechanism in the hypothalamus (53, 203). Layne et al. (110) identified progesterone in chicken ovaries, but its site of production therein is not known. Also, this steroid cannot be the only progestogen produced by the bird; far more circulating progestogen activity was identified biologically (58, 59) than could be accounted for as circulating progesterone (121). Fraps (53, 56) postulated that the maturing ovarian follicle, during its last 24 hours before ovulation, has an important secretory role in regulating ovulation, and has shown (33, 174, 175) that both it and the discharged follicle have a role in oviposition, but it has not been determined whether the latter observation is evidence for progestogen secretion or is evidence for secretion of an unknown hormone (203). The chicken follicle is not converted into a corpus luteum after ovulation, and, in fact, its rapidly resorbing structure has little resemblance to secretory tissue; however, Deo (cited in 236) did report the presence of "secretory luteal cells" in both pre- and postovulatory follicles.

3. Control of Ovarian Function—Ovulation

Understanding of the pituitary control of the ovary is complicated by differences in response to avian and mammalian gonadotropic preparations which are due either to qualitative and quantitative differences in the hormones or to the existence of a third avian gonadotropin (141), as well as to age differences in the response of avian ovaries. In chickens less than 110 days' old, the main response to any gonadotropin is medullary tissue growth and estrogen and androgen secretion; somewhat more follicular development is obtained with avian preparations than with mammalian hormones, however. After 110 days of age, avian, but not mammalian, gonadotropins (38) produce extensive follicular development with yellow yolk deposition in the immature ovary.

In the mature hen, FSH preparations or PMS stimulate follicular growth, but inhibit ovulation; purified LH, administered intravenously, induces ovulation in 6–7 hours. It is thought that the endogenous avian hormones have the same physiological functions, although there is evidence

(*138*) that the two may be secreted together as a single gonadotropic complex.

Ovulations are sequential and are timed rather accurately, usually each somewhat later (referred to as the "lag") on successive days, except that on the day following an ovulation in the early afternoon ovulation is missed (day of lapse), and the sequence (or "clutch") usually starts again on the next day with an early morning ovulation. Further, the lags are longer after the first and after the pentultimate ovulation of a clutch than in mid-clutch. Associated with this sequential activity, an active mature ovary contains a hierarchy of follicles of all stages and sizes, together, perhaps, with one in the process of ovulation and two or three that have discharged (see Fig. 1). How these can coexist with the same blood supply and the same balance of circulating hormones, and at the same time maintain the ovulation sequence, and how this elegant temporal pattern is regulated, are questions that have led to bodies of research that are too extensive and too complex to be described adequately within present space limitations, but have led to few conclusive answers as yet. The reader is referred for details to reviews by Fraps (*53*, *55*), Nalbandov (*138*), van Tienhoven (*203*), and Gilbert (*66*).

Fraps' studies have not only included the endocrine interventions just described but have given especially detailed considerations to the temporal patterns, and have led to the following theory, much of which is quite well established, but part of which remains speculation. During most of the day, the pituitary puts out a steady level of FSH and LH, which induce follicular development, but a sudden peak secretion of LH (or of both; see previous discussion) induces maturation of the largest follicle with extrusion of the first polar body, followed by ovulation. The peak release of LH is stimulated, in turn, by a feedback, or excitation, hormone from the ovary (presumably progestogen), which acts over neural pathways in the hypothalamus when it reaches the necessary threshold concentration. It is conceived that the threshold is subject to diurnal variation and is low enough to be "reached" by physiological feedback-hormone concentrations only during the night hours. It is further conceived that buildup of the excitation hormone starts at a regular time in relation to the preceding ovulation, and increases at substantially the same rate following successive ovulations. The entire process, including buildup, excitation, LH release, and ovulation, requires somewhat more than 24 hours. The hypothesized diurnal variation in threshold accounts for the day of lapse following an afternoon ovulation, for the rising level of excitation hormone misses the low threshold and cannot excite until the threshold falls next evening. It also accounts for the relatively large lag periods following the first and the penultimate ovulations of the clutch, and shorter lags in the middle, all as illustrated in Fig. 2.

The effect of alternating light and darkness on the excitation threshold must be to pace the circadian rhythm rather than an absolute effect, since birds will lay in continuous light, and some birds, for that matter, will lay in continuous darkness (*222*). Under those circumstances, ovulation cycles tend to be linked to other timing signals, such as feeding time (5). The LH release for the ovulation of a single egg clutch occurs 4–5 hours after the onset of darkness (220), and in birds kept in total darkness it occurs the same length of time after the disturbance occasioned by the regular feeding and service period. If the circadian rhythm is forcibly replaced by an abnormal "day" length of 16–18 hours, egg production is seriously reduced (1, 232). However, Byerly and Moore (26) significantly increased clutch length and egg production by supplying a 26-hour day of 14 light hours and 12 dark hours, which is, of course, close to the normal ovulation rhythm.

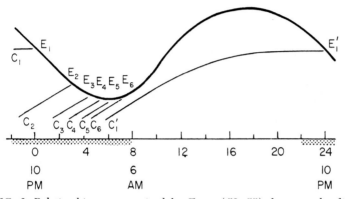

FIG. 2. Relationships, as conceived by Fraps (53, 55), between the diurnal rhythm in thresholds of response required for excitation of the ovulation inducing release of LH (E_1-E_1') and successive curves of rising excitation hormone concentration (C_1, C_2, C_3, C_4, C_5, C_6, C_1') in a sequence leading to 6 ovulations followed by 1 day with no excitation (and thus no ovulation), thus constituting a 7-day cycle. The figure is, of course, condensed; the curve of neural thresholds is understood to be repeated each day of the cycle, and the separations of the individual concentration curves exceed 24 hours by the time intervals (lags) shown in the figure. The lag between successive excitations (e.g., E_1-E_2) determines the length of lag between the succeeding curves of excitation hormone concentration (e.g., C_2-C_3). By courtesy of Dr. R. M. Fraps and the *Proceedings of the National Academy of Science.*

The peak release of the gonadotropin with LH activity has actually been demonstrated recently through blood and pituitary assays by the ovarian ascorbic acid depletion method. Nalbandov and his group (142, 143) found a peak release of LH at 8 hours before the expected ovulation, and also earlier peaks 20 and 13 hours before. They adduced evidence that the 13- and 8-hour peaks are involved directly with ovulation, and the 20-hour peak, perhaps indirectly. If that is so, it remains unexplained how a single intravenous injection of LH can induce premature ovulations in an hypophysectomized (see later discussion) or a chronically FSH-treated hen. The 13-hour peak appears to be stimulated neurally; interestingly, it was missed following the terminal egg of a clutch sequence, even though the pituitary LH content was normal for that interval after oviposition. Neural control may originate from neural afferents in the oviduct; Nalbandov (137) reached the conclusion that the presence of an egg in the anterior oviduct has an inhibitory influence, based mainly on the observation (88) that a loop of thread sewn into the lumen of the magnum or isthmus inhibits ovulation. This reported effect remains controversial, since about as many have failed to confirm it (92, 105, 189) as have succeeded in doing so (50, 201).

Perhaps the most puzzling facet of ovarian control is how the hierarchy of follicular sizes, with single-sequential ovulations, is controlled. Fraps (53, 55) describes circumstantial evidence that a peak release of LH (or of gonadotropic complex) which induces one ovulation causes maturation of the next follicle and thus renders it ovulable, but this fails to explain what makes one follicle (and one only) capable of being matured by an LH release. Nalbandov (138) has adduced evidence that ischemia developing during the last hours before ovulation reduces the supply of FSH to the follicle, thereby reducing the ovulation-inhibiting effect of this hormone. In support of his hypothesis is his striking observation that, after hypophysectomy, the follicles become progressively more sensitive to LH during the 12 hours before atresia renders them nonovulable, and very small doses of LH may cause multiple ovulations during this time. Again, however, it remains unexplained what initiates ischemia in a single follicle. Most puzzling, actually, is the mechanism that *starts* one follicle, and only one, on its terminal growth period so that the hierarchy is maintained—a puzzle not confined to avian species.

B. The Oviduct and Egg Formation

The mature oviduct is divided into five segments, each with a separate function: the infundibulum, including fimbria; magnum; isthmus; uterus or shell gland; and vagina (Fig. 3). The fimbria is thin-walled and funnel-shaped, but well supplied with smooth muscle; it becomes highly active shortly before ovulation, sometimes momentarily engulfing the follicle; thus, ovulation may occur within the fimbria. If not, the yolk is dropped into the ovarian pocket and subsequently engulfed. The yolk spends only a few minutes in the infundibulum, and fertilization occurs during this time. Albumen proteins plus about half the water of the final egg white are secreted by the magnum; the first albumen protein deposited on the vitelline membrane thickens and strengthens it; once this has happened, penetration by spermatozoa is no longer possible. The yolk requires approximately three hours to traverse the magnum and rotates as it passes down its length, so that the strands of albumen are laid on in a spiral fashion (173).

Egg white contains 10–12% dry matter, mainly a mixture of proteins most of which have characteristic biological activities that help protect the embryo against infection (51, 66), as shown in Table I. Ovomucin has the

additional property of giving egg white its gel-like spiral structure, a consequence of its filamentous nature. Egg white also contains small amounts of
sugar, riboflavin, and salt.

The egg passes through the isthmus in little more than an hour, and
during this time is covered with shell membranes composed of ovokeratin
fibers (173). It passes, thence, into the uterus, where it remains for about

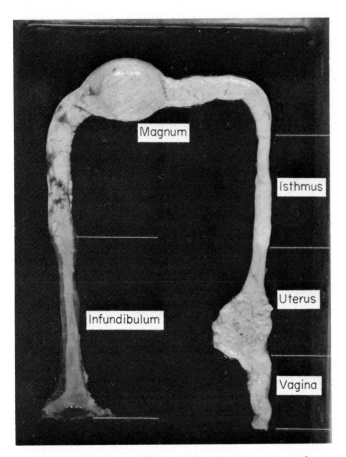

FIG. 3. Oviduct of a mature chicken with a forming egg in midmagnum.

20 hours; during the first half of this period, water and salt from the uterine
secretion pass through the membrane and dilute the egg albumen. Some
portion of this fluid actually dissolves proteins out of the ovomucin mesh-
work and forms an outer liquid layer of albumen. Meanwhile, ovomucin
fibers in some of the earlier—but not the earliest—albumen to be deposited
are breaking up into short lengths and allowing this portion of the albumen

TABLE I
COMPOSITION OF CHICKEN EGG WHITE[a]

Constituent	Approximate amount (% dry matter)[b]	Approximate molecular weight	Unique properties
Ovalbumin	54	45,000	Denatures easily, has sulf-hydryls
Conalbumin	13	77,000	Complexes iron, antimicrobial
Ovomucoid	11	28,000	Inhibits enzyme trypsin
Lysozyme	3.5	15,000	Enzyme for polysaccharides, antimicrobial
Ovomucin	1.5	?	Viscous; responsible for structure of thick egg white; high sialic acid; viral hemagglutination inhibitor
Flavoprotein-apoprotein	0.8	35,000	Binds riboflavin
"Proteinase Inhibitor"	1.0	?	Inhibits enzyme (bacterial proteinase)
Avidin	0.05	?	Binds biotin, antimicrobial
Ovomacroglobulin[c]	0.5	800,000	Strongly antigenic; extensive immunological cross reactivity
Unidentified proteins	8	?	Mainly globulins
Nonprotein	8	—	Primarily half glucose and salts (poorly characterized)

[a] Based on a table in Feeney (51) with permission of the author.
[b] Egg white usually contains 10–12% dry matter.
[c] Personal communication from Dr. Feeney.

to liquefy. The very earliest albumen deposited remains intact; this, the so-called chalaziferous layer, forms a thin coating over the yolk and strands leading from the yolk to each pole of the egg. Since the egg continues to rotate in the uterus, these strands are greatly twisted, squeezing fluid from the ovomucin meshes and forming the semiopaque twisted chalazae. Shell deposition continues throughout the stay of the egg in the uterus. In contrast to the ovary, the oviduct is a synthetic organ. All of the proteins secreted by the oviduct are synthesized by the oviducal glands.

Just 24 hours after ovulation, the hen settles on a nest (66, 235). This reflexly controlled behavior pattern brings the bird to the nest in time, of course, for the impending oviposition, but it is not conditioned by the egg in the uterus, since it occurs unaltered in "internal" layers (e.g., as a result of oviduct deformity or experimental ligation) and also after premature oviposition of a soft-shelled egg. The timing of nesting is established by the ovulation the preceding day, and its control is mediated by the discharged follicle of that ovulation, through neural or perhaps neural plus endocrine pathways; removing or ligating that follicle, and to a lesser extent cocainizing it, has interfered with the nesting reflex (68).

The act of oviposition has a certain, but incomplete, similarity to parturition. It is aided by a "bearing-down reflex" (66, 188), but can occur after that reflex has been abolished. Oviposition may be induced by posterior pituitary hormones (66), the most potent of which is the avian hormone arginine vasotocin. Demonstrated at the time of oviposition have been depletion of the neurohypophysial supply of this hormone (191) and a marked increase in its blood concentration (186). Neurohypophysectomized birds exhibiting diabetes insipidus may continue to lay, but this is not necessarily paradoxical, since numerous other factors may affect the timing of oviposition, although their physiological roles and interactions are not all understood. Acetylcholine hastens oviposition (209) and adrenaline delays it (132).

Involved in timing the oviposition are ovulations, both of the yolk of the egg to be laid and of the next egg in the clutch. The first is mediated by the discharged follicle; its removal delays oviposition (236). just as it delays the associated nesting reflex (discussed previously). The impending ovulation also exerts control, even though it normally occurs, except on the day of lapse, about 30 minutes after the oviposition. Experimental alteration of the time of ovulation is usually accompanied by a corresponding alteration in the time of oviposition if an egg is present in the uterus (53), but forcing premature oviposition mechanically does not cause premature ovulation (207). Also, a loop of thread in the uterus causes premature oviposition of a succession of membranous eggs (187), but nesting reflexes at the normal time of day indicate little or no effect on the time of ovulation (235).

IV. The Male Reproductive System

A. The Testes

Growth, development, function, and endocrine control of the testes follow quite closely the mammalian pattern described in previous chapters, so that only a few comments need be made. The most readily apparent difference is in location; whereas the testes of most mammalian species descend into a scrotum, those of birds remain at their site of origin, in the dorsal body cavity close to the kidneys. By their position, avian testes, therefore, lack the cooling and temperature-controlling mechanism of the scrotum. Since the testis surface temperature is the same as the deep-body temperature of the bird (218), an early suggestion (35) that the abdominal air sacs (which come in contact with the testes) might serve as a cooling mechanism for them appears to be without validity.

The testes, like the ovary, yield evidence that avian gonadotropins differ from those of mammals. Nalbandov *et al.* (*141*) demonstrated that injections of mammalian LH preparations maintain Leydig cells in hypophysectomized cockerels for a few days only. Avian pituitary preparations, however, maintain androgen production indefinitely and may even resensitize testes to mammalian LH. It appears that avian material is necessary to stimulate the formation of new Leydig cells, whereas mammalian LH only supports the function of those that have already been formed. The interaction of FSH and testosterone on the seminiferous tubules and spermatogenesis appears to be much like that already described for mammals in Chapter 5.

The effects of androgen on birds, as on other species, include control of growth and development of the masculine sex accessories and of certain secondary patterns of sex characters and masculine behavior. A secondary sex character in fowl which is so specifically controlled by androgen as to have become the classic organ for assay of this hormone is the characteristic comb development of the cock. Not only is the comb stimulated to grow by androgenic hormones and by no other endocrine stimulus but the response is highly quantitative as well. It is also direct; the comb is highly sensitive to inunction of androgen directly on the surface. The response may be affected by genetic differences in sensitivity (*27, 28, 45*) and is increased by keeping birds in subdued light (*230, 231*) and/or in high environmental temperatures (*108*). Estrogen, however, tends to cause comb regression (*128, 133*), but the comb is so much less sensitive to estrogen than to androgen that this is usually a minor interference. Head furnishings of certain other gallinaceous species, in a variety of shapes—such as the snood and wattles of the turkey, and the eye patches of the various pheasant species—are histologically similar to the comb and have similar sensitivity to androgen. Androgen is responsible for the development of the syrinx of the cockerel and of the spongy tissue of the male turkey, both of which are necessary for the typical masculine call, producing crowing, on the one hand, and booming, on the other. Other sexual dimorphic characteristics are either controlled genetically—for example, body size differences and the presence of spurs (though androgen may modify the shape of these)—or by estrogen—for example feather shape and color patterns. As in other animals, androgen is also important in social and sexual behavior patterns, as described in the section on mating, below.

The paired testes of the mature cock weigh some 14–33 gm and usually compose about 1% of the total body weight (*202*). Each is attached, close to the dorsal body wall at the anterior end of the kidney, by a short mesorchium. The tunica albuginea is extremely thin and forms no septa, so that the testis is not divided into lobules (*98*). The seminiferous tubules typically start from blind ends near the periphery and take tortuous courses dorsally. In transverse sections, spermatogonia may be observed close to the basement membrane; successive cell types appear progressively toward the lumen (*96*). Different sections of tubule, and even areas of the same section, may show various degrees of maturation. Multinuclear cells are common: in a careful study of spermatogenesis which used techniques minimizing cytoplasmic disruption, Lake (96) concluded that nuclei resulting from the first meiotic and subsequent divisions normally remain within a common cytoplasm, leading to multinuclear spermatids and, ultimately, to clumps of spermatozoa; this accounts, no doubt, for the arrangement of spermatozoa in testis tubules, rather than does the previously suggested chemotaxis of particular parts of the Sertoli cell cytoplasm. Sertoli cells in cock testes appear to ramify throughout interstices of the entire germinal epithelium. Synthesis of the sperm nucleoproteins requires about 2 weeks, and approximately 10 more days elapse before the spermatozoa are shed (117, 122).

B. THE ACCESSORY REPRODUCTIVE ORGANS

The accessory organs of the male fowl consist of a small epididymis closely attached to the full length of the dorsal surface of each testis, vasa deferentia which terminate in paired ejaculatory ducts in the cloaca, and a small, almost rudimentary, imperforate phallus. None of the accessory glands and vesicles characteristic of mammalian genital systems are present in the bird; the scanty seminal plasma is almost entirely the product of the seminiferous tubules and epididymis, although traces of material may be added from cells in the walls of the vas deferens (98).

The vasa deferentia are convoluted tubes extending along the medial central surface of the kidneys, lateral to the ureters. They become larger distally, primarily through increased musculature, but the lumina expand where the vasa penetrate the cloacal wall. Semen present in the expanded posterior portion is ejaculated during the bird's orgasm by contraction of the walls and pours over the surface of the phallus.

The phallus of most birds is not a true intromittent organ. In chickens, it consists of a pair of "round folds" with a small knob or "white body" terminating the groove between them, all contained in the ventral cloaca. Around the swollen endings of the vasa deferentia are a pair of "vascular bodies" consisting of lymphoid tissue, abundantly supplied with blood from the internal pudendal artery. The phallus is erectile, but the process—in contrast to that of mammals—is engorgement of the tissues with lymph. Lymph is drained through lateral "lymph folds" into the round folds of the phallus, causing these tissues to swell (144); simultaneously, the posterior retractor penis muscle relaxes and the phallus protrudes from the cloaca ventrally.

The phallus is covered with stratified squamous epithelium, but the erectile vascular tissue and lymph folds have pseudostratified columnar epithelia; in the former this forms submucosal glands and contains many goblet cells (98).

The genital apparatus of the turkey is similar grossly to that of the chicken except with regard to structures analogous to the white body of the cock's phallus; instead of a single median structure, the turkey has two, one on the top of each round fold, deeply pigmented except in white-feathered birds. Drakes and ganders have long, spirally twisted phalli which are intromittent organs, but these are also imperforate, and ejaculated semen runs along a groove on the surface. The erectile mechanism is similar to that for the very different phallus of the chicken. In some species of passerine birds, the vasa deferentia undergo tremendous hypertrophy during the breeding season, causing a considerable protuberance of the cloacal region (226, 228). These hypertrophied vasa have sometimes been miscalled "seminal vesicles," and are presumed to be involved in temperature control (229).

C. SEMEN

1. Composition

Investigations on the composition of poultry semen have recently been extensively and definitively reviewed by Lake (102), and this was supplemented by Lake and El Jack (104), with a discussion mainly of considerations relating to its origins. Accordingly, the following discussion is brief and depends primarily on those two papers, to which the reader is referred for further details and citations.

A major problem in discussing the composition of cock semen is the role to be assigned to the "transparent fluid." This fluid appears, and mixes, with the ejaculate during the conventional massage technique for semen collection (see later, Section V,B). It is regarded as lymph transudate and as an artifact of the massage method of semen collection rather than as a normal component of seminal plasma. It has been argued (145, 146) that at least a small amount is ejected during normal copulation, but even if this is true, it is not necessarily mixed with the semen prior to deposition of the latter in the hen's vagina. In any event, the proportion of transparent fluid to vas deferens fluid is highly variable and dependent on the collection technique. Furthermore, the anatomy of the avian genitalia is such that transparent fluid (and, thus, whole semen, if mixed with it) is very likely contaminated with at least traces of urine and/or feces plus blood corpuscles and desquamated cells. Consequently, it is preferable to consider the two fluids separately.

Lake and a relatively few other investigators cited by him (102) used special techniques to induce forcible ejection of semen from the ejaculatory ducts and thereby collect the fluids separately (see later, Section V,B).

Cock semen collected directly from the ejaculatory ducts usually contains some 7 or 8×10^9 spermatozoa per milliliter (97); semen, as usually collected, contains highly variable numbers, probably averaging close to 3 or 4×10^9 per milliliter, reflecting the variable quantities of transparent fluid included. Volumes obtainable vary from a small fraction of 1 ml to an occasional maximum of about 2 ml.

TABLE II

COMPOSITION OF CHICKEN SEMINAL AND TRANSPARENT FLUIDS[a,b]

	Vas deferens fluid (mg/100 ml)	Trans-parent fluid (mg/100 ml)		Vas deferens fluid (mg/100 ml)	Trans-parent fluid (mg/100 ml)
Sodium	383	369	Uric acid	7.8	*
Potassium	50	19.3	Creatine	92	
Magnesium	6.1	2.9	Glutamic acid	1068	
Calcium	4.2	8.8	Sialic acid (bound)	12	
Copper	0.03		Glucose	0	202
Zinc	0.19		Fructose	0	4
Iron	0.12		Sorbitol	*	*
Chloride	132	476.8	Inositol	10	*
Carbonic acid	120		Ascorbic acid	3	
P total	7.5		Ergothionine	2	
acid soluble	2.4		Lactic acid	34	23
inorganic	1.5		Citric acid	0	
lipid	5.0		Pyruvic acid	2.9	
Protein	800	400	2-Oxoglutaric acid	21	

[a] Based on tables in Lake (102) with permission of the author.

[b] (*) Present, or presence inferred; transparent fluid also presumably contains urea and small amounts of a large number of free amino acids. Vas deferens fluid contains, in addition to substances in the table, traces of alanine, aspartic acid, glycine, and serine and several enzymes—see text.

Information on the components of cock vas deferens fluid and of transparent fluid, brought together by Lake (102), is summarized in abbreviated form in Table II. It is obvious that vas deferens fluid differs strikingly in composition from the seminal plasmas of various mammals, which is not surprising, since it contains no secretions from accessory glands. Also, spermatozoa have been residing in it throughout their sojourn in the vas deferens, and its composition should thus reflect in some measure the metabolic processes of spermatozoa.

Thus, cock vas deferens fluid is completely lacking in reducing sugars and citric acid and almost completely so in such other prominent components of mammalian semen as inositol, phosphorylcholine, and glyceryl phosphorylcholine; it is also low in total phosphorus, most of that present being in the form of phospholipids.

The sodium content of vas deferens fluid is similar to that of blood, but potassium is higher, though not as high as in some mammalian semen. Magnesium is also higher, but calcium is low. The chloride content is definitely low; the chief anion of cock vas deferens fluid is glutamate, which is remarkably high. Traces of glycine, serine, alanine, and aspartic acid have also been found in vas deferens fluid (97); a large number of other amino acids found in small quantities in conventionally collected semen (30, 70) may have been contributed by the bloodstream via transparent fluid, as suggested by Lake (102). The remaining nonprotein nitrogen is primarily creatine. Although no claim was made for completeness, the composition of vas deferens fluid as shown in Table II must be nearly so. A calculation involving only the major components (104) accounts for the entire measured freezing-point depression, $\Delta = -0.593°$.

Vas deferens fluid is an extraordinarily rich source of acid phospho-monoesterase, but only traces of alkaline phosphomonoesterase are present. A number of other enzymes—glutamic pyruvic transaminase, glutamic oxalic transaminase, lactic dehydrogenase, and leucine aminopeptidase—have recently been identified in the fluid of conventionally collected semen (75).

Transparent fluid, in contrast to vas deferens fluid, resembles an ultra-filtrate of blood plasma, especially in regard to content of sodium, potas-sium, calcium, magnesium, and chloride (see Table II). Protein is low—0.4 gm, compared to 5 gm/100 ml of blood plasma—but the transparent fluid occasionally contains enough fibrinogen to clot—even enough to clot the entire semen collection. Transparent fluid also contains glucose and fructose in quantities similar to those in blood plasma. Transparent fluid may be damaging to spermatozoa, partly perhaps because of its high chloride and calcium content, and partly because on standing it causes agglutination of spermatozoa.

The composition of turkey semen has been little studied. It has not been collected "separately" from transparent fluid, because this material has not been identified during collection by massage, and because it is not easy to produce forcible ejection from a turkey's ejaculatory ducts. Since the sperm concentration in semen collected from the vas deferens was found to be about the same as in semen collected by massage (178), it appears unlikely that much if any transparent fluid is formed. Sperm concentration is consistently somewhat higher in turkey semen than in chicken vas deferens fluid. Turkey seminal fluid analyzed by Brown (21) had about the same sodium content (338 mg/100 ml) and tonicity ($\Delta = -0.63°C$) as chicken vas deferens fluid, and twice the potassium content (103 mg/100 ml). The present author has found that it contains up to about 7 mg fruc-tose per 100 ml, but this may arise from metabolic processes.

2. Sperm Metabolism and Motility

Recent investigations (69, 169, 184) of the energy metabolism of cock spermatozoa make clear its essential similarity to that of other species in-volved in internal fertilization. Carbohydrates are degraded through the Embden-Meyerhof glycolytic pathway. Under anaerobic conditions, lactic acid is the major end product. Aerobically, further oxidation to CO_2 and water takes place by way of the Krebs cycle, though avian spermatozoa, like mammalian germ cells but unlike most other tissues, continue to accumulate lactic acid under these conditions. These cells exhibit a pronounced Pasteur effect, but feedback coupling between aerobic energy metabolism and glycolysis is apparently less efficient than in tissues which do not accumulate lactic acid in the presence of oxygen.

Cock spermatozoa, however, differ from mammalian sperm cells which have been studied in that they exhibit the capacity to convert glucose to fructose (114). Attempts to work out the physiological mechanism of this process have fallen between the horns of the same dilemma that Mann (125) encountered in choosing one of two possible pathways for fructose synthesis in the seminal vesicles of certain mammals. 6-Phosphohexoses, formed in the early stages of the Embden-Meyerhof degradation of glycogen or glucose, may be dephosphorylated to form mixtures of free glucose and fructose. Preferential utilization of glucose by the tissues has been thought to account for the accumulation of fructose. However, appropriate enzymes for reducing glucose to sorbitol and reoxidizing the latter to fructose have been found in the seminal vesicle tissues of some mammals (125).

Although circumstantial evidence strongly favors involvement of the initial stages of the Embden-Meyerhof pathway plus phosphatase rather than the sorbitol pathway in fructose production from glucose, neither pathway has been demonstrated conclusively in cock spermatozoa. Sorbitol added to aerobic media containing cock spermatozoa is metabolized to a limited extent only; in one experiment it stimulated respiration slightly without forming lactate (169), and in another only traces of fructose at most were formed (106). Under anaerobic conditions, sorbitol is formed from fructose only when the cells are poisoned with iodoacetamide or fluoride (169). Since fructose is formed from glucose only under aerobic conditions, it appears that this phenomenon is a consequence of aerobic inhibition (the Pasteur effect) of phosphofructokinase, resulting in accumulation of fructose 6-phosphate, from which free fructose is formed by the action of phosphatases (169).

From a functional standpoint, the capacity of cock spermatozoa to form fructose from glucose bears an interesting analogy to that of mammalian seminal vesicles. In the latter, Mann (125) emphasized, fructose formed from glycogen is a source of energy to spermatozoa, whereas any glucose formed by the same process would be rapidly reutilized by the glandular tissue itself. Cocks have no seminal vesicles, and cock semen no reducing sugar, but uterovaginal host glands of the hen, in which spermatozoa reside for extended periods, do secrete quantities of glycogen (67).

As suggested by the fact that intermediates of the Kreb cycle, except oxalacetate, have little stimulatory effect on respiration (169, 240), operation of the Krebs cycle in cock spermatozoa appears to be impaired or incomplete because of a deficiency of malic dehydrogenase activity. This characteristic is shared by bovine and some other spermatozoa (125), and may account at least partially for the deficient Pasteur effect, which results in aerobic lactic acid formation.

Glycerol metabolism has been of particular interest because of its potential value in frozen storage of sperm cells. Cock spermatozoa metabolize glycerol rapidly, though with accumulation of dihydroxyacetone (169). Under some conditions of glycerol metabolism, an initial stimulation of respiration was soon followed by complete cessation. This observation was attributed circumstantially to nonenzymatic conversion of dihydroxyacetone to methylglyoxal (170), a potent inhibitor of succinic dehydrogenase (94) and other enzymes (166). Variations in the extent of inhibition may be due to a seasonal variation in the level of glyoxalase activity in successive sperm samples.

Less is known of metabolic processes involving other classes of compounds. Cock spermatozoa degrade the short-chain fatty acids formate at least through octanoate (183) with production of CO_2 but no ketone bodies; all stimulate respiration, and, in contrast to effects on mammalian spermatozoa, octanoate produces the greatest increase. Identified in cock spermatozoa (101) are a variety of complex lipids which are gradually depleted during semen storage at a rate that appears to be independent of exogenous carbohydrate. Cock spermatozoa metabolize glutamate, but not glycine (47), although both amino acids reduce fructolysis and the respiratory rate.

Still less understood are the interrelations between metabolic processes and motility. Cock spermatozoa possess the capacity to become reversibly immobilized under a variety of conditions. The most obvious are lack of O_2 and/or a reducing sugar (71, 180), suggesting the existence of respiratory processes and alternate specific glycolytic processes necessary to support motility. However, the situation is more complex; an atmosphere of CO_2 inhibits motility (180), but traces of CO_2 or HCO_3– support it (147, 148), as do traces of Mg^{++}; phosphate in the amounts used for buffer tends to be inhibitory. The requirements are apparently much more rigid at temperatures close to those of the bird's body than under cooler conditions; thus, an immobilized sperm suspension in a 40°C water bath may resume motility spontaneously when cooled to room temperature (147, 148).

Of possible biological importance is the effect of the oviduct on the motility and metabolism of introduced spermatozoa. Munro (135, 136) demonstrated that fluid expressed from the epithelium of the magnum or infundibulum permitted the temperature-linked immobilization just described, whereas uterine fluid, like seminal plasma and blood serum, supports motility at 40°C. He believed that this mechanism aids survival of spermatozoa in the female tract; this hypothesis has recently received both support and supplementation (in light of newer knowledge on the residence sites and behavior of spermatozoa in the oviduct) by the discovery of poly-α-L-glutamic acid, which immobilizes sperm cells at 40°C (80, 81). This substance was found in the infundibulum and upper magnum and in the uterovaginal junction, but nowhere else in the oviduct. What may reestablish motility in the neighborhood of the just-ovulated blastodisc, where motility is presumably necessary for sperm penetration, is unknown; of interest in this connection is the fact that material in the upper oviduct increases the respiratory rate of spermatozoa (76, 147, 148), and thus may be postulated to stimulate them to renewed activity after a period of dormancy in the host glands.

V. Reproduction

A. MATING

In wild birds generally, the gonads are active only seasonally, and gonadal recrudescence is initiated by seasonal factors such as photo-periodicity. Recrudescence does not ordinarily lead to egg production, however, unless the female has been stimulated by a sometimes elaborate sequence of events. This may or may not include pairing in individual species, but certainly includes establishment of a territory, courtship displays by the male, and nest building. Copulation is, of course, necessary for fertility, but plays no role in inducing ovulation. The extensive literature on control of the breeding season is beyond the scope of this chapter, but several excellent reviews are available (48, 49, 126, 203, 227, 239).

In briefest outline, sensory impulses from external stimuli, acting through central pathways including the hypothalamus, influence the activity of the pituitary to initiate and regulate gonadal recrudescence. The nature of the operative sensory stimuli varies from species to species, but perhaps the most nearly universal stimulus is adequate daylight, and birds are generally able to respond to photostimuli even when such stimuli are not (e.g., as with equatorial species) the normal timing mechanism (126, 127). Other initial stimuli, operative for certain species, include temperature, rainfall, and appropriate development of specific food crops. After the complement of eggs is laid, the output of the hypophysis shifts from gonadotropin to prolactin (23), which results in gonadal collapse (139), stimulates broody behavior (168), and, in pigeons and doves, induces crop milk production in both sexes (167). In some species, gonadal activity may be resumed if the environment is favorable, but ultimately the gonads become refractory to further environmental stimuli, with refractoriness persisting until dispelled by further appropriate stimuli, which usually, at least, involve a reduction in the photoperiod. In some species—e.g., crowned sparrows (130)—prepuberal refractoriness must similarly be dispelled so that a winter supervenes before the first breeding season.

Domesticated chickens and turkeys display only fragments of these patterns. They do respond to light, and although the response tends to be statistical rather than absolute, it exhibits no other features at variance with what has been observed in wild birds. Attainment of sexual maturity by female chickens is hastened by increasing the photoperiod during pre-puberal growth, though the absolute level of the photoperiod has little effect (134). The testes of White Leghorn cockerels 11 weeks' old have been shown to develop faster if the photoperiod is increased from 12 to 14 hours than if it is decreased to 8 hours (89).

Once sexual maturity is attained, reduction of the photoperiod tends to reduce the level of gonadal activity, so for this reason poultrymen often supplement the natural light period during the winter months. Like wild birds, chickens and turkeys tend to become refractory, and the longer the photoperiod the sooner this condition develops. Accordingly, a recom-mended procedure is to brood birds on a minimum photoperiod consonant with adequate feed intake and growth, and during the rearing period to increase it enough to obtain maturity at a satisfactory age (but not so early that small eggs result) and enough to stimulate maximum egg-pro-duction rate without precipitating refractoriness. With turkeys, at least, a 3-week period of short (6-hour) days late in adolesence (instead of throughout the growing period), followed by a 14-hour day, gave optimum results for males (151) as well as for females (221). For further details of the many photoperiod studies with domestic birds the reader is referred to reviews by Fraps (54) and van Tienhoven (203).

In domestic chickens and turkeys also, the ovulation mechanism has become completely independent of the presence of a male, and courtship has been reduced to precopulatory activity.* In the chicken, this consists of a number of stereotypical patterns, including "waltzing," in which the cock drops one wing and approaches the hen with short, shuffling side steps; "circling" around the hen with exaggerated high steps; and the "rear" approach, in which he sometimes grabs her comb or neck with his beak or flaps his wings over her vigorously. Wood-Gush (234) has analyzed these and other less prominent actions, and concludes that they occur most frequently before strange or relatively nonreceptive hens, are closely related to agonistic reactions, and are fundamentally displacement re-actions. In other words, before a completely familiar and receptive hen, even the most rudimentary courtship remnants are dispensed with. Never-theless, courtship aids mating activity, and cocks that display most often in a given situation are usually the ones that copulate most frequently (73, 233).

A receptive hen responds to the cock by crouching with her wings slightly spread; the cock mounts, grasps her neck feathers with his beak, and treads. Apparently, it is the rhythmic treading motion of his feet that stimulates his phallus to erect and the hen to throw her tail up to one side, everting her vagina; the cock crouches and dips his tail, his erected organ makes contact with the hen's everted vagina, and he immediately ejaculates.

* See Chapter 20 for a more detailed description of behavior patterns.

The hen withdraws the vagina, carrying a deposit of semen with it. The entire act requires only 3 or 4 seconds, and the final contact less than 1 second (97).

Even though the libido and aggressive instinct of the male are both stimulated by androgen, there appears to be little correlation between these two drives among normal, healthy cocks, except that social dominance of the males over hens does facilitate mating (72, 233). A significant negative correlation has been observed between male comb size and mating frequency; differences in comb sensitivity to androgen may be involved, but low sex drive in the large-comb group was obviously not due to androgen deficiency. Neither was it due to mechanical interference of large combs with mating, since dubbing failed to improve mating frequency (112, 237).

Individual cocks have been observed to copulate as often as 53 times in a single day, but how many of these matings resulted in ejaculation is uncertain; single matings often do not result in fertility (156). Most mating activity is late afternoon (112, 155, 233), and it is during these same hours that massage techniques have obtained the greatest volume of semen and the largest number of spermatozoa from isolated cocks (107).

Courtship and mating patterns of domestic turkeys show certain differences (74, 165). The masculine display is "strutting," in which the tom drops his wings so the tips scrape the ground as he steps forward, at the same time forcing air into the "spongy" tissue on his breast with a deep drum-like sound. This display is less specifically androgen-stimulated than is crowing or waltzing in the cock. It is occasionally performed by male turkeys only a few weeks old, and although its incidence is increased by androgen (endogenous or exogenous), it is also very strikingly increased by estrogen administration. Strutting, apparently, also has no intimidating effect on the hen, though it may have some enticement value; the turkey hen initiates mating by approaching the male (74). The hen experiences an orgasmic reaction which is followed by shaking herself, sometimes running in an arc and vocalizing. In contrast to the situation with chickens, she then suffers a loss of sexual responsiveness which may last for several days or weeks (74).

B. ARTIFICIAL INSEMINATION

Artificial insemination is used widely for improving fertility in turkey-breeding flocks and to a limited extent in chicken hatching-egg production; the technique is used almost universally as a research tool in studying avian fertility problems.

Early methods for collecting semen have all given way to the massage technique first described by Burrows and Quinn (24) or to minor variations of it. The phallus is caused to erect and protrude by stroking the back and/or abdomen and through pushing the tail forward over the bird's back, and semen is milked out of the distal vasa deferentia by deep pressure with thumb and forefinger to the base of the phallus. Lake (97) has modified this technique, using primarily lumbar massage to stimulate forcible ejection from the ducts and, thus, to collect semen free of transparent fluid from cocks who respond properly.

For successful routine insemination, deposition of semen directly into the midvagina is necessary, and to accomplish this the vaginal orifice must be everted, using gentle abdominal pressure while the tail is pushed forward, so that it protrudes beyond the lips of the cloaca (135, 164). Pressure is maintained while the syringe is inserted, but must be relaxed before semen is injected or much of the semen will be ejected alongside the syringe. Operating details of these techniques are given in the first edition of this book and in such works as those by Lake (100, 103) and Lorenz et al. (116). The importance of close attention to these details for maintaining satisfactory fertility in a commercial turkey enterprise was demonstrated in a recent study by Ogasawara and Rooney (150).

Special techniques for depositing semen more anteriorly in the oviduct are useful for certain experimental purposes. Intrauterine insemination was first accomplished by Allen and Bobr (3), using a finger as guide to traverse the vaginal bends and penetrate the uterovaginal sphincter, thus guiding the semen-containing cannula. Because this technique is usually followed by temporary stoppage of egg production, it has been abandoned in favor of a technique involving merely a prolongation and gentle intensification of the normal pressure used to cause eversion (15). With some patience, actively laying hens can be induced to evert the entire vagina and actually expose the uterovaginal junction, which can then be penetrated directly with the cannula. This technique has not interrupted or caused noticeable decline in egg production. Intraperitoneal insemination (196, 198) has been used occasionally for many years, but is very unreliable; the abdominal wall is punctured with a sharp needle and the cannula is inserted to deposit semen in the region of the ovary, whence, hopefully, it is picked up by the fimbria. Unless the semen is actually deposited in the ovarian pocket, however, it seems unlikely that spermatozoa could get to the fimbria in any numbers. For experimental purposes in the author's laboratory (199), hens are laparotimized under anesthesia and the oviduct is punctured at any desired point with a hypodermic needle to deposit semen in the lumen or between the lips of the fimbria. Depressed egg production following the laparotomy has more recently been shown to be a consequence of the intravenous anesthesia previously used. Intramuscular sodium pentothal, supplemented with a little ether by inhalation, has produced satisfactory anesthesia, and birds survived the surgery with no interruption of egg production.

C. Behavior of Spermatozoa in the Oviduct

Immediately following copulation or midvaginal artificial insemination, a small number of spermatozoa are carried rapidly to the infundibulum

(131). Perhaps 0.02% of the number inseminated may reach the infundibulum within an hour, although detectable numbers have been found within 15 minutes (4). Vigorous motility is apparently necessary for the spermatozoa to traverse the uterovaginal junction; once in the uterus, however, they are carried to the anterior end passively—for dead spermatozoa deposited in the uterus reach the the infundibulum as rapidly as live spermatozoa, and in as large numbers. Over 90% of the semen deposited in the vagina leaks out through the cloaca and is lost.

FIG. 4. Uterovaginal sperm-host gland, electron micrograph of approximately longitudinal section. Note basalar position of cell nuclei and microvilli lining the apical edges of the gland cells. Perinuclear clear areas correspond in position to lipids demonstrated in similar sections by histochemical techniques (67). The electron-dense apical granules and the cilia pictured previously (200) are seen only in sections closer to the glandular ostia. Picture, courtesy of W. H. Burke and F. X. Ogasawara.

The remainder of the spermatozoa find harbor in specialized gland tissue in the epithelial folds surmounting the uterovaginal sphincter (*14, 16, 62*), recently designated the "uterovaginal sperm-host glands" (*67*). These are simple, tubular glands made up of columnar cells with basal nuclei (Fig. 4). Following mating or insemination, spermatozoa can be found in large numbers in these glands packed tightly in bundles with heads approaching the blind ends of the glands.

Similar glands exist in much larger numbers in the posterior infundibulum (Fig. 5); these have been recognized for many years. Van Drimmelen (*197*) designated them "sperm-nests" and believed them to be the normal site of sperm residence in the oviduct. Nevertheless, spermatozoa are almost never found in infundibular glands after midvaginal artificial insemination, although they may contain small numbers following copulation. It is possible that an orgasmic response in copulation sets up oviduct movements which carry larger numbers forward than after artificial insemination.

When semen is deposited anterior to the uterovaginal junction, larger numbers reach the infundibulum (*4*) and larger numbers enter the infundibular glands; moderate numbers do so after intrauterine artificial insemination (*16*), and tremendous numbers engorge these glands following intramagnal or intrainfundibular artificial insemination (*199*).

The mechanism of discharge of spermatozoa from host glands has not yet been established, but preliminary evidence suggests that a combination of events may be involved (including mechanical distortion of the region by the passing egg, and some form of secretion). Whatever the mechanism, spermatozoa are discharged in small numbers in close temporal relation to ovulation and are responsible for successive fertilizations, but these have a short life-span in the oviduct. Spermatozoa found in the oviduct lumen more than an hour or two after ovulation already show signs of degeneration (*17*).

Attempts to discover the nature of the sperm-life-prolonging properties of the host glands have yielded a considerable amount of information, but no conclusive answers. Spermatozoa tend to pack into these glands in tight regular bundles (see Figs. 4 and 5) with their heads pointing to the blind ends (*16, 62, 197*), and these bundles appear to undergo very slow synchronous wave motion (unpublished data). Electron micrography has revealed that the acrosomes tend to be imbedded among microvilli on the apical surfaces of the gland cells (*200*). The uterovaginal glands secrete abundant quantities of glycogen and also contain large amounts of lipids of apparently complex nature (*67*). Though these lipids react at least to some phospholipid reagents, they have abnormal solubility properties and differ histochemically in the apical and basal portions of the gland cells. Fujii (*61*) interpreted the staining reactions he observed as evidence of intracellular cholesterol ester, but this could not be confirmed by Gilbert *et al.* (*67*). The biochemical environment provided by the infundibular glands is quite different from that of the uterovaginal glands. The infun-

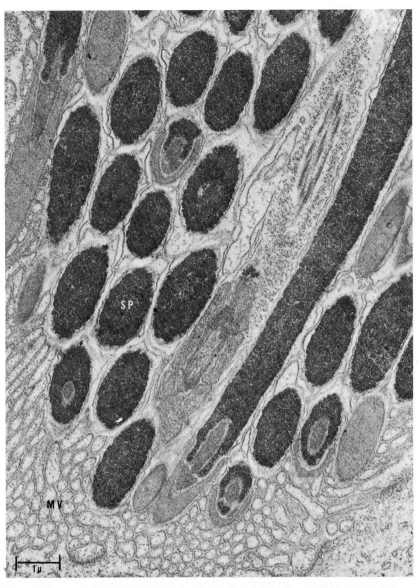

FIG. 5. Lumen of an infundibular sperm-host gland, containing a clump of sperm heads (SP) in close contact with microvilli (MV). Two spermatozoa cut in longitudinal section show the cylindrical shape of cock sperm heads and the structure of the acrosome. Reprinted from Van Krey *et al.* (*200*), with permission of the authors.

dibular glands produce no glycogen, and their intracellular lipids are both smaller in amount and—though they also resemble phospholipids—qualitatively somewhat different (119).

D. Fertility and Hatchability

Since, with an adequate semen dose, chicken hens usually remain fertile for at least a week following mating or intravaginal artificial insemination, high fertility can normally be maintained with weekly inseminations. Many hens remain fertile into the second and even the third weeks, but flock average fertility drops rapidly after the first week because individual hens become infertile, and because one or two infertile eggs frequently appear shortly before the final fertile one. The major source of variation in flock level of fertility is, nevertheless, usually a variation in the duration of the fertile period, which appears to be closely associated with the persistence of spermatozoa in the host glands, for these are ordinarily found empty or nearly so when examined immediately after oviposition of the first infertile egg following a fertile period (46).

The persistence of normal spermatozoa in the host glands appears to be controlled simply by the number of spermatozoa available. For example, Taneja and Gowe (192, 193), using intravaginal artificial insemination, obtained an average duration of fertility of about 14 days with semen doses greater than 0.01 ml; reducing the dose to 0.0002 ml decreased average persistence to 5.5 days. It may be presumed that the lower doses were inadequate to fill the host glands completely. Striking differences in duration of fertility between spermatozoa stored in infundibular glands and spermatozoa stored in uterovaginal glands are also probably a reflection of available numbers. In a recent experiment, Lorenz and Ogasawara (118) obtained an average duration of fertility of 21.3 days (maximum 26 days) after the deposition of 0.05 ml of semen in the anterior oviduct, compared with an average of 11.3 days (maximum 16 days) following midvaginal insemination with the same dose. However, the infundibulum is much more extensive than the uterovaginal region, and the glands are capable of harboring many more spermatozoa; when heavily engorged (as in anterior oviduct artificial insemination), they are capable of preserving spermatozoa much longer than are the uterovaginal glands.

Usually, poor-quality semen also shortens the fertile period; however, this may be obscured by the method of reporting fertility. In at least one instance (149), such deficient fertility was shown to be associated with more or less complete inability of the spermatozoa to enter the host glands.

The semen sample just discussed exhibited, to some degree at least, the characteristics that have been correlated with poor fertility: deficient sperm concentration, motility, and dehydrogenase activity (as measured by methylene blue or resazurin reduction time); excessive numbers "dead" (i.e., stained with nigrosin-eosin); and at least certain morphological abnormalities (*34, 40, 90, 91, 123, 177, 185, 210*). These characteristics are ordinarily so closely interrelated that it is difficult to study them separately; thus, though they are useful for predicting fertility from a mating or artificial insemination, they are not helpful in explaining the underlying causes of poor fecundity in semen. Most probably, each of these abnormalities is only one manifestation of a more general deficiency, for such semen—quite incapable of producing fertility—has contained as many *normal-appearing* spermatozoa in the dose used as are necessary for normal fertility from a high-quality sample. Also, such abnormal spermatozoa do not interfere with normal sperm cells; mixtures of semen of high and low fecundity fertilize as well as the former does alone (*149*).

Saeki (*177*) has called attention to a specific abnormality, "crooked neck," that he has often found associated with poor fertility. In this abnormality, a weakness of the neck or midpiece allows the head of the spermatozoon to fold back along the tail; such spermatozoa are presumably incapable of fertilizing, although they remain motile. Crooked-neck spermatozoa are usually observed in senescent semen (*95, 160*). When present in freshly ejaculated semen, they are probably evidence of a general weakness, for, again, enough normal-appearing spermatozoa remain to produce normal fertility, even in samples of poor fecundity. It would be of interest to follow the rate of senescence of such semen, both *in vitro* and in the host glands of inseminated hens.

Hatchability has a somewhat shorter duration than fertility, since eggs laid toward the end of the fertile period usually die early in incubation. This effect, first reported in 1918 by Phillips (*157*), was attributed a few years later by Crew (*36*) to deterioration of the "physiological qualities" of the spermatozoa as a fertilizing agent while in the oviduct so that the zygote of which they became a part is incapable of normal development. All of the numerous investigators who have since observed the phenomenon have accepted Crew's hypothesis or one closely resembling it. Dharmarajan (*42*) concluded that stale spermatozoa actually become toxic to zygotes that they induce.

This hypothesis is brought into question, however, by the experiment just described (*118*): the average duration of hatchability was 6.2 days (maximum 11 days) following midvaginal artificial insemination, and 15.6 days (maximum 24 days) following artificial insemination into the anterior oviduct. The number of spermatozoa present (and, thus, length of the fertile period) should not affect the rate of senescence per se, yet it unquestionably affected the duration of hatchability in this experiment.

Even more remarkably, anterior oviduct artificial insemination produced a high percentage of embryonic abnormality early in the fertile period—a result in striking contrast to the embryonic viability pattern after intravaginal artificial insemination. Various mechanisms were postulated to explain this effect, including a hypothesized "screening" mechanism in the uterovaginal glands or at the uterovaginal junction to keep abnormal spermatozoa from ascending the oviduct (which, of course, would be bypassed by the experimental techniques described). Quite possibly, embryonic abnormalities (both early and late in the fertile period) might be effects of sperm numbers, however. Fofanova (52) demonstrated that either excessive or deficient numbers of supernumerary spermatozoa led to abnormal cleavage patterns. Although supernumerary spermatozoa were not counted in eggs derived from the experiments described here, engorgement of the infundibular glands must have resulted in far more than usual numbers and may thus account for early abnormalities. Likewise, at the end of the fertile period, very few spermatozoa remained in the host glands and few could reach the site of fertilization, which accounts for the alternation of fertile and infertile eggs at the end of the fertile period just described; the resulting deficiency of supernumerary spermatozoa, according to Fofanova's results, should produce abnormal embryos.

Although not proved, this reasoning does fit the results obtained so far; it also leads to a further hypothesis regarding the hitherto puzzling role of the infundibular glands, which are fully capable of harboring spermatozoa, yet normally contain few or none after intravaginal artificial insemination. Quite likely, the uterovaginal and infundibular host glands work together to ensure the optimum number of spermatozoa at the site of fertilization. According to this hypothesis, the role of the infundibular glands in removing excessive numbers of spermatozoa from the site of fertilization (such as might be present, e.g., immediately after copulation) might be at least as important as their role in harboring the spermatozoa.

E. Semen Preservation

Avian semen preservation has been less successful than has, e.g., bull or ram semen, perhaps in part because of an additional requirement; whereas the storage period for mammalian spermatozoa may permissibly "use up" much of their normal life-span, avian spermatozoa must survive with their potential life-span in the sperm host glands unimpaired, or else the resulting fertile period will be reduced. Progress in development of preservative methods has been hindered by failure in some experiments to examine eggs for a period long enough after artificial insemination for the effects of the method to be assessed fully.

A large body of research, previously summarized by Lorenz (115) and by Lake (100, 103), has been based either implicitly or explicitly on the presumed necessity of preventing spermatozoa from "exhausting" certain endogenous stores, either through slowing their metabolism or by supplying exogenous sources of energy, or by both.

An obvious means of slowing metabolism is by reducing the temperature, but cold alone prolongs fertilizing capacity very little. Paradoxically, undiluted cock semen at $0°C$ loses most of its fertilizing capacity within an hour or two (25, 64, 87, 160), while motility may yet be regained after 2 or 3 days in the refrigerator. Part, but not all, of the reason for the observed rapid loss of fertilizing capacity may have been cold shock; although cock spermatozoa are much less sensitive to cold shock than are bull spermatozoa, the effect is still considerable. Chilling semen in a thin film to 0°C has caused an immediate increase in bent midpieces and an irreversible interference with certain metabolic processes. Even much less severe chilling has caused some loss of fertilizing capacity in subsequently stored semen (160), although reportedly not in semen used immediately (41).

The optimum temperature for holding undiluted semen appears to be between 10° and 15°C, but preservation without serious loss of fertilizing capacity even at this optimum has usually been limited to a few hours (see 103). Proudfoot and Stewart (162, 163) recently discovered the beneficial effects of oxygen on spermatozoa held at 10°C. Under an atmosphere of pure O_2, semen could be stored for up to 15 hours with a relatively small loss of fertilizing capacity. Thus, aerobic processes (at least at 10°C) were less damaging to cock spermatozoa than anaerobic processes, but whether O_2 would be beneficial also at lower temperatures (where metabolism is slower) was not determined; however, attempts to store undiluted semen in an O_2 atmosphere gave much poorer results at 5°C than at 10°C.

Moderate dilution aids semen storage greatly. The *mechanics* are poorly understood, but several of the *effects* of dilution are themselves now well documented. Dilution alters temperature effects on fertilizing capacity so that the optimum for diluted semen is close to 2°C (159, 160). Dilution has its price, however; it reduces fertilizing capacity in at least two ways which are essentially independent of the nature of the diluent. The first reduction is evident immediately after dilution (179, 208, 211); it may be caused partly by mechanical injury during the act of dilution, and in part by the effect of lowered sperm density on fertilizing capacity, (possibly because more widely separated spermatozoa may enter the host glands in smaller numbers). The second fertility-reducing factor is the classic "dilution effect," which is a stimulation of motility and metabolism with a shortened life-span; all increase with increasing dilution (39, 205). The dilution effect has been largely circumvented by keeping the semen-to-diluent ratio moderate; the optimum dilution rate appears to be between 1:2 and 1:3 (77, 213). The effect of sperm density has been studied with considerable success by removing the diluent through centrifugation and reconstituting the solution to the original sperm concentration shortly before inseminating (215).

Diluent composition has received a great amount of experimental attention. Studied in these investigations besides problems of exogenous energy sources and metabolic inhibition have been such factors as osmotic balance, buffering, and chelating action to protect against toxic ions. Some attention has also been paid to constructing diluents having composition and/or properties closely resembling those of seminal fluid (99), especially since replacement of the natural fluid has been shown to damage spermatozoa through altering their wall structure, but seminal plasma is by no means an ideal diluent.

Several recent studies have stressed the importance of osmotic concentration, though without complete agreement as to the exact optimum, which apparently varies somewhat with composition. What is agreed is that a diluent should be hypertonic to seminal fluid (102, 103, 115). Apparently, the midpiece has a higher tonicity than seminal fluid so that in undiluted semen or isotonic media the midpiece structure is plasmolyzed, and bent midpieces ("crooked necks") are produced (205, 238). Seminal fluid is also seriously deficient in buffering capacity, and although cock spermatozoa tolerate a moderately wide range of pH, these bounds may be exceeded if the semen is held at a temperature that allows appreciable metabolism.

Chloride in moderate amounts is quite toxic to spermatozoa (46, 217). The chloride content of vas deferens fluid is only about one-third that of blood plasma or transparent fluid (see Table I), but may still be higher than the optimum for spermatozoa, as suggested by work on diluents by Lake (99). Ca^{++} in concentrations greater than 1.2 mg/100 ml has been reported to agglutinate spermatozoa, though lower concentrations were beneficial in maintaining sperm motility (204). Thus, vas deferens fluid reportedly contains enough Ca^{++} to be damaging, and transparent fluid contains much more. Therefore, the most serious fault of seminal fluid as a diluent doubtless arises from whatever transparent fluid it may contain; its contents of Cl^- and Ca^{++}, plus its fibrinogen and perhaps other blood proteins, are undoubtedly responsible for its sperm-agglutination and inactivating effects (102).

Lake (99) described a diluent that resembled cock vas deferens fluid with respect to positive ions and glutamate, but was calcium-free and low in chloride and contained fructose. Semen collected free of transparent fluid, diluted 1:3 with Lake's solution and stored at 2°C, produced very fair fertility after 24 hours of storage, and moderate though lower fertility after 48 hours. Since the only buffer in Lake's solution is glutamate, its buffering capacity is deficient, but the pH shift was minimized by the holding temperature of 2°C.

Glutamate functions in Lake's diluent also as a chelating agent; other substances used in various diluents for this purpose have included milk (boiled to inactivate its agglutinin) (159, 160, 181), egg white (159, 160), and glycine (176). Also, the beneficial effects of certain antibiotics, frequently added to reduce the effects of bacterial contamination, may result as much from their chelating as their antibacterial properties; Wilcox and Schorb (214) found this to be true of a combination of oxytetracycline and dihydrostreptomycin.

The metabolic inhibitor 2-ethyl-5-methylbenzimidazole has been found to prolong life-span and fertilizing capacity quite strikingly at 2°C (13, 79), though a large number of other metabolic inhibitors have had no beneficial effect on cock spermatozoa (213). Carbon dioxide, which has been used to inhibit metabolism and prolong the life-span of bull spermatozoa at room temperature, has been studied briefly in cock semen diluents. When gaseous CO_2 was evolved through adding bicarbonate to a citrate-citric acid diluent and the diluted semen was stored in sealed ampuls at $2°C$, fertilizing capacity was increased moderately (86). In those experiments, sperm metabolism was not studied; however, citrate is itself a metabolic inhibitor, and observed effects of CO_2 or HCO_3^- on metabolism and motility at room temperature and $40°C$ have been inconsistent (see Section IV,C,2). What their effects would be at $2°C$, where both metabolism and motility are unapparent, is not known. Also not resolved is the potential paradox between the effects of metabolic inhibitors in diluted semen and the effects of O_2 in undiluted semen described previously.

The role of glycolyzable carbohydrate in maintaining fertilizing capacity *in vitro* is also uncertain, especially when glycolysis is also negligible at storage temperatures. Lake (99) found that a fructose-containing glutamate diluent was much superior to one in which extra NaCl replaced fructose, but was otherwise the same; however, the inferiority of the latter may have been due as much to chloride toxicity (discussed previously) as to lack of fructose. In Wilcox's studies with dilution and reconcentration, a simple phosphate buffer with antibiotics gave as good results as one containing fructose at $2°C$ (212). However, fructose added to the reconstituting solution used to replace the storage diluent just before artificial insemination gave significantly improved fertility (215). In a subsequent study (6) a tartrate buffer was found superior to phosphate for preserving fertility.

There have been surprisingly few investigations of dilution and storage of turkey semen, considering that its commercial use would potentially be more attractive than that of other domesticated avian species. The extraordinary sensitivity of undiluted turkey semen to temperatures above and below its optimum of $15°C$ was demonstrated by Bajpai and Brown (9). Enough work on diluted semen has been done to make certain that optimum conditions for turkey semen differ, in ways still not understood, from those for chicken semen. Wilcox and Shaffner (216) stored turkey semen, diluted in phosphate buffer with antibiotics, for 6 hours at $10°C$; fertility was strikingly reduced, whether or not the semen was reconcentrated before insemination. Harris *et al.* (78) diluted turkey semen in diluents of various tonicities containing citrate and bicarbonate; again, loss of fertilizing capacity was considerable within a short 6-hour storage period. Bajpai and Brown (7, 8) studied the effects of a number of diluent compositions on the maintenance of motility, morphological normality, and life-span *in vitro*. They found high levels of glutamate to be beneficial. Moderate amounts of egg yolk were beneficial *in vitro*, but were immediately detrimental to fertility. In a subsequent study (10), several diluents, including Harris's (see previous discussion), that gave promising results early in the season gave poor results when used after midseason.

Some advances have been made in the technology of frozen storage of glycerolated cock semen, but no commercially useful technique has yet been developed. Removal of glycerol by dialysis (to restore fertilizing capacity) (158) was found to be unnecessary if intrauterine artificial insemination was employed with glycerolated semen either fresh (3) or frozen (2), but the frozen semen so inseminated produced no better fertility (25%) than dialyzed semen inseminated intravaginally. Washing with centrifugation followed by intravaginal artificial insemination produced results at least as good (31); the optimum procedure, which employed 8% glycerol and fast freezing by immersing vials in an alcohol CO_2 bath at —79°C, yielded 40% fertility. Brown and Harris (19) found that a period of equilibration with glycerol before freezing also improved fertility. They confirmed the earlier results with intrauterine artificial insemination and determined that intraperitoneal artificial insemination was no better (20).

REFERENCES

1. Abplanalp, H., Woodard, A. E., and Wilson, W. O., *Poultry Sci.* **41**, 1963 (1962).
2. Allen, T. E., *Proc. Australian Soc. Animal Prod.* **2**, 118 (1958).
3. Allen, T. E., and Bobr, L. W., *Poultry Sci.* **34**, 1167 (1955).
4. Allen, T. E., and Grigg, G. W., *Australian J. Agr. Res.* **8**, 788 (1957).
5. Arrington, L. C., Abplanalp, H., and Wilson, W. O., *Brit. Poultry Sci.* **3**, 105 (1962).
6. Auger, H. V., and Wilcox, F. W., *Poultry Sci.* **43**, 834 (1964).
7. Bajpai, P. K., and Brown, K. I., *Poultry Sci.* **42**, 882 (1963).
8. Bajpai, P. K., and Brown, K. I., *Poultry Sci.* **42**, 888 (1963).
9. Bajpai, P. K., and Brown, K. I., *Poultry Sci.* **43**, 1501 (1964).
10. Bajpai, P. K., and Brown, K. I., *Poultry Sci.* **46**, 599 (1967).
11. Benoit, J., *in* "Traité de Zoologie" (P. P. Grassé, ed.), Vol. 15, p. 290. Masson, Paris, 1950.
12. Benoit, J., *in* "Traité de Zoologie" (P. P. Grassé, ed.), Vol. 15, p. 384. Masson, Paris, 1950.
13. Blackwood, U. B., and Harris, G. C., Jr., *Proc. Soc. Exptl. Biol. Med.* **103**, 60 (1960).
14. Bobr, L. W., Ph.D. Thesis, Univ. of California, Davis, California, 1962.
15. Bobr, L. W., Lake, P. E., Lorenz, F. W., Ogasawara, F. X., and Krzanowska, H., *Poultry Sci.* **44**, 659 (1965).
16. Bobr, L. W., Lorenz, F. W., and Ogasawara, F. X., *J. Reprod. Fertility* **8**, 39 (1964).
17. Bobr, L. W., Ogasawara, F. X., and Lorenz, F. W., *J. Reprod. Fertility* **8**, 49 (1964).
18. Brant, J. W. A., and Nalbandov, A. V., *Poultry Sci.* **35**, 692 (1956).
19. Brown, J. E., and Harris, G. C., Jr., *Poultry Sci.* **42**, 377 (1963).
20. Brown, J. E., Harris, G. C., Jr., and Hobbs, T. C., *Poultry Sci.* **42**, 810 (1963).
21. Brown, K. I., *Poultry Sci.* **38**, 804 (1959).
22. Burns, R. K., *in* "Analysis of Development" (B. H. Willier, P. A. Weiss, and V. Hamburger, eds.), p. 462. Saunders, Philadelphia, Pennsylvania, 1955.

23. Burrows, W. H., and Byerly, T. C., *Proc. Soc. Exptl. Biol. Med.* **34**, 841 (1956).
24. Burrows, W. H., and Quinn, J. P., *Poultry Sci.* **16**, 19 (1937).
25. Burrows, W. H., and Quinn, J. P., *Proc. 7th World's Poultry Congr. Cleveland*, p. 82 (1939).
26. Byerly, T. C., and Moore, O. K., *Poultry Sci.* **20**, 387 (1941).
27. Callow, R. K., and Parkes, A. S., *Biochem. J.* **29**, 1414 (1935).
28. Campos, A. C., and Shaffner, C. S., *Poultry Sci.* **31**, 567 (1952).
29. Chieffi, G., and Botte, V., *Experientia* **21**, 16 (1965).
30. Chubb, L. G., and Cooper, D. M., *J. Reprod. Fertility* **4**, 7 (1962).
31. Clark, C. E., and Shaffner, C. S., *Poultry Sci.* **39**, 1213 (1960).
32. Clegg, R. E., Ericson, A. T., Hein, R. E., McFarland, R. H., and Leonard, G. W., *J. Biol. Chem.* **219**, 447 (1956).
33. Conner, M. H., and Fraps, R. M., *Poultry Sci.* **33**, 1051 (1954).
34. Cooper, D. M., and Rowell, J. G., *Poultry Sci.* **37**, 699 (1958).
35. Cowles, R. B., and Nordstrom, A., *Science* **104**, 586 (1946).
36. Crew, F. A. E., *Proc. Roy. Soc. Edinburgh* **46**, 230 (1926).
37. Dantschakoff, W., *Ergeb. Physiol. Biol. Chem. Exptl. Pharmakol.* **40**, 101 (1938).
38. Das, B. C., and Nalbandov, A. V., *Endocrinology* **57**, 705 (1955).
39. DeMuelenaere, H. J. H., and Quicke, G. V., *S. African J. Agr. Sci.* **3**, 281 (1960).
40. DeSilva, P. L. B., *Ceylon Vet. J.* **11**, 43 (1963).
41. DeSilva, P. L. B., *J. Reprod. Fertility* **6**, 371 (1963a).
42. Dharmarajan, M., *Nature* **165**, 398 (1950).
43. Domm, L. V., in "Sex and Internal Secretions" (E. Allen, C. H. Danforth, and E. A. Doisy, eds.), p. 227. Williams & Wilkins, Baltimore, Maryland, 1939.
44. Domm, L. V., in "Recent Studies in Avian Biology" (A. Wolfson, ed.), p. 309. Univ. of Illinois Press, Urbana, Illinois, 1955.
45. Dorfman, R. I., and Dorfman, A. S., *Endocrinology* **42**, 7 (1948).
46. El Zayat, S., and van Tienhoven, A., *Am. J. Physiol.* **200**, 819 (1961).
47. El Zayat, S., and van Tienhoven, A., *Proc. Soc. Exptl. Biol. Med.* **106**, 803 (1961).
48. Farner, D. S., in "Recent Studies in Avian Biology" (A. Wolfson, ed.), p. 198. Univ. of Illinois Press, Urbana, Illinois, 1955.
49. Farner, D. S., *Am. Scientist* **52**, 137 (1964).
50. Farrington, A. J., Duby, R. J., and Mellen, W. J., *Poultry Sci.* **45**, 1426 (1966).
51. Feeney, R. E., in "Symposium on Foods—Proteins and Their Reactions" (H. W. Schultz and A. F. Anglemier, eds.), p. 209. Avi, Westport, Connecticut, 1965.
52. Fofanova, K. A., *Zhur. Obshchei Biol.* **25**, 22 (1964); see also *Federation Proc. Transl. Suppl.* **24**, T239 (1965).
53. Fraps, R. M., in "Progress in the Physiology of Farm Animals" (J. Hammond, ed.), Vol. 2, p. 661. Butterworth, London and Washington, D.C., 1955.
54. Fraps, R. M., in "Photoperiodism and Related Phenomena in Plants and Animals" (R. B. Withrow, ed.), p. 767. Washington, D.C., 1959.

55. Fraps, R. M., *in* "Control of Ovulation" (C. A. Villee, ed.), p. 133. Pergamon, Oxford, 1961.
56. Fraps, R. M., *Endocrinology* **77**, 5 (1965).
57. Fraps, R. M., and Dury, A., *Proc. Soc. Exptl. Biol. Med.* **52**, 346 (1943).
58. Fraps, R. M., Hooker, C. W., and Forbes, T. R., *Science* **108**, 86 (1948).
59. Fraps, R. M., Hooker, C. W., and Forbes, T. R., *Science* **109**, 493 (1949).
60. Fugo, N. W., *J. Exptl. Zool.* **85**, 271 (1940).
61. Fujii, S., *Arch. Histol.* (*Okayama*) **23**, 447 (1963).
62. Fujii, S., and Tamura, T., *J. Fac. Fisheries Animal Husbandry Hiroshima Univ.* **5**, 145 (1963).
63. Gardner, W. A., Jr., Wood, H. A., Jr., and Taber, E., *Gen. Comp. Endocrinol.* **4**, 673 (1964).
64. Garren, H. W., and Shaffner, C. S., *Poultry Sci.* **31**, 137 (1952).
65. Gilbert, A. B., *Quart. J. Exptl. Physiol.* **50**, 437 (1965).
66. Gilbert, A. B., *Advan. Reprod. Physiol.* **2**, 111 (1967).
67. Gilbert, A. B., Reynolds, M. E., and Lorenz, F. W., *J. Reprod. Fertility* **16**, 433 (1968).
68. Gilbert, A. B., and Wood-Gush, D. G. M., *Animal Behaviour* **13**, 284 (1965).
69. Goldberg, E., and Norman, C., *J. Cell. Comp. Physiol.* **58**, 175 (1961).
70. Graham, E. F., Johnson, L. A., and Fahning, M. L., *Proc. 5th Intern. Congr. Animal Reprod. Artificial Insemination, Trento* **4**, 381 (1964).
71. Grigg, G. W., *Proc. 2nd Intern. Congr. Physiol. Pathol. Animal Reprod. Artificial Insemination, Milano* **1**, 87 (1952).
72. Guhl, A. M., *Behaviour* **2**, 106 (1950).
73. Guhl, A. M., Collias, N. E., and Allee, W. C., *Physiol. Zool.* **18**, 365 (1945).
74. Hale, E. B., *Poultry Sci.* **34**, 1059 (1955).
75. Hammond, M., Boone, M. A., and Barnett, D. B., *J. Reprod. Fertility* **10**, 21 (1965).
76. Hamner, C. E., and Williams, W. L., *J. Reprod. Fertility* **5**, 143 (1963).
77. Harris, G. C., Jr., and Hobbs, T. D., *Poultry Sci.* **43**, 529 (1964).
78. Harris, G. C., Jr., Hobbs, T. D., Brown, J. E., and Warren, L. B., *Poultry Sci.* **42**, 536 (1963).
79. Harris, G. C., Jr., Wilcox, F. H., and Shaffner, C. S., *Poultry Sci.* **40**, 777 (1961).
80. Harrison, D. G., and Heald, P. J., *Proc. Roy. Soc.* **B166**, 341 (1966).
81. Harrison, D. G., Offer, M., Soo, D., and Heald, P. J., *Nature* **212**, 706 (1966).
82. Heald, P. J., and McLachlan, P. M., *Nature* **199**, 487 (1963).
83. Heald, P. J., and McLachlan, P. M., *Biochem. J.* **87**, 571 (1963).
84. Heald, P. J., and McLachlan, P. M., *Biochem. J.* **94**, 32 (1965).
85. Hertz, R., Fraps, R. M., and Sebrell, W. H., *Proc. Soc. Exptl. Biol. Med.* **52**, 142 (1943).
86. Hobbs, T. C., and Harris, G. C., Jr., *Poultry Sci.* **42**, 388 (1963).
87. Hunsaker, W. G., Aitken, J. R., and Lindblad, G. S., *Poultry Sci.* **35**, 649 (1956).
88. Huston, T. M., and Nalbandov, A. V., *Endocrinology* **52**, 149 (1953).
89. Ingkasuwan, P., and Ogasawara, F. X., *Poultry Sci.* **45**, 1199 (1966).
90. Kamar, G. A. R., *Poultry Sci.* **39**, 188 (1960).
91. Kamar, G. A. R., and Badreldin, A. L., *Poultry Sci.* **38**, 301 (1959).
92. Koga, O., *Japan. Poultry Sci.* **4**, 8 (1967).

93. Kornfeld, W., and Nalbandov, A. V., *Endocrinology* **55**, 751 (1954).

94. Kun, E., *J. Biol. Chem.* **187**, 289 (1950).

95. Lake, P. E., *Proc. World's Poultry Congr. Exposition, 10th Congr., Edinburgh, Sect. A* p. 79 (1954).

96. Lake, P. E., *Quart. J. Microscop. Sci.* **97**, 487 (1956).

97. Lake, P. E., *J. Agr. Sci.* **49**, 120 (1957).

98. Lake, P. E., *J. Anat.* **91**, 116 (1957).

99. Lake, P. E., *J. Reprod. Fertility* **1**, 30 (1960).

100. Lake, P. E., *in* "The Semen of Animals and Artificial Insemination" (J. P. Maule, ed.), p. 331. Commonwealth Agr. Bureaux, Farnham Royal, 1962.

101. Lake, P. E., *Proc. 12th World's Poultry Congr., Sydney,* **1**, 105–108 (1962).

102. Lake, P. E., *Advan. Reprod. Physiology* **1**, 93 (1966).

103. Lake, P. E., *World's Poultry Sci. J.* **23**, 111 (1967).

104. Lake, P. E., and El Jack, M. H., *in* "Physiology of the Domestic Fowl" (C. Horton-Smith and E. C. Amoroso, eds.), p. 44. Oliver & Boyd, Edinburgh and London, 1965.

105. Lake, P. E., and Gilbert, A. B., *Res. Vet. Sci.* **5**, 39 (1964).

106. Lake, P. E., Lorenz, F. W., and Reimann, W. D., *Nature* **194**, 4828 (1962).

107. Lake, P. E., and Wood-Gush, D. G. M., *Nature* **178**, 853 (1956).

108. Lamoreaux, W. F., *Endocrinology* **32**, 497 (1943).

109. Laskowski, M., *Biochem. Ztg.* **275**, 293 (1935).

110. Layne, D. S., Common, R. H., Maw, W. A., and Fraps, R. M., *Proc. Soc. Exptl. Biol. Med.* **94**, 528 (1957).

111. Layne, D. S., Common, R. H., Maw, W. A., and Fraps, R. M., *Nature* **181**, 351 (1958).

112. Long, E., and Godfrey, G. F., *Poultry Sci.* **31**, 665 (1952).

113. Lorenz, F. W., *Vitamins Hormones* **12**, 235 (1954).

114. Lorenz, F. W., *Nature* **182**, 397 (1958).

115. Lorenz, F. W., *Proc. 5th Intern. Congr. Animal Reprod. Artificial Insemination, Trento,* **4**, 7 (1964).

116. Lorenz, F. W., Abbott, U. K., Asmundson, V. S., Adler, H. E., Kratzer, F. H. Ogasawara, F. X., and Carson, J. D., *Calif. Univ. Agr. Expt. Sta. Circ.* **472** (1959).

117. Lorenz, F. W., Cavoulas, M., and Carson, J. D., *Poultry Sci.* **29**, 769 (1950).

118. Lorenz, F. W., and Ogasawara, F. X., *J. Reprod. Fertility* **16**, 445 (1968).

119. Lorenz, F. W., Reynolds, M. E., and Gilbert, A. B., *Physiologist* **10**, 236 (1967).

120. Lorenz, F. W., Reynolds, M. E., and Howard, D. L., *Federation Proc.* **25**, 190 (1966).

121. Lytle, I. M., and Lorenz, F. W., *Nature* **182**, 1681 (1958).

122. McCartney, M. G., *Poultry Sci.* **30**, 658 (1951).

123. McDaniel, G. R., and Craig, J. V., *Poultry Sci.* **41**, 866 (1962).

124. McIndoe, W. M., *Biochem. J.* **72**, 153 (1959).

125. Mann, T., "The Biochemistry of Semen and of the Male Reproductive Tract." Methuen, London, 1964.

126. Marshall, A. J., *Mem. Soc. Endocrinol.* **4**, 75 (1955).

127. Marshall, A. J., and Disney, H. J. deS., *Nature* **177**, 143 (1956).

128. Martin, J. E., Graves, J. H., and Dohan, F. C., *Am. J. Vet. Res.* **16**, 141 (1955).

129. Marza, V. D., and Marza, E. V., *Quart. J. Microscop. Sci.* **78**, 133 (1935).

130. Miller, A. H., *Condor* **56**, 13 (1954).
131. Mimura, H., *Okajimas Folia Anat. Japon.* **17**, 459 (1939).
132. Morash, R., and Gibbs, O. S., *J. Pharmacol. Exptl. Therap.* **37**, 475 (1929).
133. Morato-Manaro, J., and Albrieux, A., *Endocrinology* **24**, 518 (1939).
134. Morris, T. R., and Fox, S., *Nature* **181**, 1453 (1958).
135. Munro, S. S., *Proc. Soc. Exptl. Biol. Med.* **33**, 255 (1935).
136. Munro, S. S., *Quart. J. Exptl. Physiol.* **27**, 281 (1938).
137. Nalbandov, A. V., *in* "Comparative Endocrinology" (A. Gorbman, ed.), p. 161. Wiley, New York, 1959.
138. Nalbandov, A. V., *in* "Control of Ovulation" (C. A. Villee, ed.), p. 122. Pergamon, Oxford, 1961.
139. Nalbandov, A. V., Hochhauser, M., and Dugas, M., *Endocrinology* **36**, 251 (1945).
140. Nalbandov, A. V., and James, M. F., *Am. J. Anat.* **85**, 347 (1949).
141. Nalbandov, A. V., Meyer, R. K., and McShan, W. H., *Anat. Record* **110**, 475 (1951).
142. Nelson, D. M., and Nalbandov, A. V., *in* "Physiology of the Domestic Fowl" (C. Horton-Smith and E. C. Amoroso, eds.), p. 3, Oliver & Boyd, Edinburgh and London, 1966.
143. Nelson, D. M., Norton, H. W., and Nalbandov, A. V., *Endocrinology* **77**, 889 (1965).
144. Nishiyama, H., *J. Fac. Agr. Kyushu Univ.* **10**, 277 (1955).
145. Nishiyama, H., and Fujishima, T., *Mem. Fac. Agr. Kagoshima Univ.* **4**, 27 (1961).
146. Nishiyama, H., and Ogawa, K., *Jap. J. Zootech. Sci.* **32**, 89 (1961).
147. Ogasawara, F. X., Ph.D. Thesis, Univ. California, Davis, California, 1957.
148. Ogasawara, F. X., and Lorenz, F. W., *J. Reprod. Fertility* **7**, 281 (1964).
149. Ogasawara, F. X., Lorenz, F. W., and Bobr, L. W., *J. Reprod. Fertility* **11**, 33 (1966).
150. Ogasawara, F. X., and Rooney, W. F., *Poultry Sci.* **43**, 1348 (1964).
151. Ogasawara, F. X., Wilson, W. O., and Asmundson, V. S., *Poultry Sci.* **41**, 1858 (1962).
152. O'Grady, J. E., *in* "Physiology of the Domestic Fowl" (C. Horton-Smith and E. C. Amoroso, eds.), p. 23. Oliver & Boyd, Edinburgh and London, 1966.
153. Olsen, M. W., and Fraps, R. M., *J. Morphol.* **74**, 297 (1944).
154. Olsen, M. W., and Fraps, R. M., *J. Exptl. Zool.* **114**, 475 (1950).
155. Parker, J. E., McKenzie, F. F., and Kempster, H. L., *Poultry Sci.* **19**, 191 (1940).
156. Penquite, R., Craft, W. A., and Thompson, R. B., *Poultry Sci.* **9**, 247 (1930).
157. Phillips, A. G., *J. Am. Assoc. Poultry Husbandry* **4**, 30 (1918).
158. Polge, C., *Nature* **167**, 949 (1951).
159. Polge, C., *Proc. Soc. Study Fertility* **2**, 16 (1951).
160. Polge, C., Ph.D. Thesis, Univ. of London, 1955.
161. Poole, H. K., *Brit. Poultry Sci.* **4**, 279 (1963).
162. Proudfoot, F. G., *Poultry Sci.* **45**, 443 (1966).
163. Proudfoot, F. G., and Steward, D. K. R., *J. Reprod. Fertility* **13**, 251 (1967).
164. Quinn, J. P., and Burrows, W. H., *J. Heredity* **27**, 31 (1936).
165. Räber, H., *Behaviour* **1**, 237 (1948).
166. Racker, E., *in* "Glutathione" (S. Colowick *et al.*, eds.), p. 165. Academic Press, New York, 1954.

167. Riddle, O., and Bates, R. W., *in* "Sex and Internal Secretions" (E. Allen, G. H. Danforth, and E. A. Doisy, eds.), 2nd ed., p. 1088. Williams & Wilkins, Baltimore, Maryland, 1939.

168. Riddle, O., Bates, R. W., and Lahr, E. L., *Am. J. Physiol.* 111, 352 (1935).

169. Riddle, V., Ph.D. Thesis, Univ. of California, Davis, California, 1968.

170. Riddle, V., and Lorenz, F. W., *J. Biol. Chem.* 243, 2718 (1968).

171. Roepke, R. R., and Bushnell, L. D., *J. Immunol.* 30, 109 (1936).

172. Roepke, R. R., and Hughes, J. S., *J. Biol. Chem.* 108, 79 (1935).

173. Romanoff, A. L., and Romanoff, A. J., "The Avian Egg." Wiley, New York, 1949.

174. Rothchild, I., and Fraps, R. M., *Endocrinology* 35, 355 (1944).

175. Rothchild, I., and Fraps, R. M., *Proc. Soc. Exptl. Biol. Med.* 56, 79 (1944).

176. Rowell, J. G., and Cooper, D. M., *Poultry Sci.* 36, 706 (1957).

177. Saeki, Y., *Poultry Sci.* 39, 1354 (1960).

178. Saeki, Y., and Brown, K. I., *Poultry Sci.* 41, 905 (1962).

179. Schindler, H., Nahari, U., and Bornstein, S., *Israel J. Agr. Res.* 13, 155 (1963).

180. Schindler, H., and Nevo, A., *J. Reprod. Fertility* 4, 251 (1962).

181. Schindler, H., Weinstein, S., Moses, E., and Gabriel, I., *Poultry Sci.* 34, 1113 (1955).

182. Schjeide, O. A., and Urist, M. R., *Science* 124, 1242 (1956).

183. Scott, T. W., White, I. G., and Annison, E. F., *Biochem. J.* 83, 392 (1962).

184. Scott, T. W., White, I. G., and Annison, E. F., *Biochem. J.* 83, 398 (1962).

185. Soller, M., Schindler, H., and Borstein, S., *Poultry Sci.* 44, 424 (1965).

186. Sturkie, P. D., and Lin, Y., *J. Endocrinology* 35, 325 (1966).

187. Sykes, A. H., *Nature* 172, 1098 (1953).

188. Sykes, A. H., *Proc. 10th World Poultry Congr., Edinburgh* p. 184 (1954).

189. Sykes, A. H., *J. Reprod. Fertility* 4, 214 (1962).

190. Taber, E., and Salley, K. W., *Endocrinology* 54, 415 (1954).

191. Tanaka, K., and Nakajo, S., *Endocrinology* 70, 453 (1962).

192. Taneja, G. C., and Gowe, R. S., *Nature* 191, 828 (1961).

193. Taneja, G. C., and Gowe, R. S., *J. Reprod. Fertility* 4, 161 (1962).

194. Urist, M. R., Schjeide, O. A., and McLean, F. C., *Endocrinology* 63, 570 (1958).

195. van Deth, J. H. G. M., van Limborgh, J., and van Faassen, F., *Acta Morphol. Neerl. Scand.* 1, 70 (1956).

196. Van Drimmelen, G. C., *J. S. African Vet. Med. Assoc.* 16, 1 (1945).

197. Van Drimmelen, G. C., *J. S. African Vet. Med. Assoc.* 17, 42 (1946).

198. Van Drimmelen, G. C., *Onderstepoort J. Vet. Res. Suppl.* 1 (1951).

199. Van Krey, H. P., Ogasawara, F. X., and Lorenz, F. W., *J. Reprod. Fertility* 11, 257 (1966).

200. Van Krey, H. P., Ogasawara, F. X., and Pangborn, J., *Poultry Sci.* 46, 69 (1967).

201. van Tienhoven, A., *Anat. Record* 115, 374 (1953).

202. van Tienhoven, A., *Poultry Sci.* 36, 628 (1957).

203. van Tienhoven, A., *in* "Sex and Internal Secretions" (W. C. Young, ed.), Vol. 2, p. 1088. Williams & Wilkins, Baltimore, Maryland, 1961.

204. Wales, R. G., and White, I. G., *Australian J. Biol. Sci.* 11, 589 (1958).

205. Wales, R. G., and White, I. G., *Australian J. Biol. Sci.* 14, 637 (1961).

206. Warren, D. C., and Conrad, R. M., *J. Agr. Res.* 58, 875 (1939).

207. Warren, D. C., and Scott, H. M., *Poultry Sci.* **14**, 195 (1935).
208. Weakley, C. E., III, and Shaffner, C. S., *Poultry Sci.* **31**, 650 (1952).
209. Weiss, P., and Sturkie, P. D., *Poultry Sci.* **31**, 227 (1952).
210. Wheeler, N. C., and Andrews, F. N., *Poultry Sci.* **22**, 361 (1943).
211. Wilcox, F. H., *Poultry Sci.* **37**, 1357 (1958).
212. Wilcox, F. H., *Poultry Sci.* **39**, 459 (1960).
213. Wilcox, F. H., and Clark, R. G., *Poultry Sci.* **41**, 1091 (1962).
214. Wilcox, F. H., and Schorb, M. S., *Am. J. Vet. Res.* **19**, 945 (1958).
215. Wilcox, F. H., and Shaffner, C. S., *Poultry Sci.* **37**, 1353 (1958).
216. Wilcox, F. H., and Shaffner, C. S., *Poultry Sci.* **39**, 1580 (1960).
217. Wilcox, F. H., and Wilson, H. R., *Poultry Sci.* **40**, 701 (1961).
218. Williams, D. D., *Anat. Record* **130**, 225 (1958).
219. Willier, B. H., *in* "Sex and Internal Secretions" (E. Allen, C. H. Danforth, and E. A. Doisy, eds.), 2nd ed., p. 64. Williams & Wilkins, Baltimore, Maryland, 1939.
220. Wilson, W. O., *Ann. N.Y. Acad. Sci.* **117**, 194 (1964).
221. Wilson, W. O., Ogasawara, F. X., and Asmundson, V. S., *Poultry Sci.* **41**, 1168 (1962).
222. Wilson, W. O., and Woodard, A. E., *Poultry Sci.* **37**, 1054 (1958).
223. Winget, C. M., and Smith, A. H., *Am. J. Physiol.* **196**, 371 (1959).
224. Winget, C. M., Smith, A. H., and Hoover, G. N., *Poultry Sci.* **37**, 1325 (1958).
225. Witschi, E., *in* "Sex and Internal Secretions" (E. Allen, C. H. Danforth, and E. A. Doisy, eds.), 2nd ed., p. 145. Williams & Wilkins, Baltimore, Maryland, 1939.
226. Wolfson, A., *Bird-Banding* **23**, 159 (1952).
227. Wolfson, A., *Sci. Monthly* **74**, 191 (1952).
228. Wolfson, A., *Bull. Chicago Acad. Sci.* **10**, 1 (1954).
229. Wolfson, A., *Science* **120**, 68 (1954).
230. Womack, E. B., Koch, F. C., Domm, L. V., and Juhn, M., *J. Pharmacol. Exptl. Therap.* **41**, 173 (1931).
231. Wong, H. Y. C., and Hawthorne, E. W., *Am. J. Physiol.* **179**, 419 (1954).
232. Woodard, A. E., Wilson, W. O., and Abplanalp, H., *Poultry Sci.* **41**, 1758 (1962).
233. Wood-Gush, D. G. M., *Brit. J. Animal Behaviour* **3**, 81 (1955).
234. Wood-Gush, D. G. M., *Brit. J. Animal Behaviour* **4**, 133 (1956).
235. Wood-Gush, D. G. M., *Animal Behaviour* **11**, 293 (1963).
236. Wood-Gush, D. G. M., and Gilbert, A. B., *Animal Behaviour* **12**, 451 (1964).
237. Wood-Gush, D. G. M., and Osborne, R., *Brit. J. Animal Behaviour* **4**, 102 (1956).
238. Yamane, J., Tsukunaga, S., and Takahashi, T., *Zootech. Vet.* **17**, 523 (1962).
239. Yeates, N. T. M., *in* "Progress in the Physiology of Farm Animals" (J. Hammond, ed.), Vol. I. Butterworth, London and Washington, D.C., 1954.
240. Yoshida, S., and Masuda, H., *Zootec. Vet.* **17**, 528 (1962).

Subject Index

A

Abnormalities
  fertilization and, 369–370
  of sperm, 329, 597
Abortion
  brucellosis and, 518
  epididymis and, 527
  estrogen and, 435
  leptospirosis and, 523–524
  listeriosis and, 525
  toxoplasmosis and, 534
  trichomoniasis and, 533
  vibriosis and, 521, 523
  viral, 527–531
Absidia ramosa, 537
Acetate, conversion to short-chain fatty
  acids in milk, 463
17α-Acetoxy-9α-fluoro-11β-hydroxy-
  pregn-4-en-3,20-dione, follicular
  inhibition and, 205
Acetylcholine, oviposition and, 581
Acetyl-CoA carboxylase, fatty acid synthesis and, 464
β-N-Acetylglucosaminase, from ram
  testes, 285
Acid phosphomonoesterase, in cock
  semen, 586
Acrosome
  contents of, 280
  detachment of, 280
  hereditary anomalies in, 266
  hyaluronidase in, 364
  lipoglycoprotein of, 280
  reaction in sperm, 363
  seminiferous epithelial cycle and, 253
  of spermatid, 263–265
  zona lysin and, 365
ACTH, see Adrenocorticotropin
Actinobacillus equuli, 537
Actinobacillus seminis, 537
Actomyosin
  estrogen activation of, 418
  uterine content of, 428
Adenohypophysis, transplantation of,
  160–161

3′,5′-Adenosine monophosphate, acetate
  incorporation into steroid and,
  117–118
Adenosine triphosphate (ATP)
  lactose synthesis and, 460
  milk protein synthesis and, 461
  in semen, 292, 300
  in sperm, 286–287
ADH, see Vasopressin
Adipose tissue, effects of propionate on
  metabolism of, 464
Adrenal
  androgen: 127; biosynthesis in, 130,
    135–136; catabolism in, 138;
    during pregnancy, 427; produc-
    tion by, 90
  cortical steroids in pregnancy, 426–
    427
  corticoids and mammary gland de-
    velopment, 451
  estrogen: 99, 139; biosynthesis in,
    141–143; source, 96
  fetal, 434
  pregnancy and, 423
  progesterone in effluent blood, 116
  progestin in, 114–115
  progestin biosynthesis in, 119–122
  semen quality and, 320
  steroid secretion rate in, 146
  steroid synthesis in, 118
Adrenalectomy, libido and, 93
Adrenaline, see also Epinephrine
  milk ejection and, 467
  oviposition and, 581
Adrenocorticotropin (ACTH)
  mammary gland development and,
    451
  pregnancy and, 428
  releasing factor (CRF), 161
Adrenosterone
  biosynthesis of, 135
  in testes, 127
Age, estrus length and, 223
A.I., see Artificial insemination
Aldosterone, pregnancy levels of, 427